W9-AQN-766

Introduction to

Physics and Chemistry

Arthur Beiser

Formerly Associate Professor of Physics
New York University

Konrad Krauskopf

Professor of Geochemistry
Stanford University

McGraw-Hill Book Company
New York   Toronto   London

ST. PHILIP'S COLLEGE
Not to be taken from the Library
without permission

530
B423i

Introduction to Physics and Chemistry

Copyright © 1964 by McGraw-Hill, Inc.
All Rights Reserved. Printed in the United States of America.
This book, or parts thereof, may not be reproduced in any form
without permission of the publishers.

Library of Congress Catalog Card Number: 63–22522

04345

4 5 6 7 8 9 – M P – 9 8 7 6

Preface

Specialization in science is a mixed blessing. So vast is the terrain of modern science and so rich in detail that no contemporary name even exists for the "natural philosopher" of the past. The scientist of today is master of only a severely limited portion of his discipline, a concentration that is inevitable if he is to make his own contribution to knowledge. For the scientific novice, however, the common basis of the physical sciences must be made explicit. The traditional separation of physics and chemistry is particularly unfortunate in this respect. All matter consists of atoms and molecules, and the "physical" and "chemical" views of matter complement each other. The parochial physicist tends to forget that the atomicity of matter was a chemical discovery, and his chemist counterpart to forget that atomic theory is one of the triumphs of physics. The periodic table is a monument to chemistry, its explanation a monument to physics. A lump of matter is a lump of matter, to be studied from every angle and with every technique, and the unity of the phenomenon in the face of the diversity of our approaches to its understanding needs emphasis in any introduction to science.

The present text is an attempt to present physics and chemistry together, as parts of the same story, for students with little or no prior experience of them. No attempt is made to prepare the reader directly for advanced work in physical science or engineering, so training in problem solving is subordinated to the development of a general understanding of the methods of science and how they are used to study the natural world. Careful thought was given to the order of topics: Since the book is somewhat unconventional anyway, why follow the usual order if there is a better one? As it happens, none of the radical ideas that were explored, despite their other (and some-

13260

times considerable) merits, seemed as able to cope with the problems of the beginning student as the roughly historical sequence finally adopted. Hence we start with the traditional mechanics and heat, whose empirical basis is familiar enough, and go on to examine the fundamental notions of chemistry up through the periodic table. Then a return is made to physics with a look into electricity and magnetism. Thus the first half of the book is occupied with the classical aspects of physics and chemistry, facts and theories established by the latter part of the nineteenth century. Next come four chapters on the general subject of waves and particles, including the electromagnetic character of light, the concepts of relativity, and the wave-particle duality central to modern physical science. The atom can now be treated in some detail, and the book closes with six chapters on the structure and behavior of matter from an atomic viewpoint.

Arthur Beiser
Konrad Krauskopf

Contents

Part I

MATTER IN MOTION

CHAPTER 1 | MOTION

We shall begin our study of physics and chemistry with an analysis of motion: what it is, how things move, and why they do so. For several reasons this is the logical point of departure from the casual realm of our daily lives to the precise realm of science. Everything in the universe is in ceaseless movement, from the most minute constituents of atoms to the immense galaxies of stars that populate space, and this movement is an essential factor in the structure and evolution of the physical world. Another consideration is the simplicity of the phenomena involved in motion, which permits us to become familiar with the methods of science before applying these methods to more complicated situations. And, as a historical note, modern science had its genesis in the study of motion. The classic conflict between the Ptolemaic and Copernican concepts of the solar system brought into clear focus the relative nature of motion, while Galileo's observations on moving bodies, which contradicted ancient but unfounded beliefs, showed the power and primacy of measurement in the exploration of nature.

What Is Motion?

When a body changes its position with respect to something else as time goes on, we say that it *moves*.

The above statement is straightforward enough, but, like many other apparently simple statements in science, it contains subtleties of great importance. Here the significant idea is that all motion is relative to some reference object; so-called "absolute motion," without regard to an external reference, has no meaning. A body may go from one place to another—a train from New York to Boston—or it may repeat the same path indefinitely—a child on a merry-go-round. In either case the body travels through a certain distance *relative to the earth's surface* in each specific time interval during its motion. Under different circumstances the appropriate reference object may be something other than the earth: an atomic nucleus, the deck of a ship, the sun. All reference objects are equally "correct," provided they are properly identified, but usually a certain unique choice permits us to perceive the essential elements in a particular motion. For instance, to somebody on the earth, the sun and stars appear to circle the earth daily, while to somebody outside the earth, it is obvious that the earth is merely revolving on its axis. Both persons are correct in their observations, but the latter point of view presents a clearer picture of what is happening, a picture that can be interpreted more simply and straightforwardly than the former. Let us look into the classic argument between the Ptolemaic and Copernican views of the solar system in order to bring out the problems that may arise in selecting the proper reference for reckoning motion and why this selection is sometimes a crucial one.

A Survey of the Sky

When we go outdoors and watch the sky, the view before us is not a static one. The sun rises in the east and moves across the sky to set in the west, a journey repeated every day. The moon and stars have similar daily motions. One star in the northern sky, however, never seems to move at all. This is the North Star, or *Polaris*, used as a guide by travelers for centuries because of its unchanging position. Stars in its vicinity do not rise or set, but move around it in circles, circles that carry them under Polaris from west to east and over it from east to west. Farther from Polaris the circles get ever larger, until eventually they dip below the northern horizon. Paths of the stars in the southern sky, like the paths of the sun and moon, are simply very large circles, all with their centers near Polaris. Sun, moon, and stars rise and set because their circles lie in part beneath the horizon. Thus the whole sky, to an observer north of the equator, appears to revolve once a day about this not very conspicuous star.

That Polaris occupies a central position in this huge merry-go-round is no more than an accident. When we were children, most of us learned that the earth rotates once a day on its axis and that Polaris simply happens to lie almost directly over the North Pole. Thus, as the earth turns, everything around it appears to be in motion except this one star, which is on the line of its axis. To us this explanation seems obvious enough, since we were brought up to accept it. But let us for the moment forget this modern concept and imagine ourselves in the position of men who lived centuries ago, when a rotating earth was considered an absurd—even heretical—idea. Let

ST. PHILIP'S COLLEGE
Not to be taken from the Library
without permission

us examine the motions of heavenly objects in some detail and see why scientific ideas regarding them have changed so greatly.

Except for their circular motion around Polaris, the stars appear to remain fixed in their positions with respect to one another. Stars of the Big Dipper move about halfway around Polaris between every sunset and sunrise, but the shape of the Dipper itself remains unaltered. To emphasize the fact that stars do not perceptibly change their relative positions, they are often referred to as *fixed* stars.

In their daily east-west crossing of the sky, the sun and moon move more slowly than the fixed stars and so appear to drift eastward among the constellations. In other words, *relative* to the fixed stars, the sun and moon move eastward—just as a man on a train traveling southward may walk toward the rear car and so move northward *relative* to the train. The slow eastward motion is most easily observed for the moon; if the moon is seen near a bright star on one evening, by the next evening it will be some distance east of that star, and on succeeding nights its will be farther and farther to the east. In about a month the moon drifts eastward completely around the sky and returns to its starting point.

The sun's relative motion is less easily followed, because we cannot observe directly what stars it is near. But if we note what constellations appear just after sundown, we can estimate the sun's approximate location among the stars and follow it from day to day. We find that the sun drifts eastward more slowly than the moon, so slowly that the day-to-day change is scarcely noticeable. Because of the sun's motion, each constellation appears to rise a few minutes earlier each night, and so, after a few weeks or months, the appearance of the night sky becomes markedly different. By the time the sun has migrated eastward completely around the sky, we find that a year has elapsed. The length of the year, in fact, is determined from this apparent motion of the sun among the stars.

Five other objects in the sky, the ancients found, shift their positions with respect to the stars. These objects, to all appearances like five bright stars, were called *planets* (Greek for "wanderer") and were named for the Roman deities Mercury, Venus, Mars, Jupiter, and Saturn. Like the sun, the planets shift their positions so slowly that their day-to-day motion is difficult to detect, but unlike the sun, they move in complex paths. In general, each planet moves eastward among the stars, but its rate of motion is variable and at intervals it stops and moves for a brief time westward. Thus the path of a planet appears to consist of loops (Fig. 1.1) that recur after definite periods of time.

Thus the sun and moon, planets, and stars all appear to move in circles around a line connecting the earth and Polaris. Because of this motion, all objects except stars in the northern sky rise in the east and set in the west approximately once a day. The east-west motions of the sun, moon, and **planets** are, in general, a bit slower than the motions of the stars, and so

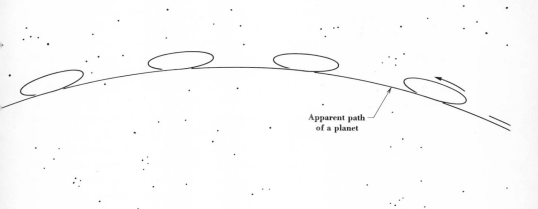

Fig. 1.1   *Apparent path of a planet in the sky as seen from the earth.* *The planets move eastward relative to the stars most of the time, but at intervals they reverse their motion and briefly move westward.*

these bodies slowly shift their positions eastward with respect to the stars. The eastward movements of the sun and moon are approximately uniform, but the planets move with variable speeds and, at intervals, even change their direction of motion for a few weeks or months.

The Ptolemaic Hypothesis

So far we have been simply listing observational facts, things that anyone can discover for himself by keeping track of the changing positions of objects in the sky. We have described the motions of celestial objects just as we see them today and just as other observers saw them many centuries ago. These observed motions are complex, but far from erratic. Each object that we have considered follows a definite path across the sky which it repeats faithfully time after time: complicated motions with an underlying regularity —to a scientific mind, such a series of motions demands an explanation. We need a hypothesis, a guess, concerning the actual space relations of objects in the sky that will account for the observed motions as combinations of simpler real motions.

As we mentioned, there are two possibilities around which a satisfactory hypothesis may be constructed: Either the earth is stationary, as it appears to be, with the celestial objects revolving about it, or the earth is moving, its motion being, then, responsible for a part of the apparent motion of other objects. Thus the apparent daily rotation of the sky may represent an actual motion of sun, moon, planets, and stars, or it may be explained by a rotation of the earth on its axis. The apparent eastward shift of the sun's position among the constellations may be a real motion of the sun, or it may be due to another motion of the earth. These alternatives were clear to the philosophers of ancient Greece, most of whom advocated a stationary earth, while a few argued for a moving earth. In their day scientific knowledge was not sufficiently advanced to settle the matter. It is hardly surprising, therefore, that most of the Greeks favored the common-sense view that the earth is stationary.

The hypothesis most widely accepted by the later Greek and Roman scholars was originally devised by Hipparchus. Ptolemy of Alexandria subsequently incorporated Hipparchus' ideas into his *Almagest,* a compendium of astronomy which was to remain the standard reference on the subject for over a thousand years, and this picture of the universe became known as the Ptolemaic system. In it our earth stands at the center, motionless, with all other objects in the universe revolving about it in paths that are either circles or combinations of circular motions—since to the Greeks the circle was the only "perfect" curve, hence the only conceivable path for a celestial object. Enclosing everything is a gigantic crystal sphere studded with the fixed stars, making approximately one revolution each day. Somewhere inside is the sun, moving around the earth exactly once a day. The difference in motion between sun and stars is just enough so that the sun appears to move among the constellations, completing its circuit once a year. Near the earth in a small orbit is the moon, revolving more slowly than the sun. The planets Venus and Mercury come between moon and sun; the planets Mars, Jupiter, and Saturn, between sun and stars.

To account for the observed peculiarities of planetary motion, Ptolemy imagined each planet to move in a small circle about a point which in turn described a large circle about the earth (Fig. 1.2). By a combination of these circular motions each planet travels in a series of loops; since we observe these loops edgewise, it appears to us as if the planets moved with variable speeds and sometimes reversed their motions.

From observations made by himself and his predecessors, Ptolemy calculated the relative speed with which each celestial object moved in its orbit. Using these speeds, he could then compute the location of an object in the sky for any date in the past or future. These computed positions checked fairly well, though not perfectly, with observed positions that had been recorded for several centuries before his time, and his predictions also agreed fairly well with observations made in succeeding years. So Ptolemy's system fulfilled all the requirements of a scientific hypothesis: It was based solidly on observational facts, it explained adequately all the facts about celestial motions that were known in his time, and it made possible the prediction of facts that could be verified in the future.

For 1,400 years no one had reason to question seriously Ptolemy's

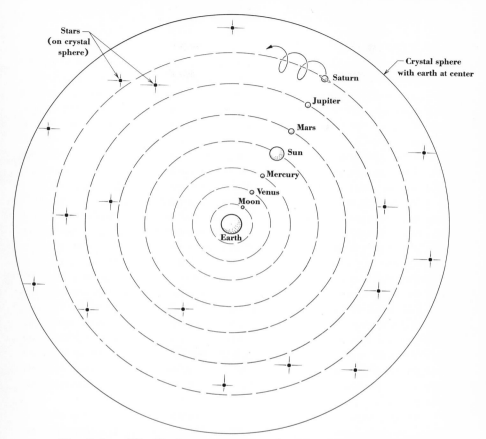

Fig. 1.2 **The Ptolemaic system, showing the assumed arrangement of the members of the solar system within the celestial
sphere.** *Each planet is supposed to travel around the earth in a series of
loops, like that shown for Saturn, while the orbits of the sun and moon are
circular. Only the planets known in Ptolemy's time are shown.*

hypothesis.   Generations of Arabian and Persian scholars found it adequate
for their limited observations, and later it was accepted without question in
the schools and monasteries of Europe.   Between the Ptolemaic system and
Christian theology in the Middle Ages there was no conflict, for both empha-
sized the importance of the earth's position as the center of all creation.   So
long a time of blind acceptance gave to Ptolemy's universe, as to many other
ideas of Greek science, a completely undeserved authority.   That such an age-
old tradition should be slow to yield to new ideas is quite understandable,
although the zeal with which Christian scholars defended a product of pagan
logic seems a bit extreme.

Copernicus and Kepler

By the sixteenth century it had become obvious that something was not quite right in the Ptolemaic system. Observed positions of the planets simply did not agree with the positions calculated from Ptolemy's complicated orbits. Discrepancies were not large, but could be detected even by inexpert observers. There were two possible ways of removing the discrepancies: Either changes could be introduced into the Ptolemaic orbits, making the system still more complicated, or the Ptolemaic hypothesis could be discarded in favor of a completely new hypothesis based on different assumptions as to the reference object relative to which the motions were to be computed.

The first to defy tradition by setting up a new explanation for the universe was Nicolaus Copernicus, a versatile and energetic Pole of the early sixteenth century. Copernicus lived in the years following Columbus' great discovery, years when mental as well as geographical horizons were receding before eager explorers. In Italy it was the time of Leonardo da Vinci and Michelangelo, a time of commercial expansion and incessant wars between rival cities, a time of great fortunes and fantastic corruption in government, a time of brilliant thinkers and inspired artists. To this Italy of the Renaissance Copernicus went as a student, learning in its universities medicine, theology, and mathematics. Back in his native Poland he practiced medicine and interested himself in currency reform, but he devoted much of his time to developing an idea that had germinated in Italy, the idea that the universe could be vastly simplified if the sun rather than the earth were taken as its center.

Let us consider the earth, said Copernicus, as one of the planets, a sphere rotating once a day on its axis. Let us further imagine that the planets, including the earth, revolve in circular orbits about the sun (Fig. 1.3), that the moon is relatively close to the earth and revolves about it, and that the stars are situated at great distances beyond. In this picture rotation of the earth on its axis explains the daily rising and setting of celestial objects. The apparent motion of the sun among the stars is due to the earth's motion in its orbit; as we swing around the sun, it appears to us as if the sun were constantly shifting its position against the background of fixed stars. The moon's eastward drift is due in large part to its actual orbital motion. Apparent movements of the planets are explained as combinations of their actual motions around the sun and our shift of position as the earth moves.

The idea behind Copernicus' hypothesis was not new, for some of the Greeks, notably Aristarchus, had been well aware that apparent celestial motions could be the result of motions of the earth. But Copernicus went beyond these earlier speculations in working out the planetary motions mathematically. From observations of the positions of the planets he calculated

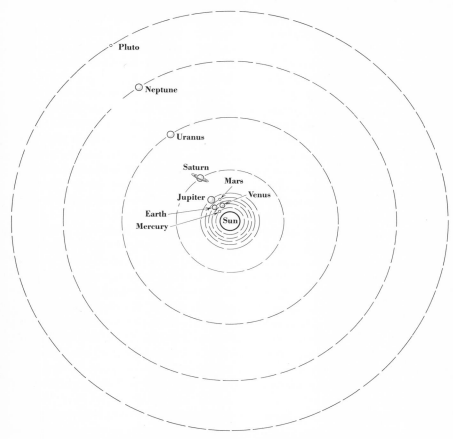

Fig. 1.3 **The Copernican system, showing the assumed arrangement of the members of the solar system.** *The planets, including the earth, are supposed to travel around the sun in circular orbits. The earth rotates daily on its axis, and the moon revolves around the earth. All the planets are shown here.*

how each orbit must be in comparison with that of the earth and how fast each planet must be moving. With these figures he could compute the apparent positions for any time in the past or future, just as Ptolemy had done with figures based on a different hypothesis. Copernicus found that these calculated positions agreed with observation fairly well, but hardly better than those calculated from the Ptolemaic system.

Despite lack of complete check with observation, Copernicus felt that his simple circular orbits gave a truer picture of the universe than the complex orbits of the Ptolemaic system. Such a belief in those days was unpopular, for many churchmen, both Protestant and Catholic, were reluctant to see the earth removed from its important place at the hub of the universe. Partly to avoid trouble with church authorities, partly from a desire to make his work as complete as possible, Copernicus delayed publication of his book for many years. As it turned out, a copy of the first printed edition reached Copernicus only a few weeks before his death in 1543.

With the publication of Copernicus' manuscript there began a long and bitter argument. To us, growing up with the idea that the earth moves, it seems odd that this simple idea was so long and so violently opposed. But in the sixteenth century, before the invention of the telescope, a decision between the Ptolemaic and Copernican systems was by no means easy. Predictions from both hypotheses agreed only moderately well with observations. Good scientific arguments could be brought forward on both sides. To settle the debate, precise observations were necessary both of celestial objects and of the earth itself, and these observations simply were not available.

In the meantime, arguments and counterarguments went on. Consider, said proponents of Ptolemy's hypothesis, how rapidly the surface of the earth must travel to complete a rotation every 24 hr. Would not all loose objects be flung into space by this whirling sphere, much as mud is thrown from the rim of a carriage wheel? And would not so dizzy a speed produce great winds to raze all rooted things, like buildings, trees, flowers? Admittedly, the earth spins rapidly, answered the disciples of Copernicus, but probably the effects of its rotation are counterbalanced by the force that holds our feet to the ground. Besides, if the speed of the earth's rotation is a problem, how much greater a problem would be the tremendous speeds of the sun, stars, and planets if they must revolve, as Ptolemy pictured them, once a day around a stationary earth. From Aristotle supporters of the older theory derived another cogent argument: If the earth moves through space around the sun, why do the stars not change position relative to one another, as trees on a distant hillside appear to change position when we drive past? Perhaps, countered the newer school, it is because the stars are so very remote. So went the dispute. The Ptolemaic hypothesis, in addition to theological support, had strong logical arguments behind it; the Copernican view rested on equally good logic and had the further merit of greater consistency and simplicity.

But the final decision rested on experiment. Fortunately, significant improvements in astronomical measurements—the first since the time of the Greeks—were not long in coming. Tycho Brahe, a Dane of noble descent, built an observatory at the Castle of Benatky, in which the instruments were as rigid and precise as possible. With the help of these instruments, Tycho, blessed with exceptional eyesight and patience, made thousands of measurements, a labor that occupied much of his life. Even without the telescope, which had not yet been invented, Tycho's observatory was able to determine celestial angles to better than one-hundredth of a degree.

At his death in 1601, Tycho left behind his own somewhat peculiar theory of the solar system, a body of superb data extending over many years, and an assistant named Johannes Kepler. Kepler regarded the Copernican scheme "with incredible and ravishing delight" and fully expected that Tycho's improved figures would prove Copernicus correct once and for all. But this was not the case; after four years of work on the orbit of Mars alone, Kepler could not reconcile the observational data with any of the models of the solar system that had by then been proposed. If the facts do not agree with the hypothesis, then the hypothesis, no matter how attractive, must be discarded. Kepler began a search for a new cosmic design that would be in better accord with Tycho's observations.

After considering every possibility, which meant years of drudgery in performing calculations by hand, Kepler found that circular orbits for the planets were out of the question even when modified in various plausible ways. He abandoned circular orbits only reluctantly, for he was something of a mystic and believed, like Copernicus and the Greeks, that circles were the only fitting type of path for celestial orbits. Discarding the circle led to consideration of other geometrical figures, and here Kepler found the key to the puzzle: *The paths of the planets around the sun are ellipses* (Fig. 1.4). This is called Kepler's first law.

Even this epochal discovery was not sufficient, as Kepler realized, for the

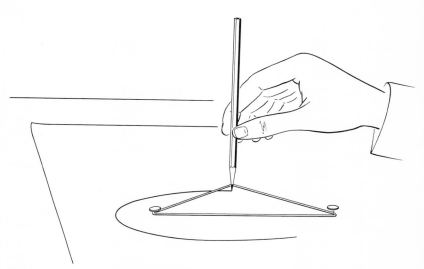

Fig. 1.4   *To draw an ellipse, place a loop of string over two tacks a short distance apart. Then move the pencil as shown, keeping the string taut. By varying the length of the string, ellipses of different shapes can be drawn. The points in an ellipse corresponding to the positions of the tacks are called* focuses; *the orbits of the planets are ellipses with the sun at one focus.*

virtue of the older hypotheses was that they could be used to *predict*—with
adequate accuracy for most purposes—the course of the planets through the
sky. What was needed now was a law that could relate the speeds of the
planets to their positions in their elliptical orbits. Kepler could not be sure
that such a law even existed, and he was overjoyed when he came upon the
answer: *The planets move so that their radius vectors* (which are imaginary
lines drawn from the sun to the planets) *sweep out equal areas in equal
times.* Thus, in Fig. 1.5, each of the shaded areas is covered in the same
period of time, which means that the planets travel more rapidly when they
are near the sun than when they are far from it. The earth, for instance,
has a speed of 18.8 miles per second (mi/sec) when it is nearest the sun
and 18.2 mi/sec when it is farthest away, a difference of over 3 percent.
This rule of equal areas is known as Kepler's second law.

A great achievement, but Kepler was not satisfied. He was obsessed
with the idea of order and regularity in the universe, and the notion that
the courses of the planets were not manifestations of some general pattern
seemed incredible to him. So Kepler persevered and, after ten more years
of labor, could announce his third law of planetary motion, the so-called
harmonic law: *The ratio between the square of the time required by a planet
to make a complete revolution around the sun and the cube of its average
distance from the sun is a constant for all the planets.*

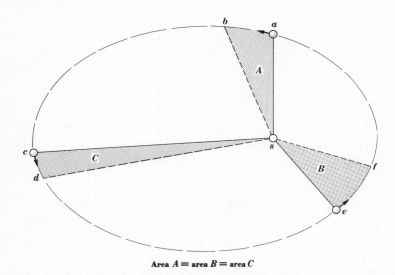

Area A = area B = area C

Fig. 1.5   Kepler's second law. *As a planet goes from a to b in its
orbit, its radius vector (an imaginary line joining it with the sun) sweeps
out the area A. In the same amount of time the planet can go from c to d,
with its radius vector sweeping out the area C, or from e to f, with its
radius vector sweeping out the area B; the three areas A, B, and C are equal.*

Thus, finally, the solar system was explained in terms of simple motions occurring in a specific frame of reference. Planetary positions computed from Kepler's ellipses agree not only with Tycho's data, but with observations made thousands of years earlier. Predictions could be made regarding positions of the planets in the future—accurate predictions this time, no longer mere approximations. Furthermore, Kepler's laws showed that the speed of a planet in different parts of its orbit was governed by a simple rule and that the speed was related to the size of the orbit. Beside this simple picture, Ptolemy's structure looked absurd indeed.

A Basic Assumption in Science

Kepler, we often say loosely, proved that Copernicus was right and that Ptolemy was wrong. It is worth pausing a moment to see in what sense such a statement has meaning.

What does it take to "prove" the correctness of a scientific hypothesis? The usual method is to test the agreement of the hypothesis with observation. If the hypothesis enables us to predict accurately the results of further observation and experiment, we accept it in preference to a hypothesis whose predictions are faulty. This is straightforward enough, but how do we proceed when two hypotheses fit the observed facts equally well?

Recall that the hypothesis of Copernicus, at the time of its publication, did not account for observed details of planetary motion any more accurately than Ptolemy's; the only real advantage Copernicus could claim was that his system made things simpler. Kepler, by introducing the further hypothesis of elliptical orbits, obtained better agreement with observation; in other words, he could predict more accurately just where each planet should appear in the sky at any future date. Does this "prove" the Copernican system correct? Hardly, for we could just as well modify the Ptolemaic system with elliptical orbits, building ellipses on ellipses instead of circles on circles, and we should obtain equally good checks with observation. Again the great advantage of the new idea is its simplicity, particularly striking now because no secondary loops at all would be required in the Copernican system, whereas they would still be needed to make Ptolemy's scheme work. We prove that Copernicus was right by showing that his idea gives a simpler but no less accurate picture; we do not prove that Ptolemy's more complicated structure could not be made to work if it were suitably patched up.

This is a situation often encountered in scientific work. Two hypotheses account equally well for a given set of data; how do we choose between them? The choice is always made as in this example. *The simpler hypothesis is the better hypothesis.*

Some such rule is necessary if science is to advance at all. Actually, for any set of observations, there are not just two possible hypotheses, but an indefinite number. To explain the sun's apparent motion, for example, we need not restrict ourselves to the earth or the sun as choices for the reference object. We might suppose that the center of motion is Venus or Jupiter, or we could try a hypothesis without an object at the center, both earth and sun moving around a point of space. A limit to the multiplying of hypotheses is set only by the inventiveness of our minds. And out of all these we choose the Copernican hypothesis as modified by Kepler, not because the other suggestions can be rigorously proved wrong, but because this hypothesis gives the simplest explanation for observed motions.

The statement that the simplest hypothesis is best needs one qualification: It must be the *simplest hypothesis that best explains all known facts.* For example, a great deal has been learned about planetary motions since the early seventeenth century. Newton showed that the motions are governed by the law of gravitation and that minor fluctuations in the motions can be explained by attractions of the various planets for one another. As telescopes increased in power and observations became more accurate, more and more of these minor irregularities in planetary motions were discovered. Hence the Copernican system today, with all the known details, is extremely complicated, much more so than the Ptolemaic system was in the time of Kepler. We do not on this account go back to the Ptolemaic system, for the obvious reason that it is totally inadequate to explain all the data we have at present. An acceptable hypothesis, then, must be both the simplest of various alternatives and the one in best agreement with the sum of accumulated knowledge.

Speed

Now that we have explored the relative nature of motion and why the proper selection of a frame of reference is so important, we shall go on to examine the quantitative language which is used to describe motion.

As we said earlier, a moving body may go from one place to another—a train from New York to Boston—or it may repeat the same path indefinitely—a child on a merry-go-round. In either case, the body travels through a certain distance in each interval of time while it is actually moving. For instance, the train may travel 68 miles during a certain hour of its trip, and the child may travel 5 ft during a certain second while the merry-go-round turns. The *speed* of a moving body is the rate at which it covers distance, that is, the distance it covers per unit time. This definition is conveniently expressed in the equation

$$\text{Speed} = \frac{\text{distance traveled}}{\text{time required}}$$

In symbolic form, letting v = speed, d = distance, and t = time,

$$v = \frac{d}{t} \tag{1.1}$$

Thus a train that covers 68 miles each hour has a speed of

$$v = \frac{68 \text{ miles}}{1 \text{ hr}} = 68 \text{ mi/hr}$$

and a child on a merry-go-round who covers 5 ft each second has a speed of

$$v = \frac{5 \text{ ft}}{1 \text{ sec}} = 5 \text{ ft/sec}$$

It is sometimes convenient to express quantities given in one set of units in terms of a different set. To perform the conversion we note first that units are treated in an equation just like ordinary algebraic quantities and may be multiplied or divided by one another. Second, we recall that multiplying or dividing a quantity by 1 does not affect its value. Let us see how these rules enable us to convert a speed of 5 ft/sec into other units. Suppose we require the speed expressed in inches per second. We note that

$$12 \text{ in.} = 1 \text{ ft}$$

so that $\quad$ 12 in./ft $= 1$

Hence, multiplying or dividing anything by 12 in./ft merely changes its units, but leaves it otherwise unaltered. If we multiply 5 ft/sec by 12 in./ft, we have

$$5 \frac{\text{ft}}{\text{sec}} \times 12 \frac{\text{in.}}{\text{ft}} = 60 \frac{\text{in.}}{\text{sec}}$$

since ft/ft $= 1$ and so cancels out. Similarly, we can express 5 ft/sec in ft/min by multiplying it by 60 sec/min:

$$5 \frac{\text{ft}}{\text{sec}} \times 60 \frac{\text{sec}}{\text{min}} = 300 \frac{\text{ft}}{\text{min}}$$

To perform the reverse conversion, we divide by 60 sec/min and so obtain

$$\frac{300 \text{ ft/min}}{60 \text{ sec/min}} = 5 \frac{\text{ft}}{\text{sec}}$$

since min/min $= 1$.

When a body moves at a constant speed, v is the same at all times. If this is the case, Eq. (1.1) may be rewritten in the useful forms

$$d = vt \tag{1.2}$$

and $\quad t = \dfrac{d}{v}$ $\hspace{6cm}$ (1.3)

The first of these permits us to determine how far the body goes in any period of time t. Thus a train whose speed is 68 mi/hr travels

$$d = 68 \text{ mi/ hr} \times 0.5 \text{ hr} = 34 \text{ miles}$$

in ½ hr and

$$d = 68 \, \text{mi/hr} \times 3 \, \text{hr} = 204 \, \text{miles}$$

in 3 hr. Equation (1.3) tells us how to find the time needed by a body whose speed is v to cover a distance d. Thus the train needs

$$t = \frac{100 \, \text{miles}}{68 \, \text{mi/hr}} = 1.47 \, \text{hr}$$

to travel 100 miles.

Velocity

Velocity is a term that is often confused with speed. The difference between them is that speed refers only to the distance covered by an object as it moves; velocity also takes into account the direction in which the object is moving. There are many situations in which it is important to know direction as well as speed. To a sailor an east wind at 32 mi/hr may be vastly different from a west wind at 32 mi/hr. An automobile traveling at 50 mi/hr to the northeast is going to find itself at the end of its trip in an entirely different place from an automobile whose velocity is 50 mi/hr to the south. When we speak of the *velocity* of a moving body, then, we refer both to its *speed* (how fast it is going) and to its *direction* (where it is headed).

The distinction between speed and velocity may seem, at first, to be a trivial matter, but we shall see that its implications are extremely important in understanding the effects of forces on motion.

Acceleration

When a body is moving with constant velocity, neither its direction nor its speed changes. A child on a merry-go-round may have a constant speed, but because he is traveling along a curved path, his velocity is not constant. A train may be proceeding on a straight track so that its direction is always the same, but if it goes faster or slower, its velocity is not constant. A body whose velocity changes is said to be *accelerated* (Fig. 1.6).

The rate of change of the velocity of an accelerated body is called its *acceleration*. In this chapter and the next we shall restrict ourselves to motion along a straight line, and in Chap. 3 we shall take up the more complicated problem of accelerations that involve a change in direction. The acceleration of a body restricted to straight-line motion can be written

$$\text{Acceleration} = \frac{\text{change in speed}}{\text{time required}}$$

In symbols,

$$a = \frac{v_2 - v_1}{t} \qquad (1.4)$$

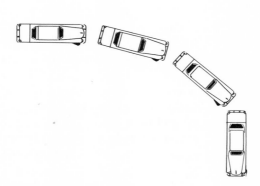

Fig. 1.6 *Three cases of accelerated motion, showing successive positions of a body after equal periods of time.* *At the top the intervals between the positions of the body increase in length because the body is traveling faster and faster. Below it the intervals decrease in length because the body is slowing down. At the bottom the intervals are the same in length because the speed is constant, but the direction of motion is constantly changing.*

where $a =$ body's acceleration

$v_1 =$ its speed at start of t

$v_2 =$ its speed at end of t

$t =$ time interval

As an example, let us consider a man traveling 30 mi/hr in a car who presses down on the gas pedal until his speedometer registers 50 mi/hr. His speed has therefore increased by

$$v_2 - v_1 = \ 50 \, \text{mi/hr} - 30 \, \text{mi/hr} = \ 20 \, \text{mi/hr}$$

Suppose that 2 min is required for his car to reach the higher speed. Then his acceleration is

$$a = \frac{20 \text{ mi/hr}}{2 \text{ min}} = 10 \frac{\text{mi/hr}}{\text{min}}$$

It is usually desirable to use the same unit for time throughout. In terms of hours,

$$a = 10 \frac{\text{mi/hr}}{\text{min}} \times 60 \frac{\text{min}}{\text{hr}} = 600 \frac{\text{mi/hr}}{\text{hr}}$$

which can be written more simply as 600 mi/hr². This means that the speed of the car increases by 600 mi/hr during each hour the acceleration continues. Of course, the acceleration is only a few minutes long in the case of a car, and the mere fact that *if* this acceleration persisted unchanged for an hour the car's speed would be hundreds of miles per hour does not mean that it is *possible* for the acceleration to go on for so long. In actuality, friction and air resistance would prevent more than a fraction of such a high speed from being achieved.

Equation (1.4) may be rewritten in the form

$$v_2 = v_1 + at \tag{1.5}$$

This equation states that the final speed of an object undergoing the acceleration *a* is equal to its speed at the start of the acceleration v_1 plus the product of the acceleration *a* and the time *t* during which it acts. Thus a ball rolling across the floor may be retarded by friction so that it slows down at the rate of 2 cm/sec². If its initial speed is 10 cm/sec, at the end of 1 sec its speed is

$$v_2 = 10 \text{ cm/sec} - 2 \text{ cm/sec}^2 \times 1 \text{ sec}$$
$$= 8 \text{ cm/sec}$$

at the end of 2 sec its speed is

$$v_2 = 10 \text{ cm/sec} - 2 \text{ cm/sec}^2 \times 2 \text{ sec}$$
$$= 6 \text{ cm/sec}$$

and so on. The acceleration is negative since its effect is to reduce the ball's speed.

Let us suppose we have a body of initial speed v_1 which experiences an acceleration *a*. We have seen that its speed after a time *t* is $v_2 = v_1 + at$. How far does it go during this time? To answer this basic question we note that, during the time interval *t*, the body's *average* speed $\bar{v}$ is

$$\bar{v} = \frac{v_1 + v_2}{2} \tag{1.6}$$

Since its speed is increasing uniformly, the body travels as far as if it had the constant speed *v* equal to its average speed $\bar{v}$, and we have just

$$d = \bar{v}t$$

Substituting for $\bar{v}$,

$$d = \tfrac{1}{2}(v_1 + v_2)t$$

and inserting $v_2 = v_1 + at$, we finally find that

$$d = v_1 t + \tfrac{1}{2}at^2 \tag{1.7}$$

Equation (1.7) gives the distance traveled by a body of initial speed v_1 during the time t in which it undergoes the acceleration a. If there is no acceleration, the speed is constant and

$$d = v_1 t$$

which is Eq. (1.2), while if its initial speed is 0,

$$d = \tfrac{1}{2}at^2 \tag{1.8}$$

Freely Falling Bodies

The most familiar acceleration is that of gravity. When something is dropped, it does not fall with uniform speed (neglecting air resistance). A stone released from the top of a cliff strikes the ground with a much higher speed than a stone released at shoulder level (Fig. 1.7). If we jump off a table, we strike the floor with greater impact than if we jump off a chair.

The significant aspect of the acceleration of freely falling bodies is that it is always the same. Large objects and small, heavy ones and light, all descend with an acceleration of 32 ft/sec² (9.8 m/sec² in metric units). This acceleration is usually abbreviated g. Because of it, a body falling from rest has a speed of 32 ft/sec at the end of the first second, 64 ft/sec at the end of the next second, and so on. To adapt Eq. (1.5) to the case of a body falling from rest, we note that $v_1 = 0$ and $a = g$. Hence we can simply write

$$v = gt \tag{1.9}$$

where v is the downward speed of the body after falling for the time t. Similarly, from Eq. (1.8), the body will drop

$$d = \tfrac{1}{2}gt^2 \tag{1.10}$$

during this time.

For simplicity, in the preceding paragraph we have neglected air resistance. In the motion of small, light objects like raindrops, air resistance exerts a retarding influence opposing the accelerating tendency of gravity; otherwise raindrops would attain bulletlike velocities, and we could not safely venture out in the lightest shower. But for moderately heavy objects dropping at moderate speeds, air resistance is only a minor correction.

The retarding action of the air often gives an erroneous idea of the

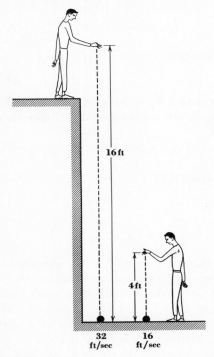

16 ft

4 ft

32
ft/sec

16
ft/sec

Fig. 1.7 *A stone released from the top of a cliff strikes the ground with a much higher velocity than a stone released at shoulder level.*

relative rates with which different objects fall. A feather and a lead bullet indisputably fall with very different velocities. But the difference is wholly due to the buoyancy and large surface of the feather; if the two objects or any other two objects are enclosed in an evacuated cylinder, they fall at precisely the same rate (Fig. 1.8). Since the acceleration of gravity is the same for everything, the velocities of any two objects dropped simultaneously will increase at the same rate, and the objects will reach the ground together.

It does not matter whether a falling body starts out from a stationary position or is initially moving. If a ball is simply held in the air and dropped, its velocity increases steadily until it strikes the ground. If it is thrown in a horizontal direction, its motion is determined both by its tendency to keep on moving in the direction it was thrown and by the pull of gravity. The pull of gravity accelerates its motion downward, so that the ball moves in a curved path which grows steeper as it nears the ground (Fig. 1.9). If the ball is tossed vertically upward (Fig. 1.10), the acceleration, acting downward, at first is in a direction opposite to the ball's motion. Hence the ball's velocity steadily diminishes, becoming zero at the top of its climb, and then increases steadily downward, the acceleration remaining constant throughout.

Galileo

The conclusion that objects near the earth's surface fall with the same acceleration regardless of their weight was first clearly stated by Galileo Galilei as a result of careful experiments on the speeds of balls rolling down inclined planes. This directly contradicted part of the teachings of Aristotle, whose ideas were widely accepted in the early seventeenth century. Aristotle's reasoning depended on a general theory of the universe, in which each different kind of material had a "natural" place appropriate to it and toward which

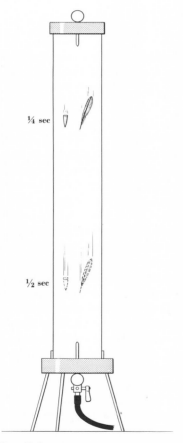

Fig. 1.8   *In a vacuum all bodies fall with the same acceleration since air resistance and buoyancy do not act.*

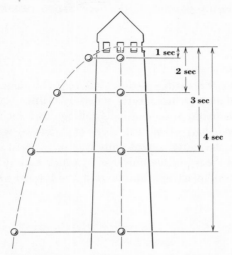

Fig. 1.9 *When one ball is thrown horizontally from a building at the same time that a second ball is dropped vertically, the two reach the ground simultaneously because both have the same downward acceleration.*

it tried to move. Thus fire had a "natural motion" upward toward the sun and stars, whereas rocks or sticks of wood had an "earthy" quality that caused them to move downward toward their natural home in the earth. Furthermore, objects might contain different proportions of earthiness or fieriness, and their motions upward or downward would be accordingly fast or slow. It followed that a big stone, possessing more earthiness than a small one, ought to move downward more rapidly.

This fragment of Aristotle's reasoning, taken out of context, sounds rather absurd in the light of present knowledge. Actually, this is not fair to the great philosopher, for the conclusion about falling bodies is only a minor detail in a grand scheme that sought to explain the operation of the universe and man's relation to it. The central ideas of Aristotle's universe— a stationary earth at the center of things, with mankind as the most important part of creation—fitted well into Christian theology and were in fact made a part of Church dogma in the writings of St. Thomas Aquinas and his followers. With this powerful backing, it is small wonder that Aristotle's ideas survived almost unaltered for nearly 2,000 years and that to challenge them in the early 1600s took more than ordinary courage.

Yet challenge them Galileo did. The particular question of falling bodies he worked on as a young professor at the University of Pisa and when he found that his experiments contradicted prevailing ideas, he attacked the conclusions of Aristotle with all the brashness and heedlessness of youth. A story has come down to us that he sought to dramatize his ideas by climbing to the top of Pisa's famous leaning tower and dropped from there a bullet and a cannon ball, thus demonstrating to a skeptical crowd that two objects would indeed reach the ground together. The story is not confirmed by historical records, but history does tell us that his outspoken championing of experimental results in opposition to the authority of Aristotle caused him to lose his professorship at Pisa. This was only a momentary setback in a brilliant career. Galileo continued his experimental work in other Italian cities, his learning bringing him fame as a scholar and his personal charm winning him friends among the ruling families of Italy. Despite fame and friends, his continued criticism of accepted opinions brought recurrent trouble with Church authorities. Especially serious was his advocacy of the Copernican system. For many years he managed to escape serious reprisals, but finally, as an old man, he was hailed before the Inquisition at Rome and forced, under threat of torture, to recant his heretical beliefs.

The most radical new idea that Galileo introduced, which no amount of recanting could obliterate, was not a specific scientific discovery, but the general concept that useful information about the world can be gained from accurate observation and experiment. Aristotle had sought to explain the world largely by reasoning alone—reasoning based on supposedly self-evident principles, like the principle that all materials seek to move toward their natural levels. He would have regarded Galileo's experiments as trivial, as a wrong-headed way of getting information, because they did not relate motion to general principles. Galileo, on the other hand, ignored hypothetical principles in favor of finding out by actual trial just how falling bodies

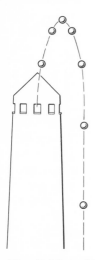

Fig. 1.10 *When a ball is thrown upward, its downward acceleration eventually causes its velocity to decrease to zero. This point is the top of its path, and it then begins to fall as if it had been dropped from there.*

do behave. From his experiments he could derive mathematical rules or laws describing how fast a falling body will move and how far it will go in a given time, and he could check the rules by further experiment; but these rules are entirely different from the broad principles of Aristotle. The emphasis on conclusions drawn from observation and experiment rather than from "self-evident" principles is the characteristic that distinguishes modern science from all previous methods of trying to gain understanding and control of the natural world.

Self-examination

1. The object in the sky that apparently moves least in the course of time is
   a. the North Star
   b. the sun
   c. the moon
   d. one of the other planets

2. The Copernican system replaced the Ptolemaic system primarily because it
   a. made calculations easier
   b. was favored by the medieval church
   c. provided a simpler picture of the heavens
   d. placed the sun at the center of the solar system

3. The most precise early measurements of the planetary motions were made by
   a. Johannes Kepler
   b. Galileo Galilei
   c. Isaac Newton
   d. Tycho Brahe

4. Kepler modified the Copernican system by showing that the planetary orbits are
   a. ellipses
   b. circles
   c. combinations of circles forming looped orbits
   d. the same distance apart from one another

5. A scientific hypothesis is
   a. a law of nature
   b. a diagram showing the paths taken by the planets
   c. a proposed explanation for observations made on some aspect of the physical world
   d. a statement of experimental results

6. An airplane travels at constant speed a distance of 160 miles in a time of ½ hr. Its speed is
   a. 80 mph

b. 160 mph
c. 320 mph
d. 640 mph

7. An object with a constant *speed*
   a. is not accelerated
   b. might be accelerated
   c. is always accelerated
   d. also has a constant velocity

8. In which of the following examples is the motion of the car not accelerated?
   a. A car turns a corner at the constant speed of 20 mi/hr.
   b. A car climbs a steep hill with its speed dropping from 60 mi/hr at the bottom to 15 mi/hr at the top.
   c. A car climbs a steep hill at the constant speed of 40 mi/hr.
   d. A car climbs a steep hill and goes over the crest and down on the other side, all at the same speed of 40 mi/hr.

9. When a body is accelerated,
   a. its velocity always changes
   b. its speed always changes
   c. its direction always changes
   d. it falls toward the earth

Problems

1. To the naked eye, a planet looks only slightly different from a star. If you watched the sky each night for a month or so, how could you definitely distinguish a planet from a star?

2. If you were standing at the North Pole, along what paths would the stars appear to move?

3. In terms of what you would actually observe, what does it mean to say that the moon apparently moves eastward among the stars?

4. In terms of what you would actually observe, what does it mean to say that the sun apparently moves eastward among the stars?

5. Why does the moon not rise at the same hour every night?

6. From observations of the moon and its motion, why would you conclude that it is not another planet revolving around the sun but rather a relatively small body revolving about the earth?

7. If you could measure accurately the sun's apparent diameter as seen from the earth, what changes in the diameter would you anticipate finding in the course of a year? Why?

8. The sun, moon, and planets all follow approximately the same path across the sky, from east to west; none of them is ever seen in the far northern or far southern sky. What does this suggest to you about the arrangement in space of these members of the solar system?

9. Sometimes Venus and Jupiter are seen close together in the western sky early in the evening. Draw a diagram to show the relative positions of earth, sun, and the two planets when this happens. Draw the diagram as though you were looking down on the North Pole from above, and indicate the directions of the earth's rotation and revolution.

10. To an observer on the earth, the heavenly bodies all appear to be moving with respect to him. Why, then, do we regard the Copernican hypothesis as a better representation of the universe than the Ptolemaic hypothesis?

11. Light from the sun requires about $8\frac{1}{3}$ min to reach the earth, a distance of about 150 million kilometers or 93 million miles. What is the speed of light, in kilometers per second and in miles per second?

12. If an airplane has a cruising speed of 300 mi/hr and is bucking a 60 mi/hr head wind, what distance can it cover in 6 hr? If the same airplane has a tail wind of 60 mi/hr, what distance can it cover in 6 hr?

13. The speed of sound in air is about 1,100 ft/sec. If a gun is fired 1 mile from you, how long will it take before you hear the sound?

14. It is approximately 2,300 miles by car from Chicago to San Francisco. If a motorist averages 40 mi/hr and drives for 9 hr each day, how many days will he require for the trip?

15. A car moving at 50 mi/hr is brought to a stop in 3 sec. What is its average acceleration in this period?

16. A pitcher requires about 0.1 sec to throw a baseball. If the ball leaves his hand with a speed of 120 ft/sec, what was its acceleration?

17. A car is moving with a speed of 20 ft/sec. Four seconds later its speed is 14 ft/sec. What is its acceleration?

18. A stone dropped from a cliff falls, as we know, with an acceleration of 9.8 m/sec². How fast will the stone be moving 1 sec after it is dropped? 3 sec after it is dropped?

19. A ball is thrown vertically downward with an initial velocity of 10 m/sec. What is its velocity after 1 sec? After 5 sec?

20. A ball is thrown vertically upward with an initial velocity of 10 m/sec. What is its velocity after 1 sec? After 5 sec?

21. A ball is thrown vertically upward with an initial velocity of 96 ft/sec. How long will it take the ball to reach the highest point in its path? How long will it take the ball to return to its starting place? What will the ball's velocity be there?

22. Suppose that you are in a barrel going over Niagara Falls and that, during the fall of the barrel, you drop an apple inside the barrel. Would it appear to move toward the top of the barrel or toward its bottom, or would it remain stationary within the barrel?

23. A car whose acceleration is constant attains a speed of 50 mi/hr in 20 sec starting from rest. How much additional time is required for it to attain a speed of 80 mi/hr?

24. An object whose initial speed is 90 m/sec is acted upon by an acceleration of —20 m/sec². How far will the object go while its speed decreases to 30 m/sec?

25. A man in an ascending elevator drops a stone from a height of 6 ft above the elevator floor. How long does the stone take to reach the floor when the elevator is rising (*a*) at a constant speed of 10 ft/sec and (*b*) at a constant upward acceleration of 2 ft/sec²?

26. A man in a descending elevator drops a stone from a height of 6 ft above the elevator floor. How long does the stone take to reach the floor when the elevator is falling (*a*) at a constant speed of 10 ft/sec and (*b*) at a constant downward acceleration of 2 ft/sec²?

CHAPTER 2 | THE LAWS OF MOTION

In the previous chapter we learned how to analyze the motion of a body in terms of velocity and acceleration, time and distance, and saw how these quantities are related. Now it is appropriate to inquire into the origin of motion. Why does anything move? Why do some bodies maintain constant velocities while others go faster or slower or change direction? These are fundamental questions, and the answers to them constitute the equally fundamental laws of motion formulated nearly three centuries ago by Isaac Newton.

The First Law of Motion

Imagine a ball at rest on a level table. Given a gentle push, the ball rolls a short distance and gradually comes to a stop. This is common experience. The harder and smoother the ball and table top are made, the farther the ball rolls before stopping. Suppose that the ball could be made perfectly round and the table flawlessly smooth and perfectly level. In other words, suppose there were no friction between them; suppose, further, that all air (which resists motion through it) could be removed from the path of the ball and that the table were infinitely long. If the ball were now set in motion, would it ever stop rolling?

The conditions of this experiment cannot, of course, be realized in our laboratories. But they can be closely approximated, and the result is that, as resistance to its motion becomes less and less, the ball shows less and less inclination to stop. It is reasonable to conclude that, under ideal conditions, it would keep on rolling forever.

This conclusion was first expressed in the writings of Galileo. Later it was stated by Isaac Newton in a general form that has come to be known as Newton's first law of motion: *Every body continues in its state of rest or of uniform motion in a straight line if no force acts upon it.*

In other words, objects about us do not start moving of their own accord; once set in motion, they continue with constant speed in a straight line until some resistance (for instance, friction) makes them stop. In our daily life such influences as friction and air resistance cannot be eliminated, and, consequently, all moving bodies in our experience tend to stop. To keep them moving at constant speed it is necessary that something push them continually, the push being used to overcome friction and air resistance. But here and throughout this chapter we are considering ideal conditions, under which friction and air resistance are absent. When we speak of balls, we shall mean perfectly smooth, hard spheres; our tables and floors and roads will be smooth, level surfaces of indefinite extent. Granted these conditions, a moving ball has no reason to stop. A push is required to set it moving, but once started, it continues of its own accord. Ideally, motion at constant speed in a straight line is a condition quite as natural as a state of rest.

Inertia and Mass

When we say that a motionless body tends to remain at rest, we imply that it offers a definite resistance to any attempt to make it begin moving. This fact is strikingly evident when we try to move a stalled car by pushing it. Newton's first law states that a body, once in motion, resists attempts at stopping it or changing its motion. For the same reason, if we have managed to push the car hard enough to get it rolling, we find great difficulty in stopping it.

The resistance that a material object offers to any change in its motion is an important property of matter called *inertia*. Inertia is significant because it gives us a means of measuring the quantity of matter present in an object.

The expression *quantity of matter* is another of those phrases whose meaning seems to be clear, yet which science insists upon providing with a very specific definition that may seem at first to be rather peculiar. The trouble is that a number of different concepts are mixed up in most of our minds when we speak of matter. There is, first, the notion of bulk, the feeling that one of the essential properties of matter is that it occupies space. This is a very difficult idea to put into the precise terms of science, because, as we shall see later, it is impossible to ascribe a definite volume to the fundamental building blocks of which matter is composed.

Another concept involved in our mental picture of matter is *weight*. In everyday life we measure the amount of matter present in an object by simply weighing it. Something weighing 2 pounds (lb) contains twice as much matter as something else weighing 1 lb. The reason that weight is unsatisfactory for an adequate definition of quantity of matter is that *weight is the gravitational pull of the earth on an object*. This pull is not the same everywhere on the earth; it is less at high elevations (on mountaintops, for example) than at sea level, less near the equator than near the North and South Poles. These differences are not large, of course, but they do exist. For example, a body weighing exactly 1 ton (2,000 lb) in Lima, Peru, would weigh about 8 lb more if taken to Oslo, Norway. Also, the idea of weight becomes confusing if we leave the vicinity of the earth altogether. A 150-lb man "weighs" 25 lb on the moon (that is, the moon exerts a pull of 25 lb on him), but he would weigh 2 tons on the sun and nothing at all in empty space far from the solar system and other stars. It is hard to believe that it is the amount of matter in an object that varies so greatly when we take it from place to place, and so weight is not a suitable quantity to use in describing matter from a scientific point of view.

The property of matter that gives rise to inertia, though, is much more promising. Imagine two balls of equal size, one made of lead, the other of wood. Here on earth we should say immediately that the lead ball contains more matter because it weighs more. If we were blindfolded and forbidden to weigh them, we could still tell the balls apart by kicking them along a level floor because the inertia of the lead ball would resist our kick more than that of the wooden ball. Now suppose that we and the two balls are transferred to some point in the depths of space. Can we find any method of establishing the greater quantity of matter in the lead ball under these new conditions? Weighing them would be quite useless, for neither ball would exert any downward push on our hand or on the pan of a balance. But inertia would still give the answer. The lead ball would again appear to contain more matter, because our toe would again hurt more after kicking it. The resistance that the two balls offer to any attempt to make them move is a property quite independent of their weights—and much more fundamental than their weights since it does not depend upon their position with respect to the earth (Fig. 2.1).

The name *mass* is given to the property of matter that manifests itself as inertia. Since this property is an intrinsic characteristic of matter and does not depend upon the location, shape, size, etc., of a particular object, mass may properly be thought of as quantity of matter; the more mass something has, the more matter it contains.

In the metric system mass is measured in units of *grams*. The gram was originally defined as the mass of a cubic centimeter of water [a cubic centimeter is the volume of a box in the shape of a cube each of whose sides measures a centimeter (cm)]. Because the gram (g) is such a small unit (1 g is equivalent to 0.0353 oz), the *kilogram* (kg), equal to 1,000 g, has come into common use. Today, masses in the metric system are all referred

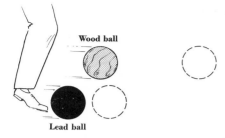

Wood ball

Lead ball

Fig. 2.1   *The inertia of a lead ball is greater than that of a wood ball everywhere in the universe. When both are kicked with the same force, the wood ball receives the greater acceleration because its mass is less.*

to the mass of a *standard kilogram,* a platinum-iridium cylinder kept at the International Bureau of Weights and Measures in France.   The mass of the standard kilogram is, by definition, exactly one kilogram.   The weight of 1 kg in British units is 2.2 lb.

The unit of mass in the British system, the *slug,* is unfamiliar to most people, because we normally deal with the weights of things rather than with their masses.   We shall consider mass and weight in the British system later in this chapter.

Force and Acceleration

Let us now return to the last clause of Newton's first law of motion, which states that the motion of a body can be altered by the action of a force.   Most of us have a hazy notion of what force means; we think of a horse pulling a wagon, a man pushing a wheelbarrow or lifting a flour sack.   Other familiar examples we have met in the preceding discussion are the force of gravity, which pulls us and objects about us to the earth's surface, and the force of friction, which retards the motion of any object moving in contact with another.   The pull of a magnet and the force of water pushing against the vanes of a turbine are further illustrations.   In all these examples the central idea is one of pushing or pulling, lifting or throwing—a process either involving muscular effort or producing the same results as the exertion of muscular effort. We shall speak of forces immensely greater than any muscle could produce and forces immeasurably smaller than the most delicate touch could detect, but we call them *forces* because they produce results on a larger or smaller scale similar to results accomplished by muscular effort.   Force is thus a concept based on the direct evidence of our senses and is difficult to define satisfactorily.   The most workable definition is a restatement of the first law of motion which specifies the result of a force's action: *A force is any influence capable of producing a change in the motion of a body.*   Actual change of motion need not result from the application of a force.   We may push with all our strength against a stone wall without affecting its motion in the slightest degree, yet we still call this muscular exertion the application of a force, since the same exertion would be capable of producing motion if applied to a more suitable object.

What we have called simply "change of motion" in the above paragraph is, of course, *acceleration*. A moving body with no forces acting upon it proceeds with constant velocity. If a force should act on the body, the velocity of the body changes, either in magnitude or direction or both, and the body is therefore *accelerated*. A force, then, is something capable of causing an acceleration, and, conversely, every acceleration is the result of an applied force.

It is important to remember that a body continues to be accelerated as long as a force acts upon it, and no longer. A force does not merely make a body move faster, for example, than it moved before; it causes the speed to increase steadily until the force is removed. Here again, results that would be obtained under ideal conditions seem to contradict everyday experience. Theoretically, as just stated, a small force acting on a ball rolling without friction would cause its speed to increase steadily, and the ball could be made to move with any conceivable speed if only the force acted for a long enough time. Theoretically, again, the accelerator in an ideal automobile would not be needed at all to maintain a constant speed of 30 or 60 mi/hr; once set in motion at either of these speeds, an ideal car would keep on moving without any further force being applied to its wheels. To change from 30 to 60 mi/hr would require use of the accelerator, that is, the application of a force. We might say, then, that the force would have effected a change from one constant speed to another; but the direct effect of the force, the effect while the force was acting, would have been to make the speed increase continually, and unless the force was removed when 60 mi/hr was attained, the speed would go right on increasing. An ideal car could be made to go at any desired speed, however fast, merely by a slight momentary pressure on the accelerator. Ordinary cars cannot, because at high speeds friction and air resistance increase, so that most of the force that the engine applies to the rear wheels is used up merely in counteracting these opposing forces.

From similar reasoning we conclude that no force at all, or better an infinitely small force, is required to move an ideal ball from one position of rest on a level table to another. Applying any finite force would set the ball moving forever, with constant velocity if the force were removed, with steadily increasing velocity if the force were continuous. Practically, we have to supply a force: We strike the ball and let it roll to a stop in its new position. During the fraction of a second while we are striking it, the force we exert changes the ball's velocity from zero to some small value; when the striking force is removed, friction begins to alter this velocity, reducing it to zero when the ball reaches its new position of rest. We apply a force to make the ball change position, but the force is used entirely in overcoming the opposing force of friction. Ideally, the initial force needed would be infinitely small.

Newton's Second Law of Motion

Newton's second law of motion is a quantitative expression of the ideas we have discussed in the foregoing paragraphs. It gives us a relation among force, mass, and acceleration that can be treated mathematically: *The acceleration that a force can give an object is directly proportional to the magnitude of the force and inversely proportional to the mass of the object; the acceleration is in the direction of the applied force.*

This means that, if we measure the accelerations produced by different forces on the same mass, doubling the force will double the acceleration, and that, if we let the same force act on different masses, doubling the mass will cut the resulting acceleration in half (Fig. 2.2). Provided that proper units are employed, the law can be stated mathematically in the form

$$\frac{F}{m} = a$$

or, equivalently, as

$$F = ma \tag{2.1}$$

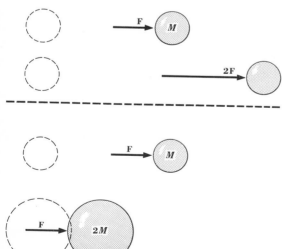

Fig. 2.2 *When different forces act upon the same mass, the greater force produces the greater acceleration. When the same force acts upon different masses, the greater mass receives the smaller acceleration.*

where $F = $ force

$m = $ mass

$a = $ acceleration

In words, the second expression says that force is equal to the product of mass and acceleration. This is a precise statement of the definition of force given above.

It is impossible to exaggerate the importance of Newton's second law of motion. Replacing vague, intuitive feelings about the effects of forces with a definite, quantitative statement, this apparently simple law provides the foundation for much of the science of physics.

The second law permits us to define a unit for force in the metric system. If we express mass m in kilograms and acceleration a in meters per second per second (m/sec^2), the force F is given directly in terms of a unit called the *newton*. For example, if we apply a force of 15 newtons (about $3\frac{1}{2}$ lb) to a ball of mass 0.3 kg, the ball will experience an acceleration of

$$a = \frac{F}{m} = \frac{15 \text{ newtons}}{0.3 \text{ kg}} = 50 \text{ m/sec}^2$$

On the other hand, if we measure the acceleration of an object of known mass, we can compute what force must have been applied to it.

Another aspect of Newton's second law concerns direction. The direction of the acceleration is always the same as the direction of the force. An automobile begins to go faster and faster; therefore the force exerted on it is the same direction as the one in which it is moving. The same automobile slows down; therefore the force exerted on it is in the direction *opposite* to that in which it is moving. This conclusion follows from the fact that the velocity of the automobile is decreasing, implying an acceleration (rate of

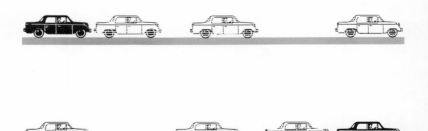

Fig. 2.3   *A force applied in the direction in which a body is moving produces a positive acceleration (increase in speed). A force applied opposite to the direction of motion produces a negative acceleration (decrease in speed).*

change of velocity) that is negative in terms of its forward movement. A forward acceleration produces an increase in speed, whereas a backward acceleration produces a decrease in speed (Fig. 2.3). When the automobile rounds a curve at a constant speed, its direction changes, and there is an acceleration present. This acceleration is toward the inside of the curve; thus the force that produced the turning must have been pointing toward the inside of the curve. We shall have more to say about force and acceleration with respect to bodies moving along curved paths in the next chapter, but the essential thing to keep in mind is that every change in velocity, whether a change in speed or direction of motion, is caused by a force acting in the same direction as the change.

Mass and Weight

The force with which the earth attracts a body is called the weight of the body. If your weight is 160 lb, that means that the earth is pulling you down with a force of 160 lb. Weight is different from mass, which is a measure of the quantity of matter an object contains. There is a very intimate relationship between weight and mass, though, and it is extremely important for us to understand it.

Let us look at the problem in the following way. Whenever a force F is applied to a mass m, Newton's second law of motion tells us that the mass will be so accelerated that its acceleration a will be in accordance with the formula

$$F = ma$$

In the case of a body on the earth, the force exerted upon it by gravity is its weight W. This force causes the body to fall with the constant acceleration $g = 32$ ft/sec^2. We may therefore substitute W for F and g for a in the above formula, so that

$$W = mg \qquad (2.2)$$

Since g is a constant, the weight W of a body and its mass m are always directly proportional to each other; a large mass is heavier than a small one.

In the British system of units we use pounds (lb) for weight and feet per second per second (ft/sec^2) for acceleration. The corresponding unit of mass is the *slug*. In order to find the mass in slugs of some object whose weight W we know, we need only rearrange Eq. (2.2) in the form

$$m \text{ (slugs)} = \frac{W \text{ (lb)}}{g \text{ (ft/sec}^2)}$$

Since g is 32 ft/sec^2,

$$m \text{ (slugs)} = \frac{W \text{ (lb)}}{32 \text{ ft/sec}^2} \qquad (2.3)$$

In other words, dividing by 32 the weight of something measured in pounds gives its mass in slugs.

It is legitimate to ask at this point why we should ever want to know the mass of a body in terms of so peculiar-sounding a unit as the slug, when, after all, weights rather than masses are what we normally deal with. We go to the store for 10 lb of onions, not for $\frac{1}{3}$ slug of onions. The usefulness of knowing the mass of some object comes in whenever we wish to apply Newton's second law of motion to its behavior. Suppose that we push a car weighing 3,200 lb with a force of 50 lb. To find its acceleration we must first find its mass; since

$$m \text{ (slugs)} = \frac{W \text{ (lb)}}{32 \text{ ft/sec}^2}$$

we have
$$m = \frac{3,200}{32} = 100 \text{ slugs}$$

Now we can use this mass value in the second law of motion,

$$F = ma$$

to find the value of the acceleration a. With $F = 50$ lb and $m = 100$ slugs,

$$a = \frac{F}{m} = \frac{50 \text{ lb}}{100 \text{ slugs}}$$
$$= \frac{1}{2} \text{ ft/sec}^2$$

If there were no friction present, the car's acceleration would be $\frac{1}{2}$ ft/sec^2. At the end of 1 sec its speed would be $\frac{1}{2}$ ft/sec; at the end of 10 sec its speed would be 5 ft/sec; and so forth.

The second law of motion can be used in reverse, so to speak, to determine the force that is producing a known acceleration. The same car we spoke of above might increase its speed, say, from 20 to 50 mi/hr in 20 sec. Again neglecting friction, what force did the car's motor have to supply in order to cause this acceleration? We start by calculating the acceleration. The car increased its speed by $50 - 20$, or 30 mi/hr in 20 sec. Since 30 mi/hr is equal to 44 ft/sec,

$$\text{Acceleration} = \frac{\text{change in velocity}}{\text{time interval}}$$
$$a = \frac{44 \text{ ft/sec}}{20 \text{ sec}} = 2.2 \text{ ft/sec}^2$$

Thus the force acting on the car was

$$F = ma = 100 \text{ slugs} \times 2.2 \text{ ft/sec}^2$$
$$= 220 \text{ lb}$$

How is weight measured in the metric system? In the metric system, as we know, mass rather than weight is normally specified; a customer in a French grocery might ask for a kilogram of bread or 5 kg of potatoes. To find the weight in newtons (the metric unit of force) of something whose mass in kilograms is known, we simply turn to Eq. (2.2) and set $g = 9.8$ m/sec², its value in the metric system. Then we have

$$W \text{ (newtons)} = m \text{ (kg)} \times 9.8 \text{ m/sec}^2$$

Thus the weight of 5 kg of potatoes is

$$W = 5 \times 9.8 = 49 \text{ newtons}$$

This is the force with which the earth attracts a mass of 5 kg.

Newton's Third Law of Motion

Forces in the world about us always turn out, upon close examination, to consist of combinations of forces. When we think we have a case of just one force at work, further inspection reveals others—less obvious perhaps, but nevertheless present. Let us look into the question of whether it is ever possible for a single force to exist.

We push downward on a table. As far as we are concerned, that seems to be a single force—an elemental push, giving us the sort of sensation which we must use in any ultimate definition of force. But immediately we are conscious of a second force: the resistance of the table, pushing upward against our hand as we push downward on its top. The harder we press down, the more stubbornly the table resists. Seemingly, we cannot exert a force on the table without its exerting a force on us.

Suppose that we transfer ourselves and the table to the frozen surface of a lake—to a sheet of ice, which we shall imagine to be smooth and slippery, so that it can offer no resistance to the table's sideward motion. Again we push on the table, horizontally now instead of vertically, and watch it accelerate, as it should under the influence of a single constant force (Fig. 2.4). But again we meet difficulties: We can stick to the ice no better than the table can, and as we push it away from us, we find ourselves starting to

Force exerted by table on man

Force exerted by man on table

Fig. 2.4 *Pushing a table on a frozen lake results in man and table moving apart in opposite directions.*

move in the opposite direction. Even here we cannot seem to exert a force on the table without its pushing back on us, as revealed by our motion.

Considerations of this sort led Newton to his third law of motion: *For every force there is an equal and opposite force.* More precisely, whenever one object exerts a force on a second, the second exerts an equal force in the opposite direction on the first.

No force ever occurs singly. A weight hangs on a spring balance; the weight pulls downward on the spring, and the spring pulls upward on the weight (Fig. 2.5). A chair pushes downward on the floor; the floor presses upward on the chair. The firing of a rifle exerts force on a bullet; the bullet simultaneously pushes backward (recoil) on the rifle.

Sometimes the reality of the opposite force is difficult to appreciate. A book resting on a table exerts the downward force of its own weight; but just how can an inert object like the table exert a real upward force on the book? If the table top were made of rubber, the book would depress it, and the upward force would obviously result from the elasticity of the rubber. A similar explanation actually holds for table tops of wood or metal, although the depression is extremely small. Again, a falling apple experiences a

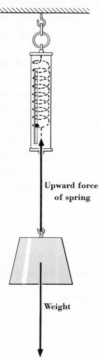

Upward force
of spring

Weight

Fig. 2.5 *For every force there is an equal and opposite force: The spring pulls upward on the weight with the same force as that with which the weight pulls downward on the spring.*

downward pull from the earth and, by the third law, must itself pull upward on the earth with an equal force. We cannot observe the effects of this latter force because the earth is so very much more massive than the apple, but we have no reason to doubt that the force exists.

Newton's third law applies always to *two objects*—the force that one exerts on the other and the opposite force that the second exerts on the first. Let us look at a stone hanging at the end of a string. By Newton's third law, the string pulls upward on the stone, and the stone pulls downward on the string. Here are equal and opposite forces, *but these act, respectively, upon two different objects*, the stone and the string.

It is not always entirely clear how the third law of motion operates in various situations. A boy pulls a cart with a force of 10 lb. According to the third law, the cart pulls right back on the boy with the same force, 10 lb, but in the opposite direction. How can the cart move? Seemingly, the boy's force is matched by the reverse force of the cart, leaving a total of zero force. What we have overlooked in making this statement is the fact that the two forces, that of the boy and that of the cart, act on different things. The boy pulls the cart; the cart experiences this force; the cart begins to move. The cart pulls backward on the boy; the boy must exert himself to overcome this force, which is what he is doing when he pulls on the cart. The third law of motion is sometimes called the law of action and reaction in order to make clear the distinction between the natures of the forces involved.

Vectors

Until now we have restricted our attention to single forces acting on objects that are free to move. Force problems in the real world are never so simple; always several forces are in operation simultaneously. A falling stone, for example, is subject not only to the force of gravity, but to the resistance of the air through which it moves. The motion of an automobile depends on the force supplied to its drive shaft by the engine, on friction on its bearings, on friction between tires and pavement, on air resistance, on gravity if the car is going up- or downhill.

The most interesting problems that involve forces acting in combination occur when two or more forces act in different directions. Suppose, for instance, that we set out to cross a lake in a canoe on a windy day, as in Fig. 2.6. We paddle straight for the opposite shore, propelling the boat against the frictional resistance of the water with an average force of, say, 40 lb. At the same time a cross wind pushes against the side of the canoe with an average force of 20 lb. Obviously, the canoe will not actually travel in the direction in which it is pointing; the effect of the wind is to make it proceed somewhat to one side. What we should like to find out is the extent of this deflection.

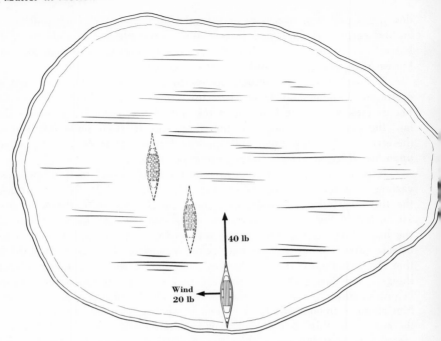

40 lb

Wind
20 lb

Fig. 2.6 *A canoe crossing a lake. A force of 40 lb is supplied by the paddle, while the wind exerts a force of 20 lb against the side of the canoe. Each force acts separately, and the canoe moves both forward and to one side under the action of both of them.*

A simple and graphic method of making such a calculation is to use a *scale drawing* of the forces that act. Figure 2.7 shows the forces on the canoe. The force due to the paddling is shown as the arrow **A**, and the force of the wind on the canoe is shown as the arrow **B**. The length of each arrow is proportional to the magnitude of the force it represents; that is, if we set a scale of 1 in. = 10 lb, arrow **A** would be 4 in. long and arrow **B** 2

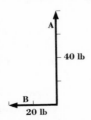

A

40 lb

B
20 lb

Fig. 2.7 *Vector diagram of the forces acting on the canoe. The arrow* **A** *represents the force caused by the paddling, and the arrow* **B** *represents that caused by the wind. These arrows are called vectors.*

in., corresponding to a 40-lb force and a 20-lb force, respectively. (We can, of course, choose any scale that is convenient. If large forces are being treated, it might be more suitable to let 1 in. equal 100 or even 1,000 lb, for example.) Arrows of this sort, representing the direction as well as the size of some quantity, are called *vectors*. They are useful in discussions of quantities like force, velocity, and acceleration in which direction is important. Other quantities, like mass, speed, and volume, have no directional significance, and for them vectors have no meaning. Vectors are customarily printed in boldface type, for example, **A**, whereas their magnitudes are printed in italics, *A*.

The combination of forces **A** and **B** is equivalent to a single force **C** directed at an angle between **A** and **B**. In other words, we can replace **A** and **B** with the force **C**, provided that **C** is properly chosen, and **C** will have the same effect on the motion of the canoe that **A** and **B** have together. This is illustrated in Fig. 2.8. What we are saying is merely that the canoe is a single object, which can move in only one direction at a time. Even though two different forces are pushing it simultaneously, its behavior is just the same as though one force were acting in such a way as to combine the effects of the two applied forces.

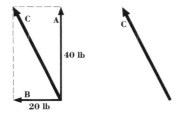

Let us examine another situation. Imagine a 20-lb pail of water supported by two people, each pulling at the end of a rope passed under its handle (Fig. 2.9). To support the pail requires a force of 20 lb pulling straight upward, as shown by arrow **R**. This force is supplied by the combination of two oblique forces of 12 lb each, arrows **P** and **Q**. Evidently, the required forces **P** and **Q** would be changed if the angle between them were changed: Each would be less if the angle were smaller, greater if the angle were larger. Or the forces might be altered by attaching another rope to the pail, thus supplying a third supporting pull. But changing the angle or the number of ropes does not alter the fundamental situation: Oblique forces in combination are producing the effect of a single vertical upward force.

Vectors are useful not only as crude representations in diagrams, but

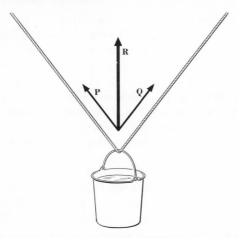

Fig. 2.9 *A pail of water may be supported by the single force* **R** *or by the two smaller forces* **P** *and* **Q**. *The combined upward pull of* **P** *and* **Q** *is equal to* **R**.

also in exact mathematical computations. For example, in the problem diagramed in Fig. 2.10, two forces are given: one force of 40 lb, represented by vector **A**, the other of 20 lb, represented by vector **B**. Intuitively, we know that the resulting single force produced by their combined effects must lie somewhere between them; but how can we obtain exact numerical values for the strength and direction of this force? No obvious way of handling the problem suggests itself with ordinary mathematical methods, but vectors make the solution easy.

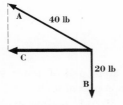

Fig. 2.10 *Two forces,* **A** *and* **B**, *act on a single body. The single force that can replace both of them is shown.*

First let us try vectors with the simpler case of forces acting in a straight line. Suppose that two horses pull on a wagon, one with a force of 350 lb, the other with a force of 200 lb. A diagrammatic top view of the wagon is shown in Fig. 2.11, with the horses represented only by vector arrows. Lengths of the arrows are determined by letting 1 cm represent 100 lb. Here, obviously, the total pull is the sum of the two forces, that is, 550 lb. In terms

Fig. 2.11 *One horse pulls the wagon with a force of 200 lb, and the other with a force of 350 lb. Together they exert a force of 550 lb.*

of vectors, the sum is obtained by moving **B** to a new position with its tail at the tip of **A** and drawing another arrow from the tail of **A** to the tip of **B**. This new vector **C** has a length of 5.5 cm, representing a force of 550 lb, and it points in the same direction as **A** and **B**.

Figure 2.12 shows a situation in which two forces are again acting in a straight line, but in opposite directions. We obtain the resulting single force by applying the rule stated in the last paragraph: Lay one arrow with its tail at the tip of the second (actually a little to one side, to avoid any confusion) and then draw a third vector (**F**) from the tail of the second (**G**) to the tip of the first (**R**).

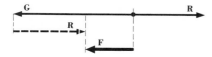

Fig. 2.12 *When two forces act parallel to one another but in opposite directions, their action is equivalent to that of a single force whose magnitude is the difference between those of the two forces. Here* **F** *is the net force that results from the application of the opposing forces* **G** *and* **R**.

Now let us return to the canoe problem of Fig. 2.6. Here the two forces are no longer in a straight line, but the procedure suggested in the last two paragraphs is still applicable. Figure 2.13 shows, first, the two force vectors redrawn from Fig. 2.6 with the lake and canoe omitted. In the second

Fig. 2.13 *To add the vectors* **A** *and* **B**, *shift* **B** *parallel to itself so that its tail is at the head of* **A**; *the sum of* **A** *and* **B** *is a vector drawn from the tail of* **A** *to the head of* **B**.

diagram, vector **B** is moved to a new position with its tail at the tip of vector **A**; during this transfer, the length and direction of **B** remain the same. The heavy arrow of the third diagram is drawn from the tail of **A** to the tip of **B**. This is the desired combined effect of **A** and **B**. The arrow's length can be measured directly on the diagram, and the angle it makes with **A** or **B** can be found with a protractor.

The same rule is always followed: Place one vector with its tail at the tip of the other, keeping its length and direction unchanged, then draw a third vector from the tail of the second to the tip of the first. This process is called *vector addition*. It may be applied to any number of vectors by

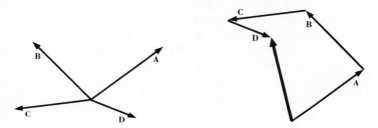

Fig. 2.14   *To add a number of vectors together, string them together head to tail and draw a vector from the tail of the first to the head of the the last; this vector is the sum of all the others. The order in which the vectors are added together is immaterial.*

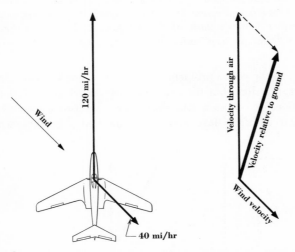

Fig. 2.15   *An airplane is heading north at 120 mi/hr in a 40 mi/hr wind from the northwest. Adding together the vectors representing these velocities yields a single vector which indicates that the airplane will actually move at about 100 mi/hr in a direction between north and northeast.*

stringing the arrows together, tip to tail, and drawing the arrow representing the vector sum from the tail of the first to the tip of the last (Fig. 2.14).

To show the usefulness of vectors in dealing with other quantities besides forces, let us try an example with velocities. Suppose that the speedometer of an airplane heading due north shows a speed of 120 mi/hr and that it is bucking a 40 mi/hr wind from the northwest. In what direction will it actually move and with what speed? Figure 2.15 shows the solution; first the velocities are drawn as vectors, then they are combined according to the usual rule. Evidently the plane will move in a direction between north and northeast, at a speed of about 100 mi/hr.

Self-examination

1. If two objects of the same size and shape but one twice as heavy as the other are dropped simultaneously from a tower,
   a. the heavy object strikes the ground before the light one
   b. they strike the ground at the same time, but the heavy object has the higher velocity
   c. they strike the ground at the same time and have the same velocity
   d. they strike the ground at the same time, but the heavy object has the lower acceleration because it has more mass

2. Weight is
   a. the same thing as mass but expressed in different units
   b. the force with which the earth pulls something to it
   c. the quantity of matter in some object
   d. inertia

3. Which of the following is *not* a unit of mass?
   a. the slug
   b. the gram
   c. the kilogram
   d. the ton

4. An object weighing 16 lb has a mass of
   a. ½ slug
   b. 2 slugs
   c. 32 slugs
   d. 512 slugs

5. When a force of 100 newtons is applied to a body whose weight is 39.2 newtons, the body's acceleration is
   a. 0.04 m/sec²
   b. 9.8 m/sec²

    c. 25 m/sec^2
    d. 400 m/sec^2

6. If we know the magnitude and direction of the force exerted on a body of given mass, Newton's second law of motion permits us to calculate its
    a. position
    b. speed
    c. velocity
    d. acceleration

7. Of the following quantities, the one that is *not* a vector is
    a. velocity
    b. acceleration
    c. mass
    d. force

8. According to Newton's third law of motion,
    a. there is no such thing as a single force acting on a body
    b. for every force there is an equal and opposite reaction force, but each may act on a different body
    c. action and reaction forces need not be equal, but must act along the same straight line
    d. action and reaction forces must be equal, but need not act along the same straight line

9. Two forces, one of 10 lb and another of 6 lb, act upon a body. The directions of the forces are unknown. The resultant force on the body is
    a. between 6 and 10 lb
    b. between 4 and 16 lb
    c. more than 6 lb
    d. more than 10 lb

10. When a boy pulls a cart, the force that causes *him* to move forward is
    a. the force the cart exerts on him
    b. the force he exerts on the cart
    c. the force he exerts on the ground with his feet
    d. the force the ground exerts on his feet

Problems

1. Is the moon's motion around the earth accelerated? Is a force acting on the moon? What is the direction of the force?

2. When you whirl a stone at the end of a string, the stone seems to be pulling outward against your hand. When you release the string, however, the stone moves along a straight path. Explain each of these effects.

3. What force is required to impart a 5 m/sec² acceleration to a 6-kg body?

4. A force of 4,000 newtons is applied to a 1,400-kg car. What is its acceleration? What will its velocity be after 8 sec if it started from rest?

5. A man whose mass is 80 kg is riding in an elevator whose upward acceleration is 2 m/sec². What force does he exert on the floor of the elevator?

6. What is the mass of a 160-lb man? With how much force is he attracted to the earth? If he falls from a cliff, what will his downward acceleration be?

7. How much force is required to give a 5-slug mass an acceleration of 12 ft/sec?

8. A loaded elevator weighs 2 tons. The cable supporting it can safely withstand a tension of 5,000 lb. What is the maximum upward acceleration that the elevator can have if the tension in the cable is not to exceed this figure?

9. An automobile weighing 3,500 lb goes from 30 mi/hr (44 ft/sec) to 60 mi/hr (88 ft/sec) in 5 sec. What is the force acting upon it?

10. The brakes of the above automobile are able to exert a force of 500 lb. How long will it take for them to slow the automobile down to a stop from an initial speed of 60 mi/hr?

11. In going from one town to another a car travels 40 miles north, 40 miles west, and then 10 miles south. What is the actual straight-line distance between the towns?

12. A body weighing 75 lb is acted upon by a horizontal force of 75 lb. What is the magnitude and direction of the resultant force on the body?

13. An ocean liner is steaming due west at a speed of 25 mi/hr. There is a wind from the northwest at 10 mi/hr. What is the speed of the smoke from the liner's funnel relative to the boat? What is the direction of the smoke?

14. A motor boat whose speed through the water is 10 mi/hr heads directly across a river 1 mile wide. The current in the river is 2 mi/hr. When the boat reaches the other side of the river, how far downstream will it be?

15. A bullet is fired horizontally from a great height at a speed of 300 m/sec. As soon as it leaves the gun it starts falling with an acceleration of 9.8 m/sec. By means of vector diagrams find its approximate speed after 1, 5, and 10 sec, respectively. (Neglect air resistance and winds.)

16. A book rests on a table. What is the reaction force equal and opposite to the force the book exerts on the table? To the force that gravity exerts on the book?

17. If you were set down in the center of a frozen lake whose surface was so smooth and slippery that it offered no frictional resistance to any kind of motion, how could you get off the lake?

18. Two forces, one of 12 newtons and the other unknown, act at right angles on an object. If the net force on the object is 30 newtons, what is the magnitude of the unknown force?

19. A horizontal and a vertical force combine to produce a force of 10 newtons that acts in a direction 40° above the horizontal. Find the magnitudes of the horizontal and vertical forces.

CHAPTER 3 | GRAVITATION

One of the truly great triumphs of the human mind is the law of universal gravitation, which has lost none of its luster in the three centuries since its discovery. At one stroke this seemingly simple relationship showed that the motions of the planets about the sun, which follow Kepler's three laws as we saw in Chap. 1, the motion of the moon about the earth, and the behavior of falling bodies on the earth are all manifestations of the same basic phenomenon of nature, gravitation. The man who first perceived the law of gravitation together with all its implications was Isaac Newton, to whom we also owe the laws of motion that formed the subject of the last chapter. Newton proved that the same laws of nature that apply in the universe are valid on the earth's surface, so that the gravitational force that attracts apples to the ground is identical with the gravitational force that keeps the planets in their orbits. Newton accomplished more than merely explaining the elliptical paths of the planets, the law of equal areas, and the harmonic law; he showed that these features of the solar system, so puzzling at first glance, are absolutely inevitable consequences of natural laws, thereby establishing the existence of a much more profound kind of order in the universe than his predecessors had conceived.

Newton

The facts of Newton's life are simple and undramatic. He was the son of an obscure farmer who died before Isaac was born. At first an undistinguished student, young Newton soon revealed his scientific aptitude and was sent to Cambridge to complete his studies.   In his twenties Newton was appointed professor of mathematics there, and he remained at Cambridge, living quietly and never marrying, for thirty years.   Then, at fifty-four, Newton was appointed an official of the British Mint, where he stayed for the rest of his life.   Honors came to Newton in profusion, and he was buried in Westminster Abbey with the noblest of England's dead.

In contrast to this uneventful life are the adventures of his far-ranging mind, adventures which cannot but amaze all who read of his work.   In the law of gravitation Newton found the solution to the problem of planetary motion and gave science a powerful tool for understanding natural phenomena.   His formulation of the three laws of motion placed the science of mechanics on a solid foundation.   By inventing the calculus, Newton gave physical science a new and powerful kind of mathematics whose possibilities are still being explored.   Finally, his work in optics was among the earliest systematic investigations of the properties of light.   Newton's great work, the *Principia*, was published in 1687, the last year of Charles II's reign. This event is one of the most important landmarks in the whole history of science.

Of all the resounding tributes that have been paid to Newton's greatness, perhaps the most elegant is that by the mathematician Joseph Louis Lagrange: "Newton was the greatest genius who ever lived, and the most fortunate, for there cannot be more than once a system of the world to establish."

Centripetal Force

We shall begin our study of gravitation by considering the general problem of motion along a curved path, the kind of motion we must be able to understand before we tackle the forces at work on the planets.

A simple example of motion along a curved path is the whirling of a ball tied to the end of a string (Fig. 3.1).   Even though the speed of the ball may be the same at all times, its direction constantly changes and therefore the ball must be accelerated. We find that to hold the ball in its circular path requires the continual exertion of a force by our hand on the string, which is the force responsible for the continual acceleration of the ball.   The force that we exert on the ball through the string is called *centripetal* ("center-seeking") force.   It is the force that must be applied from the outside in order to cause an object to move in a curved path.   The acceleration produced by a centripetal force is called centripetal acceleration, and, like the force that gives rise to it, is directed toward the center of curvature of the object's path.

Let us consider the ball's motion between any two points fairly close together on the circle it describes, such as A and B in Fig. 3.2.   At A the ball moves with a velocity represented by the tangent vector v_A and, if unrestrained, would continue to move with this velocity along the line AP.   At

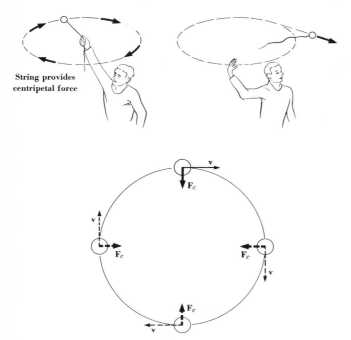

Fig. 3.1   *An inward centripetal force* **F**$_C$ *acts upon every object that moves in a curved path. If the force is removed, the object continues moving in a straight line tangent to its original path.*

B the ball's velocity vector is v_B, and, as shown, the total change in its velocity between positions A and B is given by the vector Δv. The ball's velocity at B is the vector sum of v_A, its velocity at A, and Δv, its change in velocity, as shown in the right-hand diagram in Fig. 3.2. If the centripetal force acting from 0 is of the proper magnitude to keep the ball moving with uniform speed in a circle, v_B will have the same length as v_A and will be tangent to the circle at B.

From Fig. 3.2 it is evident that the vector triangle whose sides are v_A, v_B, and Δv is similar to the space triangle whose sides are $0A$, $0B$, and the chord s, since v_A, v_B, and Δv are perpendicular to $0A$, $0B$, and s, respectively. Since corresponding sides of similar triangles are proportional in length,

$$\frac{\Delta v}{v} = \frac{s}{r} \tag{3.1}$$

where Δv = length of Δv

v = length of both v_A and v_B

r = radius of circle

  = $0A$ and $0B$

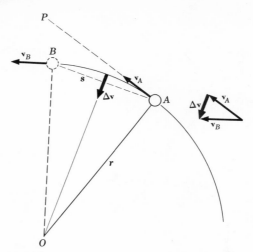

Fig. 3.2 *As a ball moves in a circular path its velocity changes constantly. The difference between the ball's velocity* $\mathbf{v}_A$ *at the point A and its velocity* $\mathbf{v}_B$ *at the point B is* $\Delta\mathbf{v}$. *Since* $\Delta\mathbf{v}$ *is directed toward the center of the circle, the force causing the circular motion must also be directed toward the center. This inward force is the* centripetal force.

The actual distance the ball travels in going from A to B is vt, where t is the time required for it to cover this distance (Fig. 3.3). In the diagram, vt, an arc of the circle, is clearly longer than s, the chord that joins A and B. However, the closer together the points A and B are, the more nearly equal vt and s are. When A and B are infinitely close together, $vt = s$. This is the situation we are primarily concerned with, since the quantity of interest here is the *instantaneous acceleration* of the ball (that is, its acceleration at any particular moment). Hence we can substitute vt for s in Eq. (3.1) and obtain

$$\frac{\Delta v}{v} = \frac{s}{r} = \frac{vt}{r}$$

so that
$$\frac{\Delta v}{t} = \frac{v^2}{r} \tag{3.2}$$

In Chap. 1 we learned that the acceleration of a body is given by the change in its velocity during a certain time interval divided by that time interval. Here the ball changes its velocity by Δv during the time t, so its acceleration is

$$a_c = \frac{\Delta v}{t} = \frac{v^2}{r} \tag{3.3}$$

The quantity a_c is the centripetal acceleration of a body of speed v which moves along a circular path of radius r.

Newton's second law of motion permits us to relate the centripetal force F_c on an object in circular motion to its centripetal acceleration a_c. Because, in general,

$$F = ma$$

here we have

$$F_c = ma_c \qquad (3.4)$$

The centripetal force on a body is the product of its mass m and its centripetal acceleration. The direction of the force is the same as that of the acceleration, so $\mathbf{F}_c$, as we know from experience, points toward the center of the circular path. Combining Eqs. (3.3) and (3.4), we see that

$$F_c = \frac{mv^2}{r} \qquad (3.5)$$

To whirl a given object in a circle requires a greater force if it moves fast or if the circle is small, and the more massive the object, the more force is needed.

From Eq. (3.5) we can see, for example, why cars rounding a curve are so difficult to steer when the curve is sharp (small r) or the speed is high

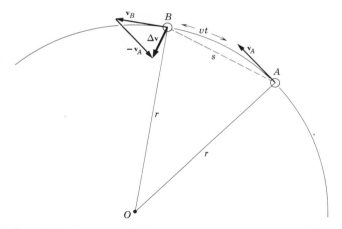

Fig. 3.3   A and B are two successive positions t sec apart of a ball undergoing uniform circular motion at the speed v in a circle of radius r. The chord joining A and B is s, while the actual distance the particle traverses is vt. In calculating the instantaneous acceleration of the particle we are restricted to having A and B an infinitesimal distance apart, in which case the chord and arc have the same length and Δv points radially inward to the center of the circle at O. Here A and B are shown relatively far apart for clarity, and so Δv is not quite radially inward.

(a large value for v means a very large value for v^2). A heavy car (large m) is evidently going to be generally harder to maneuver than a light car (small m). In the case of a car, the centripetal force is supplied by friction between the car's tires and the road; if the force needed to make a particular turn at a particular speed is too great, the car skids.

Let us consider a car weighing 2,400 lb and traveling at 10 mi/hr around a turn 100 ft in radius. The car's mass is

$$m = \frac{W}{g} = \frac{2,400 \text{ lb}}{32 \text{ ft/sec}^2} = 75 \text{ slugs}$$

and its speed in feet per second is

$$v = 10 \text{ mi/hr} \times 5,280 \text{ ft/mi} \times \frac{1}{3,600 \text{ sec/hr}}$$

$$= 14.7 \text{ ft/sec}$$

Hence the centripetal force involved in the turn is

$$F_c = \frac{mv^2}{r} = \frac{75 \text{ slugs} \times (14.7 \text{ ft/sec})^2}{100 \text{ ft}}$$

$$= 162 \text{ lb}$$

This force is readily transmitted by the road to the car if the pavement is dry and in good condition. However, if the car's speed were 50 mi/hr, the required force would be twenty-five times greater (4,050 lb, or over 2 tons), and the car would be unlikely to be able to make the turn.

Centrifugal Force

When we round a curve in a train or automobile, we experience the familiar sensation of a force pushing us toward the outside of the curve. Mud thrown from a moving wheel and the pull of a stone whirled on the end of a string are other manifestations of this force, which is known as *centrifugal* ("center-fleeing") force. However, strictly speaking, it is no more than another name for inertia: When our car rounds a corner, we tend to keep going in a straight line and therefore *feel* as if we were being pushed toward one side of the car (Fig. 3.4). Centrifugal force is simply an expression of the reluctance of moving bodies to change their direction of motion.

The force that must be applied from the outside in order to cause an object to move in a curved path is centripetal force, as we know. Centrifugal force, on the other hand, is only an *apparent* force, which arises because of the tendency of moving things to travel in straight lines. We can think of centrifugal force as being the equal and opposite force that Newton's third law of motion requires to be present whenever a centripetal force acts.

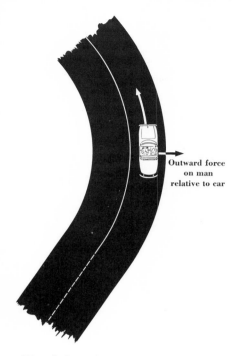

Outward force
on man
relative to car

Fig. 3.4 *A person in an automobile rounding a curve feels as though he is being pushed sideways toward the outside of the curve. This centrifugal force is a manifestation of inertia and arises from the tendency of moving bodies to continue in motion along a straight line.*

Universal Gravitation

That some force is necessary to hold the planets in their elliptical orbits had been recognized before Newton, but the nature of the force had remained a matter of speculation. It was Newton's great inspiration that this force might be the same as the force that pulls objects to the surface of the earth. Perhaps, thought Newton, the moon revolves around the earth much as a stone on the end of a string revolves around a finger, with gravity taking the place of a pull on the string. In other words, perhaps the moon is a falling object, pulled toward the earth just as we are pulled, but moving so fast that the pull is just sufficient to keep it from flying off in a straight line away from the earth (Fig. 3.5). Further, the earth and its sister planets might well be held in their orbits by a greater gravitational attraction from the sun.

It was a remarkable idea, but would it work? Galileo had discovered certain relationships among distance, velocity, and time for ordinary objects falling freely toward the earth, as we saw in Chap. 2; could it be shown that the moon falls according to the same laws? Kepler had set down three exact

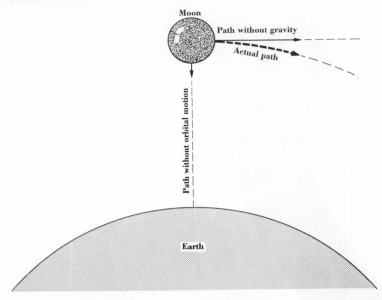

Fig. 3.5   *The motion of the moon around the earth represents a balance between the downward pull of gravity and the tendency of the moon to travel in a straight line; gravity provides the centripetal force required to keep the moon in its orbit.*

statements concerning planetary motion; could a gravitational force between planets and sun explain those three laws?

Newton's problem was to express in mathematical terms the gravitational force between different bodies. His method of attack had essentially three steps. He began with Kepler's second law, which states that the line joining any planet with the sun sweeps out equal areas in equal time intervals. Newton showed, with the help of his newly invented calculus, that the force must act directly along the line between sun and planet, just as gravity on the earth pulls objects directly toward the earth's surface.

Kepler's third law gave a more specific hint about the nature of the force. This law states, we recall, that the square of the time T required for a planet's revolution is proportional to the cube of the radius r of its orbit, so that T^2/r^3 has the same value throughout the solar system. This law, together with the fact that the gravitational attractive force on a planet must provide for the exact amount of centripetal force involved in holding it in its orbit, was all that Newton needed to determine the way in which gravitational force varies with distance. His result states that the force of gravitation exerted by the sun on a planet is inversely proportional to the square of the average distance r between them; that is, the force varies as $1/r^2$. All other things staying the same, a planet twice as far from the sun as it normally is would feel only $1/2^2$, or one-fourth as much attractive force, while if it were half as far from the sun, the force on it would be $1/(\frac{1}{2})^2$, or four times greater. This dependence upon distance is shown in Fig. 3.6.

The important conclusion that Newton reached regarding the variation of gravitational force with distance was bolstered by Kepler's first law: Each planet moves in an ellipse with the sun at one focus. Again making use of the calculus, Newton showed that a planet attracted to the sun with a force inversely proportional to the square of its distance away must travel in an ellipse.

Galileo's work on falling bodies supplied the final clue. All objects in free fall at the earth's surface have the same acceleration g, and

$$\text{Weight of object} = \text{mass of object} \times \text{value of } g$$

Therefore the weight of an object, which is the force of gravity upon it, is always proportional to its mass m. Newton's third law of motion (action-reaction) requires that if the earth attracts an object, the object also attracts the earth. If the earth's attraction for a stone depends upon the stone's mass, then the reaction force exerted by the stone on the earth depends upon the earth's mass. Hence the gravitational force between two bodies is proportional to *both* of their masses.

We can summarize the above conclusions in a single statement: *Every particle in the universe attracts every other particle with a force that is directly proportional to the product of their masses and inversely proportional to the square of the distance between them.* In equation form, Newton's law of gravitation states that the force F between two bodies whose masses are m_1 and m_2 is

$$F = \frac{Gm_1m_2}{r^2}$$

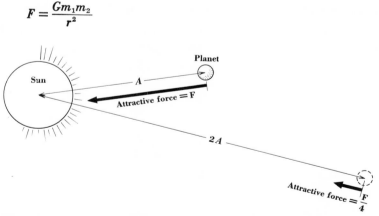

Fig. 3.6   *The gravitational force on a planet would drop to one-fourth its usual amount if the distance of the planet from the sun were to be doubled. If the distance is halved, the force would increase to four times its usual amount.*

where r is the distance between them and G is a constant of nature, the same number everywhere in the universe. The value of G is 6.670×10^{-11} newton-m^2/kg^2.

Newton was still confronted with one difficult problem: From what points in two objects should r be measured? The force between an apple and the earth is inversely proportional to the square of their distance apart; but what distance? From the apple to the earth's surface, to the earth's center, or to some other point in the earth's interior? Again using the calculus, Newton succeeded in showing that, for two uniform spherical objects, r is the distance between their centers; in other words, spheres behave as if their masses were concentrated at their centers (Fig. 3.7). Solving the problem is more diffi-cult for objects of other shapes, but in general, for any body, a *center of mass* can be found from which r is to be measured.

The inverse-square relationship between gravitational force and distance of separation r is a most important one. Let us see what this law means in terms of the earth's attraction for a ball whose weight at sea level is 1 lb. At sea level the force of gravity on the ball is, of course, 1 lb, and the ball is roughly 4,000 miles from the earth's center. If this distance is multiplied by 2, so that the ball is 8,000 miles from the earth's center (in other words, the ball is at an altitude of 4,000 miles above sea level), the force of gravity decreases by a factor of 2^2, or 4; thus its weight would be only $\frac{1}{4}$ lb. If we take the ball much farther out, so that it is 40,000 miles from the earth's center, or ten times farther out than it is at sea level, its weight drops by a factor of 10^2, or 100, to only 0.01 lb. As the distance increases, the gravita-tional force decreases very rapidly.

Experimental Proof of the Law of Gravitation

Nearly a century after Newton's time another great English scientist, Henry Cavendish, succeeded in measuring directly the force of gravitation. His

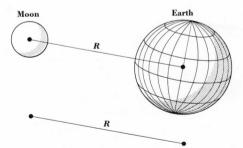

Fig. 3.7 *For computing gravitational effects, spherical bodies (such as the earth and moon) may be regarded as if their masses are located at their geometrical centers, provided that they are uniform spheres or consist of concentric uniform spherical shells.*

method was simple: Two small metal spheres were attached to the ends of a light rod, which was suspended at its center from a slender wire; two heavy lead spheres were brought near the small ones, and the twist in the wire was observed (Fig. 3.8). Simple as it sounds, the completion of the experiment was a real feat, for the forces involved are incredibly small. By these delicate measurements Cavendish obtained experimental proof of the law of gravitation.

An even more direct experiment was performed later by a German named Phillip von Jolly, who weighed a few pounds of mercury carefully and then measured the increase in the weight of the mercury when 6 tons of lead was placed directly below it (Fig. 3.9). The Cavendish method, however, is superior in practice and figured in the most recent (1930) determination of the constant G at the National Bureau of Standards in Washington. In the latter experiment 1½-oz gold spheres were placed at the ends of an 8-in. rod, and the external masses were in the form of steel cylinders weighing 145 lb each. In the absence of the cylinders, the rod required about 30 min to swing back and forth; when the cylinders were put in position, the period of vibration was reduced to about 25 min because of the gravitational attraction between them and the gold spheres at the ends of the rod; and from this difference G could be calculated with great accuracy.

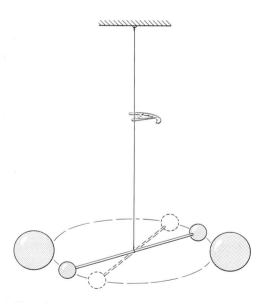

Fig. 3.8   Scheme employed by Cavendish in demonstrating the law of gravitation.   The gravitational force between each pair of spheres can be determined from the amount of twist in the wire when the two large spheres are brought near the apparatus.

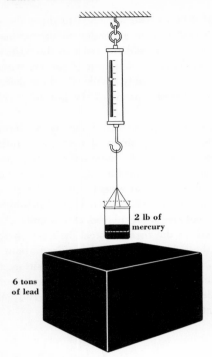

2 lb of
mercury

6 tons
of lead

Fig. 3.9   Another method for measuring gravitational forces.
The increase in the downward force on the mercury when the lead is placed
underneath it is a measure of the gravitational attraction between them.

It is hard to realize just how small gravitational forces are, so that enormous masses, such as that of the sun or that of the earth, are needed to exert an appreciable pull on nearby objects. Two 40,000-ton ocean liners, for instance, if they are ½ mile apart, attract each other with a force of only ½ oz!

The Shape of the Earth

The earth, as we are all told, is a sphere. Actually, it is an *oblate spheroid,* meaning that it is somewhat flattened at the poles and bulges slightly at the equator. Why does it have this particular shape? Why is it not shaped like an egg, like a pyramid, or like a corkscrew?

We can answer this question by considering the pressures beneath the earth's surface. Pressures in water are familiar enough: Swimmers can descend only a few dozen feet, submarines only a few hundred, before the pressure becomes dangerously high. These crushing forces are due simply to the weight of overlying liquid, to the earth's gravitational attraction for the upper layers of water. Less familiar are pressures in solid rocks. Most ordinary rocks are between two and three times as heavy as water, which means that pressures in rocks, due simply to their weight, should be more than twice as great as pressures at similar depths in the ocean. With increasing distance beneath the earth's surface, rock pressures quickly become enormous. Below a depth of about 12 miles, the pressure is so great that solid rock will flow in response to it. We have no direct information about what kinds of material exist 12 miles down, but we can be sure that they behave somewhat like very thick liquids in response to pressure changes. This means that one part of the earth cannot project out very much farther than other parts; if it did, pressures beneath it would be greater than under surrounding regions, and the underlying rock would flow out to the sides until pressures were equalized.

In other words, gravity alone tends to give the earth a spherical shape, to keep all parts of its surface at the same distance from the center. Such minor irregularities as mountains and ocean basins do not greatly disturb the pressure balance, but no large protuberances can exist.

The cause of the bulge at the equator is centrifugal force. The apparent outward force on a rotating object due to inertia is

$$F = \frac{mv^2}{r}$$

where r is the distance away from the axis of rotation. At the equator, r is large, but v^2 is extremely large, whereas in the polar regions, r is small, but v^2 is extremely small; hence the centrifugal force is considerably greater at the equator, where it amounts to about 1/300 of the gravitational force there. As Fig. 3.10 indicates, this centrifugal force distorts the earth into the form

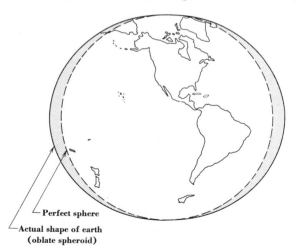

— Perfect sphere

— Actual shape of earth
(oblate spheroid)

Fig. 3.10 *Centrifugal force distorts the earth into an oblate spheroid. The effect is greatly exaggerated in the figure; the equatorial diameter of the earth is actually only 27 miles more than its polar diameter.*

of an oblate spheroid. The total distortion is not great, for the earth is only 27 miles greater in equatorial diameter than in polar diameter.

The earth is about 0.34 percent away from being a perfect sphere. Venus, which rotates very slowly, has negligible centrifugal distortion; Jupiter, Saturn, and Uranus, all of which turn rapidly on their axes, exhibit distortions of 6.2, 9.6, and 6 percent, respectively, and are conspicuously flattened at their poles.

Variations of Gravity on the Earth

A man's weight changes as he travels about over the earth. The change is never large—not more than a pound or so at most—but he would have no trouble detecting it with delicate instruments. If he is sufficiently curious, he will discover that there are three major types of variation in his weight:

1. *Variation with altitude.* On a mountaintop he will weigh less than in adjacent valleys. This observation can be explained simply as an effect of changing distance from the earth's center.
2. *Variation with latitude.* Near the equator he will find his weight a minimum, near the poles a maximum. A little reflection will show two reasons for this variation: The centrifugal force arising from the earth's rotation, which works against gravity, is greatest at the equator, and points along the equator are farthest from the earth's center because of the earth's equatorial bulge.
3. *Variation with density of subsurface material.* In addition to the well-defined variations with latitude and altitude, our investigator will discover erratic minor changes in weight whose explanation is not so obvious. At least in part, these minor variations are due to differences in the rocks immediately below the surface: in regions where the subsurface rocks are unusually heavy, the force of gravity is somewhat greater than in regions underlain by light materials.

The Mass of the Earth

On the basis of what we know already, we can find the total mass of the earth. It sounds, perhaps, like a formidable job, but it is really a fairly simple and straightforward calculation, and it is worth following as a good illustration of the indirect way in which scientists go about performing such incredible-sounding feats as "weighing" the earth, the sun, other planets, and even distant stars.

Let us focus our attention on a 1-kg mass on the earth's surface. Its weight W, which is the force with which the earth attracts it, is given by

$$W = mg$$
$$= 1 \text{ kg} \times 9.8 \text{ m/sec}^2$$
$$= 9.8 \text{ newtons}$$

There is another way of finding the force of attraction on this 1-kg mass. Newton's law of gravitation states that, in general,

$$F = \frac{Gm_1m_2}{r^2}$$

Here, if the force is that exerted by the earth on the 1-kg mass, we can let m_1 be 1 kg and m_2 be the unknown mass of the earth m_{earth}. The quantity r is the distance between the center of the earth and the surface of the earth, which we know is 4,000 miles, or in metric units, 6.4×10^6 (6,400,000) m. The constant G is 6.67×10^{-11} newton-m^2/kg^2. Thus

$$F = \frac{6.67 \times 10^{-11} \times 1 \times m_{earth}}{(6.4 \times 10^6)^2} \qquad \text{newtons/kg}$$
$$= 1.63 \times 10^{-24} m_{earth} \qquad \text{newtons/kg}$$

But this force of attraction is just the weight of the 1-kg mass, which we found to be 9.8 newtons. Therefore

$$9.8 \text{ newtons} = 1.63 \times 10^{-24} m_{earth} \qquad \text{newtons/kg}$$

$$m_{earth} = \frac{9.8}{1.63 \times 10^{-24}} \text{ kg}$$
$$= 6.0 \times 10^{24} \text{ kg}$$

The mass of the earth is 6.0×10^{24} kg, which, in more familiar units, turns out to be 6.6×10^{21} tons, or 6,600,000,000,000,000,000,000 tons!

The Discovery of Neptune and Pluto

We have seen something of the immense usefulness of the law of gravitation in astronomical explanations and calculations. But historically the most spectacular application of this law was the prediction of the two outermost members of the sun's family.

The planet Uranus was found by accident in 1781. Observations during the next few years enabled astronomers to work out details of the new planet's orbit and to predict its future positions in the sky. To make these predictions, it was necessary to consider not only the sun's gravitational attraction, but the minor attractions of the neighboring planets Jupiter and Saturn as well. The calculations were long and tedious, but their results were accepted unquestioningly. For forty years, about half the time required for Uranus to make one complete revolution, calculated positions of the planet agreed accurately with observed positions. Then a discrepancy appeared. Little by little the planet moved away from its predicted path among the stars. The calculations were checked and rechecked, but no mistake could be found; the attractions of all known bodies had been correctly allowed for. One of two conclusions seemed necessary: Either the law of gravitation, on which the calculations were based, was not strictly accurate, or else some unknown body was attracting Uranus away from its predicted path.

So firmly established was the law of gravitation that two young men, Urbain Leverrier in France and John Couch Adams in England, set themselves the prodigious task of calculating the position of an unknown body that might be responsible for the discrepancies in Uranus' position. Adams, completing his computations first, sent them to England's Astronomer Royal. Busy with other matters, the Astronomer Royal put the calculations away for future checking. Meanwhile, Leverrier sent his paper to a young German astronomer, Johann Gottfried Galle, who lost no time in turning his telescope to the part of the sky where the new planet should appear. Very close to the position predicted by Leverrier, Galle found a faint object, which proved to be the eighth member of the sun's family. A little later the Astronomer Royal showed that Neptune's position had been correctly given in Adams' work also.

When Neptune had been observed for several decades, very slight discrepancies between the observed and calculated positions of this planet led the American astronomer Percival Lowell to predict the existence of yet another planet. The discovery of Pluto was hardly as dramatic as that of Neptune; the discrepancies in Neptune's orbit were so small that Pluto's position could not be predicted with accuracy, and the search dragged on for twenty-five years before the ninth planet was finally located in 1930.

The Scientific Method

We have already made considerable progress in our exploration of the physical universe. Ours has been a passive role, in the sense that we have confined ourselves to learning facts and interpretations based on centuries of scientific work. It is appropriate at this point to pause and look into the procedures by which scientists acquired this knowledge in the first place. Diverse as these procedures are, we find underlying them in all scientific work a basic pattern of inquiry, a general scheme of attacking problems, which has become known as the *scientific method*.

In grossly simplified terms, we may describe the scientific method as comprising three steps: (1) observation, (2) generalization from the observed facts, and (3) checking the generalization by further observations. Observations of the material world are at the beginning and the end of scientific reasoning. Observed facts serve both as the foundation on which a scientist builds his theories and as the ultimate check on the correctness of the theories.

1. *Scientific observation* is carried out painstakingly, to be sure that all pertinent facts are collected and that each fact is accurate. If the number of facts is large, a considerable amount of classification and analysis of the observational data may be necessary before generalization is possible.
2. *Generalization* may be merely the statement of a rule or pattern to which the observed facts seem to conform. Or it may be a more ambitious attempt to explain the observations in terms of simpler rules and processes. In any case it involves the extension of results from one series of observations to similar observations in new and untried circumstances, in other words, the *prediction* of results in other experiments.
3. *Checking a generalization* implies the setting up of new experiments whose results can be predicted from the generalization. If the new observations agree with the predictions, the generalization has proved its usefulness. The new observations may lead to further generalizations or to refinements of the old one, which in turn must be checked by further experiment, and so on indefinitely.

As put forward originally, a scientific generalization is commonly called a *hypothesis.* When checked and rechecked in a variety of ways, so that there is no longer any doubt of its correctness, the hypothesis becomes a *law.* The word *theory* is usually reserved for a larger logical structure, built on two or three fundamental generalizations, designed to explain a wide variety of phenomena. But there is no complete uniformity in the use of these three terms.

A breakdown of the scientific method into three steps does not mean that a working scientist consciously follows these steps. Certainly he does not set one day aside for observing, a second day for generalizing, and a third for checking. Sometimes all three processes go on nearly simultaneously and quite unconsciously; while he is collecting data a possible hypothesis may suggest itself as a hunch, and almost immediately he may be aware that the hunch has already been tested by previous experiments designed for some other purpose. And often different persons or groups of persons perform each of the steps. The scientific method as described above is merely a formalized expression of a process that a scientist, consciously or unconsciously, uses over and over again as he works.

Nor does this simple description of the scientific method mean that any neophyte going into a laboratory can make startling discoveries merely by telling himself to observe, generalize, and check. He would not know, first and most important, what questions to ask of nature; nor would he know the techniques of observation or how to devise experiments to serve as valid checks; worst of all, he would not have the background or the intuition or the trained imagination to arrive at reasonable generalizations. Making the scientific method sound simple as a logical process does not make the individual steps simple, nor does it detract from the greatness of scientists who are unusually skillful in formulating problems, in securing data, or in originating hypotheses.

An appropriate example of the scientific method is the history of attempts to explain planetary motions. The original observations are records of the positions of the planets with respect to the earth and the fixed stars. From these data the Greeks made several attempts to piece together a reasonable generalization, the most successful being the Ptolemaic hypothesis. From this hypothesis future positions of the planets could be predicted, and observations checked the predictions satisfactorily. As centuries passed and observational methods were improved, it appeared that the check was not quite accurate. Some modification of the original hypothesis was necessary, but modification seemed impossible without introducing unreasonable complexities.

Then appeared a rival generalization, the hypothesis of Copernicus. Predictions from this hypothesis gave at first no better checks with observation than Ptolemy's hypothesis. Kepler refined Copernicus' idea, basing his more accurate generalizations on the observations of Tycho Brahe. With these modifications the Copernican system now made possible predictions of planetary positions which agreed well with the observations. Because of these accurate checks and because of its greater simplicity, the Copernican hypothesis soon replaced the Ptolemaic hypothesis. Its correctness was established even more firmly by the telescopic observations of Galileo and his successors.

Behind Kepler's laws and Galileo's observations on falling bodies Newton discerned an even broader generalization, the law of gravitation. We should note in passing that this law could hardly be formulated in terms of a Ptolemaic solar system. Newton confirmed his initial hypothesis by observations of the moon's motion. Newton and the physicists who followed him used his law to make one prediction after another, which have been checked by observation. The most spectacular of these predictions led to the discovery of Neptune and Pluto.

It is safe to say that the scientific method has made possible the technological civilization of today. Without it, science and engineering would still be in a primitive trial-and-error stage, far removed from the present-day advanced state of these disciplines.

But we must remember that the scientific method has strict limitations. It is a means of discovering and organizing facts about the physical world, and no more than that. Observed facts are the foundation of its structure and the ultimate proof of its results. Usually, all the facts must be based on observations that can be repeated at will; always they must be facts that would be clear to anyone with normal senses and sufficient training to understand them. Scientists may disagree about how observations should be interpreted, but about the observations themselves there should be no dispute. Of course, this insistence on accurate observational data is one of the great virtues of scientific reasoning. But it is likewise a severe limitation, a limitation that must be clearly recognized, especially if the scientific method is to serve any useful purpose in disciplines into which human values enter— because human values are by nature subjective, the products of an individual's emotions, and therefore more difficult to deal with in an objective, quantitative fashion.

Self-examination

1. The acceleration of gravity *g*
   a. is a fundamental constant of nature
   b. is the same for all stars, planets, and other astronomical bodies
   c. varies slightly around the earth
   d. is caused by the moon

2. In order to cause something to move in a circular path, we must supply
   a. centrifugal force
   b. centripetal force
   c. inertial force
   d. gravitational force

3. If the earth were three times farther from the sun than it is now, the gravitational force exerted on it by the sun would be
   a. three times as large as it is now
   b. nine times as large as it is now
   c. one-third as large as it is now
   d. one-ninth as large as it is now

4. The gravitational force with which the earth attracts the moon
   a. is less than the force with which the moon attracts the earth
   b. is the same as the force with which the moon attracts the earth
   c. is more than the force with which the moon attracts the earth
   d. varies with the phase of the moon

5. Scientific theories
   a. must constantly be reviewed to see if they are in accord with new experimental observations
   b. represent guesses that have not yet been compared with observational data
   c. are summaries of particular experiments
   d. are laws of nature that are not subject to revision

6. The earth resembles most closely in shape
   a. a perfect sphere
   b. a grapefruit
   c. a football
   d. an egg

7. An object is traveling in a circle with a constant speed. Its acceleration is constant in
   a. magnitude only
   b. direction only
   c. both magnitude and direction
   d. neither magnitude nor direction

8. A ball of mass 0.2 kg is whirled in a circle at the end of a string 1.0 m long whose breaking strength is 10 newtons. Neglecting gravity, the maximum speed of the ball is approximately
   a. 2 m/sec
   b. 7 m/sec
   c. 10 m/sec
   d. 50 m/sec

9. An imaginary planet has twice the mass and twice the radius of the earth. The acceleration of gravity at its surface is
   a. 4.9 m/sec^2
   b. 9.8 m/sec^2
   c. 19.6 m/sec^2
   d. 39.2 m/sec^2

Problems

1. A track team on the moon could set new records for the high jump or pole vault because of the smaller gravitational force. Could sprinters also improve their times for the 60-yd dash?

2. Why would a stone dropped down a deep well land a short distance east of a point vertically below the point from which it is dropped?

3. Where on the earth's surface is the centrifugal force due to its rotation greatest? Where is it least? Why?

4. What centripetal force is required to keep a 1-kg mass whose speed is 5 m/sec moving in a circle of radius 2 m?

5. What centripetal force is required to keep a 1-lb weight whose speed is 10 ft/sec moving in a circle of radius 4 ft?

6. The maximum force a road can exert on the tires of a certain 3,500-lb automobile is 800 lb. What is the greatest speed with which the automobile can round a turn of radius 1,200 ft?

7. A string 3 ft long is used to whirl a 2-lb stone in a vertical circle at a speed of 12 ft/sec. What is the tension in the string when the stone is at the top of the circle? At the bottom? Halfway between?

8. The minute hand of a clock is 0.1 m long. Find the centripetal acceleration of its tip.

9. Is the sun's gravitational pull on the earth the same at all seasons of the year? Explain.

10. According to the basic premise of gravitation, the earth must be continually "falling" toward the sun. If this is true, why does the average distance between earth and sun not grow smaller?

11. According to Kepler's second law, the earth travels fastest when it is closest to the sun. Is this consistent with the law of gravitation? Explain.

12. An artificial satellite is placed in orbit half as far from the earth as the moon is. Would its time of revolution around the earth be longer or shorter than the moon's if its orbit is to be stable?

13. Calculate the speed an artificial satellite must have if it is to occupy a stable orbit close to the earth's equator. (Neglect the resistance of the atmosphere, and assume that the radius of the orbit is that of the earth.)

14. What is the acceleration of a meteor when it is 8,000 miles from the earth's surface?

15. What is the apparent weight in a rocket 20,000 miles from the earth's surface of a man whose weight on the earth is 160 lb?

16. Venus has a diameter of 7,700 miles and a mass 0.8 of the earth's mass. How much will a girl whose weight on the earth is 100 lb weigh on the surface of **Venus**?

CHAPTER 4 | ENERGY

We use the word *energy* so often and in such a variety of ways that the very specific definition of this term given in physics may be something of a surprise. Usually we associate energy with activity or motion: a falling stone possesses energy, an energetic person is constantly doing things. Sometimes, though, we speak of certain foods as being rich in energy or of the earth as receiving radiant energy from the sun. What is it that a piece of pie and a falling stone have in common? To the physicist the answer is obvious: the ability to do *work*. Let us begin our discussion of energy, then, by considering work.

Work

Changes that take place in the physical world are invariably the result of forces. Forces are needed to pick things up, to move things from one place to another, to squeeze things, to stretch things, and so on. However, not all forces produce changes, and it is the distinction between forces that accomplish them and forces that do not that is central to the idea of energy.

If we push against a stone wall, nothing happens. We have applied a force, but the wall has not yielded in any way and shows no effects. However, if we apply the same force to one of the stones that make up the wall, the stone flies through the air for some distance (Fig. 4.1). Now something has been accomplished as the result of our push. The basic difference between the two situations is that, in the first case, our hand did not move while it pushed against the wall. The force was a stationary one. In the second case, when we threw the stone, our hand

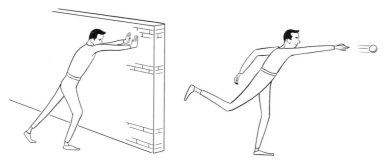

Fig. 4.1 *For a force to do work on a body, the body must undergo a displacement while the force acts on it.*

did move while the force was being applied and before the stone actually left our grasp. It is the motion of the force that constitutes the difference between the two cases and that is responsible for the difference in the two results.

When we analyze the problem of forces and the actions that they produce, we find that all forces that produce effects such as motion or distortions in an object undergo displacements in so doing; that is, a moving force accomplishes something, while the stationary force does not. The physicist makes this concept definite by defining a quantity called *work*. To a physicist, *the work done by a force is equal to the magnitude of the force multiplied by the distance through which the force acts.* If the distance is zero, no work is done by the force, no matter how great it is. And even if something moves through a distance, it does not do work unless it exerts a force on something else, so that merely moving our hand without a stone in it means that no work is done.

The above formal definition is in agreement with our observations. However, it is clear that a person can become tired without doing work, so how tired he becomes is no valid index of the amount of work he has performed. Surely, pushing against a wall for an afternoon in the hot sun is more exhausting than simply throwing a stone, but in the latter case work is being done while in the former nothing is being accomplished at all.

In algebraic form,

$$W = Fd \qquad (4.1)$$

where W = work

F = applied force

d = distance through which force has acted

In this equation F is assumed to be in the same direction as d. If it is not, for example, in the case of a boy pulling a wagon with a rope not parallel

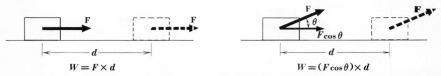

Fig. 4.2 *When a force and the distance through which it acts are parallel, the work done is equal to the product of* F *and* d. *When they are not in the same direction, the work done is equal to the product of* d *and the component of* F *in the direction of* d, *namely* (F cos θ) × d.

to the ground, we must use for F the projection of the applied force that acts in the direction of the motion (Fig. 4.2).

The projection of a force in the direction of a displacement d is

$$F \cos \theta$$

where θ is the angle between F and d. Hence the most general equation for work is

$$W = Fd \cos \theta \qquad (4.2)$$

Where F and d are parallel, $\theta = 0$ and $\cos \theta = 1$, so that Eq. (4.2) reduces to Eq. (4.1). A force that is perpendicular to the motion of an object can do no work upon it. Thus gravity, which results in a downward force on everything near the earth, does no work on objects moving along the earth's surface. However, if we drop an object, as it falls to the ground work is definitely done upon it.

In the British engineering system of units, the unit in which work is measured is called the *foot-pound*. One foot-pound is the amount of work done by a force of one pound that acts through a distance of one foot. In the metric system, work is measured in *joules*, where 1 joule is the amount of work done by a force of 1 newton that acts through a distance of 1 m. Hence

$$1 \text{ joule} = 1 \text{ newton-m}$$

To convert from one system of units to another, we note that

$$1 \text{ joule} = 0.738 \text{ ft-lb}$$
$$1 \text{ ft-lb} = 1.36 \text{ joules}$$

As an example, lifting a 50-lb crate to a height of 4 ft means that a force of 50 lb acts through a distance of 4 ft. Hence the work done is

$$W = Fd = 50 \text{ lb} \times 4 \text{ ft}$$
$$= 200 \text{ ft-lb}$$

In metric units the work done is

$$W = 200 \text{ ft-lb} \times 1.36 \text{ joules/ft-lb}$$
$$= 272 \text{ joules}$$

Power

It is often of interest to know the rate at which work is being done by some force. This quantity is called *power*, P, and, by definition, is equal to the work W performed in some period of time t divided by t:

$$P = \frac{W}{t} \qquad (4.3)$$

In the metric system the unit of power is the *watt*, where

$$1 \text{ watt} = 1 \text{ joule/sec}$$

Thus a motor with a power output of 500 watts is capable of doing 500 joules of work per second.

In the British system the proper unit of power is the foot-pound/second (ft-lb/sec). However, the horsepower (hp) is the customary unit of power in much engineering work. The origin of this unit is interesting. In order to sell the steam engines he had invented, James Watt was usually compelled to compare their power outputs with that of a horse. After various tests he found that a typical horse could perform work at the rate of 22,000 ft-lb/min for as much as 10 hr/day. To avoid possible disputes about full measure, Watt increased this figure by one-half in establishing the unit that he called the horsepower. Thus Watt's horsepower represents a rate of doing work of 33,000 ft-lb/min, or 550 ft-lb/sec. In metric units 1 hp is equal to 746 watts. (The early steam engines ranged from 4 to 100 hp, with the 20-hp model the most popular.)

Kinetic Energy

What is it that makes it possible for a force to do work? The answer is *energy*. Energy may be thought of as that property of something which enables it to do work. When we say that something has energy, we suggest that it is capable of exerting a force on something else and performing work on it. When work is done on something, on the other hand, energy has been added to it. Energy is measured in the same units as those of work, the foot-pound and the joule.

Energy may take on many forms. A familiar example is the energy a moving body possesses by virtue of its motion. Every moving object has the capacity to do work. By striking another object that is free to move, the moving object can exert a force and cause the second object to shift its

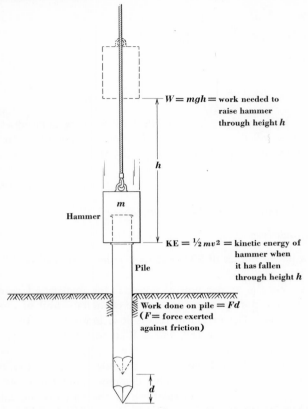

Fig. 4.3 *In the operation of a pile driver, work done in raising the hammer is converted into kinetic energy when the hammer is released. The kinetic energy is converted into work when the hammer strikes the pile.*

position. It is not necessary that the moving object actually do work; it may keep on moving, or friction may slowly bring it to a stop. But while it is moving, it has the *capacity* for doing work. It is this specific property that defines energy, since energy means the ability to do work, and so all moving things have energy by virtue of their motion. This type of energy is called *kinetic energy.*

A good example of the relation between work and kinetic energy is furnished by the pile driver, a simple machine that lifts a heavy weight and allows it to fall on the head of a pile, thereby driving the pile into the ground (Fig. 4.3). Just before the pile is struck, the hammer possesses considerable kinetic energy, which it loses by exerting a force on the pile. During the fraction of a second in which the force acts, the pile moves a short distance against the frictional resistance of the ground; hence work is accomplished by the energy of the falling weight.

The energy that an object possesses because it is moving, its kinetic energy (KE), is described formally by the expression

$$KE = \tfrac{1}{2}mv^2 \tag{4.4}$$

in which m is the mass of the object and v its speed. That mass and speed should determine kinetic energy seems reasonable enough; a train going 60 mi/hr should have more energy than a hummingbird traveling at the same rate and more energy than a similar train going 10 mi/hr. But it is not obvious why the m and v should be combined in this particular fashion.

Let us derive formula (4.4) for kinetic energy from the relationship between work and energy. The force required to lift a pile-driver hammer of mass m is its weight of mg. If the hammer is raised to a height h, the work done is

$$W = Fd = mgh$$

Now we drop the hammer, and when it reaches the ground it must have a kinetic energy equal to W; that is,

$$KE = W = mgh$$

The vertical distance h is related to the time of fall t of the hammer by

$$h = \tfrac{1}{2}gt^2$$

as we saw in Chap. 1, and so

$$KE = \tfrac{1}{2}m\,(gt)^2$$

The hammer's speed v at the bottom of its fall is its acceleration a multiplied by the time t,

$$v = gt$$

and we therefore obtain

$$KE = \tfrac{1}{2}mv^2$$

Even though we have obtained this formula for the specific case of a falling body, it is a perfectly general conclusion that holds for all moving things. The v^2 term means that kinetic energy increases very rapidly with increasing speed. At 90 mi/hr a car has nine times as much kinetic energy as at 30 mi/hr—and requires nine times as much force to bring it to a stop in the same distance (Fig. 4.4). A meteor entering the earth's atmosphere at 50 km/sec and slowed by friction to 5 km/sec thereby has its kinetic energy reduced a hundredfold. The variation with mass is, of course, less spectacular: A 2-ton car going 50 mi/hr has just twice the kinetic energy of a 1-ton car at the same speed.

A numerical example may be helpful to illustrate the calculation of

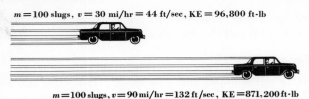

$m = 100$ slugs, $v = 30$ mi/hr $= 44$ ft/sec, KE $= 96,800$ ft-lb

$m = 100$ slugs, $v = 90$ mi/hr $= 132$ ft/sec, KE $= 871,200$ ft-lb

Fig. 4.4   *Kinetic energy is proportional to the square of the velocity; a 90 mi/hr car has nine times the kinetic energy of a 30 mi/hr car.*

kinetic energy in the British system. What is the kinetic energy of a 2-ton car going 50 mi/hr? The mass of this car is

$$m = \frac{w}{g}$$
$$= \frac{4,000 \text{ lb}}{32 \text{ ft/sec}^2}$$
$$= 125 \text{ slugs}$$

and its speed is

$$v = 50 \text{ mi/hr} \times 1.47 \frac{\text{ft/sec}}{\text{mi/hr}}$$
$$= 73.5 \text{ ft/sec}$$

The kinetic energy of the car is therefore

$$KE = \tfrac{1}{2}mv^2$$
$$= \tfrac{1}{2} \times 125 \text{ slugs} \times (73.5 \text{ ft/sec})^2$$
$$= 3.38 \times 10^5 \text{ ft-lb}$$

Potential Energy

The statement that energy is the capacity to do work is not restricted to kinetic energy, but is a perfectly general definition. Many objects possess energy because of their position. Consider the pile driver of the preceding section: When the hammer has been lifted to the top, it has only to be released to fall and do work on the pile. The capacity for doing work is present in the hammer as soon as it has been lifted, simply because of its position several feet above the ground. The actual work on the pile is done at the expense of kinetic energy gained during the hammer's fall, but the capacity for working is present before the fall starts. Energy of this sort, depending merely on the position of an object, is called *potential energy*.

Examples of potential energy are everywhere. A book on a table has potential energy, since it can fall to the floor; a skier poised at the top of a slide, water at the brink of a cataract, a car at the top of a hill, anything capable of moving toward the earth under the influence of gravity has energy because of its position. Nor is the earth's gravity necessary: A planet has potential energy with respect to the sun, since it can do work in falling toward the sun; a nail placed near a magnet has potential energy, because it can do work in moving to the magnet.

It is easy to obtain an equation for the gravitational potential energy (PE) an object has at or near the earth's surface. The work

$$W = mgh$$

is required to raise a body of mass m to a height h above its original position, as in Fig. 4.5, and so its potential energy at this height must be

$$PE = mgh \qquad (4.5)$$

When the weight w of a body is specified instead of its mass, Eq. (4.5) becomes

$$PE = wh \qquad (4.6)$$

since mass and weight are related by the formula

$$w = mg$$

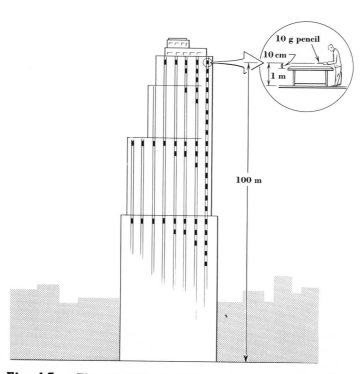

Fig. 4.5 *The gravitational potential energy of a body depends upon the choice of reference level.*

The gravitational potential energy of an object depends upon the level from which it is reckoned. Often the earth's surface is convenient, but sometimes other references are more appropriate. Suppose we hold a 10-g (0.01-kg) pencil 10 cm (0.1 m) above a table whose top is 1 m above the floor (Fig. 4.5). The pencil has a potential energy of

$$PE = mgh = 0.01 \text{ kg} \times 9.8 \text{ m/sec}^2 \times 0.1 \text{ m}$$
$$= 0.0098 \text{ joule}$$

relative to the table, and a potential energy of

$$PE = mgh = 0.01 \text{ kg} \times 9.8 \text{ m/sec}^2 \times 1.1 \text{ m}$$
$$= 0.108 \text{ joule}$$

relative to the floor. The room in which we are might well be, say, 100 m above the ground, so that the potential energy of the pencil is

$$PE = mgh = 0.01 \text{ kg} \times 9.8 \text{ m/sec}^2 \times 100 \text{ m}$$
$$= 9.8 \text{ joules}$$

relative to the ground. What, then, is its true potential energy? The answer is that there is no such thing as "true" potential energy; potential energy is intrinsically a *relative* quantity, meaningful only in terms of a specific reference location. However, the *difference* between the potential energies of a body at two points in its motion *is* significant. If we drop the pencil and want to compute its speed upon striking the floor, we equate its kinetic energy of

$$KE = \tfrac{1}{2}mv^2$$

with its loss of potential energy in falling through 1.1 m. Hence

$$PE = KE$$
$$mgh = \tfrac{1}{2}mv^2$$
$$v = \sqrt{2gh}$$
$$= \sqrt{2 \times 9.8 \text{ m/sec}^2 \times 1.1 \text{ m}}$$
$$= 4.6 \text{ m/sec}$$

The fact that the floor of the room in which the pencil falls may be at ground level or 100 m above it is irrelevant; only the actual distance of fall is involved. It is important to note that h in Eqs. (4.4) and (4.5) is always the vertical distance (not necessarily the total distance the body may travel) between the starting point and the lowest point of fall.

In the British system of units, where weights rather than masses are customarily given, the potential energy of a body is just its weight (in pounds) multiplied by its height (in feet) above the selected reference level. Thus a 2-ton car at the top of a hill 100 ft high has a potential energy of

$$PE = wh$$
$$= 4{,}000 \text{ lb} \times 100 \text{ ft}$$
$$= 4 \times 10^5 \text{ ft-lb}$$

relative to the foot of the hill, which is only a trifle more than its kinetic energy when moving at 50 mi/hr. If a 50 mi/hr car crashes into some fixed object, nearly as much work (that is, damage) will be done on car and object as if the car drops through 100 ft of free fall.

Energy Transformations

Nearly all familiar mechanical processes actually consist of interchanges of energy among its kinetic and potential forms and work. An example is the case of a pile driver. The first step in the operation of a pile driver is the raising of its hammer above the ground by an engine, which performs an amount of work equal to the weight of the hammer multiplied by the height to which it is raised. The hammer in its upper position now has potential energy. When the hammer is released, it falls faster and faster, its potential energy becoming converted to kinetic energy. When the pile is struck by the hammer, the hammer's kinetic energy becomes work as the pile is driven into the ground, and the hammer comes to a halt.

We can obtain a great deal of insight into mechanical processes by thinking in terms of such transformations of energy. Thus, when the car of Fig. 4.6 drives to the top of a hill, its engine must do work in order to lift the car up. At the top, the car has an amount of potential energy equal to the work done in getting it up there (neglecting friction). If the engine is turned off, the car can still coast down the hill, and its kinetic energy at the bottom of the hill will be the same as its potential energy at the top.

Fig. 4.6 *In the absence of friction, a car can coast from the top of one hill into a valley and then up to the top of another hill of the same height as the first. In doing this the initial potential energy of the car is converted into kinetic energy as it goes downhill, and this kinetic energy is then converted back into potential energy as it climbs the second hill.*

Changes of a similar nature, from kinetic energy to potential and back, are exhibited in the motion of a planet in its orbit around the sun (Fig. 4.7) and in the motion of a pendulum (Fig. 4.8). The orbits of the planets are ellipses with the sun at one focus, and each planet is therefore at a constantly varying distance from the sun. At all times the total of its potential and kinetic energies remains the same. When the planet is close to the sun, its potential energy is low and its kinetic energy high. The additional speed due to the increased kinetic energy keeps the planet from being pulled into the sun by the greater gravitational force it experiences at this point in its path. When the planet is far from the sun, its potential energy is high and its kinetic energy correspondingly lower, the reduced speed exactly keeping pace with the reduced gravitational force.

A typical pendulum, as in Fig. 4.8, consists of a ball suspended by a string whose mass is negligible compared with that of the ball. When the ball is pulled to one side with its string taut and then released, it swings back and forth indefinitely. When it is released, the ball has a potential energy relative to the bottom of its path of mgh. At its lowest point all this potential energy has become kinetic energy, and the speed of the ball is found by setting PE and KE equal:

$$PE_{top} = KE_{bottom}$$
$$mgh = \tfrac{1}{2}mv^2$$
$$v = \sqrt{2gh}$$

This is the same speed the ball would have if dropped from a height h, but here the ball is moving horizontally because of the constraining influence

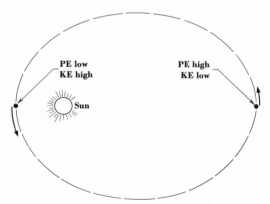

Fig. 4.7 **Energy transformations in planetary motion.** *Near the sun the potential energy of a planet is a minimum and its kinetic energy a maximum, while far from the sun its potential energy is a maximum and its kinetic energy a minimum. The total energy of the planet is the same at all points in its orbit.*

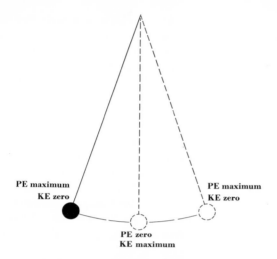

PE maximum
KE zero

PE maximum
KE zero

PE zero
KE maximum

Fig. 4.8   Energy transformations in pendulum motion. *The constant total energy of the ball is continuously exchanged between kinetic and potential forms.*

of the string.   However, energy is not a vector quantity, and the direction of the ball's motion has no bearing on its kinetic energy.   Since h is the vertical distance through which an object falls in acquiring the speed $\sqrt{2gh}$, the fact that the ball's path is an arc of a circle, and not merely straight down, is also irrelevant.   After reaching the bottom, the ball continues in its motion until it rises to a height h on the opposite side from its initial position. Then, momentarily at rest since all its kinetic energy is now potential energy, the ball begins to retrace its path back through the bottom to its initial position.

Energy in Other Forms

The two kinds of energy—kinetic and potential—we have spoken of are not the only kinds that occur in nature.   Energy in other forms can also perform work.   The *chemical energy* of gasoline is used to drive our automobiles; the chemical energy of food enables our bodies and the bodies of domestic animals to perform work.   *Heat energy* from burning coal or oil is used to form the steam that drives locomotives.   *Electric energy* and *magnetic energy* turn motors in home and factory.   *Radiant energy* from the sun, though man has yet to learn how to harness it efficiently, performs very necessary work in lifting water from the earth's surface into clouds, in producing inequalities in atmospheric temperatures that cause winds, and in making possible chemical reactions in plants that produce foods.

Just as kinetic energy can be converted into potential energy and potential into kinetic, so other forms of energy can readily be transformed. In the cylinders of an automobile engine, for example, chemical energy stored in gasoline and air is changed first to heat energy when the mixture is ignited, then to mechanical energy as the expanding gases push down on the pistons. This mechanical energy is in large part transmitted to the wheels, but some is used to turn the generator and thus produce electric energy for charging the battery, and some is changed to heat by friction in bearings. Energy transformations go on constantly, all about us.

If energy changes are followed backward into the past, it becomes apparent that almost all the energy available to us on the earth today has come ultimately from a single source—the sun. Light and heat reach us directly from the sun; food and wood owe their chemical energy to sunlight falling on plants; water power exists because the sun's heat evaporates water constantly from the oceans. Coal and petroleum were formed from plants and animals that lived and stored energy derived from sunlight millions of years ago.

Modern civilization owes its spectacular development in large measure to the discovery of vast sources of energy and to the development of new methods for storing and transforming it. Within less than two centuries man has learned to use efficiently the chemical energy of coal and petroleum, to change heat into useful mechanical energy, to store chemical energy in explosives, to get electric energy from moving water, and to use electric energy for heating, lighting, mechanical work, and communication. In the development of atomic bombs and nuclear reactors, a new energy source has been tapped—the energy stored in the interiors of atoms. Other possible sources, still being explored by industry, are the energy of tides and radiant energy direct from the sun.

Heat as a form of energy deserves special attention. Heat is invariably one of the products of any energy transformation, appearing whether we wish it to or not. In some transformations heat is almost the only product, as when electric energy is used in a heater, when wood burns in an open fire, or when sunlight is absorbed at the earth's surface. More often heat appears as a secondary product accompanying another form of energy, due, for instance, to friction in mechanical processes and to resistances in electric circuits. Sometimes the amount of heat produced is very small, but its presence cannot be avoided altogether. We shall find later that heat and its effects provide the key to understanding many of the properties of matter.

Momentum

Another quantity that must often be taken into account in problems concerning moving bodies is called *momentum*. The momentum of a body of mass m and velocity v is, by definition, the product of m and v:

$$\text{Momentum} = mv \tag{4.7}$$

The important thing about momentum is that it is a *vector quantity*, meaning that it has a direction associated with it, namely, the direction of motion of the body. Kinetic energy, given by the somewhat similar formula $\frac{1}{2}mv^2$, has a completely different significance, since it is a quantity having only magnitude. In the early days of physics, even after the time of Newton, the distinction between momentum and kinetic energy was as troublesome to scientists as it frequently is to students today.

Momentum finds its greatest usefulness in situations involving (in general terms) explosions and collisions. When external forces do not act upon the bodies involved, their momentum is *conserved*; the total momentum of all the bodies before they interact is exactly the same as their total momentum afterward. When two objects collide and stick together, for instance, the sum of the initial momenta of the objects (taking into account their directions of motion), which we might write m_1v_1 and m_2v_2, must be equal to the momentum mv of the composite body they form when they stick together (Fig. 4.9).

A rocket illustrates conservation of momentum. When the rocket stands stationary on its launching platform, its momentum is zero. When it is fired, the momentum of the gases rushing out downward is balanced by the momentum in the other direction of the rocket body moving upward; the total momentum of all the constituents of the rocket, gases and body, remains zero, because momentum is a vector quantity and the upward and downward momenta cancel out. Thus a rocket does not operate by "pushing" against anything and functions best in the near vacuum of space, where friction is virtually absent. Energy also is conserved in a rocket, the kinetic energy

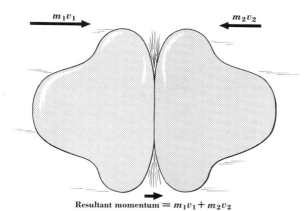

Fig. 4.9 *When two objects collide, the sum of their initial momenta is equal to the momentum of the composite body they form when they stick together. Momentum is a vector quantity, and the directions of motion of the objects must be taken into account when their momenta are added together.*

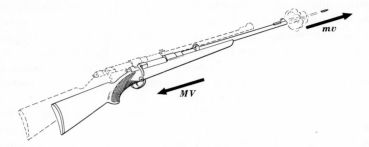

Fig. 4.10   *When a rifle is fired, the backward momentum of the rifle is equal to the forward momentum of the bullet. The speed of the bullet is greater than that of the rifle because it is lighter. The initial momentum of the system of rifle plus bullet is zero, and so the final momentum of the system must also be zero since no external forces act upon it.*

of the rocket and of the exhaust gases after firing being equal to the chemical energy expended in producing the gases at high velocity.

Let us examine the similar problem of a rifle being fired (Fig. 4.10). Before the trigger is pulled, both rifle and bullet are stationary, so the initial momentum is zero. When the trigger is pulled, however, the bullet flies out of the barrel with the momentum mv, where m is its mass and v its velocity. Because no outside forces are acting on the bullet and rifle at the moment of firing, the total momentum after firing must be the same as it was initially. This means that the rifle itself must move *backward* if its momentum is to balance out the forward momentum of the bullet. If the mass of the rifle is M and its backward velocity is V,

$$MV = mv$$

Suppose that the bullet has a mass of 10 g (0.01 kg) and a muzzle velocity of 800 m/sec. This gives it a momentum of

$$mv = 0.01 \times 800 = 8 \text{ kg-m/sec}$$

If the rifle's mass is 3 kg, its velocity can be found from the fact that

$$MV = mv = 8 \text{ kg-m/sec}$$

to be $$V = \frac{8 \text{ kg-m/sec}}{3 \text{ kg}} = 2.67 \text{ m/sec}$$

It is this momentum that is felt as the recoil of a rifle or shotgun; the heavier the bullet and the greater its muzzle velocity, the more "kick" will be felt by the shooter. Notice that the idea of conservation of energy in transitions from one form to another gives us no indication that there will be any recoil.

Self-examination

1. Of the following units, the one that is *not* a unit of energy is the
   a. foot-pound
   b. newton
   c. joule
   d. watthour

2. A stationary object may have
   a. potential energy
   b. kinetic energy
   c. momentum
   d. velocity

3. When the velocity of a body is doubled,
   a. its kinetic energy is doubled
   b. its potential energy is doubled
   c. its momentum is doubled
   d. its acceleration is doubled

4. A moving body need *not* have
   a. velocity
   b. momentum
   c. potential energy
   d. kinetic energy

5. Conservation of energy means that
   a. energy can be created but not destroyed
   b. energy can be destroyed but not created
   c. energy can both be created and destroyed
   d. energy can neither be created nor destroyed

6. Two spheres of the same size, one of mass 5 kg and the other of mass 10 kg, are dropped simultaneously from a tower. When they are 1 m above the ground, the two spheres have the same
   a. momentum
   b. kinetic energy
   c. potential energy
   d. acceleration

7. A bomb dropped from an airplane explodes in mid-air.
   a. Its total kinetic energy increases.
   b. Its total kinetic energy decreases.
   c. Its total momentum increases.
   d. Its total momentum decreases.

8. An 8-slug mass is raised through a height of 10 ft. The increase in its potential energy is
   a. 2.4 ft-lb
   b. 10 ft-lb
   c. 80 ft-lb
   d. 2,560 ft-lb

9. A child on a swing is 3 ft above the ground at the lowest point and 6 ft above the ground at the highest point. The horizortal speed of the child at the lowest point of the swing is
   a. 11 ft/sec
   b. 14 ft/sec
   c. 18 ft/sec
   d. 32 ft/sec

Problems

1. Two objects, one with a mass of 1 kg and the other with a weight of 1 newton, both have potential energies of 1 joule relative to the ground. What are their respective heights above the ground?

2. Two objects, one with a mass of 1 slug and the other with a weight of 1 pound, both have potential energies of 1 ft-lb relative to the ground. What are their respective heights above the ground?

3. A total of 490 joules of work is needed to lift a body of unknown mass through a height of 10 m. What is its mass?

4. Can you suggest any kinds of energy found on the earth that do not have their ultimate source in the sun's radiation?

5. Is it correct to say that all changes in the physical world involve energy transformations of some sort? Why?

6. A force of 20 lb is required to move a 50-lb crate across a floor. How much work must be done to move the crate 30 ft?

7. Ten thousand joules of work is expended in raising a 90-kg box. How high was it raised? What is its potential energy?

8. In what part of its orbit is the earth's potential energy greatest with respect to the sun? In what part of its orbit is its kinetic energy greatest? Explain your answers.

9. A 3,200-lb car, initially at rest, coasts down a hill 50 ft high. If there were no frictional forces present, what would its speed be at the foot of the hill?

10. If the frictional retarding force on the car of Prob. 9 is 100 lb and if the length of the road is 1,500 ft from the top of the hill to its foot, what will the car's speed be at the foot of hill?

11. An automobile weighing 3,500 lb and traveling at 30 mph (44 ft/sec) strikes a stationary automobile of the same weight. The two cars stick together after the collision. What is their final velocity? How much kinetic energy has been lost?

12. A 180-lb man dives horizontally from a 300-lb boat with a speed of 5 ft/sec. What is the recoil speed of the boat?

13. A bullet weighing 0.08 lb is fired from a 10-lb rifle at a muzzle velocity of 2,000 ft/sec. What is the recoil speed of the rifle?

14. Is it possible for a body to have simultaneously more kinetic energy but less momentum than another body? Is the converse possible?

15. Two boys, one weighing 75 lb and the other 100 lb, are facing each other on frictionless roller skates. The smaller boy pushes the larger one, so that the latter moves away at a speed of 2 mi/hr. With what speed does the smaller boy move, and in what direction?

16. A centripetal force of 50 lb is used to keep a 0.2-slug ball moving in a circle with uniform speed at the end of a string 3 ft long. How much work is done by the force in each revolution of the ball?

CHAPTER 5 | HEAT

Not always does the disappearance of kinetic or potential energy result in the performance of work. A skier slides down a high slope and comes to rest at the bottom. What has become of the potential energy he originally had? The engine of an automobile is shut off, while the automobile itself is permitted to coast along a level road from some initial speed; eventually the automobile slows down and comes to a halt. What has become of its original kinetic energy? All of us can give many similar illustrations that exhibit the apparent disappearance of kinetic or potential energy. What these examples have in common, as careful examination would reveal, is that *heat* is always produced. As a general observation, whenever mechanical energy disappears from a system of objects that does not interact with its surroundings, all this energy is converted either into mechanical work or into heat. This is one way of stating the law of conservation of energy, one of the most fundamental of all physical principles. In this chapter we shall explore the related topics of heat and temperature, together with the conservation of energy.

Temperature

Heat and temperature are often confused. We say commonly, and usually correctly, that the higher its temperature, the more heat an object possesses. But we cannot say that one object possesses more heat than *another* object because its temperature is higher. The filament of a light bulb, for instance, has a much higher temperature than a piece of burning wood, yet we should hardly choose to warm ourselves on a

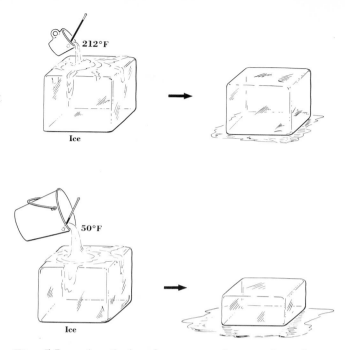

Fig. 5.1 *A pail of cool water contains more heat than a cup of boiling water.*

cold day by a light bulb in preference to a wood fire. A cup of boiling water is hotter than a pailful of cool water, but the cool water would melt a larger quantity of ice. The cupful of boiling water evidently contains a smaller amount of heat despite its higher temperature (Fig. 5.1).

Temperature, like force, is a physical quantity primarily meaningful to us in terms of the responses of our sense organs. We can touch an object and estimate its temperature, but just how we do this is not easy to explain in words. Some objective means of specifying the notion of temperature is required. We shall postpone the proper interpretation of temperature in terms of molecular motion until the next chapter and for the moment invoke a familiar experimental observation. When a hot and a cold body are placed in contact, they eventually reach the same intermediate temperature. Hot coffee poured into a cold cup becomes cooler, while the cup simultaneously becomes warmer. A working definition of temperature can be based upon this phenomenon: When heat flows from one body to another, the former is at a higher temperature than the latter.

A *thermometer* is a device that measures temperature. Most substances expand when heated and shrink when cooled, and the thermometers we use in everyday life are designed around this property of matter. More precisely, they are based upon the fact that different materials react to a given temperature change to different extents. The familiar mercury-in-glass thermometer (Fig. 5.2) functions because mercury expands more than glass when heated and contracts more than glass when cooled. Thus the length of the mercury column in the glass tube provides a measure of the surrounding temperature. Another common thermometer makes use of the different rates of expansion of different kinds of metals. Two straight strips of dissimilar metals are joined together at a particular temperature (Fig. 5.3). At higher temperatures the bimetallic strip bends so that the metal with the greater expansion is on the outside of the curve, and at lower temperatures it bends in the opposite direction. In each case the exact amount of bending depends upon the temperature. Thermometers of this kind are often employed in measuring fairly high temperatures, such as in ovens and furnaces.

Thermal expansion is not the only property of matter that can be used to construct a thermometer. As another example, the color and amount of light emitted by a very hot body vary with temperature. A poker thrust in a fire first glows dull red, then successively bright red, orange, yellow, and finally, if the poker achieves a high enough temperature, it becomes "white hot." The precise color of the light given off by an incandescent object is thus a measure of its temperature.

Given a physical property that varies with temperature, the next step is to establish a scale of temperature to make possible quantitative measurements. Unfortunately, two such scales are in common use, one devised by Fahrenheit in 1724 and the other by Celsius in 1742. Fahrenheit chose for

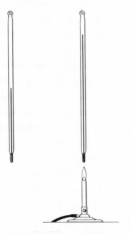

Fig. 5.2 *A mercury-in-glass thermometer. Mercury responds to temperature changes to a greater extent than glass does, and so the length of the mercury column is a measure of the temperature of the thermometer bulb.*

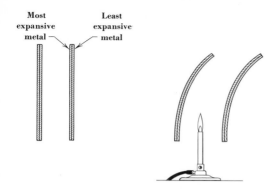

Most expansive metal

Least expansive metal

Fig. 5.3 *A bimetallic strip thermometer. No matter on which side the heat is applied, the bend is away from the more expansive metal. The higher the temperature, the greater the deflection. At low temperatures the deflection is in the opposite sense.*

the zero point of his scale the lowest temperature he could obtain with an ice-salt mixture and arbitrarily picked 96° as the temperature of the human body. (His measurement was inaccurate; today we regard 98.6° as normal body temperature.) Such temperatures are difficult to reproduce accurately, and so today the Fahrenheit scale is defined by calling 32° the freezing point of water and 212° its boiling point.

More practically, Celsius chose the easily determined temperatures of freezing and boiling water as the 0° and 100° marks on his scale. The Fahrenheit scale is an awkward makeshift and remains in use only because England and America cling to it with the same obstinacy that preserves the British system of weight and measures. Most other civilized countries, and scientists throughout the world, use the more convenient Celsius (or centigrade) scale. A comparison of the two is shown in Fig. 5.4. To go from a Fahrenheit temperature T_F to a Celsius temperature T_C, and vice versa, we note that Fahrenheit degrees are five-ninths as large as Celsius degrees. Hence, also taking into account the difference between the zero point on the two scales, we see that

$$T_F = \tfrac{9}{5}T_C + 32° \tag{5.1}$$
$$T_C = \tfrac{5}{9}(T_F - 32°) \tag{5.2}$$

Thus the Celsius equivalent of the normal body temperature of 98.6°F is

$$T_C = \tfrac{5}{9}(98.6° - 32°)$$
$$= \tfrac{5}{9} \times 66.6°$$
$$= 37.0°C$$

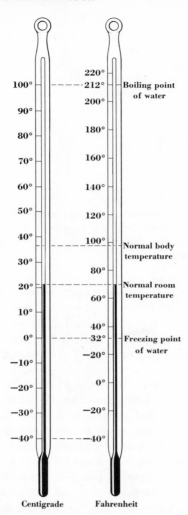

Centigrade   Fahrenheit

Fig. 5.4   Comparison of Celsius and Fahrenheit temperature scales. A Celsius temperature T_C *may be changed to its equivalent Fahrenheit temperature* T_F *by means of the formula* $T_F = (9/5)T_C + 32$; *to change from a Fahrenheit temperature to its equivalent Celsius temperature, the formula* $T_C = (5/9)(T_F - 32)$ *may be used.*

Heat

The *heat* possessed by an object depends not only on its temperature, but on the amount and kind of material in it. A cup of water at 100°C has less heat than a pailful at 30°C simply because less water is present. To heat the cupful on a stove from 0 to 100°C would require less time than to heat the pailful from 0 to 30°C. In order to include quantity of material as well as temperature in the idea of heat, we define the unit of heat, the *kilocalorie,* as *the amount of heat required to raise the temperature of one kilogram of water by one degree centigrade.* Raising the temperature of 1 kg of water from 20 to 25°C would require 5 kilocalories (kcal); raising the temperature of 5 kg of water through the same range would require 25 kcal; and so on. The kilocalorie is an energy unit, like the joule and the foot-pound.

If we wish to lower the temperature of something, heat must be removed from it. The amount of heat involved is the same as would be needed to raise the temperature through the same temperature interval; thus, to cool 1 kg of water through 1°C, exactly 1 kcal has to be extracted.

The temperatures of most other substances can be changed by the transfer of less heat than that required by an equal mass of water. For instance, to increase or decrease the temperature of 1 kg of ice by 1°C we must add or remove only 0.5 kcal, and to do the same for 1 kg of silver a mere 0.056 kcal need be added or removed. The *specific heat* of a substance is defined as the heat required to change the temperature of 1 kg of the substance by 1°C. A list of the specific heats of various substances is given in Table 5.1. For a given mass, the smaller the specific heat, the less the amount of heat needed to effect a given temperature change.

Table 5.1. Specific heats of various substances. *The values given are averages, since the actual specific heats vary to some extent with temperature.*

Substance	Specific heat, kcal/kg-°C
Alcohol (ethyl)	0.58
Aluminum	0.22
Copper	0.093
Glass	0.20
Granite	0.19
Ice	0.50
Iron	0.11
Lead	0.030
Mercury	0.033
Silver	0.056
Steam	0.48
Water	1.00
Wood	0.42

From the definition of specific heat (symbol c) we can obtain a simple formula for the heat (symbol Q) involved in changing the temperature of a mass m of a substance by ΔT. This formula is

$$Q = mc\,\Delta T \tag{5.3}$$

and it holds whether the heat is added or removed provided that the substance does not change state (from solid to liquid, for example) during the process. Thus, in order to raise the temperature of 10 kg of iron from 20 to 50°C, we must supply

$$Q = 10 \text{ kg} \times 0.11 \text{ kcal/kg-}°\text{C} \times 30°\text{C}$$
$$= 33 \text{ kcal}$$

since ΔT is 30°C.

Changes of State

An important effect brought about by an appropriate change in temperature is the change of one form of matter to another. All gases can be liquefied and all liquids frozen if the temperature is decreased sufficiently. Nearly all solids can be liquefied and vaporized, except for those like paper and coal which decompose below their melting points. Since almost every substance can exist as a solid, liquid, and gas, these are considered as different *states* of matter rather than different kinds, and changes from one to another are called *changes of state*.

Let us consider the temperature changes accompanying the melting of ice and the vaporization of water under ordinary conditions (normal atmospheric pressure). If we start with a dish of chipped ice below its melting point, the first effect of supplying heat is to raise the temperature. The rise continues steadily up to 0°C, then stops abruptly as the ice begins to melt. During the melting the temperature remains at 0°C, no matter how much heat we supply, provided the ice-water mixture is kept well mixed. If heating continues after the last of the ice disappears, the temperature again starts upward and rises continuously to 100°C. During this rise we find vapor given off in increasing quantities. Water vapor itself is a colorless gas and therefore invisible, but above the heated dish it may cool and condense into visible white clouds of tiny liquid droplets. If we had had the proper means of detecting it, we should have found that vapor was given off during the entire heating process, from the cold ice as well as the heated water; rising temperature simply increases the rate of vaporization. At 100°C the liberation of vapor becomes so rapid that it no longer takes place from the surface alone: Bubbles of vapor form all through the liquid, and we say that the water is boiling. At the boiling point, as at the melting point, the temperature remains constant. We may use as hot a flame as we like, or as many burners, but the thermometer will remain at 100°C until the water disappears. Thereafter, if we arrange to heat the water vapor (usually called *steam* above the boiling point of water) in a closed container, its temperature will rise indefinitely as more heat is supplied. This sequence of changes is shown graphically in Fig. 5.5.

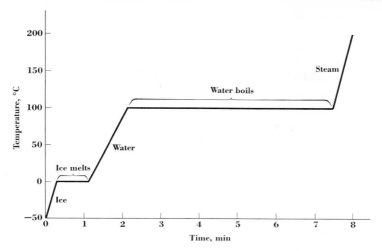

Fig. 5.5 *Graph of temperature versus time for 1 kg of water, initially ice at* $-50°C$, *to which heat is added at the constant rate of 100 kcal/min. The process is assumed to take place with no loss of heat to the surroundings of the water.*

When steam (under 1 atmosphere pressure) is cooled to 100°C, it condenses to liquid water, and the liquid freezes to ice at 0°C; that is, the sequence of changes shown in Fig. 5.5 is exactly reversed by decreasing the temperature. The condensation point of steam and the freezing point of water are identical, respectively, with the boiling point of water and the melting point of ice. Because these temperatures are the same from whichever side approached, and because they remain constant while heat is added or removed, they are eminently suitable for fixing the points on a thermometer scale, as Celsius noted two centuries ago. The only factors that influence the temperatures of freezing and boiling are the surrounding pressures and the purity of the water. The boiling point is particularly susceptible to pressure changes: The decrease in atmospheric pressure in going from sea level to a high mountain, for instance, lowers the boiling point so markedly that eggs and vegetables, to be thoroughly cooked, must be boiled considerably longer. The advantage of a pressure cooker lies in the fact that increased pressure raises the boiling point and hence decreases the time necessary for cooking.

Note that, in the melting of ice and the vaporization of water, the material *absorbs heat without becoming hotter.* Just to melt 1 kg of ice, with the temperature constantly at 0°C, requires the addition of 80 kcal of heat—enough to raise the temperature of 1 kg of liquid water from room temperature to the boiling point. To vaporize 1 kg of water at its boiling point, without any change in temperature, requires the addition of considerably more heat—nearly 540 kcal. These two figures are called, respectively, the *heat of fusion* and the *heat of vaporization* of water.

The reverse changes of state give off heat instead of absorbing it. The condensation of 1 kg of steam liberates 540 kcal, and the freezing of 1 kg of water liberates 80 kcal. That steam indeed gives off heat when it condenses is attested by the severe burns which live steam can produce. The liberation of heat when lakes freeze in winter is sufficient to keep their shores temporarily at a somewhat higher temperature than that of surrounding regions.

Changes of state in other substances are similar to those we have just discussed for water. Most substances have definite melting points and boiling points and characteristic latent heats of fusion and vaporization. A few materials, like glass, have no sharp melting point, but gradually soften when heated. Some solids vaporize readily on heating and ordinarily pass directly into the gaseous state without liquefying; iodine, dry ice (solid carbon dioxide), and camphor are familiar examples. The direct formation of vapor from a solid, called *sublimation*, is not a peculiar property of these few substances—a light snowfall, for example, gradually disappears by sublimation even on a very cold day—but for most solids the amount of vaporization is so slight that we do not ordinarily observe it.

The Nature of Heat

The work done in raising an object through a height h is transformed into potential energy, and this potential energy is available for further conversion into kinetic energy or back into work. When work is done against friction, however, it ceases to be directly available for such conversion. To give a specific example, we might push a crate 50 ft across a warehouse floor by exerting a horizontal force of 30 lb on it, and in so doing we perform

$$W = Fd = 30 \text{ lb} \times 50 \text{ ft} = 1{,}500 \text{ ft-lb}$$

of work. But at the end of its path the crate is stationary, so it has acquired no kinetic energy, and it is at the same level as when it started, so it has gained no potential energy. At first glance the work we did seems to have vanished, but a closer look reveals a new phenomenon: The crate and floor are now at a higher temperature than they were before. This is hardly a novel observation; even primitive man must have found that rubbing two sticks together both involves effort on his part and causes the sticks to grow warm. But a more basic question is less easy to answer: Does the dissipation of a given amount of energy always liberate *exactly* the same amount of heat? Only if this is true can we be sure that heat is really a form of energy.

While it comes as no surprise to us today to learn that heat is a form of energy, our predecessors were not so clear on this point. Not much more than a century ago most scientists regarded heat as an actual substance, which they called *caloric*. The absorption of caloric caused an object to rise in temperature, while the escape of caloric from something caused its temperature to fall. Because the weight of an object does not change when it is heated, caloric was considered to be a weightless or imponderable substance, one of several imponderables whose convenient behavior was invoked by learned men in the latter part of the eighteenth century to account for mysteries in nature for which no other explanation was known. Caloric was invisible, odorless, and tasteless, as well as weightless, attributes which, of course, were responsible for its failure to be perceived directly.

Actually, the idea of heat as a substance worked fairly satisfactorily for materials heated over a flame, but it did not furnish an explanation for the heat generated by friction. One of the first to appreciate this difficulty was an adventurous American, born Benjamin Thompson in 1763, who fled this country during the Revolution and was made Count Rumford during a spectacular career in Europe. One of Rumford's many occupations was supervising the boring of cannon for a German prince, and he was impressed by the large amounts of heat evolved by friction in the boring process. He showed that the heat could be used to boil water and that heat could be produced again and again from the same piece of metal. If heat was a fluid, it was not unreasonable that boring a hole in a piece of metal should liberate it. However, even a dull drill which cut no metal liberated a large quantity of heat. It was hard to conceive of a piece of metal as containing an infinite amount of caloric, and Rumford preferred to regard heat as a form of energy. Actually, in his own terminology, Rumford considered heat to be "motion" rather than a substance; but his inference is clear.

James Prescott Joule was an English brewer after whom the metric unit of energy is named in recognition of his classic experiment which settled the nature of heat. Joule's experiment employed a small paddle wheel within a container of water (Fig. 5.6). Work was done in turning the paddle wheel against the resistance of the water, and Joule determined exactly how much heat was supplied to the water by friction during this process. He found that a given amount of mechanical energy invariably produced the same amount of heat. Not only was heat intimately associated with motion, as Rumford had found, but the *amount of work* performed against friction precisely determined the *amount of heat* produced. This was a clear demonstration that heat is energy, and not matter.

The amount of mechanical energy that produces 1 kcal of heat, according to modern experiments, is 4,185 joules. This figure is often called the *mechanical equivalent of heat*.

Conservation of Energy

Joule's work led to one of the basic laws of physical science. His experiments showed clearly that, in the transformation of mechanical energy into

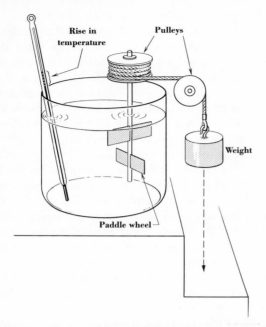

Fig. 5.6 *Joule's experimental demonstration that energy is conserved. As the weight falls, it turns the paddle wheel, which heats the water by friction. The potential energy of the weight is converted first into the kinetic energy of the paddle wheel and then into heat energy (4,185 joules of mechanical energy is equivalent to 1 kcal of heat).*

heat, no energy is lost, nor is any new energy created. One kind of energy is simply converted into another, and every bit of mechanical energy expended reappears as heat energy. In further experiments on other changes of mechanical energy into heat and in conversions of electric, magnetic, and radiant energy into heat, the amount of heat produced was always shown to be precisely equal to the amount of some other kind of energy that had vanished.

In other types of energy transformation, from potential to kinetic, for instance, some energy at first glance does seem to disappear; thus the hammer of a pile driver never has quite so much kinetic energy when it strikes the pile as it had potential energy before it fell, because some energy is lost in friction. But if the heat energy produced by the friction is added to the kinetic energy, the sum of the two is precisely equal to the original potential energy. For all ordinary transformations of energy that have been studied in detail, a similar statement holds: If all the different sorts of energy that go into a transformation are added together and if all the energy produced **is accounted** for, the two sums are precisely equal. In other words, so far as we know, *energy cannot be created or destroyed.* This sweeping generalization is the law of conservation of energy.

Modern physics has discovered what seem, at first, to be violations of the law of conservation of energy. In the theory of relativity, however, Einstein proved that *mass* must be thought of as a form of energy, and this equivalence has restored conservation of energy to its place as one of the basic principles of physics. We shall learn later of the various ways in which mass is converted into energy and energy into mass in nature.

Just how far-reaching the law of conservation of energy is can perhaps be appreciated only by a physicist, who has applied it to a great variety of situations and seen it time and again bring order into tangled mazes of observational data. It is probably the broadest exact principle in all science, applying with equal force to remote stars and to the intricate biological processes in living cells. In the practical world, it enables technicians to calculate accurately the amount of energy obtainable from a machine, and it has shown clearly the fallacy in the age-old dream of perpetual motion.

Self-examination

1. Heat is most closely related to
   a. temperature
   b. energy
   c. momentum
   d. friction

2. A temperature of 20°C is the same as
   a. −20.9°F
   b. −6.4°F
   c. 68°F
   d. 93.6°F

3. Two bars of lead, one twice as heavy as the other, are heated to a temperature of 200°C. The heavy bar
   a. contains half as much heat as the lighter bar
   b. contains the same amount of heat as the lighter bar
   c. contains twice as much heat as the lighter bar
   d. may contain more or less heat than the lighter bar, depending upon the precise shapes of the bars

4. On the basis of what has been said in this chapter about energy and heat, we should expect the water at the bottom of a waterfall to be
   a. warmer than at the top
   b. at the same temperature as at the top
   c. cooler than at the top
   d. warmer or cooler, depending upon the height of the waterfall

5. In order for a vapor to condense into a liquid,
   a. its temperature must drop
   b. its temperature must rise
   c. it must give off heat
   d. it must absorb heat

6. The ratio between the energy dissipated in a particular process and the heat that it is converted to is known as the
   a. specific heat
   b. mechanical equivalent of heat
   c. joule
   d. kilocalorie

7. A typical daily diet has an energy content of 2,400 kcal. If this energy were expended in lifting a mass of 1 kg, the height through which it would be raised would be roughly
   a. 1 m
   b. 100 m
   c. 10,000 m
   d. 1,000,000 m

Problems

1. The boiling point of oxygen is −183°C. What is this temperature on the Fahrenheit scale?

2. What is the Fahrenheit equivalent of a temperature of 25°C?

3. What is the Celsius equivalent of a temperature of 100°F?

4. How many kilocalories are required to raise the temperature of 20 kg of water from the freezing point to the boiling point?

5. How much heat is required to raise the temperature of 1 kg of copper from 100 to 140°C? From 140 to 180°C?

6. How much steam at 120°C is required to melt 2 kg of ice at 0°C?

7. Why is a piece of ice at 0°C more effective in cooling a drink than the same weight of cold water at 0°C?

8. How much heat is required to change 50 g of ice at 0°C into water at 20°C?

9. How much heat is given off when 1 kg of steam at 100°C condenses and cools to water at 20°C?

10. How much energy does an 80-kg man use in climbing a staircase 8 m high? To how many calories of heat does this energy correspond?

11. A 10-kg stone is dropped into a pool of water from a height of 100 m. How much energy in joules does the stone have when it strikes the water? If all this energy goes into heat, how many calories of heat are added to the water? If the pool contains 10 m³ of water, by how much is its temperature raised?

12. How high is a waterfall if the water at its base is 1°C higher in temperature than the water at the top?

13. How many kilocalories of heat are evolved per hour by a 600-watt electric heater?

Part II

PROPERTIES OF MATTER

CHAPTER 6 | SOLIDS, LIQUIDS, AND GASES

We now turn to matter itself and the characteristics of its three states, solid, liquid, and gas. As we shall see, what we have learned about energy finds direct application in the study of matter; in fact, throughout all the physical sciences, knowledge of the transformation of energy from one form to another and its conversion into work permits us to gain insights into the universe that would not otherwise be possible.

Almost everyone has a fairly clear idea of the distinctions among solids, liquids, and gases. Solids maintain their sizes and shapes no matter where they are placed. Liquids, however, spread out and assume the shapes of their containers while maintaining their volumes constant. Gases maintain neither shape nor volume, but expand until they fill completely whatever container they are placed in (Fig. 6.1).

A related distinction involves the ability of gases and liquids to flow readily, which is why these phases of matter together are called *fluids*. Solids resist deformation, although, of course, if enough force is applied, they too will change shape. Thus the dividing line between solids and liquids is not always perfectly clear-cut. Pitch, for instance, is hard and brittle like a solid; yet, if it is allowed to stand long enough, it will spread out to fill its container in the manner of a liquid.

Solids surround us in bewildering variety. To such naturally occurring substances as rocks, minerals, and products of plant and animal life, man has added an endless list of artificial materials. Iron, wood, feathers, and salt are all solids, since all will retain their shapes

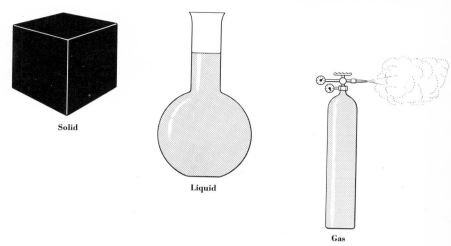

Solid

Liquid

Gas

Fig. 6.1 *A solid maintains its shape and volume no matter where it is placed; a liquid assumes the shape of its container while maintaining its volume; a gas expands indefinitely unless stopped by the walls of a container.*

indefinitely regardless of the shapes of their containers. Some solids occur in the beautiful geometric shapes called crystals. The formation of a crystalline solid is a wonderful sight if the time is taken to watch it carefully. When water freezes to ice, for example, slender ice needles radiate out over the liquid surface, branching and interlocking, each new-formed bit of solid seeming to know by some uncanny instinct just where it should appear to preserve the shapes and pattern of the interlaced needles. We can hardly miss the conclusion that the shape of an ice needle or the shape of any other growing crystal reflects something about the inner structure of the solid and that perhaps the secret of this inner structure might be revealed by a painstaking study of the crystal, a notion we shall return to.

When a solid is bent, stretched, or squeezed, it does not flow as a fluid would. If the deforming force is small, the solid changes shape only slightly and then springs back to its original form when the force is removed. This behavior is called *elastic*; some materials, of course, are much more elastic than others. Subjected to a great force, a solid may be permanently deformed. Thus an iron wire, if bent slightly, springs back to its original shape, but if subjected to a greater force, is permanently bent. Brittle solids, like ceramics, can undergo almost no permanent deformation without breaking; other solids, like some metals, can be deformed almost indefinitely—gold, for instance, can be hammered into thin, translucent foils, and platinum can be drawn into wires so fine that they are scarcely visible.

An important property of most solids is that an applied stress produces a deformation whose extent is proportional to the magnitude of the stress, provided that the latter is not too great. If a certain wire stretches by 0.1 in. when it is used to support a weight of 50 lb, a 100-lb weight would cause it to stretch by 0.2 in., a 150-lb weight would cause it to stretch by 0.3 in., and so on (Fig. 6.2). When the weight is removed, the wire contracts to its initial length. Because of this proportionality between the force F and the resulting elongation s, we can write

$$F = ks \qquad (6.1)$$

where k, the force constant, varies with the size, shape, and nature of the material under stress. A thick wire stretches less than a thin one of the same kind under the same tension, so it has a higher force constant, as does a steel wire compared with an identical strand of rubber. In all cases, though, the ratio between s and the original length of the wire stays the same during the elongation, so that a long wire stretches more than a short one. Equation (6.1) is known as Hooke's law.

Figure 6.3 is a graph that shows the response of a particular iron rod to an applied force. With increasing tension the curve is at first a straight line, reflecting Hooke's law. Eventually a point called the elastic limit is reached, where further elongation leads to a permanent deformation. When the force exceeds that corresponding to the elastic limit, the rod stretches at a more rapid rate, until the breaking point is reached. Some metals, such as copper, can be stretched well beyond their elastic limits without rupture, while others, such as cast iron, are so brittle that they cannot go far beyond their elastic limits without breaking.

Liquids

Water is the only common naturally occurring liquid, although petroleum, molten lava, and liquids produced by plants and animals occur in small

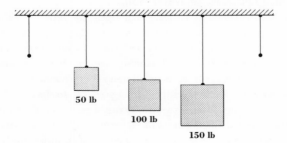

Fig. 6.2   *The elongation of a wire is proportional to the force applied to it. As long as the elongation is not too great, when the force is removed, the wire returns to its original length.*

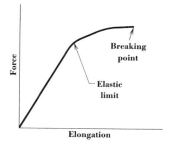

Fig. 6.3 *Elongation of an iron rod as a function of the force applied to it. The approximate proportionality between the force and the elongation it produces is called Hooke's law; this proportionality only holds over a limited range.*

amounts. Artifically, a great variety of liquids have been prepared, but no other liquid is remotely comparable with water in abundance or in multiplicity of uses.

In contrast to gases, liquids are virtually incompressible. The highest pressures obtainable with modern laboratory equipment are able to squeeze water only into about three-fourths of its original volume. Some liquids, water and alcohol, for instance, are *miscible* ("mixable") with each other in all proportions, but others, like water and oil, are immiscible, which is also behavior very different from that of gases. Two immiscible liquids shaken together give a cloudy mixture, with tiny globules of one liquid suspended in the other; when the shaking stops, the globules coalesce and the liquids separate into distinct layers. If two miscible liquids are placed in contact without stirring, one will diffuse into the other, but the process is very much slower than diffusion in gases. If a heavy gas (like carbon dioxide) is placed in the bottom of a container and a light gas (hydrogen) in the top, after a few hours the two will be completely mixed; but if the lighter of two miscible liquids (for instance, alcohol) is poured carefully on top of the heavier (for instance water), months may pass before diffusion can make the mixing complete.

Like gases, liquids flow readily, but their rate of flow is much smaller. A thick liquid like honey, particularly when full of tiny bubbles or solid specks, reveals the details of liquid flow. As honey creeps slowly down an inclined surface, the bubbles gather in lines along the direction of flow, the distinctness of the lines showing roughly the amount of liquid movement in their vicinity. The lines are most evident at the top of the flow, while scarcely detectable at its bottom. If the motion of the honey is confined to channels of different shapes, the bubble lines form graceful curves around obstacles and irregularities in the channel walls (Fig. 6.4). Always the most distinct lines are at the surface of the liquid, far from the confining walls. These observations suggest that the liquid moves by the sliding of one layer over

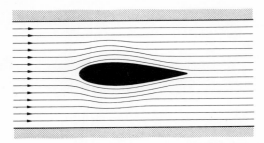

Fig. 6.4   Flow lines in fluid motion around an obstacle. *Each line represents paths taken by successive fluid particles. These lines are often called* streamlines.

another, layers near the bottom and sides of the channel clinging to the solid surfaces and scarcely moving at all (Fig. 6.5). How fast the liquid flows depends on how freely layers within the liquid can slide past one another. In honey there is evidently considerable resistance to the sliding motion; in water or alcohol, much less. This inner resistance of liquids to flowing movement is called *viscosity*. Honey is a viscous liquid; water and alcohol are less viscous. Gases show some slight resistance to fluid motion, but their viscosities are extremely low compared with liquid viscosities.

In rapidly flowing liquids and gases the mechanism of flow is not so simple as that just described. Flow lines are not straight or in smooth curves, but follow complex, ever-changing loops and eddies. Turbulent flow of this sort is well shown in a swift mountain brook.

Some curious properties of liquids are associated with their free surfaces. For instance, steel is heavier than water, but a steel needle can be made to float if lowered very carefully to a water surface. The needle rests in a slight depression of the surface, the water showing no tendency to "wet" the

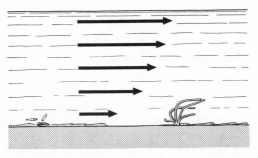

Fig. 6.5   Relative motion at different levels in a slowly moving liquid. *The liquid moves by the sliding of one layer over another; at the bottom the motion is least, and it is fastest at the surface.*

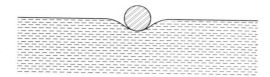

Fig. 6.6 ***Enlarged cross section of needle on water surface.*** *The elastic character of a liquid surface is the result of surface tension.*

metal (Fig. 6.6). When we disturb the needle so that any part cuts through the surface, it sinks immediately to the bottom. If we touch the water surface very carefully with the end of a glass rod, at first contact the glass, like the needle, simply depresses the surface without being "wet" by the liquid. Further lowering causes the surface to break, and a little ridge of water climbs up around the rod (Fig. 6.7). When we lift the rod out, its end is now "wet," covered with a thin film of water. The water surface, after the momentary disturbance, then becomes smooth and flat as before. In experiments like these the surface layer of water seems to behave differently from the rest of the liquid; water will "wet" both glass and steel, but the surface layer must be broken before liquid and solid can make intimate contact. It is almost as if the water were covered with a thin, stretched sheet of rubber, which must be ruptured before the water can make contact with metal or glass. Unlike rubber, the surface layer has the capacity for repairing itself: No matter how many times the surface is broken, it shows the same behavior to each new disturbance. The apparent stretched, elastic character of liquid surfaces is shown also by the spherical shape of raindrops and by the spherical shape of globules formed when immiscible liquids are shaken together. Here each liquid fragment has a free surface on all sides, and the surface contracts to give the drop a shape with the least possible surface area—the sphere. The force tending to decrease the area of liquid surface is a property of the liquid called *surface tension*.

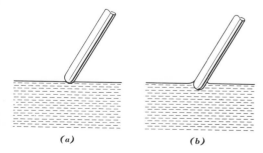

(a)   (b)

Fig. 6.7 ***Glass rod (a) before breaking water surface and (b) after breaking surface.***

Gases

Gases have become familiar articles of commerce: the light gases hydrogen and helium, the heavy gas carbon dioxide, the evil-smelling, yellow-green, poisonous gas chlorine. Surrounding us always is the mixture of colorless and odorless gases that we call air. The odors of flowers, foods, and perfumes are all due to gaseous materials. Yet the ways of gases remain mysterious to the layman, because without special techniques he cannot isolate and handle them as he can liquids and solids. He often finds it startling even to learn that gases have weight (the air in a good-sized room, for instance, weighs close to a hundred pounds), since they spread so easily outward and upward in apparent defiance of gravity.

To the scientist, on the other hand, gases are by far the best understood of the three forms of matter. He knows that all gases have certain important characteristics that are much alike, and he has discovered simple laws to describe their properties. We shall discuss some of these important laws later, but for the moment let us simply note a few of the more obvious facts about gas behavior.

The defining property of gases is their ability to expand indefinitely. Coupled with this is their extreme compressibility, with even a small increase in pressure causing a marked reduction in the volume of a gas. A gas will expand either into a vacuum or into another gas, the second gas serving merely to slow down the rate of expansion. The diffusion of one gas into another can be exhibited by opening a bottle of ammonia in one corner of a room: The irritating odor of ammonia gas spreads quickly through the air into all parts of the room. Nor is there any limit to the amount of one gas that can diffuse into another: Gases are miscible with one another in all proportions. Finally, gases, unless highly compressed, are characterized by extreme lightness in comparison with liquids and solids.

Pressure

We have already noted the great compressibility of gases and the near incompressibility of liquids and solids. Let us examine a little more closely the influence of pressure on various materials.

First of all, what do we mean by pressure? By definition, pressure is the force per unit area acting perpendicular to a surface. To see what this means, let us consider the cylinder of Fig. 6.8, which has some fluid within it. A piston weighing 30 lb rests on the fluid. Since the piston has an area of 60 in.^{2}, the pressure exerted on the fluid is 30 lb per 60 in.^{2} = 0.5 lb/in.^{2}, which is the force exerted on each square-inch column of the fluid. Symbolically,

$$P = \frac{F}{A} \tag{6.2}$$

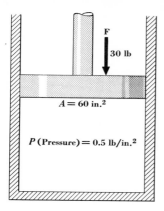

Fig. 6.8 *Pressure is force per unit area. A 30-lb piston whose area is 60 in.² exerts a pressure of 0.5 lb/in.² on the liquid it is resting on.*

where P, F, and A represent pressure, force, and area, respectively. Pressure may be expressed in such units as pounds per square inch (lb/in.²), pounds per square foot (lb/ft²), newtons per square meter (newtons/m²), and so on; the usual engineering units are pounds per square inch.

In a fluid, since gravity pulls downward on all parts of it, the bottom layers are under pressure from the weight of overlying fluid whether external pressure is acting or not. At the bottom of the cylinder just described, for instance, the pressure must be slightly greater than 0.5 lb/in.², since the bottom layer must support not only the piston's weight but a considerable weight of fluid as well. In ordinary laboratory experiments with gases, pressures due simply to the weights of the gases involved are usually negligible, but in experiments with liquids such pressures are important.

Except for the steady downward increase due to gravity, pressures in all parts of a fluid are the same. It would be unthinkable, for instance, to have the fluid confined in the cylinder of Fig. 6.8 under a pressure of 20 lb/in.² in the upper part of the cylinder and under a pressure of 3 lb/in.² in the lower part. Since the fluid is capable of flowing, it would move from the region of high pressure to the region of low pressure until the pressure was equalized. If the air pressure in a tire is 30 lb/in.², then the air exerts an outward force of 30 lb on every square inch of the tire's inner surface. Different parts of a solid, on the other hand, can be under very different pressures, since the solid cannot flow. One end of a timber can be placed under immense pressure in a vise, while the other end is under no pressure except that of the surrounding atmosphere.

Also, because a fluid can flow, the pressure at any one point within it must be the same in all directions. It is this fact that makes pressure so useful a quantity in physics. Suppose that a piece of paper can be supported horizontally in the middle of the cylinder of Fig. 6.8. If the downward

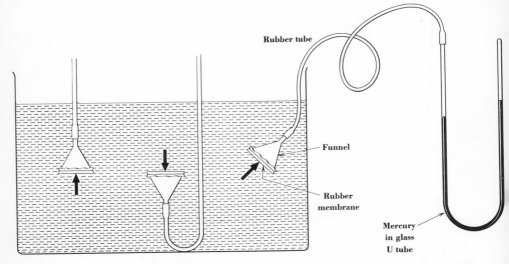

Fig. 6.9   *Pressure is the same in all directions at the same level in a fluid.*

pressure on its upper surface is 0.5 lb/in.^{2}, then the upward pressure on its lower surface must be 0.5 lb/in.^{2}.   If the two pressures were different, the paper would move toward the direction of lower pressure; in other words, the fluid would flow until the pressure at each point became the same in all directions.   This characteristic of fluid pressure is well shown by the device of Fig. 6.9, which consists of a funnel capped with a thin rubber sheet and connected with an instrument for measuring pressure.   If the funnel is held with the center of the membrane at any one level in a liquid or gas, turning the funnel in different directions has no effect on the indicated pressure.

Since we live at the base of the atmosphere, we are under pressure from the weight of gas above us—a pressure amounting to nearly 15 lb/in.^{2} at sea level, sufficient to crush a container from which air has been removed unless its walls are fairly stout.   We are not conscious of the 15-lb force pushing inward on every square inch of our bodies simply because our bodies are sufficiently permeable to air so that pressures inside are maintained equal to those without.   Atmospheric pressures are measured with instruments called *barometers*, of which the commonest type is a closed tube of mercury about 1 m long inverted in a dish of mercury (Fig. 6.10).   The upper part of the tube is evacuated, either directly with a vacuum pump or by taking care that no air enters the tube when it is inverted in the dish.   At the bottom of the tube, the downward force on the portion of mercury A is equal to the weight of the mercury column.   This must be balanced by an upward force, or else the mercury would flow out of the tube.   The upward force on

A is maintained by the downward push of the atmosphere on the mercury surface in the dish. Thus the pressure of 100 miles or so of atmosphere is balanced by the pressure of 30 in. of mercury. The pressure of the atmosphere at any one time is measured by the height of the mercury column, which fluctuates with varying weather conditions over a range of about 5 in.

Normal atmospheric pressure at sea level corresponds to a barometric height of 76 cm (about 30 in.). This pressure (14.7 lb/in.^{2}) is frequently used as a pressure unit, called the *atmosphere*. Thus a pressure of 2 atmospheres (atm) would correspond to 152 cm of mercury, or about 30 lb/in.^{2}. Smaller pressures, since they are often measured with mercury columns, are commonly described in terms of mercury heights; thus a pressure of 5 cm of mercury is equal to about 0.066 atm, or roughly 1 lb/in.^{2}.

Archimedes' Principle

Pressures in liquids rapidly become greater with increasing depth, as anyone knows who has swum even a few feet below the surface of a lake or pool. The stoutest submarine must be wary of venturing more than a few hundred

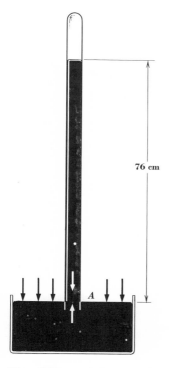

76 cm

Fig. 6.10 **A barometer.** *The weight of the mercury column is balanced by atmospheric pressure.*

feet down for fear of collapsing. At a depth of 6 miles in the ocean the pressure is about 8 tons/in.², or roughly 1,000 atm, sufficient to compress water by some 3 percent of its volume. Fish that inhabit these depths can withstand such enormous pressures for the same reason that we can endure the pressures at the bottom of our ocean of air: Pressures inside their bodies are kept constantly equal to pressures outside. When brought quickly to the surface, deep-ocean fish often explode because of their high internal pressures.

Let us determine precisely how the pressure in a fluid depends upon the density of the fluid, which is its mass per unit volume, and the depth below the surface. Table 6.1 is a list of the densities of various common substances both in kilograms per cubic meter and slugs per cubic foot. To pose a definite problem, we shall inquire into the pressure at the bottom of a tank of height h and cross-sectional area A that contains a fluid of density d (Fig. 6.11). The tank's volume V is its area multiplied by its height.

$$V = Ah$$

The total mass m of the fluid it contains is the product of its volume and the density of the fluid, so that

$$m = dV = dAh$$

Table 6.1. Densities of various substances. *The values given hold for atmospheric pressure and room temperature.*

Substance	Density kg/m³	Density slugs/ft³
Air	1.3	2.5×10^{-3}
Alcohol (ethyl)	7.9×10^2	1.5
Aluminum	2.7×10^3	5.3
Balsa wood	1.3×10^2	0.25
Bromine	3.2×10^3	6.2
Carbon dioxide	2.0	3.8×10^{-3}
Concrete	2.3×10^3	4.5
Gasoline	6.8×10^2	1.3
Gold	1.9×10^4	38
Helium	0.18	3.5×10^{-4}
Hydrogen	0.09	1.7×10^{-3}
Ice	9.2×10^2	1.8
Iron	7.8×10^3	15
Lead	1.1×10^4	22
Mercury	1.4×10^4	26
Nitrogen	1.3	2.4×10^{-3}
Oak	7.2×10^2	1.4
Oxygen	1.4	2.8×10^{-3}
Water, pure	1.00×10^3	1.94
Water, sea	1.03×10^3	2.00

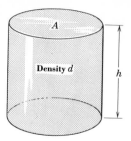

Fig. 6.11   *The volume of a tank of height h and cross-sectional area **A** is Ah. When it is filled with a fluid of density d, the mass of the fluid is dAh and its weight is dgAh.*

The *weight* of the fluid is

$$w = mg = dgAh$$

and this is the force with which the fluid presses down on the base of the tank. Pressure is force per unit area, and so

$$P = \frac{F}{A} = \frac{w}{A} = \frac{dgAh}{A}$$
$$= dgh \qquad\qquad (6.3)$$

where the quantity dgh is the pressure exerted on the base of the tank by the fluid. In addition, of course, the atmosphere also exerts the pressure P_{atm} on the fluid surface, which in turn is passed on to the base of the tank. Hence the total pressure is

$$P = P_{atm} + P_{fluid}$$
$$= P_{atm} + dgh \qquad\qquad (6.4)$$

This equation holds for any depth h in a fluid of density d, since the fluid below this depth does not affect the weight of the fluid *above* it, and the actual dimensions of the container are irrelevant, since only the vertically downward force of the overlying fluid affects the pressure.

When something is immersed in water (or other fluid), it seems to weigh less than it does in air. This effect is called *buoyancy,* and it is responsible for such diverse phenomena as balloons floating in the atmosphere, ships floating in the sea, and the continents floating in the plastic rock that constitutes most of the earth's interior. If the upward buoyant force on a submerged body is greater than its weight, the body floats; if the force is less than its weight, the body sinks. We shall use Eq. (6.4) to calculate this buoyant force.

Let us examine the block shown in Fig. 6.12, which is L high and has the cross-sectional area A. The top of the block is a depth h below the

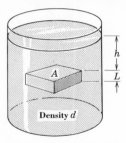

Fig. 6.12 *According to Archimedes' principle, the buoyant force on a submerged object is equal to the weight of fluid it displaces.*

surface of a fluid whose density is d. The downward force F_{down} on the upper face of the block is the product of the pressure P_1 there and the area A of this face, so that

$$F_{\text{down}} = P_1 A$$
$$= P_{\text{atm}} A + dghA$$

in view of Eq. (6.4). The upward force F_{up} on the bottom face of the block is, similarly,

$$F_{\text{up}} = P_{\text{atm}} A + dg(h + L)A$$

since this face is at a depth of $h + L$ below the fluid surface. Hence the net force F on the block is

$$F = F_{\text{up}} - F_{\text{down}}$$
$$= dgLA$$

This force is always upward since the pressure on the bottom of the block is always greater than that on the top of the block. We note that the *volume V* of the block is

$$V = LA$$

the block's area multiplied by its height. Therefore

$$F = Vdg \tag{6.5}$$

The quantity Vdg is just the weight of a volume of the fluid equal to the volume of the block, and so Eq. (6.5) states that

Buoyant force = weight of fluid displaced by body

This statement is *Archimedes' principle.*

As an illustration of Archimedes' principle, we can compute the proportion of an iceberg that is below the surface. In order for the iceberg to float in equilibrium, its weight must be exactly balanced by the buoyant force of the sea water. If we let the iceberg's area be A and its height be L, as in Fig. 6.13, and call its submerged depth L_{sub}, we have

$$\text{Weight of iceberg} = \text{weight of displaced sea water}$$
$$LAd_{ice}g = L_{sub}Ad_{water}g$$
$$\frac{L_{sub}}{L} = \frac{d_{ice}}{d_{water}} = \frac{1.8 \text{ slugs/ft}^3}{2.0 \text{ slugs/ft}^3} = 0.9$$

Ninety percent of the volume of an iceberg is under water.

The Gas Laws

In many ways the gaseous state is the one whose behavior is the easiest to describe and account for. As an important example, the pressures, volumes, and temperatures of gas samples are related by simple formulas that have no counterpart in the cases of liquids and solids. The existence of these formulas led to a search for their explanation in terms of the microscopic structure of gases, a search rewarded by the discovery of the kinetic theory of matter, which we shall explore in the following chapter.

Suppose that a cubic foot of some gas is placed in the cylinder of Fig. 6.14 and compressed by a 100-lb force that is the sum of the weight of the piston and the weight of the column of atmosphere above the piston. If a 100-lb weight is placed on top of the piston, so that the pressure on the gas is doubled, the piston will move down until the gas volume is 0.5 ft³, half its original amount. If the total pressure is made ten times greater, the piston will move down farther, until the gas occupies only 0.1 ft³. Thus we can say that the volume of a given quantity of gas is inversely proportional to the pressure applied to it. If the volume of the gas when the pressure is

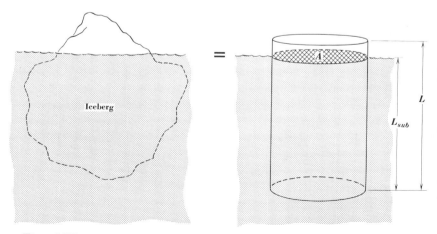

Fig. 6.13 *Ninety percent of the volume of an iceberg is submerged.*

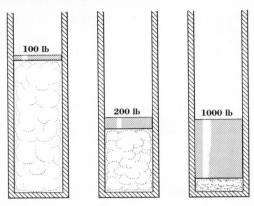

Fig. 6.14 *Boyle's law: At constant temperature, the volume of a given quantity of gas is inversely proportional to the pressure applied to it.*

P_1 is V_1 and if the volume when the pressure is changed to P_2 changes to V_2, the relationship among the various quantities is

$$\frac{P_1}{P_2} = \frac{V_2}{V_1} \qquad (6.6)$$

This relationship is called *Boyle's law*, in honor of the English physicist who discovered it.

Just as changes in gas volume are simply related to pressure changes, so they are simply related to temperature changes. If a gas is cooled steadily, starting at 0°C, while its pressure is maintained constant, its volume decreases by $\frac{1}{273}$ of its volume at 0°C for every degree the temperature falls. If the gas is heated, its volume increases by the same fraction (Fig. 6.15). If volume rather than pressure is kept fixed, the pressure increases with rising temperature and decreases with falling temperature, again by the fraction $\frac{1}{273}$ of its 0°C value for every degree change.

These figures suggest an awkward question: What would happen to a gas if we could lower its temperature to −273°C? If we should try to maintain constant volume, the pressure at this temperature would seem to fall to zero; if the pressure remained constant, the volume should fall to zero. It is hardly probable, however, that our experiment would have so startling a result. In the first place, we should find great difficulty in attaining so low a temperature, and in the second place, all known gases liquefy before that temperature is reached. Nevertheless, this temperature, −273°C, has apparently some special significance, a significance that will become clearer shortly. It is called *absolute zero*.

For many scientific purposes it is more convenient to reckon temperatures from absolute zero than from the freezing point of water. Temperatures on such a scale, given as degrees Celsius above absolute zero, are called *abso-*

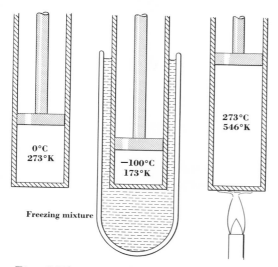

Fig. 6.15 *Charles' law: At constant pressure, the volume of a given quantity of a gas is directly proportional to its absolute temperature. (To change a Celsius temperature to its equivalent absolute temperature, add 273°.)*

lute temperatures. Thus the freezing point of water is 273° absolute, written 273°K in honor of the English physicist Lord Kelvin, and the boiling point of water is 373°K. Any Celsius temperature can be changed to its equivalent absolute temperature by adding 273°.

Using the absolute scale, we may express the above relationship between gas volumes and temperatures very simply: The volume of a gas is directly proportional to its absolute temperature (Fig. 6.16). This relation may be expressed mathematically as

$$\frac{V_1}{V_2} = \frac{T_1}{T_2} \qquad (6.7)$$

where the V's are volumes and the T's are absolute temperatures. Discovered by two eighteenth-century French physicists, Jacques Alexandre Charles and Joseph Gay-Lussac, this relation is commonly known as Charles' law. Like Boyle's law, it holds to a fair approximation for all gases at ordinary pressures, but becomes inaccurate at high pressures.

Boyle's law and Charles' law can be combined in the single formula

$$\frac{P_1 V_1}{T_1} = \frac{P_2 V_2}{T_2} \qquad (6.8)$$

At constant temperature, $T_1 = T_2$ and Eq. (6.8) becomes Boyle's law, while

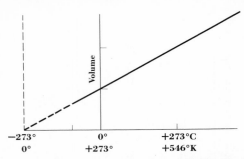

Fig. 6.16 *Graphic representation of Charles' law, showing the proportionality between volume and absolute temperature for gases.*

at constant pressure, $P_1 = P_2$ and Eq. (6.8) becomes Charles' law. A common way of writing this formula is

$$\frac{PV}{T} = \text{constant} \tag{6.9}$$

since it reflects the fact that this particular combination of variables does not change in value even though the individual variables P, V, and T may vary. It is very significant that Eq. (6.9) holds fairly well for *all* gases, and it therefore furnishes a specific goal for theories which attempt to explain the gaseous state of matter.

Self-examination

1. The pressure in a liquid at a given depth below the surface
   a. is always exerted downward
   b. is the same in all directions
   c. equals the total weight of liquid above that depth
   d. depends upon the amount of liquid below that depth

2. Which of the following statements is correct?
   a. Solids cannot be deformed.
   b. Liquids do not expand to fill their containers.
   c. Gases cannot exert pressure.
   d. All liquids pour easily.

3. The pressure of the earth's atmosphere at sea level is due to
   a. the gravitational attraction of the earth for the atmosphere
   b. the heating of the atmosphere by the sun
   c. the fact that most living things constantly breathe air
   d. evaporation of water from the seas and oceans

4. Viscosity is most closely related to
   a. density
   b. velocity
   c. friction
   d. honey

5. Which of the following is *not* a unit of pressure?
   a. lb/ft^2
   b. slug/ft-sec^2
   c. newton-m^2
   d. kg/m-sec^2

6. The pressure at the bottom of a tank of liquid is *not* proportional to
   a. the height of the liquid
   b. the area of the liquid surface
   c. the density of the liquid
   d. the acceleration of gravity

7. A certain container holds 10^{-2} kg of air at atmospheric pressure. When an additional 10^{-2} kg of air is pumped into the container, the new pressure is
   a. ½ atm
   b. 1 atm
   c. 2 atm
   d. 4 atm

8. The volume of a gas sample is directly proportional to its
   a. pressure
   b. Fahrenheit temperature
   c. Celsius temperature
   d. absolute temperature

9. The pressure on 1 ft^3 of helium is increased from 20 lb/in.^{2} to 80 lb/in.^{2}. The new volume of the helium is
   a. 0.25 ft^3
   b. 0.5 ft^3
   c. 4 ft^3
   d. 16 ft^3

Problems

1. A certain spring has a force constant of 2 lb/ft. By how much will it stretch when it is used to support an object whose mass is 0.1 slug?

2. A certain steel wire stretches by 0.01 in. when it is used to support a weight of 50 lb. What is its force constant in pounds per foot?

3. A man whose mass is 60 kg is standing on a rectangular swimming raft 3 m long and 2 m wide which is floating in fresh water. By how much does the raft rise when he dives off?

4. A 180-lb man wears shoes whose area is 20 in.² each. How much pressure does he exert on the ground?

5. A 120-lb woman balances on the heel of her right shoe, which is ¼ in. in diameter. How much pressure (in atmospheres) does she exert on the ground?

6. Mercury is 13.6 times as heavy as water. If water were used in a barometer instead of mercury, how high would the column of liquid be?

7. A small amount of water is boiled for a few minutes in a large tin can, and the can is then covered tightly while it is still hot. As the can cools, it collapses. Why does this happen?

8. Would a barometer on Mars show a higher or a lower reading than on earth? Would water boil at a lower or a higher temperature?

9. What is the pressure on a gas confined in a cylinder 4 in. in diameter if the force on the piston is 100 lb? (Do not consider atmospheric pressure.)

10. A certain quantity of hydrogen occupies a volume of 1,000 cm³ at 0°C (273°K) and ordinary atmospheric pressure. If the pressure is tripled but the temperature is held constant, what will the volume of the hydrogen be? If the temperature is increased to 273°C but the pressure is held constant, what will the volume of the hydrogen be?

11. Find the buoyant force on a 160-lb man in air under the assumption that his density is the same as that of fresh water.

12. An automobile tire gauge measures the amount by which the air pressure in a tire exceeds the atmospheric pressure of 14.7 lb/in.². If the "gauge" pressure of a certain tire is 24 lb/in.² at 0°C, what will it be at 27°C if the tire volume remains the same?

CHAPTER 7 | KINETIC THEORY OF MATTER

Suppose there were no limit to the power of our microscopes, so that we could examine a drop of water under stronger and stronger lenses indefinitely. What sort of a microscopic world would we discover when the drop was enlarged, say, a million times? Would we still see structureless, transparent, liquid water? Or would we perhaps see distinct particles, the building blocks, as it were, of the substance that to our gross senses is structureless, transparent, and liquid? These are questions as old as civilization, posed whenever men have speculated deeply on the nature of things. Our first record of an intelligent approach to the problem dates from the fifth century B.C. in Greece, where Democritus championed our modern view that matter ultimately consists of individual particles. Four centuries afterward, in the Rome of Caesar and Cicero, Democritus' views were elaborated by the great scholar-poet Lucretius.

Lucretius and Democritus used their hypothesis that matter is made up of tiny particles chiefly for philosophical speculation and tried only superficially to connect it with actual observations. Physicists of the nineteenth century, less interested in philosophy than in factual knowledge, found in the 2,000-year-old idea a powerful tool for explaining and correlating a great variety of observations and simple experiments like those described in the last chapter. This extension of the theory of Democritus is known as the *kinetic theory of matter*. The word kinetic suggests the nature of the extension: Matter seems to consist of myriad particles in constant motion, not a static assembly of them.

Molecules

Like any other scientific theory, the kinetic theory starts with a group of assumptions. The assumptions were made originally as guesses, intelligent guesses, of course, describing the peculiarities of the particles supposed to make up gases, liquids, and solids. Physicists then tried to show that the familiar characteristics of matter follow from an application of ordinary physical laws to particles with these assumed peculiarities. This attempt was highly successful; the behavior of matter could be described accurately, or *explained*, in terms of the assumptions. Furthermore, use of the assumptions enabled scientists to predict unsuspected quirks in the behavior of matter, and these predictions could be checked by experiment. As the original guesses proved themselves capable of explaining more and more known experiments and of predicting the results of new ones, they were accepted ever more widely as probable facts rather than as mere assumptions.

The basic assumptions of the kinetic theory are (1) that matter is composed of tiny, discrete particles called *molecules* and (2) that these molecules are in constant motion.

In brief, a molecule may be defined as the smallest particle of a substance that is representative of the essential characteristics of the substance. Today we have much information about the actual sizes, speeds, even shapes of the molecules in various kinds of matter, which, of course, was not available when the kinetic theory was formulated. Our information is obtained indirectly, since even today we cannot directly measure the dimensions of most molecules, but it is confirmed in so many different ways that we have every reason to believe it to be accurate. For example, a molecule of nitrogen, the chief constituent of air, has a diameter of about 1.8 ten-billionths of a meter (1.8×10^{-10} m) and weighs 4.7×10^{-26} kg. It travels (at $0°C$) with an average speed of 50.0 m/sec (1,500 ft/sec, or about the speed of a rifle bullet) and in each second collides with over 5 billion other molecules. Of similar dimensions and moving with similar speeds in each cubic centimeter of air are nearly 3×10^{19} other molecules.

The extreme smallness of ordinary molecules will probably make it impossible for us ever actually to see them because the resolving power of our microscopes is limited by the wave nature of light. But particles not many times larger than molecules are visible in the highest-powered microscopes, particles small enough to move in response to the blows of swiftly traveling molecules against their sides. Molecular motions are highly erratic, and so the visible particles are buffeted about in irregular, zigzag paths (Fig. 7.1). The smallest visible particles move rapidly under molecular bombardment, darting this way and that, now brought to a stop, now starting out in a new direction. Larger particles show only a slight jiggling motion or do not move at all, since so many molecules strike them that, at any one instant, the forces on all sides are nearly the same. This motion of micro-

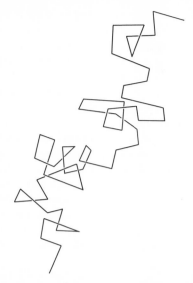

Fig. 7.1 *Irregular path of a microscopic particle bombarded by molecules.* *The line joins the positions of a single particle observed at 10-sec intervals. This phenomenon is called* Brownian movement *and is direct evidence of the reality of molecules and their random motions.*

scopic particles, called the *Brownian movement,* is well shown by particles of certain dyes and by tiny oil droplets suspended in water and by smoke particles suspended in air. Brownian movement is the most direct and convincing evidence we have of the reality of molecules and their motions.

The Kinetic Theory of Gases

We go on now to discuss the specific assumptions of the kinetic theory regarding gas molecules. We begin with gases, because the uniformity in behavior of different gases and the simple mathematical rules that describe this behavior suggest that the structure of gases is simpler than that of liquids and solids.

The three basic assumptions of the kinetic theory for gas molecules are these:

1. Gas molecules are small compared with the average distance between them.
2. Gas molecules collide without loss of kinetic energy.
3. Gas molecules exert practically no forces on one another, except when they collide.

A gas, then, is assumed to be mostly empty space, its isolated molecules moving helter-skelter, like a swarm of angry bees in a closed room. Each molecule collides with others several billion times a second, changing its speed and direction at each collision but uninfluenced by its neighbors between collisions. If a series of collisions brings it momentarily to a stop, new collisions will set it in motion; if its speed becomes greater than the average, successive collisions will slow it down. There is no order in the motion, no uniformity of speed or direction; we can say merely that the molecules maintain a certain average speed and that at any instant as many molecules are moving in one direction as in another.

This animated picture suggests immediately some general explanations for the more obvious properties of gases. The ability of a gas to expand and to leak through small openings is a consequence of the rapid motion of its molecules and their lack of attraction for one another. Gases are easily compressed, because the distances between molecules can be shortened with scarcely any deformation of the molecules themselves. One gas mixes readily with another, because the wide spaces between molecules leave ample room for others. Gases are light in weight, because their volume consists so largely of empty space.

Gas pressure is the effect of bombardment of millions and millions of molecules, the same sort of bombardment that causes suspended smoke particles to show the Brownian movement; the myriad tiny, separate blows affect our crude senses and measuring instruments as a continuous force. When a gas is squeezed into a smaller volume, more molecules strike a square centimeter of surface each second, and the pressure is increased. When the gas is expanded to a larger volume, each square centimeter is struck less often, and the pressure decreases (Fig. 7.2). This is the general relationship summarized in Boyle's law.

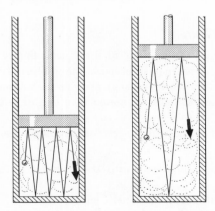

Fig. 7.2   When a gas is compressed into a smaller volume its molecules strike the walls of the container more often than before, leading to an increase in pressure. For simplicity, only vertical molecular motions are shown.

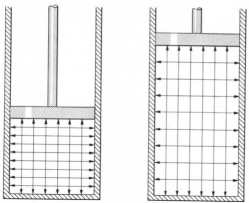

Fig. 7.3   Origin of Boyle's law according to the kinetic theory of gases. *Expanding a gas sample means that its molecules must travel farther between successive impacts on the container wall and that their blows are spread over a larger area, so the gas pressure drops.*

The kinetic theory is able to show that the pressure and volume of a gas at constant temperature should be exactly inversely proportional to one another. Suppose that the molecules of a gas confined in a cylinder (Fig. 7.3) are thought of as moving in a completely regular manner, some of them moving vertically between the piston and the base of the cylinder and the remainder horizontally between the cylinder walls. If the piston is raised so that the gas volume is doubled, the vertically moving molecules have twice as far to go between collisions with top and bottom and hence will strike only half as often; the horizontally moving molecules must spread their blows over twice as great an area, and hence the number of impacts per unit area will be cut in half. Thus the pressure in all parts of the cylinder is exactly halved, as Boyle's law would predict. It is not hard to extend this reasoning to a real gas whose molecules move at random.

The third assumption mentioned above is not strictly accurate: Gas molecules do exert slight attractions on one another. These attractions become conspicuous when a gas is greatly compressed and account (in part) for the fact that Boyle's law does not hold at high pressures.

To explain the effects of temperature, one further assumption is required:

> 4. The absolute temperature of a gas is directly proportional to the average kinetic energy of its molecules.

Just why this assumption is stated in this particular manner is not obvious without a mathematical discussion. As a matter of fact, it is more like a conclusion than an assumption, because it is the key to agreement between the kinetic theory and the experimental data. Assumption 4 is not un-reasonable: The fact that temperature should be closely related to molecular speeds, and hence to molecular energies, follows from the simple observation that the pressure of a confined gas increases as its temperature rises. In-creases in pressure must mean that the molecules are striking their confining walls more forcefully and so must be moving faster.

Earlier in this chapter we learned that the pressure of a gas approaches zero as its temperature falls toward $-273°C$. For the pressure to become zero, molecular bombardment must cease. Thus absolute zero finds a logical explanation, in terms of the kinetic theory, as the temperature at which gas molecules would lose their kinetic energies completely. There can be no lower temperature, simply because there can be no smaller amount of energy than none at all. The regular increase of gas pressure with absolute tem-perature if the volume is constant and the similar increase of volume if the pressure is constant (Charles' law) are understandable from this definition of absolute zero, although the formal demonstration of direct proportionality is a bit complicated.

As a prediction from our temperature assumption, we might guess that compressing a gas in a cylinder should cause its temperature to rise. While the piston is moving down, molecules rebound from it with increased energy (Fig. 7.4), just as a baseball rebounds with increased energy from a moving bat. Hence the average kinetic energy of the gas molecules should be raised, and the temperature of the gas should increase. To verify this prediction, one need only pump up a bicycle tire and observe how hot the pump becomes after the air in it has been compressed a few times. If, on the other hand, a gas is expanded by pushing a piston outward, its temperature should fall, since each molecule that strikes the retreating piston gives up some of its kinetic energy. In a steam engine, for instance, compressed steam at a temperature well above the boiling point of water is cooled nearly to its condensation point as it expands by pushing against the piston of the engine.

The fourth assumption may be stated in slightly more general fashion as a definition of temperature: The temperature of a gas is a measure of its average molecular kinetic energy. It follows that all gases at the same tem-perature have the same average molecular kinetic energies.

From this fact about temperature we might venture another prediction: Heavy molecules should move more slowly than light molecules at the same temperature. The average kinetic energy of a molecule is

$$\text{KE} = \tfrac{1}{2}m\overline{v^2} \qquad\qquad (7.1)$$

where m is the molecule's mass and $\overline{v^2}$ is its average squared speed; a light molecule (small m) must have a greater speed than a heavy molecule if $\tfrac{1}{2}m\overline{v^2}$ is to be the same for both. One easy way to test this prediction is to measure the rates at which two gases leak out through small openings. The gas carbon dioxide, for instance, has molecules over twenty times heavier

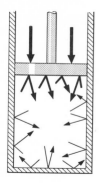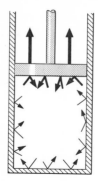

Fig. 7.4 *Compressing a gas causes its temperature to rise because molecules rebound from the piston with increased energy; expanding a gas causes its temperature to drop because molecules rebound from the piston with decreased energy.*

than molecules of hydrogen; through small openings hydrogen escapes much more rapidly, with the difference in rates (about 4.7:1) being just sufficient to make the average kinetic energies of the two kinds of molecules the same.

Escape of Atmospheres

Some of the members of the solar system possess atmospheres and some do not. Since all the planets and their satellites almost certainly originated in similar processes, there is the problem of why *all* planets and satellites do not have atmospheres. The kinetic theory of gases, which suggests that all gas molecules are in rapid motion, provides the answer. A planet holds a moving molecule, as it holds any other object, by gravitational attraction. To escape from a planet's attraction, a molecule need only acquire sufficient speed in an outward direction. The necessary speed, called the *escape velocity,* is high for a massive planet like Jupiter, low for a light body like the moon. The earth's escape velocity is not quite 7 mi/sec: This is the speed which an interplanetary rocket must possess in order to leave the earth behind and, similarly, the speed which a molecule at the top of the atmosphere must attain before it can wander off into space. The moon's escape velocity is much smaller, about 1.5 mi/sec. Now air molecules at ordinary temperatures move with average speeds of less than ½ mi/sec, so their chances of escaping from either earth or moon may not seem very good. But this ½ mi/sec is an *average speed;* many air molecules at any given instant are moving more slowly, many others considerably faster. And temperatures on the moon's surface at midday approach 100°C, a temperature at which the average molecular speed is somewhat higher than ½ mi/sec. If a sample of air could be placed on the moon today, a few of its faster molecules would attain speeds over 1.5 mi/sec and drift off into space. As these escaped, collisions in the remaining gas would presently restore the original distribution of molecular speeds and thus give a few more molecules the necessary speed. The air would slowly vanish, molecule by molecule. Probably the moon has been for ages without an atmosphere because the original gas surrounding it escaped by just this process.

To leave the earth, an air molecule would have to reach a speed of 7 mi/sec in the cold upper atmosphere. Attaining this speed at lower elevations would, of course, do no good, for collisions would cause it to lose energy before it could escape. The number of molecules with speeds so far above the average in the upper atmosphere is negligible, so that our planet is in no danger of losing its valuable air blanket. Even molecules of hydrogen, lightest, and hence fastest, of all gas molecules at a given temperature, probably cannot now escape the earth's attraction, although if the earth was hotter in the remote past, they may have then escaped in large numbers.

Thus a planet's ability to hold gas molecules depends primarily on its gravitational pull and to a lesser extent on its temperature. Mercury, small and hot, is as barren as the moon. Venus, nearly the size of the earth, has an atmosphere as dense as ours. Mars is heavy enough to hold a thin atmosphere, but the swift molecules of hydrogen, helium, and neon must have escaped from it long since. The four giant planets have enormously thick atmospheres containing abundant hydrogen.

Heat

As we have mentioned, heat is a form of energy. What meaning can we attach now to the heat energy of a gas, in the language of the molecular theory? Since supplying heat to a gas raises its temperature, thereby increasing the kinetic energy of its molecules, we might reasonably guess that the heat energy of a gas is precisely this energy of molecular motion. But such a guess must be examined carefully.

Up to now, *energy of molecular motion* has implied energy associated with the movement of molecules from place to place, or translational movement. If heat energy is merely the kinetic energy of translational motion, then a given amount of heat ought to affect the temperatures of all gases alike. But this is emphatically not true; heat energy absorbed by a gas is not all used in making its molecules move around more quickly.

Studies of the effects of heat on different gases, coupled with results of other research, have shown that complex molecules may absorb heat energy in three principal ways: (1) their translational motion may be increased; (2) one part of a molecule may be set to vibrating with respect to another part, as if the parts were connected by a spring; and (3) each molecule may be set in rotation (Fig. 7.5). When heat is supplied to a gas, it becomes molecular energy in one or more of these different forms, but only the energy that goes into one particular form, kinetic energy of translation, affects the temperature of the gas.

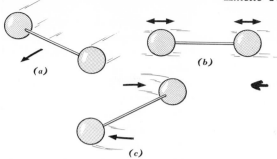

Fig. 7.5 *Three types of motion possible for dumbbell-shaped molecules (like those of hydrogen, oxygen, and chlorine): (a) translation, (b) vibration, (c) rotation.*

Count Rumford and several other scientists before him had surmised that heat was a form of motion. The kinetic theory finally presented, for gases at least, a definite picture of just what kind of motion heat is—a complex, disordered motion of tiny particles, spinning around, vibrating back and forth, flying in all directions.

This view of heat answers an awkward question that bothers many a novice in physics: What keeps the molecules moving? We picture them as something like tiny billiard balls, moving rapidly, colliding with one another many times a second. Real billiard balls, after a few seconds of such motion, would lose their energy in the friction of collisions and come to rest at the bottom of their container. All other motions of our experience, save perhaps the motion of stars and planets, are similarly brought to a halt by friction unless some outside force maintains them. Molecular motions are maintained by no outside force, yet continue indefinitely with no sign of diminishing speed. Why is it that friction does not bring these tiny particles to rest, as it does other moving objects?

The answer is that friction involves a transformation of mechanical energy into heat energy, which is the same as molecular energy. Friction between molecules would mean simply a transformation of molecular energy into molecular energy, which is not a transformation at all. Molecules keep moving because there is nothing to make them stop. The question of the last paragraph is, in fact, nearly meaningless; it appears to make sense only because we are so accustomed to thinking of heat and motion as distinct concepts. Motion in the molecular world cannot produce heat, as it does in the larger world of everyday life, because molecular motion *is* heat.

Liquids and Solids

The kinetic theory grew from the efforts of several nineteenth-century physicists to find an explanation for the behavior of gases. Its greatest triumphs have come from work on gases, but in recent years the theory has been applied with much success to the vastly more complicated inner structures of liquids and solids.

The incompressibility of liquids and solids suggests the assumption that their molecules are close together, probably in actual contact. The Brownian movement in liquids is ample basis for assuming that liquid molecules, like gas molecules, are in constant, random motion. The assumption that particles in solids are held more or less rigidly in fixed positions follows from the definite shapes that solids maintain and from their inability to diffuse.

Strong attractive forces are assumed to be holding together the particles of liquids and solids. Some of these intermolecular attractions are the same as the very slight attractions between gas molecules that are responsible for deviations from Boyle's law at high pressures. In liquids and solids the forces are more conspicuous because the molecules are so much closer together. The nature of the attractive forces, which are largely of electrical origin, is discussed in Part IV.

To explain the effects of temperature on liquids and solids, we may keep the assumption that was so useful for gases: Absolute temperature is proportional to average kinetic energies of moving particles. (This is not quite accurate for solids.) In liquids, a rise in temperature means an increase in average speed of translational motion; in solids, a rise in temperature means an increase in vibrational motion of the particles about their fixed positions. As for gases, we further assume that liquid and solid particles can take up heat energy in other ways, so that absorption of 1 kcal of heat by 1 kg of different materials may produce different increases in temperature.

If a gas resembles a swarm of angry bees, the particles of a liquid may fairly be likened to bees in a hive, crawling over one another incessantly, each one continually in contact with its neighbors. The slowness of liquid diffusion is explained by the difficulties of motion when each particle is closely surrounded by others. Liquids can flow because their molecules slide easily over one another, but they are more viscous than gases because intermolecular attractions impede the motion. The viscosity of a liquid is a rough measure of how strongly its particles attract one another.

Attractive forces between the particles of solids are stronger than in liquids, so strong that the particles are no longer free to move about. They are far from motionless, however: Held in position as if by springs attached to its neighbors, each particle oscillates back and forth rapidly and continuously. A solid is elastic because its particles bounce back into their normal positions after being stretched apart or pushed together. A solid breaks or is permanently deformed when it is subjected to a force larger than the forces of attraction between its particles. In a brittle solid, rupture takes place suddenly along a single surface, and the particles are pulled so far apart that healing is impossible. In a solid that can yield by slow deformation to excessive forces, we may imagine tiny fractures developing all through the solid, each fracture healing itself as the particles slide to new positions and find new partners for their attractive forces.

Crystal form and crystal growth suggest arrangements of particles in patterns of equally spaced rows and planes. Each particle, so to speak, faces the same way, and the distances to its neighbors on all sides are determined by its attractive forces in various directions. The smooth faces and sharp angles of the crystal are, then, the outer expression of this inner regularity. The microscope and X rays prove convincingly that many solids that do not show crystal faces nevertheless have a regular pattern in their inner structures. Solids of this sort, whether or not they occur in well-shaped crystals, are called *crystalline solids;* salt, diamond, quartz, and most metals are familiar examples (Fig. 7.6). Solids whose particles have no regularity of arrangement (for instance, glass and rubber) and which, of course, never show crystal forms are called *amorphous solids.*

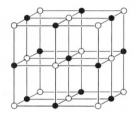

Fig. 7.6 *Arrangement of particles in space in a crystal of ordinary salt.*

Changes of State

To illustrate once more how molecules and their motions account for the ordinary properties of matter, let us consider the peculiar temperature-energy relationships involved in changes of state, that is, changes from solid to liquid, liquid to solid, solid to gas, gas to solid, liquid to gas, or gas to liquid.

Suppose that two liquids, water and ether, are placed in open dishes. Particles in each are moving in all directions with a variety of speeds. At any instant some particles are moving fast enough upward to break through the liquid surface and escape into the air, in spite of the attractions of their slower neighbors. By this loss of its faster molecules each liquid gradually evaporates; since the molecules remaining behind are the slower ones, evaporation leaves cool liquids behind. The ether evaporates more quickly (or is more *volatile*) and cools itself more noticeably because the attraction of its particles for one another is smaller and a greater number can escape (Fig. 7.7).

Now suppose that a tight cover is placed on each dish. Molecules of

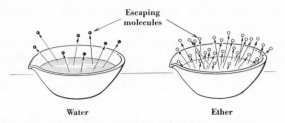

Escaping molecules

Water   Ether

Fig. 7.7 *Ether evaporates more rapidly than water because the attractive forces between its molecules are smaller.*

vapor can no longer escape completely; by collisions with one another and with the cover, they are sooner or later knocked back into the liquid. So the fast particles that leave each liquid return to it, and it no longer is cooled. Evaporation goes on as before, but is balanced now by the reverse process of condensation. How many molecules are present in the space above each liquid at any given instant is determined by how rapidly they leave its surface; over the ether considerably more vapor is present than over the water, since ether evaporates more easily. The amount of vapor is expressed best in terms of its pressure; thus we say that the *vapor pressure* of the ether is higher than that of water. More formally, we may define the vapor pressure of any liquid at a given temperature as the pressure that its vapor exerts when confined above the liquid. The vapor pressure of a substance is a measure of how readily its particles escape from its surface.

Let us now remove the covers from our dishes of water and ether and heat each liquid slowly. We aid the process of evaporation by supplying heat, giving more and more particles the energy necessary to escape. Vapor rises from each dish in steadily increasing quantities; if we stop the heating at intervals, cover each dish, and measure the vapor pressures, we find that these pressures are growing rapidly larger. At a temperature of 35°C even the particles of average speed in the ether dish apparently gain sufficient energy to vaporize, for bubbles of vapor begin to form all through the liquid. We say now that the liquid is *boiling.* Its vapor pressure has become equal to the pressure of the surrounding atmosphere; particles within the liquid form bubbles because now the pressure that they exert as vapor is sufficient to overcome the downward pressure of the atmosphere on the liquid surface. At this temperature the vapor pressure of water is still only a small fraction of an atmosphere (4.2 cm of mercury); only when the temperature approaches 100°C does its vapor pressure also become equal to atmospheric pressure, so that the liquid can boil. We may define the boiling point of a liquid as the temperature at which its vapor pressure becomes equal to the surrounding pressure. Standard boiling points listed in tables are the temperatures at which vapor pressures become equal to normal atmospheric pressure, 76 cm of mercury (Fig. 7.8).

Whether evaporation takes place spontaneously from an open dish or is aided by heating, the formation of vapor from a liquid requires energy. In the one case, energy is supplied from the heat energy of the liquid itself (since the liquid grows cooler); in the other case from the external source of heat. For water at its boiling point, 540 kcal (the *latent heat of vaporization*) is used up in changing each kilogram of liquid into vapor. Here there is no difference in temperature between liquid and vapor, hence no difference in their average molecular kinetic energies. If not into kinetic energy, into what form of molecular energy does the 540 kcal of heat energy go?

Intermolecular forces suggest an answer. In the liquid these forces are strong, because the molecules are close together. To tear the molecules apart, to separate them by the wide distances that exist in the vapor, requires that these strong forces be overcome. Each molecule must be moved against the attraction of its neighbors, moved to a new position in which their attraction for it is very small. Just as a stone thrown upward against the earth's attraction acquires potential energy, so molecules moved apart in this fashion acquire potential energy—potential energy with reference to intermolecular forces. So heat supplied in evaporating a liquid goes into another form of molecular energy besides the translational, vibrational, and rotational energies we have considered: molecular potential energy. When a vapor condenses

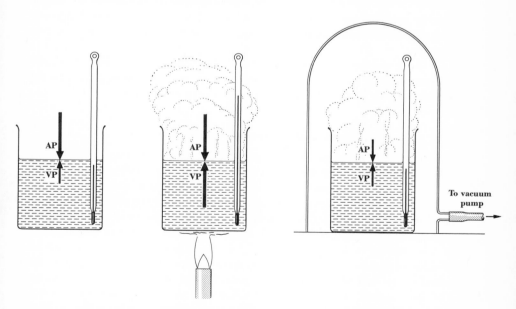

Fig. 7.8 *A liquid boils when its temperature is high enough for its vapor pressure* (VP) *to equal the atmospheric pressure* (AP). *A liquid may be made to boil at a lower temperature than usual by reducing the external pressure.*

to a liquid, its molecules "fall" toward one another under the influence of their mutual attractions, and their potential energy must be taken up as heat energy by the surroundings.

Temperature changes accompanying the melting of crystalline and amorphous solids are quite different and afford one easy experimental method for distinguishing the two types of material. A crystalline solid like ice melts sharply at one definite temperature, and requires the addition of a certain quantity of energy at this temperature simply to effect the change from solid to liquid. An amorphous solid like glass softens gradually on heating, so that no one temperature can be given as its melting point.

In terms of the kinetic theory, this difference in behavior is a consequence of differences in inner structure. Particles of a crystalline solid are arranged in a definite pattern, each one oriented so that the forces binding it to its neighbors on all sides are as large as possible. To overcome these forces and give the particles the disorderly arrangement of a liquid structure requires that they gain potential energy, just as liquid particles must gain potential energy during evaporation. This potential energy is the *latent heat of fusion* (80 kcal/kg for water), which must be supplied to melt any crystalline solid and which is given out when the liquid crystallizes again. Particles of amorphous solids, on the other hand, have no definite pattern, but are already in the random, disorderly arrangements characteristic of liquids. Melting involves merely a gradual loosening of the ties between adjacent particles, without any marked increase in potential energy at a certain temperature.

Thus, without any new assumptions, the kinetic theory offers a rational interpretation of vaporization and melting in terms of the motions, the potential energies, and the arrangements of molecules in matter.

The Second Law of Thermodynamics

Different kinds of energy can be transformed from one into another. But heat energy is peculiar in that it cannot be transformed into other kinds *efficiently*. From the heat energy of burning coal we may obtain mechanical, chemical, or electric energy, but always in these transformations a large fraction of the heat energy is wasted. There is no escape from this waste; the transformations will not take place without it. This distinctive characteristic of heat energy was discovered early in the nineteenth century, at the beginning of the Industrial Revolution, as a result of attempts to improve the recently invented steam engine. Attacked both by engineers trying to get as much mechanical work as possible out of a ton of coal and by scientists more interested in the properties of heat as a form of energy, the problem of why transformations involving heat should be so wasteful was finally solved by the kinetic theory's picture of heat as random, disorderly motion of molecules.

The only practical method of obtaining mechanical energy directly from heat, the method used in both steam and internal-combustion engines, is to supply heat to a compressed gas and let it expand against a piston or the vanes of a turbine. Without concerning ourselves with the details of a real engine, we may picture the fundamental process involved as follows. Suppose that a gas under pressure in a cylinder (Fig. 7.9) is heated and allowed to expand by pushing the piston outward. Heat energy is thereby converted into mechanical energy of the piston, which may be used for turning a dynamo, running a pump, or for any purpose we wish. Now when expansion has reduced the pressure of the heated gas to atmospheric pressure, or when the piston reaches the end of the cylinder, further heating accomplishes little. To give the piston more mechanical energy, we must somehow recompress the gas and let it expand again. Recompressing the gas, however, requires the application of mechanical energy from outside. If the gas is compressed while hot, just as much energy will be needed as the gas has given out by expansion, so that the net gain will be zero. But if we cool the gas first, we find that less energy is required to compress it than we gain from the expansion. To make the engine do useful work, we must arrange to compress the gas while it is cold, then heat it and allow it to expand while hot, then cool it again for the next compression.

Note carefully what happens to the heat supplied to the gas: A part of it is used to drive the piston, but some is deliberately allowed to escape when the gas is cooled before compression. For the engine to run, we need both a source of heat and something to which the gas can give part of its heat, usually the surrounding atmosphere. In effect, heat flows through the engine from the heat source to the atmosphere, and during the flow we manage to

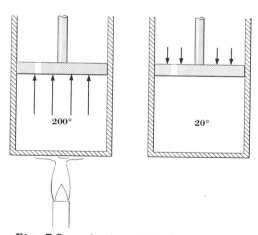

Fig. 7.9   *A gas at 200° gives out more energy in expanding than is required to compress the gas at 20°.*

change some of the heat into mechanical energy. All heat engines work on this principle, taking advantage of the flow of heat from a hot object to a cold object in order to recover some of it as mechanical energy. A *difference of temperature* between two objects or two places is essential.

Contained in the molecular motions of the atmosphere is a vast quantity of heat energy, but we cannot recover it because no cold object is available to which the heat can flow. Of course, we might set up a refrigerating machine to maintain a low temperature, but we should find that more energy is required to run the refrigerator than we could get by using it as the cold side of a heat engine. A refrigerator, in fact, is the reverse of a heat engine: It employs mechanical energy to force heat from a cold object to a warmer object, while a heat engine uses the natural flow of heat from hot objects to cold as a means of obtaining mechanical energy. Setting up a refrigerator to maintain a low temperature for running a heat engine is just the old perpetual-motion dream in a new guise.

We are strictly limited, then, in our ability to turn heat energy into mechanical energy. We can obtain mechanical energy only by letting heat flow from a region of high temperature to a region of low temperature, and in the best of circumstances the conversion is incomplete. This limitation is not due to friction, which saps the energy of all kinds of mechanical devices, but is a limitation imposed by the fundamental nature of heat. Why should heat energy in this respect be so different from other forms?

The kinetic theory states that heat is energy of random, disorganized motion. When heat is supplied to a gas, its molecules increase their speeds in all directions. We use only the increase in speed in a particular direction, the direction in which the piston moves; but to obtain an increase in this direction, we must speed up motions in all other directions as well. If we could line up the molecules and fire them all, like tiny bullets, straight at the piston, then all the energy we give them would go to make the piston move. In a real gas most of our bullets go astray, only a few of them giving their excess energy to the piston. From the energy of random, disorderly motion we can extract only a fraction as the energy of ordered motion in definite directions which we need to run the world's machinery.

In contrast to the difficulty of obtaining mechanical energy efficiently from heat is the ease with which other forms of energy may be converted into heat energy. When coal burns, its chemical energy changes directly to heat. When a pendulum swings, kinetic energy is transformed to potential and back again, but with each swing, friction removes some energy as heat. Electric energy in a light filament is changed partly to heat, partly to light; the light, falling on walls and furniture, is absorbed and converted into heat energy. In all the energy transformations of our acquaintance some, and more often all, of the original energy becomes eventually energy of disordered molecular motion.

Once in the form of heat, energy cannot easily be restored to its original form. A little may be recovered, as we have seen, by making the heat flow to a cooler object, but even to recover this little is possible only for a brief time after the heat is produced. Heat energy spreads quickly into its surroundings, and the temperature difference necessary to make a heat engine operate soon disappears. A stone falls to the pavement, and kinetic energy turns into heat; for a few moments particles in the stone and concrete move a little faster, then the faster movement affects neighboring molecules, and the heat energy spreads in ever-widening circles. Coal burning in a fireplace warms the air of a room; when the fire goes out, the warmth persists for a little while, but spreads gradually to the walls, to adjoining rooms, to the outside air, and presently is distributed so widely through the surroundings that we can no longer detect it. From any hot object heat flows in like manner to cooler objects about it, spreading indefinitely until it becomes a part of the general molecular motion of earth and atmosphere. From this reservoir of heat we cannot recover even a fraction of the original energy, for a perceptible temperature difference no longer exists. The energy has not disappeared, but it is no longer available for conversion into other forms.

We may summarize these observations on heat by the statement: *In every energy transformation, some of the original energy is always changed into heat energy not available for further transformations.* This statement is the law of dissipation of energy, known to scientists as the second law of thermodynamics. The law is merely a scientific expression of the everyday observations that other forms of energy commonly become heat energy and that heat spreads out, or is dissipated, into its surroundings.

So far as we know, this law of the wastage of energy applies quite as universally as the law of conservation of energy, which is the *first* law of thermodynamics. The radiant energy of stars, the mechanical energy of planetary motions, the chemical energy of food, all are being steadily changed into the energy of disordered molecular motion. The law seems to imply that the universe in the past had more energy in forms capable of doing work than at present. It seems to imply also that the distant future will bring a time when there is no energy but heat energy, heat energy evenly distributed so that no part of the universe is warmer than another, the so-called "heat death" of the universe.

Self-examination

1. According to the kinetic theory of matter, at a given temperature
   a. light gas molecules have the same average energy as heavy gas molecules
   b. all the molecules in a gas have identical speeds
   c. light gas molecules have lower average energies than heavy gas molecules
   d. light gas molecules have higher average energies than heavy gas molecules

2. Absolute zero may be thought of as the temperature at which
   a. all molecular motion in a gas would cease
   b. all gases have become liquids
   c. water freezes on the centigrade scale
   d. we have reached the lowest temperature that can be reached with a good refrigerator

3. The energy of molecular motion is manifested as
   a. potential energy
   b. heat
   c. chemical energy
   d. friction

4. Molecules are, in general, farthest apart from one another in
   a. gases
   b. liquids
   c. crystalline solids
   d. amorphous solids

5. When a vapor condenses into a liquid,
   a. the temperature always drops sharply
   b. there is no change in the heat content of the substance
   c. heat is absorbed
   d. heat is given off

6. A molecule is
   a. the smallest particle found existing by itself in nature
   b. any very tiny particle
   c. the smallest particle of a substance that is representative of the substance
   d. the ultimate particle of which all matter is composed

7. The kinetic theory of matter
   a. can be derived directly from the law of conservation of energy
   b. is based entirely on experimental data with no arbitrary assumptions
   c. contains assumptions accepted because the resulting theory agrees with experimental data
   d. cannot be considered valid because molecules cannot be readily seen or measured

8. The temperature of a gas sample in a rigid container is raised. The pressure the gas exerts on the container walls increases because
   a. the molecules are in contact with the walls for briefer intervals
   b. the molecular masses increase
   c. the molecules have higher average speeds and so strike the walls more often
   d. the molecules lose more kinetic energy each time they strike the wall

9. In the operation of a heat engine heat is taken in at a particular temperature and
   a. is completely converted into mechanical energy
   b. is partly converted into mechanical energy and partly exhausted at a lower temperature
   c. is partly converted into mechanical energy and partly exhausted at the same temperature
   d. is partly converted into mechanical energy and partly exhausted at a higher temperature

Problems

1. Why does bombardment by air molecules not produce Brownian movement in large objects such as chairs and tables?

2. Can you account for the ability of gases to leak rapidly through very small openings?

3. Each molecule of the gas sulfur dioxide has a mass almost exactly double that of an oxygen molecule. If both gases are at the same temperature, which will have molecules with the higher average speed? If the speed of oxygen molecules at a particular temperature averages 4×10^4 cm/sec, what is the average speed of the sulfur dioxide molecules?

4. Each molecule of nitrogen has a mass very close to fourteen times greater than that of a hydrogen molecule. Find the temperature of a hydrogen sample in which the average molecular speed is equal to that in a sample of nitrogen at a temperature of 300°K.

5. The average speed of a hydrogen molecule at room temperature and atmospheric pressure is about 1 mi/sec. What is the average speed of a nitrogen molecule, fourteen times heavier, under the same conditions?

6. A sample of hydrogen is compressed to half its original volume, while its temperature is held constant. What happens to the average speed of the hydrogen molecules?

7. How can the conclusion of kinetic theory that molecular motion ceases only at absolute zero be reconciled with the observation that solids have definite shapes and volumes at temperatures much higher than absolute zero?

8. The first assumption of the kinetic theory of gases is that gas molecules are small compared with the average distance between them. The oxygen and nitrogen molecules in air are roughly 2×10^{-10} m in diameter, and there are 2.7×10^{25} molecules in a cubic meter of air at sea level and room temperature. How many molecular diameters is the average molecular separation?

9. How could you tell experimentally whether a fragment of a clear, colorless material is glass or a crystalline solid?

10. How does perspiration give the body a means of cooling itself? Why is moving air apparently cooler than still air?

11. In order to cool a room during the summer, a man turns on an electric fan and leaves. If the room is completely insulated from the outside, what will happen to its temperature and why?

12. The oceans contain an immense amount of heat energy. Why can a submarine not make use of this energy for propulsion?

CHAPTER 8 | CHEMICAL CHANGE

Before we go into some of the basic ideas that underlie chemistry, it is worth our while to consider the relationship between this branch of physical science and the other one we have been studying, physics. In general, it is impossible to set up rigid boundaries to divide one science from another. Even the broad categories of physical science, which deals with inorganic matter, and biological science, which deals with living matter, tend to overlap, as we can see in such hybrids as biophysics and biochemistry. The separation of physical science into such pigeonholes as physics, chemistry, geology, and astronomy is in many respects artificial, but it is a convenient way of gaining insight into the complex workings of nature. The universe presents a tangled skein to the scientist, who must consider each of its strands separately before he is able to comprehend the pattern in which they are found.

Chemistry and Physics

Astronomy and geology can be defined without much ambiguity. Geology, the "earth science," deals with all the naturally occurring inorganic materials and phenomena of the earth, embracing those parts of physics and chemistry and biology that are relevant. Astronomy considers things and processes beyond the earth and the earth as it is related to other objects in space. Since the earth in its motions and history is a part of the solar system, astronomy overlaps geology to a certain extent.

The distinction between physics and chemistry is more subtle, depending on different points

143

of view rather than on differences in subject matter. A physicist would analyze a dynamite explosion, for instance, in terms of the gas pressure produced, the strength of the rocks blown apart, the amount of heat lost to the rocks and the surrounding air. A chemist observing the same explosion would consider the elements and compounds involved in the reaction that converts dynamite into gas, the source of the heat liberated, the possible changes produced in the rock material by heat and pressure. Physics deals with the more general properties of matter, its density, its motion in response to forces, its ability to absorb and radiate heat; chemistry deals rather with specific properties of different kinds of matter and with changes from one kind of matter to another. Physics is concerned, too, with energy of all varieties, its source, its measurement, its changes from one form to another; chemistry is concerned with energy only in so far as it influences or is produced by chemical reactions.

Early physics was an offspring of astronomy, early chemistry an outgrowth of alchemy, which was a misguided effort to accomplish impossible changes in the form of matter. Inevitably, the better minds in both sciences sought an explanation of the phenomena they discovered in terms of the ultimate structure of matter, and research in this field cannot properly be assigned to one science or the other. Modern inquiries have so broadened our knowledge of the structure of matter that this borderland field might well be considered a science in its own right.

Although any attempt to separate the two sciences is futile, certain of the fundamental concepts of the two fields are distinct from each oher. The *physical properties* of a substance, for instance, are those with which physics is primarily concerned—color, density, hardness, boiling and melting points; its *chemical properties* involve its capacity to react with other substances. Again, *physical change* refers to a change like that from solid to liquid or liquid to gas or the change in form produced by crushing a solid or emulsifying a liquid; *chemical change* involves a change from one compound to another or from elements to compounds. We say that the compounds of a solution or a heterogeneous material can be separated by *physical means*, by which we mean processes like distillation, settling, and filtration. *Chemical means*, on the other hand, are necessary to effect separation of the elements in a compound. Since the boundary between physics and chemistry is so hazy, terms like physical and chemical properties, physical and chemical change, cannot be precisely defined, but do serve a purpose in rough descriptions of matter and its alterations.

The difference in viewpoint between physics and chemistry can hardly be appreciated without a background in both sciences. Such a background in physics we have partially acquired in preceding chapters; in this and the next three chapters we shall try to get the chemist's slant on things, and then we shall return to physics for more information regarding matter before completing our work in chemistry.

Properties of Substances

The essential characteristics of a substance that enable us to distinguish it from other substances are called its *properties*. We describe water as a color-less, odorless, tasteless material, liquid at ordinary temperatures, freezing at 0°C and boiling at 100°C, noninflammable, capable of dissolving sugar, salt, and many other materials, miscible with alcohol in all proportions, im-miscible with oils—these are all properties of the substance water.

The list of properties by which we describe a substance ordinarily in-cludes such features as its color, taste, odor, whether it is solid or liquid or gaseous, its relative heaviness compared with other substances, to what extent it will dissolve other materials or be dissolved by them, and how easily it will burn. For a liquid we might add its viscosity and its ability to mix with other liquids; for a solid we should describe its hardness, its brittleness, its crystal form. We could go on to mention the behavior of a substance near a magnet, the ease with which it conducts heat and electricity, its behavior when mixed with all manner of different substances. Often in scientific work it is useful to express some of these properties quantitatively; thus, instead of describing ethyl alcohol as a liquid that boils readily but is difficult to freeze, we may say more precisely that ethyl alcohol boils at 78°C and freezes at about −117°C.

Chemical Change

Properties of materials undergo profound changes in many familiar processes. We have already discussed the melting of solids and vaporization of liquids, changes brought about by alterations in molecular speeds and distances. Other processes, such as the rusting of iron, the burning of wood, and the explosion of dynamite, involve more drastic changes in properties and altera-tions in the molecules themselves rather than merely in their motions. Proc-esses of this sort that consist of molecular changes are called *chemical reactions*.

Let us examine a specific chemical reaction in detail in order to gain an understanding of just what is implied by this term. Suppose that we mix some powdered zinc metal with a somewhat greater amount of powdered sulfur on a sheet of asbestos and ignite the mixture with the flame from a bunsen burner. The result is an explosion, and light and heat are given off. When the fireworks have died down and any excess sulfur has burned away, we are left with a brittle, white substance that resembles neither the original zinc nor the original sulfur. What has happened?

Further experiment would quickly show that neither zinc nor sulfur alone gives any such reaction on heating, that explosion of the mixture takes place as well in a vacuum as in air, and that a metal or porcelain surface may be substituted for asbestos without influencing the reaction. In other words, the process requires the presence of both zinc and sulfur, but no other materials. We are forced to conclude that the two substances have *combined* to form the new material. To convince the most skeptical, we could find ways to change the white, brittle product back into zinc and sulfur, but to accomplish this change would require considerable time and resourcefulness.

This is a simple example of the kind of alteration in the properties of matter that we call a *chemical reaction*. Let us analyze it by examining in detail the properties of the three substances concerned. Sulfur is a yellow solid, rather soft, with a low density, melting at about 114°C, not dissolved by water or acid but easily dissolved by a liquid called carbon disulfide. Every grain of the yellow powder exhibits these properties, and if we should crush the grains, their fragments would still show the same properties. Because every particle of sulfur is like every other particle, we call it a *homogeneous* substance. Zinc, too, is homogeneous, with such characteristic properties as a light gray color, fairly high density, a melting point of 419°C, solubility in dilute acids, and insolubility in carbon disulfide. The brittle, white product of reaction is a third homogeneous substance, called zinc sulfide, with properties different from those of either zinc or sulfur: a very high melting point, a fairly low density, insolubility in either very dilute acids or carbon disulfide.

Now suppose we prepare two identical zinc-sulfur mixtures, heating one until it reacts but leaving the second unheated. Both the resulting zinc sulfide and the unheated mixture contain zinc and sulfur, and both differ from pure zinc and sulfur in such properties as color and density. But the mixture is *a heterogeneous* material: Its properties change from one particle to the next. With a microscope and a needle we can separate particles of zinc from particles of sulfur. Either carbon disulfide or dilute acid will dissolve part, but not all, of the mixture. Properties of individual particles in the mixture have not changed at all.

In the zinc sulfide, on the other hand, every particle has the same properties as every other particle, and these properties are quite different from those of zinc and sulfur particles. Two substances can be mixed, often very intimately, simply by stirring them together, but their properties are radically altered only if they undergo a chemical reaction.

Most familiar chemical changes do not involve so spectacular a liberation of energy as the zinc-sulfur reaction. Rust, for example, is the product of a slow combination of iron with certain gases of the atmosphere. Silverware slowly tarnishes because the metal combines with small amounts of sulfur contained in certain foods and in compounds in the air. Cooking involves many complex but hardly spectacular reactions. In the growth and decay of living things, even more complex types of slow chemical change occur. Among commonplace chemical processes only the reactions involved in burning result in rapid liberation of energy.

To interpret a chemical change, for instance the zinc-sulfur reaction, in terms of the kinetic theory, we might guess tentatively that it involves a combination of the ultimate particles of zinc and sulfur to form particles of zinc sulfide. This explanation is a bit too simple and will need modification later, but at least the conclusion is safe that the original particles of zinc and sulfur have disappeared and a new type of particle has been formed. Just how the change from one type of particle to another comes about, in this reaction and in others, is the central problem of chemistry.

Elements, Compounds, and Mixtures

Chemistry as a science is relatively new, since its early history was occupied almost exclusively with a search for a way of converting ordinary metals into gold. This fruitless quest, called *alchemy* by the Arabs, was not abandoned until the seventeenth century, when men like John Mayow and Robert Boyle in England, Jean Rey in France, and Georg Stahl in Germany began a realistic inquiry into the properties of matter and their changes during chemical reactions.

From the long, disheartening search of the alchemists ultimately emerged the idea that certain materials, like iron, mercury, gold, and sulfur, were simple substances that could be neither decomposed nor transformed into one another. Such simple substances were called *elements*. Belief slowly grew that the earth contains only a limited number of these elements and that all other materials are combinations of them in various proportions. The formation of a new substance from others by chemical change, then, is possible only if its elements are present in the other substances. Never expressed as a law, this statement is nevertheless the fundamental axiom that distinguishes chemistry from alchemy.

These modern elements are concrete, tangible substances. Our belief that they are the building materials of all matter is founded on the fact that every other variety of matter that we can bring into the laboratory can be broken down into two or more of them. Of the known elements, 11 are gases, 2 are liquids, and the remaining 90 are solids at ordinary temperatures and pressures. Hydrogen, oxygen, chlorine, and neon are familiar gaseous elements; bromine and mercury are the two liquids; iron, zinc, tin, aluminum, copper, lead, silver, gold, carbon, and sulfur are among the solid elements.

Elements are put together to form the other materials of the earth in a variety of ways. Some materials contain two or more elements united in a chemical *compound*, as zinc and sulfur are united in the compound zinc sulfide. Other materials consist of *mixtures* of elements or mixtures of compounds. The distinction between compounds and mixtures is of fundamental importance, since chemical reactions always involve the formation or the breaking down of one or more compounds.

Let us consider first the kinds of material that can be formed from two elements only. The elements may form a *heterogeneous mixture*, like the mixture of zinc and sulfur we have been considering; in such a mixture each element retains its own distinguishing properties, and small fragments of each can be separated mechanically from the mixture. The elements may be mixed more intimately to form a *homogeneous mixture,* or *solution;* thus the gases hydrogen and oxygen when placed in the same container will mix so thoroughly that no ordinary means will show that any one part of the mixture is different from any other part. Finally, the elements may form a *compound;* if an electric spark is allowed to jump through a mixture of hydrogen and oxygen, the two react violently, and liquid droplets of the compound water are formed.

The distinction between compounds and heterogeneous mixtures is easy, since the separate elements are still recognizable in the mixtures. It is not always a simple matter, however, to tell whether two elements have formed a solution or have undergone a chemical reaction to produce a compound. We may say in general that their properties are more profoundly altered if they have united chemically, and we may put the matter to experimental test in one of the three following ways:

1. Measure the freezing point or boiling point of the material. For a compound the freezing point or boiling point is a constant temperature, but for a solution the temperature changes during both boiling and freezing. Thus water, a compound of hydrogen and oxygen, boils at precisely 100°C (if the pressure is 1 atm); liquid air, a homogeneous mixture of nitrogen and oxygen, starts to boil at about −192°C and boils at various temperatures up to −182° as vaporization continues.

2. See whether the material can be separated into its elements by boiling or freezing. Ordinarily, the composition of a compound is not altered by a change of state, but a solution is wholly or partially separated into its constituents. Water shows no tendency to decompose into its elements at 100°C or even far above this temperature; when liquid air boils, however, the vapor that comes off first is largely nitrogen, and the vapor that comes off in the last stages is largely oxygen.

3. Add more of one of the constituent elements to the material, and see whether the material remains homogeneous. Elements in a compound are combined in a definite invariable proportion, whereas the composition of a solution or mixture is variable. In water every gram of oxygen is combined with precisely 0.126 g of hydrogen; if more oxygen or more hydrogen is added, it does not mix with the water, but forms a heterogeneous mixture of gas and liquid. With liquid or gaseous air, on the other hand, more nitrogen or oxygen will mix readily, and the material remains homogeneous.

Experiments of this sort will determine whether any unknown material is a compound or a solution. The experiments, of course, reflect the fact that in a compound the elements have combined to form a new substance, with characteristic properties of its own, whereas in a mixture each element retains its identity.

The distinction between heterogeneous mixtures and homogeneous mixtures holds as well for mixtures of compounds as for mixtures of elements. Thus the common rock granite is a heterogeneous mixture of several compounds, the various compounds being easily distinguishable by their differences in color, in crystal form, in hardness, and so on. Whole milk that has not been "homogenized" is a heterogeneous mixture which separates into milk and cream on standing. A solution of salt in water, on the other hand, is a homogeneous mixture of two compounds; the boiling point of the solution is not constant, the salt may be separated by boiling off the water, more salt or more water may be added to the solution without destroying its homogeneity. Ordinary soda water is a homogeneous mixture of carbon dioxide dissolved under pressure in water; when the pressure is released it becomes a heterogeneous mixture of liquid water and gas bubbles.

To sum up, all the earth's materials may be classified as elements, compounds, homogeneous mixtures, and heterogeneous mixtures. Formally, the classification may be expressed as follows:

> *Heterogeneous matter*—mixtures of elements, compounds, or both
> *Homogeneous matter*—pure substances (elements and compounds)
> —homogeneous mixtures (solutions)

Combustion

The first chemical change to be studied intensively by methods that we can call modern was the process of burning, or combustion. The transformation from wood to smoke and ashes, with its accompanying heat and dancing flames, is by all odds the most spectacular chemical change with which men of earlier times had immediate contact, and it has piqued the curiosity of thoughtful individuals from remotest antiquity to the present. Primitive man based his explanation on ever-present demons and spirits. In the religions of many advanced civilizations the fire god has a respected place. The more scientifically minded Greeks gave the first rational explanation in nonsupernatural terms, recorded in the writings of Aristotle: Every inflammable material was supposed to contain the elements "earth" and "fire," the fire escaping while the material burned and the earth (ashes) remaining behind. In various guises this explanation of Aristotle's persisted through the centuries of alchemy down even to the time of the French Revolution.

The particular form this explanation took in the eighteenth century was the *phlogiston hypothesis* developed by two Germans, Johann Joachim Becher and Georg Stahl. The essential idea was the same as Aristotle's, but Becher and Stahl showed how it could be extended to many other reactions besides burning; and for the substance that supposedly escaped during burning, they abandoned Aristotle's simple word *fire* and coined the more esoteric term *phlogiston.* The story of the overthrow of the phlogiston hypothesis and the establishment of modern conceptions of chemical change is an impressive chapter in the history of ideas.

Today we never hear the word phlogiston, but in its day there was no more respected concept in all chemistry. Early scientists explained combustion in the following way. All substances that can be burned contain phlogiston, and the phlogiston escapes as the burning takes place. We observe that air is necessary for combustion, but this is explained by assuming that phlogiston can leave a substance only when air is present to absorb it. Many metals when heated in air change slowly to soft powders; zinc and tin give white powders, mercury a reddish powder, iron a black scaly material. These changes, like the changes in ordinary burning, were ascribed to the escape of phlogiston; a metal was assumed to be a compound of powder plus phlogiston, and heating the metal simply caused the compound to decompose. Now, many of the powders can be changed back to metal by heating with charcoal, an observation interpreted to mean that charcoal must be a form of nearly pure phlogiston that simply reunited with the powder to form the compound (the metal). When hydrogen was discovered in 1766, its ability to burn without leaving any ash suggested that it was another form of pure phlogiston; one could predict, then, that heating an ore or a powder with hydrogen would form a metal, and this prediction was confirmed by experiment.

So far so good, but soon the phlogiston hypothesis ran into serious trouble. When wood burns, its ashes weigh less than the original wood, and the decrease in weight can reasonably be ascribed to the escape of phlogiston. But when a metal is heated until it turns into a powder, the powder weighs *more* than the original metal! The believers in phlogiston were forced to assume that phlogiston sometimes could have negative weight, so that, if it left a substance, the remaining material could weigh more than before. To us this notion of negative weight is nonsense, but in the eighteenth century it was taken quite seriously.

The French scientist Antoine Lavoisier conducted a series of experiments in the latter part of the eighteenth century that effectively demolished the phlogiston hypothesis. Son of a wealthy lawyer, Lavoisier was given a good education and had more than ample means for carrying on his scientific work. For many years of his busy life he served as a public official and showed himself keenly aware of the acute social problems that France was facing. But neither an immense scientific reputation nor long public service could save him during the Revolution; denounced by Marat, he was sent to the guillotine in 1794.

Lavoisier knew that tin could be converted to a white powder when it was heated, and the powder definitely weighed more than the original metal. To study the change in greater detail, Lavoisier placed a piece of tin on a wooden block floating in water (Fig. 8.1), covered the block with a glass jar, and heated the tin by focusing the sun's rays upon it with a magnifying

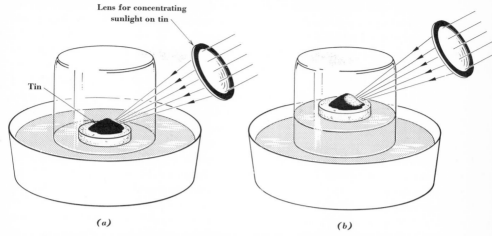

Fig. 8.1   Lavoisier's experiment showing that tin, upon heating, combines with a gas from the air. (*a*) *Before heating;* (*b*) *after heating. The tin is partly changed to a white powder, and the water level rises until only four-fifths as much air is left as there was at the start. Further heating causes no additional change.*

glass—a common method of heating before gas burners and electric heaters were invented. The tin was partly changed to white powder, and the water level rose in the jar until only four-fifths as much air was left as there had been at the start. Further heating caused no detectable change. In another experiment Lavoisier heated tin in a sealed flask until as much as possible was converted to powder. The flask was weighed accurately before and after heating, and the two weights proved to be identical. Then the flask was opened, and air rushed in. With the additional air, the weight of the flask was greater than it had been at the start, and by the same amount as the increase in weight of the tin.

Oxygen

To Lavoisier these experiments suggested clearly that the tin had absorbed a gas from the air. We need only imagine that one-fifth of the air consists of a gas that can combine with tin; then the powder is a compound of this gas with the metal, and the increase in weight is the weight of the gas. Water rises in the jar to take the place of the gas that has been removed; when the sealed flask is broken, air rushes in to replace the gas that the tin has absorbed. This explanation is simple and direct, involving no phlogiston but only substances that have definite weights.

At about the time these experiments were completed, Lavoisier learned that an English experimenter, Joseph Priestley, had prepared a new gas with strange properties. Priestley was the poverty-stricken minister of a small church, with only limited time and equipment; yet his experimental talents led him to a number of significant discoveries. The gas that he had found caused lighted candles to flare up brightly and glowing charcoal to burst into flames, and a mouse kept in a closed jar of the gas lived longer than one kept in a closed jar of air. Lavoisier gave the gas its modern name, *oxygen*, and found it useful not only for explaining the changes in metals on heating, but for explaining the processes of combustion as well. The burning of candles, wood, coal, according to Lavoisier, involves a combination of their materials with oxygen. They appear to lose weight because the products of the reaction are gaseous; actually, as he showed by experiment, the gaseous products weigh more than the original material. Thus burning and the re-actions of metals in air both received a rational explanation in terms of real substances, and the necessity for assuming the mysterious phlogiston dis-appeared.

Oxygen, under ordinary conditions, is a colorless, odorless, tasteless gas. If cooled sufficiently, it condenses to a clear blue liquid with the unusual property of being strongly attracted to a magnet. The boiling point of liquid oxygen is $-183°C$, and its freezing point is about $-218°C$. Oxygen is chemically active even in the liquid state, the closer packing of its molecules offsetting the very low temperature. Iron, for example, will burn so vigor-ously in liquid oxygen that the metal is melted by the heat of the reaction, in spite of the intensely cold liquid surrounding it.

Oxygen is by far the most abundant of the elements that make up the earth's crust, its total amount (by weight) being nearly equal to that of all the rest put together. Most of the oxygen is in compounds, compounds which are the chief constituents of rocks, soil, and living things. Water is a com-pound of hydrogen and oxygen. The free element is one of the important constituents of the atmosphere.

Air owes its ability to support combustion to the free oxygen which it contains; it cannot support combustion as well as pure oxygen because the element is so diluted with inactive gases. (Air is about one-fifth oxygen, four-fifths nitrogen, with small amounts of other gases.) That air is a mix-ture (or solution) of oxygen and nitrogen rather than a compound may be readily shown by liquefying it and allowing the liquid to boil. Boiling com-mences near the boiling point of nitrogen ($-196°C$), and the vapor that comes off first consists mostly of this element; as boiling proceeds the tem-perature rises, and toward the end practically pure oxygen is left in the liquid. The ease with which oxygen can be separated from nitrogen by letting liquid air boil makes this a convenient method for preparing pure oxygen for commercial use.

When oxygen combines chemically with another substance, the process is called *oxidation*, and the other substance is said to be *oxidized*. Rapid oxidation accompanied by the liberation of noticeable heat and light is the process of *combustion*, or burning. In the experiments of Lavoisier, tin and mercury oxidized slowly when heated. A lighted candle oxidizes rapidly in air, still more rapidly in pure oxygen. Slow oxidation is involved in many familiar processes, such as the rusting of iron, the decay of wood, the hardening of paint. The energy to maintain life comes from the slow oxidation of food in our bodies by oxygen breathed in through the lungs and transported by the blood stream.

A substance formed by the union of another element with oxygen is called an *oxide*. The white powder that Lavoisier obtained by heating tin is tin oxide. Rust is largely iron oxide. In general, oxides of metals are solids. Oxides of other elements may be solid, liquid, or gaseous. The oxide of sulfur is an evil-smelling gas (the odor of burning sulfur) called sulfur dioxide; carbon forms two gaseous oxides, called carbon monoxide and carbon dioxide; the oxide of silicon is found in nature as the solid called quartz, the chief constituent of ordinary sand; the oxide of hydrogen is water. Oxides of nearly all the elements can be prepared, most of them simply by heating the elements with oxygen. A few oxides (mercuric oxide, lead oxide, barium peroxide) are easily decomposed by heating, giving one convenient laboratory method for preparing oxygen; other oxides, such as lime (calcium oxide), are not decomposed even at the temperature of the electric arc, 3000°C.

Conservation of Mass

Lavoisier's discovery of the true nature of combustion was made possible by his use of the balance and by his insistence on the importance of weights in studying chemical reactions. This emphasis on weights marked a profound change in viewpoint and is one of Lavoisier's great contributions to chemistry. From his day to ours the balance has remained the chemist's most valuable tool.

The balance not only enabled Lavoisier to overthrow the phlogiston hypothesis; it also led him to a generalization as fundamental to modern chemistry as the law of energy conservation is to physics. Accurate weighing of many substances before and after undergoing chemical reaction convinced him that *the total mass of the products of a chemical reaction is always the same as the total mass of the original materials,* no matter how startling the chemical change may be. This is the *law of conservation of mass.* It may be stated more tersely: *Matter can be neither created nor destroyed.* When wood burns, mass seems to disappear because some of the products of reaction are gases; if the mass of the original wood is added to the mass of the oxygen that combined with it and if the mass of the resulting ash is added to the mass of the gaseous products, the two sums will turn out exactly equal. Iron increases in weight on rusting because it combines with gases from the air, and the increase in weight is exactly equal to the weight of gas consumed. In the thousands of reactions that have been tested with accurate chemical balances, no deviation from the law has ever been found.

Modern physics has made necessary some modification in our ideas about the conservation of mass and energy. We can no longer assert that matter and energy are indestructible, for such processes as the explosion of an atomic bomb and the reactions that produce the sun's radiation involve the transformation of matter into energy. To take account of these processes we must, for strict accuracy, combine the two conservation laws in the single statement: *The total amount of energy, including its mass equivalent, in the universe is constant.* Transformations of matter into energy will be discussed in future chapters; for the present our concern is with more ordinary processes, in which the older conservation laws hold rigidly within the limits of experimental error.

Self-examination

1. When salt is dissolved in water, the result is
   a. a compound
   b. a heterogeneous mixture
   c. a solution
   d. an element

2. When a substance burns,
   a. it gives off phlogiston
   b. it absorbs phlogiston
   c. it gives off oxygen
   d. it absorbs oxygen

3. Elements *cannot*, by chemical means, be combined to make
   a. other elements
   b. compounds
   c. mixtures
   d. gases

4. Of the following characteristics of a sample of a substance, the one that is *not* a physical property is its
   a. color
   b. odor
   c. hardness
   d. temperature

5. Rust is an example of
   a. an element
   b. a solution
   c. a mixture
   d. a compound

6. The alchemists were
   a. early physicians
   b. French chemists at the time of the Revolution
   c. primarily interested in making gold from base metals
   d. the men who first developed scientific method

7. When a piece of metal is oxidized, the resulting oxide is
   a. heavier than the original metal
   b. the same weight as the original metal
   c. lighter than the original metal
   d. sometimes heavier and sometimes lighter, depending upon the metal

Problems

1. List as many properties as you can of ice and of water. Why do we call the change from water to ice a physical change?

2. List the properties of iron and of rust. Why do we call the change from iron to rust a chemical change?

3. How can you show that water is a compound rather than a homogeneous mixture of hydrogen and oxygen?

4. Air was long considered an element. How could you show that this idea is false?

5. When a large jar is placed over a lighted candle, the candle burns for a few minutes and then goes out. Can you explain why this occurs?

6. On what kind of experimental evidence is the law of conservation of mass based? Can you suggest a reason why this law was not formulated before the time of Lavoisier?

7. Can iron be prepared from rust? Sulfur from zinc sulfide? Lead from iron? Hydrogen from oxygen?

8. Compare the history of the phlogiston hypothesis with that of the Ptolemaic hypothesis. In what ways was each a successful hypothesis? What were the chief flaws in each? What special assumptions had to be introduced to rescue each hypothesis, and how were these avoided in the hypotheses that replaced them? Is it really proper to group the phlogiston and Ptolemaic hypotheses together?

CHAPTER 9 | ATOMS AND MOLECULES

It is characteristic of the sciences that their greatest progress occurs when quantitative methods are used in studying nature. We have already learned how the measurements of Galileo and others led directly to Newton's laws of motion and the law of gravitation. In chemistry a similar development took place, the work of Lavoisier initiating a train of thought that culminated in the atomic theory upon which modern chemistry is based.

Law of Definite Proportions

A major question arose in the years immediately following Lavoisier's death: Are the elements in a chemical compound combined in a definite, constant ratio by weight, or can the ratio vary? Let us look at water, for example, a simple compound we are all familiar with. Analysis shows that the oxygen contained in a water sample weighs eight times as much as the hydrogen there; that is, for every gram of hydrogen, there are 8 g of oxygen. Does this mean that in *every* sample of water the ratio between oxygen and hydrogen is 8:1, or could it sometimes be 7:1 or 9:1? At that time this problem was difficult, because analytical procedures were still primitive and really pure substances were seldom available.

Ultimately the question was resolved by an apothecary named Joseph Louis Proust, who had been given a magnificent laboratory in Madrid by Charles IV of Spain. Proust's experiments permitted him to put forward the *law of definite proportions: The elements that make up a chemical compound are always combined in the same definite proportions by weight.* For water, this law means that the 8:1 ratio by weight between its oxygen and hydrogen constituents always holds, regardless of where the water came from or when the measurement is made. If we mix, say, 3 g of hydrogen gas and 24 g of oxygen gas together and ignite them, the result will be the formation of 27 g of water, since the ratio is 8:1. However, if 4 g of hydrogen is mixed with 24 g of oxygen and ignited, the result is a heterogeneous mixture of 27 g of water and 1 g of unused hydrogen gas.

Modern research has shown that the law of definite proportions as stated above, although correct in most ordinary chemical situations, must be modified somewhat under certain circumstances. We shall have more to say about this matter when we discuss *isotopes* of elements, in a subsequent chapter.

The Atomic Theory

The discoveries of Lavoisier and Proust were highly significant, but they were isolated facts in a sea of ignorance. At the start of the nineteenth century nobody had any defensible ideas about the structure of matter, of how elements go to make up compounds. The bold theory that answered these

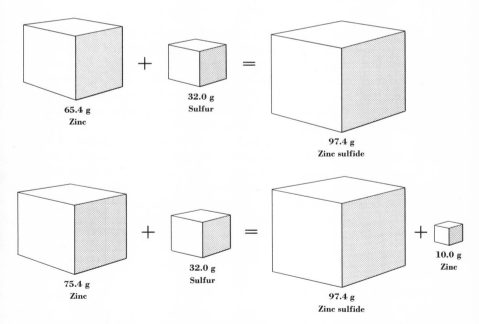

Fig. 9.1   The law of definite proportions. *Zinc and sulfur always combine in the same ratio of weights when they form zinc sulfide even though the actual weights may vary. Any excess of either constituent is left over after the reaction.*

questions came from a somewhat unlikely individual, a poorly educated teacher named John Dalton. Dalton was a literal thinker who had had no formal instruction in physics or chemistry, but these liabilities turned out to be assets, because they meant that he constantly sought simple explanations for complex phenomena without being hampered by the misconceptions of other people.

The atomic theory of matter emerged from Dalton's crude attempts at picturing the ultimate particles of which gases were composed. He began with the notion of Democritus and Lucretius that everything was composed of *atoms* and made this idea quantitative by making the following assumptions:

1. Every element consists of tiny particles called atoms.
2. The atoms of any one element are all exactly alike.
3. Atoms are indestructible: They cannot be divided, created, or destroyed.
4. When two or more elements unite to form a compound, their atoms join together to make molecules of the compound.
5. In general, atoms combine in small numbers. Thus one atom of an element *A* may combine with one atom of *B* or with two atoms or with three, but not with 50 or 100.

The first four assumptions are sufficient to explain the laws of conservation of mass and of definite proportions. The fifth is justified by the simple predictions that can be made with its help regarding weight relationships among the constituent elements in various compounds. We shall not go into the indirect methods that Dalton employed in attempting to determine the numbers of various kinds of atoms, even though he spent much time and effort on this problem, because not long afterward Avogadro was to put forward a profound hypothesis that both confirmed the atomic theory and provided a method for finding the composition of molecules.

We may note in passing that assumptions 2 and 3 above are valid only so long as we restrict ourselves to chemical processes and properties; modern physics has revealed that all atoms of the same element need not be identical and that atoms can be broken down into small constituent particles under the proper circumstances. Modern research into organic chemistry has shown that assumption 5, also, is not always true.

Avogadro's Hypothesis

In the year 1808 the French scientist Joseph Gay-Lussac concluded, on the basis of very careful experiments, that, when gases undergo chemical reactions, the *volumes* of the reacting and product gases are related by simple whole numbers. Thus, when water is decomposed into hydrogen and oxygen, the volume of the hydrogen is exactly twice the volume of the oxygen; when nitrogen and oxygen unite to form the colorless gas nitric oxide, one volume each of nitrogen and oxygen produce two volumes of nitric oxide. Here were some numerical relations that the atomic theory ought to explain but could not. According to Dalton, each molecule of nitric oxide should contain an atom each of oxygen and nitrogen. Since the molecules in a gas are far apart, their size should make no difference in the volume occupied by gas, and so Dalton reasoned that one volume of nitrogen plus one volume of oxygen should yield one volume of nitric oxide. Dalton therefore dismissed Gay-Lussac's measurements as incorrect.

The young Italian physicist Amadeo Avogadro was not so hasty. Three years after Gay-Lussac's work, he put forward two important ideas. First, he asserted that *equal volumes of all gases, under the same conditions of pressure and temperature, contain the same number of molecules.* He suggested further that the molecules of some gaseous elements might not consist simply of individual atoms of the element, but that they might be composed of two or more identical atoms joined together.

Let us see how Avogadro's ideas fit Gay-Lussac's measurements into the framework of the atomic theory. Consider, for example, the formation of nitric oxide, in which two volumes of product are obtained from one volume each of nitrogen and oxygen (Fig. 9.2). Since each volume represented contains the same number of molecules (Avogadro's hypothesis), a given number of oxygen molecules must react with the *same* number of nitrogen molecules to give *twice* as many molecules of nitric oxide. Thus 1,000 oxygen molecules would give 2,000 nitric oxide molecules; 10 oxygen molecules would give 20 of nitric oxide; 1 oxygen molecule would give 2 of nitric oxide. Now each nitric oxide molecule contains some oxygen; hence the oxygen molecule must have split, half of it going to each molecule of product. Avogadro interpreted this deduction to mean that an oxygen molecule consists of at least two atoms.

Similar reasoning applied to other reactions shows that oxygen molecules apparently often split into two parts, but never into more than two. We may safely infer that each molecule has no more than a pair of atoms. Also, for the other common gaseous elements—nitrogen, hydrogen, chlorine—Gay-Lussac's volume relationships suggest molecules made up of two atoms apiece.

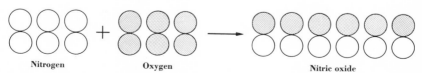

Nitrogen   Oxygen   Nitric oxide

Fig. 9.2 *Formation of nitric oxide from nitrogen and oxygen.* *Because one volume each of nitrogen and oxygen combine to yield two volumes of nitric oxide, nitrogen and oxygen must consist of molecules each containing two atoms.*

How does the formation of water from its constituent elements fit into this picture?   Gay-Lussac had shown that, at temperatures above 100°C, two volumes of hydrogen reacting with one volume of oxygen produce two volumes of water vapor (Fig. 9.3).   In terms of molecules, then, a given number of hydrogen molecules react with half as many oxygen molecules to give the same number of water molecules.   Two hydrogen molecules plus one oxygen molecule give two water molecules.   Now, each of the original molecules contains two atoms apiece; hence four hydrogen atoms and two oxygen atoms go into the building of the two water molecules.   Accordingly, each water molecule must contain two hydrogen atoms and one oxygen atom, a 2:1 ratio.

So Avogadro's simple idea about the structure of molecules cleared away the outstanding difficulties in Dalton's theory and showed the relationship between the molecules of physics and the atoms of chemistry.   But Dalton, strangely, did not see the importance of this addition to his theory.   Stubbornly he clung to his indivisible atoms as the ultimate particles of gases. Dalton was famous, Avogadro all but unknown; science for once followed reputation rather than reason, and the younger man's work was forgotten. Not until 1860, fifty years after Avogadro had made his suggestions, did chemists open their eyes to its value.   In those fifty years, difficulties in the atomic theory had grown so formidable that even the existence of Dalton's atoms was seriously questioned.   But once the distinction between molecules and atoms became clearly recognized, discrepancies in the theory vanished, and atoms were henceforth accepted as a fundamental concept in chemistry.

Avogadro's idea that the volume of a gas at any given temperature and pressure is determined only by the number of molecules present, in his day merely a daring hypothesis, has been so well confirmed in recent years that today we regard it as an established law.

Symbols and Formulas

In order to make the atomic theory useful and understandable, some means was needed for clearly representing atoms and the molecules that they form. The system of notation that we use today was invented by the Swedish chemist Jöns Jakob Berzelius, a contemporary of Dalton and Avogadro.

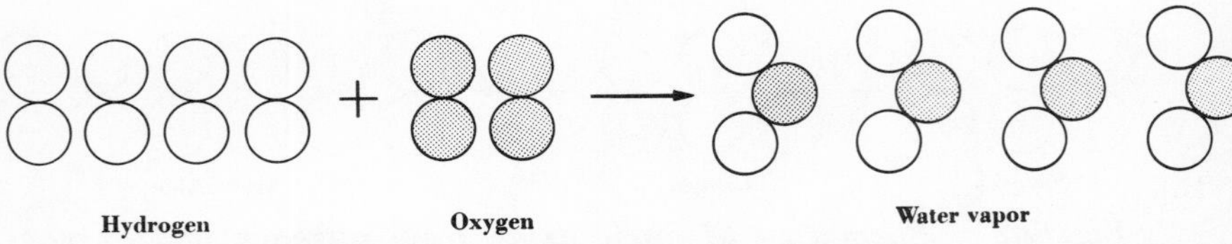

Hydrogen   Oxygen   Water vapor

Fig. 9.3   *Two volumes of hydrogen reacting with one volume of oxygen yield two volumes of water vapor.   Hydrogen and oxygen molecules each contain two atoms, and therefore water molecules must each contain two hydrogen atoms and one oxygen atom.*

In Berzelius' scheme an atom of an element is represented by an abbreviation of the element's name. For many elements the first letter is used; an atom of oxygen is O, an atom of hydrogen H, an atom of carbon C. When the names of two elements begin with the same letter, two letters are used in the abbreviation for one or both: Cl stands for an atom of chlorine, He for helium, Zn for zinc. For some elements abbreviations of Latin names are used: a copper atom is Cu (cuprum), an iron atom Fe (ferrum), a mercury atom Hg (hydrargyrum). These abbreviations are called *symbols* for the elements. Table 9.1 is a list of the elements in alphabetical order together with their chemical symbols.

Table 9.1. Atomic weights and chemical symbols of the elements.
Those elements whose atomic weights are given in parenthesis are not found on the earth but have been prepared artificially in nuclear reaction. The number given in those cases is the mass number of the most stable isotope of the element (Chap. 20).

Element	Symbol	Atomic weight	Element	Symbol	Atomic weight
Actinium	Ac	227	Fluorine	F	19.00
Aluminum	Al	26.98	Francium	Fr	(223)
Americium	Am	(243)	Gadolinium	Gd	157.25
Antimony	Sb	121.75	Gallium	Ga	69.72
Argon	Ar	39.95	Germanium	Ge	72.59
Arsenic	As	74.92	Gold	Au	196.97
Astatine	At	(210)	Hafnium	Hf	178.49
Barium	Ba	137.34	Helium	He	4.003
Berkelium	Bk	(249)	Holmium	Ho	164.93
Beryllium	Be	9.01	Hydrogen	H	1.008
Bismuth	Bi	208.98	Indium	In	114.82
Boron	B	10.81	Iodine	I	126.90
Bromine	Br	79.91	Iridium	Ir	192.2
Cadmium	Cd	112.40	Iron	Fe	55.85
Calcium	Ca	40.08	Krypton	Kr	83.80
Californium	Cf	(249)	Lanthanum	La	138.91
Carbon	C	12.01	Lawrencium	Lw	(257)
Cerium	Ce	140.12	Lead	Pb	207.19
Cesium	Cs	132.91	Lithium	Li	6.94
Chlorine	Cl	35.45	Lutetium	Lu	174.97
Chromium	Cr	52.00	Magnesium	Mg	24.31
Cobalt	Co	58.93	Manganese	Mn	54.94
Copper	Cu	63.54	Mendelevium	Md	(256)
Curium	Cm	(245)	Mercury	Hg	200.59
Dysprosium	Dy	162.50	Molybdenum	Mo	95.94
Einsteinium	Es	(253)	Neodymium	Nd	144.24
Erbium	Er	167.26	Neon	Ne	20.18
Europium	Eu	151.96	Neptunium	Np	(237)
Fermium	Fm	(255)	Nickel	Ni	58.71

Table 9.1.   The atomic weights and chemical symbols of the elements (continued).

Element	Symbol	Atomic weight	Element	Symbol	Atomic weight
Niobium	Nb	92.91	Silicon	Si	28.09
Nitrogen	N	14.01	Silver	Ag	107.87
Nobelium	No	(253?)	Sodium	Na	22.99
Osmium	Os	190.2	Strontium	Sr	87.63
Oxygen	O	16.00	Sulfur	S	32.06
Palladium	Pd	106.4	Tantalum	Ta	180.95
Phosphorus	P	30.97	Technetium	Tc	(99)
Platinum	Pt	195.09	Tellurium	Te	127.60
Plutonium	Pu	(242)	Terbium	Tb	158.92
Polonium	Po	210	Thallium	Tl	204.37
Potassium	K	39.10	Thorium	Th	232.04
Praseodymium	Pr	140.91	Thulium	Tm	168.93
Promethium	Pm	(145)	Tin	Sn	118.69
Protactinium	Pa	(231)	Titanium	Ti	47.90
Radium	Ra	226.05	Tungsten	W	183.85
Radon	Rn	222	Uranium	U	238.03
Rhenium	Re	186.2	Vanadium	V	50.94
Rhodium	Rh	102.91	Xenon	Xe	131.30
Rubidium	Rb	85.47	Ytterbium	Yb	173.04
Ruthenium	Ru	101.07	Yttrium	Y	88.91
Samarium	Sm	150.35	Zinc	Zn	65.37
Scandium	Sc	44.96	Zirconium	Zr	91.22
Selenium	Se	78.96			

Two or more atoms joined to form a molecule Berzelius represented by writing their symbols side by side: A carbon monoxide molecule is CO, a zinc sulfide molecule ZnS, a mercuric oxide molecule HgO. When a molecule contains two or more atoms of the same kind, a small subscript indicates the number present; the familiar expression H_2O means that a molecule of water contains two H atoms and one O atom; a molecule of oxygen, containing two O atoms, is written O_2; a molecule of carbon tetrachloride (CCl_4) contains one C atom and four Cl atoms; a molecule of nitrogen pentoxide (N_2O_5) contains two N (nitrogen) atoms and five O atoms. Each subscript applies only to the symbol immediately before it. These expressions for molecules are called *formulas*.

Symbols and formulas give the chemist a convenient shorthand for expressing the joining together and separating of atoms, which, according to Dalton's theory, are the fundamental processes of chemical change.

Chemical Equations

As a shorthand method of expressing the results of a chemical change, Berzelius suggested that the formulas of the substances involved be combined into a *chemical equation.* An equation includes the formulas of all the substances entering the reaction on the left-hand side with the formulas of all the products on the right-hand side. The formulas may be written in any order and are connected by + signs; between the two sides of the equation is placed an arrow. Thus, when carbon burns, the two substances that react are carbon (C) and oxygen (O_2), and the only product is carbon dioxide (CO_2):

$$C + O_2 \rightarrow CO_2$$

This equation means, in words: "Carbon reacts with oxygen to form carbon dioxide."

In an equation, the number of atoms of any one kind must be the same on both sides of the equation. This provision ensures that the law of conservation of mass is expressed in every chemical equation, corresponding to the fact that this law is obeyed in the actual reaction being described. For example, the decomposition of water that occurs when an electric current is passed through a water sample (a process called electrolysis) might be written in words as

Water $\rightarrow$ hydrogen + oxygen

Using the formulas for these substances, we might write

$$H_2O \rightarrow H_2 + O_2$$

Here two atoms of oxygen are shown on the right-hand side, only one atom on the left; in chemical terms, the equation is *unbalanced*. We cannot help matters by simply writing O instead of O_2 on the right, for we know that oxygen has the formula O_2. Nor is it legitimate to write a subscript 2 under the O in H_2O, for H_2O_2 is the formula of hydrogen peroxide, not water. The remedy is to show two units of H_2O on the left, giving two molecules of hydrogen and one of oxygen:

$$2H_2O \rightarrow 2H_2 + O_2$$

Now the equation is *balanced*, for there are two O atoms and four H atoms on each side. Note that a number placed in front of a formula multiplies everything in the formula, whereas a subscript applies only to the atom immediately in front of it.

Balancing an equation consists in making the number of atoms of each kind the same on both sides by writing the proper numbers in front of various formulas. For simple equations, balancing involves no more than careful inspection. We shall consider three examples:

1. Mercury heated in oxygen is changed to red mercuric oxide:

Mercury + oxygen $\rightarrow$ mercuric oxide

Unbalanced equation:

$$Hg + O_2 \rightarrow HgO$$

Balanced equation:

$$2Hg + O_2 \rightarrow 2HgO$$

2. Zinc added to a solution of hydrochloric acid liberates hydrogen and forms a solution of zinc chloride:

Zinc + hydrochloric acid → hydrogen + zinc chloride

Unbalanced equation:

$$Zn + HCl \rightarrow H_2 + ZnCl_2$$

Balanced equation:

$$Zn + 2HCl \rightarrow H_2 + ZnCl_2$$

3. When hydrogen sulfide is burned in oxygen, water and sulfur dioxide are formed:

Hydrogen sulfide + oxygen → water + sulfur dioxide

Unbalanced equation:

$$H_2S + O_2 \rightarrow H_2O + SO_2$$

Balanced equation:

$$2H_2S + 3O_2 \rightarrow 2H_2O + 2SO_2$$

Two facts about equations need emphasis: (1) An equation shows simply what chemical change has taken place; it tells nothing about the conditions (temperature, pressure, etc.) that are necessary to bring about the change. (2) An equation is not a means of predicting what chemical change *will take place*, but is a concise summary of a change that *has taken place*. To write an equation, the formulas of all products as well as those of all the substances that react must be known.

An equation in itself is not a means of predicting chemical changes, but if a chemist is familiar enough with the chemical behavior of an element, he can often express by means of an equation his inference about the reaction of the element in a new set of circumstances.

Atomic Weight

Since the days of the alchemists, a total of over 100 different chemical elements have been discovered. Not all of them are found on the earth; the missing elements, however, can be made from existing elements with the help of modern "atom smashers" and nuclear reactors.

An element, as we know, is a substance that cannot be decomposed into simpler constituents or transformed into another substance by ordinary chemical means, that is, by means of chemical reactions. The elements all have physical and chemical properties that enable us to distinguish them. There are many similarities among various elements: Hydrogen and helium are light gases; aluminum and magnesium are light, silvery metals; lead and uranium are very heavy metals; mercury and bromine are liquids at room temperature; silicon and germanium have similar electrical properties; and so on. But none of the elements found in nature have the same atomic weights, so that atomic weight is an unambiguous physical property that can serve to tell one element from another despite superficial resemblances between them in other ways.

When we speak of *atomic weight,* we do not imply, of course, that we actually place a single atom of a given element on a balance and weigh it, any more than, when we speak of the weight of the planet Jupiter, we imply that we possess a cosmic balance upon which we have placed Jupiter. Instead we use an indirect method of comparing one atom with another. For instance, we know that in water the ratio between the weights of the oxygen and hydrogen constituents is always 8:1. But every water molecule consists of two atoms of hydrogen for every one atom of oxygen, and so we conclude that oxygen is 16 times heavier than hydrogen. Comparisons of this kind can be carried out on all the elements, so that we are able to find out just how much heavier or lighter the atoms of one element are than those of another element. In doing this we learn nothing about the *actual* weights of the individual atoms, to be sure, but the chemist is normally interested only in the *relative* values.

The atomic-weight scale that is in use today has the most abundant type of carbon atom as its standard. (We shall learn about the existence of different kinds of atoms, called *isotopes,* of the same chemical species in Chap. 20.) The atomic weight of this type of carbon atom is *defined* as exactly 12, and the atomic weights of all the elements are expressed in terms of their weight relative to this atom. Thus ordinary carbon, some of whose atoms are heavier than the most abundant kind, has an atomic weight of 12.01. Table 9.1 lists the 103 known elements in alphabetical order, together with their chemical symbols and atomic weights. The atomic weights range from 1.008 for hydrogen to 257 for lawrencium. A curious fact shown by this table, whose significance we shall discuss later, is that *atomic weights for many elements are very nearly whole numbers.*

Avogadro's Number

No matter how small may be the samples of matter involved in a chemical experiment, they contain enormous numbers of atoms. However, if the numbers of atoms in two samples of different elements are the same, the ratio of the masses of the samples is equal to the ratio of the atomic weights of the corresponding elements. A quantity of helium that contains as many helium atoms as there are oxygen atoms in a quantity of oxygen always has a mass

$$4.003/16.00 = 0.2502$$

of that of the oxygen, while a quantity of lead whose atoms are equal in number to the oxygen atoms has a mass

$$207.19/16.00 = 12.95$$

times greater, since the atomic weights of helium, oxygen, and lead are, respectively, 4.003, 16.00, and 207.19.

Since it is impossible to count the atoms in a sample directly, while determining its mass is easy, the above argument is most useful stated in reverse: When the masses of two samples of different elements are in proportion to their atomic weights, they contain the same number of atoms. Because of this, it is convenient to define a quantity called the *gram atom*. *A gram atom of any element is that amount of it whose mass is equal to its atomic weight expressed in grams.* A gram atom of oxygen is 16.00 g; a gram atom of helium is 4.003 g; and a gram atom of lead is 207.19 g. A gram atom of any element contains the same number of atoms as a gram atom of any other element. This number is a constant of nature known as *Avogadro's number* (N_o), whose value is

$$N_o = 6.02 \times 10^{23} \text{ atoms/g atom}$$

We shall look into two of the ways by which N_o can be determined in later chapters.

A knowledge of Avogadro's number permits us to calculate the number of atoms in a sample of any element. For example, we might wish to know how many atoms there are in a pound of copper. We begin by noting that a weight of 1 lb is equivalent to a mass of 454 g and that the atomic weight of copper is 63.54. Hence a gram atom of copper has a mass of 63.54 g, and there are

$$\frac{454 \text{ g}}{63.54 \text{ g/g atom}} = 7.15 \text{ g atoms}$$

of copper per pound. We now multiply the number of gram atoms by the number of atoms per gram atom, which is N_o, and find that there are

$$7.15 \text{ g atoms} \times 6.02 \times 10^{23} \text{ atoms/g atom} = 4.30 \times 10^{26} \text{ atoms}$$

in a pound of copper.

Avogadro's number also makes it possible to obtain the mass of an individual atom of any element. The procedure is simply to divide the atomic weight of the element by N_o. Thus, in the case of copper, we have

$$\frac{63.54 \text{ g/g atom}}{6.02 \times 10^{23} \text{ atoms/g atom}} = 1.06 \times 10^{-22} \text{ g/atom}$$

Molecular Weight

The molecular weight of any compound is the ratio between the weight of any of its molecules and the weight of the most common carbon atom, where the latter, as before, is assigned the value 12.000. . . . The molecular weight of a compound is therefore the sum of the atomic weights of its constituent elements, each multiplied by the number of its atoms per molecule of the compound. The molecular weight of gaseous oxygen, for instance, is 32, since its formula is O_2 and the atomic weight of oxygen is 16. The molecular weight of the more complex compound sodium sulfate (Na_2SO_4) may be calculated as follows:

$$2Na = 2 \times 22.99 = 45.98$$
$$1S = 1 \times 32.06 = 32.06$$
$$4O = 4 \times 16.00 = 64.00$$
$$\text{Total} = \overline{142.04}$$

The molecular weight of sodium sulfate is 142.04.

The useful notion of the gram atom can be extended to molecules by defining the *gram molecule*, usually called the *mole*. *A mole of any compound is that amount of it whose mass is equal to its molecular weight expressed in grams.* A mole of oxygen has a mass of 32 g, and a mole of sodium sulfate a mass of 142.04 g. A mole of any substance contains the same number of molecules as a mole of any other substance, and this is the same as the number of atoms in a gram atom. Hence Avogadro's number N_0 may also be written

$$N_0 = 6.02 \times 10^{23} \text{ molecules/mole}$$

As an example of a calculation facilitated by the use of the mole we shall find the percentage by weight of the sodium in sodium sulfate (Na_2SO_4). According to its formula, each mole of Na_2SO_4 contains 2 g atoms of Na, namely 45.98 g. Hence a mole of Na_2SO_4, which is 142.04 g, since the molecular weight of Na_2SO_4 is 142.04, contains

$$\text{Percent sodium} = \frac{\text{mass of Na per mole}}{\text{mass per mole}} \times 100$$
$$= \frac{45.98 \text{ g}}{142.04 \text{ g}} \times 100$$
$$= 32.4$$

Once we know this percentage, of course, we can immediately establish the mass of sodium in any given quantity of sodium sulfate. Thus a ton of sodium sulfate contains

$$0.324 \times 2,000 \text{ lb} = 648 \text{ lb}$$

of sodium.

Earlier in this chapter we discussed Avogadro's hypothesis, which holds that equal volumes of all gases, under the same conditions of pressure and temperature, contain the same number of molecules. Careful measurements show that, at $0°C$ and atmospheric pressure, 1 mole of any gas occupies a volume of exactly 22.4 liters. (The *liter*, equal to 1,000 cm^3, or 10^{-3} m^3, is a metric unit of volume; it is a little larger than a quart.) This fact makes it possible to deal quantitatively with gas volumes in chemical reactions.

As an illustration, let us compute how much potassium chlorate ($KClO_3$) must be decomposed to yield exactly 1 liter of oxygen at $0°C$ and atmospheric pressure. When $KClO_3$, a white solid, is heated, it turns into KCl, another white solid, and evolves oxygen as a gas. The balanced equation of this reaction is

$$2KClO_3 \rightarrow 2KCl + 3O_2$$

Because 1 mole of any gas occupies 22.4 liters under the specified conditions, 1/22.4 mole occupies 1 liter. From the equation, 2 moles of $KClO_3$ produce 3 moles of O_2; hence $\frac{2}{3}$ mole of $KClO_3$ produces 1 mole of O_2, and 1/22.4 of that $\frac{2}{3}$ mole produces 1 liter of O_2. Thus

$$\frac{2}{3} \times 1/22.4 = 0.030 \text{ mole } KClO_3$$

is needed to evolve 1 liter of O_2. What mass of $KClO_3$ does this represent? First we determine the molecular weight of $KClO_3$:

$$
\begin{aligned}
1K &= 1 \times 39.10 = & 39.10 \\
1Cl &= 1 \times 35.45 = & 35.45 \\
3O &= 3 \times 16.00 = & \underline{48.00} \\
& \text{Total} = & 122.55
\end{aligned}
$$

The molecular weight of $KClO_3$ is 122.55, and a mole of this compound has a mass of 122.55 g. Our conclusion, then, is that

$$0.030 \times 122.55 \text{ g} = 3.68 \text{ g}$$

of potassium chlorate will yield 1 liter of oxygen at $0°C$ and atmospheric pressure when it is decomposed.

Self-examination

1. The law that states that the elements making up a chemical compound are always combined in the same weight ratios is called
   a. the law of conservation of mass
   b. the law of definite proportions
   c. Avogadro's law
   d. the atomic theory

2. Of the following natural laws, that with the least application to chemistry is the law of
   a. conservation of energy
   b. conservation of momentum
   c. conservation of mass
   d. definite proportions

3. Of the following assumptions that Dalton made in developing his atomic theory, the one that is still wholly valid is
   a. every element consists of tiny particles called atoms
   b. the atoms of any one element are all exactly alike
   c. atoms are indestructible
   d. atoms combine in small numbers

4. According to Avogadro's hypothesis, equal volumes of all gases, under the same conditions of pressure and temperature,
   a. have the same molecular weight
   b. contain the same number of molecules
   c. contain numbers of molecules directly proportional to their molecular weights
   d. contain numbers of molecules inversely proportional to their molecular weights

5. Which of the following chemical equations is balanced?
   a. $Fe_2O_3 + CO \rightarrow 2Fe + 2CO_2$
   b. $Na_2S + SO_2 \rightarrow Na_2S_2O_3 + S$
   c. $3CuO + 2NH_3 \rightarrow 3Cu + 3H_2O + N_2$
   d. $4Al + 3Fe_3O_4 \rightarrow 4Al_2O_3 + 9Fe$

6. Which of the following chemical equations is unbalanced?
   a. $2Hg + O_2 \rightarrow 2HgO$
   b. $2H_2S + 3O_2 \rightarrow 2H_2O + 2SO_2$
   c. $Na_2O + H_2O \rightarrow 2NaOH$
   d. $SO_2 + H_2O \rightarrow H_2SO_4$

7. The mass of a mole of any element
   a. is always equal to the mass of a gram atom of the element
   b. is always greater than the mass of a gram atom of the element
   c. may be greater than the mass of a gram atom of the element, depending upon its physical state
   d. may be less than the mass of a gram atom of the element, depending upon its physical state.

8. Elements can be distinguished unambiguously by their
   a. boiling points
   b. colors
   c. atomic weights
   d. electrical properties

Problems

1. The gas ammonia is a compound of the elements nitrogen and hydrogen. Analysis shows that there are 14 g of nitrogen for every 3 g of hydrogen in a sample of ammonia. How many grams of nitrogen would 51 g of ammonia contain? How many grams of ammonia could be prepared from 100 g of hydrogen?

2. The most common ore of iron, hematite, is an iron oxide with 7 g of iron to every 3 g of oxygen. How much iron could be recovered from 100 tons of pure hematite?

3. The formula for liquid water is H_2O, for solid zinc sulfide ZnS, and for gaseous nitrogen dioxide NO_2. Precisely what information do these formulas convey? What information do they *not* convey?

4. How many molecules of water vapor could be made from two molecules of hydrogen?

5. Nitrogen and oxygen are present in air in the virtually constant ratio of 3.2 g of nitrogen to every 1 g of oxygen. These elements can also combine chemically to form the compound nitric oxide, which contains 7 g of nitrogen to every 8 g of oxygen. Both air and nitric oxide are colorless gases. Suggest methods for showing experimentally that one is a compound and one a mixture.

6. One volume of hydrogen reacts with one volume of chlorine to give two volumes of the gas hydrogen chloride. Show from these figures that each hydrogen molecule must contain at least two atoms.

7. The analysis of ammonia, a compound of nitrogen and hydrogen, shows that 14 g of nitrogen is combined with every 3 g of hydrogen. A nitrogen atom is approximately fourteen times heavier than a hydrogen atom. What is the ratio of nitrogen to hydrogen atoms in the ammonia molecule?

8. Find the mass of a 0.2-mole sample of gaseous oxygen. How many molecules are there in the sample? What volume does the sample have at $0°C$ and atmospheric pressure?

9. Find the number of molecules in 0.0042 g of gaseous nitrogen.

10. Find the mass of 2 moles of Fe_2O_3.

11. How many atoms are there in a ton of lead?

12. How much aluminum is required to react with 10 g of oxygen to form Al_2O_3? How much Al_2O_3 will be formed?

13. The oxygen present in the compound $KClO_3$ is given off when it is heated. How many moles of O_2 gas are evolved when a mole of $KClO_3$ is decomposed?

14. What is the percentage by weight of the oxygen in $C_{12}H_{22}O_{11}$?

15. Does Ag_5SbS_4 or Ag_3AsS_3 contain more silver per ton?

CHAPTER 10 | *BASIC CHEMISTRY*

The chemical properties of several elements are illustrative of certain fundamental aspects of chemical behavior as well as being interesting in themselves. One of these elements, oxygen, was described in Chap. 8, and the properties of five other important elements, hydrogen, carbon, sulfur, chlorine, and sodium, are outlined below. Then we go on to consider the specialized vocabulary of chemistry, which permits chemists to present information clearly and concisely. We shall learn no new theories in this chapter, but instead expand our store of basic chemical knowledge.

Hydrogen

Hydrogen is the lightest of all substances, having a density of only 0.09 kg/m^3 at 0°C and atmospheric pressure. It is a colorless, tasteless, and odorless gas above its boiling point of −253°C (20°K); its freezing point is −259°C (14°K). At ordinary temperatures hydrogen molecules contain two atoms each, and its formula is accordingly H$_2$.

Hydrogen is a fairly abundant element, making up about 1 percent by weight of the earth's crust. Most of it is combined with oxygen in water. In compounds with carbon and oxygen, hydrogen is present in all animal and vegetable tissue. Free hydrogen, uncombined with other elements, is very scarce; it sometimes occurs as a minor constituent of volcanic gases and of natural gas.

In the laboratory, hydrogen is commonly prepared by the reaction between certain metals and water or acids and by the electrolysis of

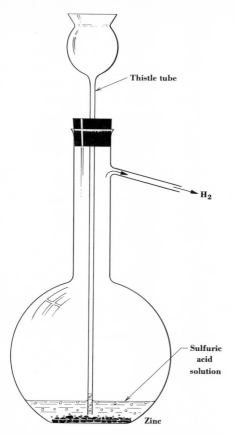

Thistle tube

H₂

Sulfuric
acid
solution

Zinc

Fig. 10.1   Preparation of hydrogen by the reaction between a metal and an acid. *Here sulfuric acid dissolved in water reacts with zinc to evolve gaseous hydrogen.*

water.   A convenient apparatus for the first method is shown in Fig. 10.1. Acid is poured down the thistle tube onto pieces of metal in the flask, and the gas bubbles off steadily as long as both acid and metal are present.   Zinc is often used as the metal, and sulfuric acid as the acid; the reaction between these two may be written

Zinc + sulfuric acid (soln) → hydrogen + zinc sulfate (soln)

Zn + H_2SO_4 → H_2 + $ZnSO_4$

In words, this statement reads, "Zinc added to a solution of sulfuric acid gives hydrogen and a solution of zinc sulfate."   After reaction, the zinc sulfate is not visible, but may be obtained as a white, crystalline solid by evaporating the remaining liquid.   The second method for preparing hydrogen, *electrolysis,* involves the passage of an electric current through a fluid, with resulting decomposition of the fluid (Fig. 10.2). Here the fluid is water, made a conductor by addition of a little acid or alkali, and the current passes between small platinum plates (marked "Pt") connected to a battery or generator. Hydrogen bubbles collect at one plate, oxygen bubbles collect at the other, and each gas rises to the top of its tube. As the gases accumulate, the volume of hydrogen remains always twice as great as the volume of oxygen. This reaction may be summarized

$$\text{Water} \rightarrow \text{hydrogen} + \text{oxygen}$$
$$2H_2O \rightarrow 2H_2 + O_2$$

Such a statement says nothing about how the reaction was carried out, but merely describes the chemical change that has occurred.

Hydrogen burns readily in air or oxygen with a hot, colorless flame. The gas produced in the flame is water vapor, as may be shown by condensing some of it. This reaction is the reverse of the decomposition of water by electrolysis:

$$\text{Hydrogen} + \text{oxygen} \rightarrow \text{water}$$
$$2H_2 + O_2 \rightarrow 2H_2O$$

A mixture of hydrogen and oxygen will not react at ordinary temperatures, but once the mixture is ignited by the heat of a flame or an electric spark, the reaction generates sufficient heat to keep itself going. If the gases are

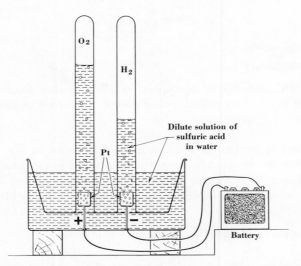

Fig. 10.2   *Electrolysis of water.* *An electric current decomposes water into gaseous hydrogen and oxygen. The volume of the hydrogen evolved is twice that of the oxygen, since both are diatomic gases and water contains twice as many hydrogen atoms as oxygen atoms. A trace of sulfuric acid is used to enable the water to conduct electricity.*

mixed in the proper proportions, an explosion results, because of the sudden expansion of the mixture as it is heated by the reaction. Miniature explosions produced by bringing a flame near hydrogen-air mixtures in a test tube give a convenient method of testing for the element.

One other compound of hydrogen and oxygen may be prepared indirectly. This is *hydrogen peroxide* (H_2O_2), an explosive liquid when pure which is commonly used in dilute solution as a disinfectant and bleaching agent. Its formula is written H_2O_2 rather than HO because its molecular weight, determined by comparison of the density of its vapor with that of oxygen (and in other ways), is 34 and not 17.

Hydrogen is an active element at moderately high temperatures, combining directly with a number of other nonmetallic elements besides oxygen and less readily with several of the metals. Thus with nitrogen it forms *ammonia* (NH_3); with chlorine, *hydrogen chloride* (HCl); with calcium, *calcium hydride* (CaH_2). With many metallic oxides hydrogen reacts to form water and the free metal; thus

$$\text{Copper oxide} + \text{hydrogen} \rightarrow \text{copper} + \text{water}$$
$$\text{CuO} \quad + \quad H_2 \quad \rightarrow \quad \text{Cu} \quad + \quad H_2O$$

In a reaction of this sort, where oxygen is removed from combination with a metal, the oxide is said to be *reduced*. Reduction is the opposite process to oxidation.

The low density of hydrogen makes it useful for filling high-altitude research balloons, although its inflammability is a constant source of danger. The intense heat produced when hydrogen burns in oxygen is made use of in cutting and welding metals with the oxyhydrogen blowtorch. Hydrogen is a principal constituent of artificial gas fuels. The hardening of oils to form solid fats and the production of synthetic ammonia and wood alcohol are among the other commercial uses of the element.

Carbon

Diamond and graphite are two naturally occurring forms of the pure element carbon. Diamond is the hardest known natural substance, clear and colorless when strictly pure, not breaking easily in any direction, and a very poor conductor of electricity. Graphite is soft, opaque, steel gray to black, composed of tiny flakes that split apart easily, and a fairly good electrical conductor. Ordinary carbon in the form of coke, soot, and charcoal is highly impure graphite in minute crystals. Both diamond and graphite are extremely resistant to heat, vaporizing appreciably only at temperatures near 3500°C. Carbon has never been liquefied.

That two materials as different in properties as diamond and graphite can be forms of a single element seems at first incredible. That this is so may be proved by burning each in oxygen at temperatures above 700°C;

Fig. 10.3   The arrangement of carbon atoms in a diamond crystal. *The unit of structure is a tetrahedron consisting of four atoms around a central atom; one of these units is shown by heavy lines.*

both give carbon dioxide gas as the only product. The differences between the two arise from a difference in crystal structure. The carbon atoms of diamond are arranged in a compact framework in which each atom is surrounded by four others at the corners of a tetrahedron (Fig. 10.3), while the carbon atoms of graphite lie in parallel planes, each plane made up of hexagonal rings (Fig. 10.4). Distances between the planes in a graphite crystal are greater than distances between the atoms within each plane, so that the crystal splits easily in a direction parallel to the planes. In diamond the atoms are closer together (as shown by its greater density), and each atom is separated from the four that surround it by equal distances; hence diamond is not easily split in any direction. Many other solids besides carbon, both elements and compounds, can exist in two or more different forms, the properties of each depending on the particular arrangement of particles in its crystal lattice.

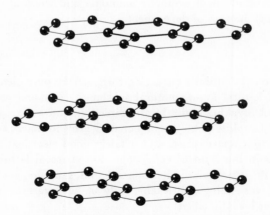

Fig. 10.4   The arrangement of carbon atoms in the crystal lattice of graphite. *The unit of structure is a hexagonal ring of six atoms; one of these units is shown by heavy lines.*

Inactive at ordinary temperatures, carbon at high temperatures reacts readily with many substances. It burns in air or oxygen to form the gas *carbon dioxide* (CO_2) if abundant oxygen is available, or the gas *carbon monoxide* (CO) if the oxygen supply is limited. Carbon combines slowly with a few other nonmetallic elements: with sulfur to form the volatile, inflammable liquid carbon disulfide (CS_2), with hydrogen to form the gas methane (CH_4) and related compounds. Some metals react with carbon to form solids called carbides, such as calcium carbide (CaC_2) and iron carbide (Fe_3C). Like hydrogen, hot carbon reduces the oxides of many metals; for instance,

$$\text{Zinc oxide} + \text{carbon} \rightarrow \text{zinc} + \text{carbon monoxide}$$
$$\text{ZnO} \quad + \quad \text{C} \quad \rightarrow \quad \text{Zn} + \quad \quad \text{CO}$$

The two oxides of carbon, carbon monoxide and carbon dioxide, are colorless, odorless, tasteless gases. One or the other, depending on the amount of oxygen available, is formed, not only from the burning of carbon, but from the burning of any carbon compound. The slow oxidation of carbon compounds in the bodies of animals produces carbon dioxide, which is exhaled from the lungs. The monoxide is inflammable and forms an important constituent of artificial gas fuels. It is also a deadly poison, especially dangerous because it has no odor. Carbon dioxide is heavy, nonpoisonous, and neither inflammable nor able to support combustion. Dissolved in water under pressure, it forms ordinary soda water. It is the gas responsible for the "rising" of bread and cakes during baking. Solid carbon dioxide, "dry ice," is used extensively in refrigeration.

Carbon is a relatively scarce element in the earth's crust, making up only about 0.03 percent by weight of the crust's materials. But its importance to humanity is out of all proportion to its abundance. In the form of coal, carbon is an important industrial fuel. Coal and coke are indispensable in winning many of the common metals from their ores. The compound carbon dioxide is an important minor constituent of air, since plant growth depends on its presence. Combined with calcium and oxygen in calcium carbonate ($CaCO_3$), carbon is a constituent of the common and useful rock limestone. Compounds of carbon with hydrogen (hydrocarbons) make up natural gas, gasoline, and lubricating oils. More complex carbon compounds are the chief constituents of our bodies, of the food we eat, of the clothes we wear, of the wood from which our houses are built. Artificially produced carbon compounds include an endless variety of dyes, perfumes, explosives, drugs, and plastics. In the number, variety, and importance of its compounds, carbon outranks all other elements.

Sulfur

Sulfur, a yellow, odorless, and tasteless solid, is the brimstone of ancient times. It melts at 115°C and boils at 445°C, and its density is about twice that of water. The common occurrence of sulfur near active volcanoes, together with the blue flame and sharp odor produced when it burns, probably explains its long literary association with the subterranean abode of deceased sinners. The free element is also found among the deposits of volcanoes long extinct and in marine deposits associated with gypsum and rock salt. Gypsum is a familiar naturally occurring sulfur compound $(CaSO_4 \cdot 2H_2O)$; the sulfides pyrite (FeS_2), galena (PbS), and cinnabar (HgS) are others.

Liquid sulfur has the peculiar property of becoming highly viscous as its temperature is raised toward 200°C and then losing viscosity as the boiling point is approached. When sulfur near its boiling point is quickly cooled by pouring into water, it solidifies to a brown, pliable, elastic material called amorphous sulfur which is quite different from the familiar yellow, crystalline form.

Chemically, sulfur is a moderately active element. It burns readily in air or oxygen to form *sulfur dioxide* (SO_2), a gas whose strong odor is that often described as "the odor of sulfur." Sulfur unites with many metals on heating to form compounds called *sulfides*, for example, copper sulfide (CuS) and silver sulfide (Ag_2S). With active metals this reaction may liberate considerable energy, as in the zinc-sulfur reaction described in Chap. 8. With hydrogen, sulfur combines to form hydrogen sulfide (H_2S), a gas whose odor is like that of rotten eggs. Other common sulfur compounds contain both metals and oxygen: "Epsom salts," magnesium sulfate $(MgSO_4 \cdot 7H_2O)$; "blue vitriol," copper sulfate $(CuSO_4 \cdot 5H_2O)$; gypsum, calcium sulfate $(CaSO_4 \cdot 2H_2O)$. (The H_2O in these formulas indicates water, loosely held in the solid crystals, which may be removed on mild heating.)

Industrially the most important sulfur compound is sulfuric acid (H_2SO_4), a heavy, colorless, viscous liquid that is highly corrosive and dissolves readily in water with evolution of much heat. A solution of the acid is a common laboratory reagent, and among its countless industrial uses the most important are in petroleum refining and in the manufacture of fertilizers and explosives.

Chlorine

Chlorine is a poisonous, greenish-yellow gas with a disagreeable odor. Chlorine melts at −102°C and boils at −35°C, and its density at 0°C and atmospheric pressure is 3.16 kg/m³. At ordinary temperatures chlorine molecules contain two atoms each, and so its chemical formula is Cl_2.

Chlorine is far too active to exist free in nature. Its most abundant compound is sodium chloride $(NaCl)$, familiar to us as ordinary salt, which occurs in solution in the ocean and in salt lakes and in solid form as deposits of rock salt. In the laboratory, chlorine may be prepared from sodium chloride by heating it with sulfuric acid and a black powder called manganese dioxide, while industrially the gas is prepared by electrolysis of a concentrated sodium chloride solution.

Chemically, chlorine is one of the most active of all elements, combining directly with all metallic elements and many nonmetallic elements. Oxygen is one of the few with which it will not react, but unstable oxides can be prepared indirectly. The more active metals burn brilliantly in chlorine just as they do in oxygen, forming *chlorides* instead of oxides. Thus copper foil burns to form *copper chloride* ($CuCl_2$), and sodium burns with an intense yellow flame to form white clouds of tiny *sodium chloride* crystals. This spectacular reaction between the active gas chlorine and the active metal sodium, both highly poisonous, to produce the harmless substance salt is one of the most impressive examples of the profound changes in properties that chemical reaction can bring about.

A jet of hydrogen burns in chlorine as readily as in oxygen, forming a colorless gas with a sharp, unpleasant odor called *hydrogen chloride* (HCl). A mixture of hydrogen and chlorine will react at room temperature, provided that the mixture is exposed to light; if the mixture is prepared in darkness and then brightly illuminated, the reaction is explosive. For either this *photochemical* ("caused by light") reaction or the burning of hydrogen, the chemical change may be summarized

$$\text{Hydrogen} + \text{chlorine} \rightarrow \text{hydrogen chloride}$$
$$H_2 \quad + \quad Cl_2 \quad \rightarrow \quad 2HCl$$

A solution of hydrogen chloride in water is a common strong acid called hydrochloric acid (the "muriatic acid" of commerce).

Chlorine reacts with many colored compounds of carbon, changing them to colorless compounds. This property accounts for the extensive use of the element in bleaching. It is used also as a disinfectant and in the preparation of dyes, explosives, and poison gases.

Sodium

Sodium is a silver-gray solid that rapidly tarnishes when exposed to air. It melts at $98°C$ and boils at $880°C$. Sodium is one of the more abundant elements, making up nearly 2.5 percent of the earth's crust, but its extreme chemical activity prevents it from occurring free in nature. Its compounds are widely distributed in rocks, soil, and, in solution, in bodies of water.

Sodium is so soft that it can be cut like cheese; so light that it will float on water; so easily corroded by air and water that it must be kept under oil. By ordinary standards these properties suggest that sodium should be called anything but a metal, yet to the chemist sodium is strongly metallic in every way. It has a silvery luster on freshly cut surfaces, and it is an excellent conductor of electricity—two characteristically metallic properties. Its chemical behavior shows in an exaggerated form certain properties common to all the more active metals. Among these are:

1. Its ability to burn brightly, with the evolution of much heat, in both oxygen [forming *sodium peroxide* (Na_2O_2)] and chlorine.

Some nonmetallic elements will burn in oxygen or chlorine, a few in both, but the energy liberated is in general not as great as for the metals.

2. Its ability to liberate hydrogen from acids. Many common metals, for instance zinc, iron, and aluminum, liberate hydrogen slowly from acids, but with sodium the reaction is violent and the liberation of gas exceedingly rapid.

3. Its ability to liberate hydrogen from water. This reaction produces, in addition to hydrogen, a solution of a compound called *sodium hydroxide* (NaOH):

$$\text{Sodium} + \text{water} \rightarrow \text{hydrogen} + \text{sodium hydroxide (soln)}$$
$$2\text{Na} \quad + \quad 2\text{H}_2\text{O} \rightarrow \quad \text{H}_2 \quad + \quad 2\text{NaOH}$$

Several of the commoner metals, even iron, can be made to react slowly with hot water, but a little chunk of sodium need only be dropped on cold water to start a reaction that sets it skimming over the surface and generates enough heat to melt the metal.

Sodium combines readily with most of the nonmetallic elements, but not in general with other metals. Like hydrogen and carbon, it reduces many metallic oxides to the pure metal. Of the simple compounds of sodium, the more familiar are ordinary salt (NaCl), washing soda or sodium carbonate (Na_2CO_3), baking soda or sodium bicarbonate ($NaHCO_3$), caustic soda or sodium hydroxide (NaOH).

The Language of Chemistry

Every element has its own special name, but when it is part of a compound this name may undergo a change or may even not be mentioned specifically in the name of the compound. The way in which compounds are named is quite ingenious, and as a prelude to further work in chemistry, it is useful for us to learn something about this special language. We shall find that the order in which the chemical symbols representing the various elements in a compound are placed in the formula for that compound follows a special pattern. The first time we face all the various rules for naming and symbolizing compounds, they seem bewilderingly complicated, and we must not lose sight of the fact that these rules were actually devised to bring some order into the complex world of chemistry.

The first rule we consider is straightforward: In a compound containing a metal and one or more elements that are not metals, the name of the metal comes first and its symbol appears first in the formula. Thus common salt is

Sodium chloride   NaCl

For compounds containing only nonmetallic elements there is no simple rule. If carbon or hydrogen is present, it usually stands first:

Carbon dioxide	CO_2
Hydrogen sulfide	H_2S
Carbon tetrachloride	CCl_4

An exception that has become standard usage is

Ammonia	NH_3

If oxygen or chlorine is present, it is usually written last:

Carbon monoxide	CO
Phosphorus trichloride	PCl_3
Sulfur dioxide	SO_2

In compounds containing more than two elements, oxygen is very often one of the constituents. In such cases oxygen usually does not appear explicitly in the name of the compound and it is last in the formula:

Calcium carbonate	$CaCO_3$
Sodium sulfate	Na_2SO_4

An exception occurs in the case of certain compounds containing both hydrogen and oxygen, called hydroxides, in whose formulas hydrogen comes last, for instance,

Sodium hydroxide	$NaOH$

Names of compounds made up of only two elements always end in *-ide*, which is used as a suffix to the name of the second element in the name. Thus we have

Hydrogen chloride	HCl
Zinc chloride	$ZnCl_2$
Aluminum chloride	$AlCl_3$
Hydrogen sulfide	H_2S
Iron carbide	Fe_3C

A number of other compounds also have names that end in *-ide,* for instance, the hydroxides, which contain hydrogen and oxygen in the combination OH.

When two or more compounds contain the same pair of elements, they are distinguished by one of two methods:

1. A prefix (*mono-, di-, tri-*, etc.) may be added to the name of the second element in each, indicating the number of its atoms per molecule:

Carbon monoxide	CO
Carbon dioxide	CO_2
Phosphorus trichloride	PCl_3
Phosphorus pentachloride	PCl_5

2. The suffixes *-ic* and *-ous* may be added to the name of the first element, the *-ic* referring to a compound containing more atoms of the second

element relative to the first (for iron, the suffixes are added to the Latin name, ferrum):

Ferric chloride	$FeCl_3$
Ferrous chloride	$FeCl_2$
Mercuric oxide	HgO
Mercurous oxide	Hg_2O
Cupric sulfide	CuS
Cuprous sulfide	Cu_2S

In general, the second method is used for compounds of a metal with a nonmetal and the first for compounds of two nonmetals, but this rule has several exceptions.

The term *peroxide*, often applied to dioxides, refers properly only to a group of dioxides with special properties. The only common peroxides are

Hydrogen peroxide	H_2O_2
Sodium peroxide	Na_2O_2
Barium peroxide	BaO_2

Most compounds with three elements, as we said, contain oxygen, another nonmetallic element, and a metal. Normally, the suffix *-ate* is added to the name of the nonmetal to indicate the presence of oxygen:

Sodium sulfate	Na_2SO_4
Calcium sulfate	$CaSO_4$
Potassium nitrate	KNO_3
Magnesium carbonate	$MgCO_3$

Atomic Groups

A great many compounds contain the group of atoms SO_4 united with a metal. In addition to the two listed above, common examples are

Potassium sulfate	K_2SO_4
Copper sulfate	$CuSO_4$
Zinc sulfate	$ZnSO_4$
Magnesium sulfate	$MgSO_4$

Collectively these compounds are referred to as the sulfates, and the atomic group SO_4 is called the *sulfate group*. This group may remain intact through many chemical reactions. For instance, if we mix solutions of magnesium sulfate and barium chloride, we obtain barium sulfate, which appears as a solid, and a solution of magnesium chloride. A chemist would write the reaction in the form

$$MgSO_4 + BaCl_2 \rightarrow BaSO_4 + MgCl_2$$

Other atomic groups which remain intact in chemical reactions and which appear as parts of many compounds are

Nitrate group	NO_3
Carbonate group	CO_3
Hydroxide group	OH

When two or more groups of a single kind are present in each molecule of a compound, the formula is written with a pair of parentheses around the group:

| Calcium nitrate | $Ca(NO_3)_2$ |
| Ferric hydroxide | $Fe(OH)_3$ |

instead of CaN_2O_6 and FeO_3H_3, respectively; the parentheses are used to indicate that the elements they enclose behave as a unit rather than individually, in chemical reactions.

Acids and Bases

We shall not attempt rigorous definitions of these important classes of compounds at this point. In general, acids are characterized experimentally by the facts that (1) their solutions have a sour taste, and (2) their solutions will change the color of certain dyes; for example, they will turn blue litmus paper red. Their formulas are characterized by the presence of hydrogen combined with one or more nonmetallic elements. If only one element besides hydrogen is present, the acid is named by adding the prefix *hydro-* and the suffix *-ic* to the name of the second element:

| Hydrochloric acid (hydrogen chloride) | HCl |
| Hydrosulfuric acid (hydrogen sulfide) | H_2S |

If the acid contains oxygen in addition to another nonmetal, the prefix *hydro-* is omitted from the name:

Sulfuric acid (hydrogen sulfate)	H_2SO_4
Nitric acid (hydrogen nitrate)	HNO_3
Carbonic acid (hydrogen carbonate)	H_2CO_3

The hydroxides, for instance,

| Sodium hydroxide | $NaOH$ |

violate the rules of naming that have been set up for other compounds and are exceptional also in their chemical properties. Soluble hydroxides of metals are characterized by (1) their bitter taste, and (2) their ability to reverse the changes in the color of dyes brought about by acids; for instance, a soluble hydroxide will turn red litmus paper blue. In many respects opposite in behavior to acids, the hydroxides of metals are called collectively *bases* even though the term does not appear in their names.

The rules we have described enable us to name most of the compounds we shall study in future chapters. Note that these rules start out by assuming that we already know the formula of a compound in question—but if all we know is the name of the compound, this information is not enough for us to figure out its formula. If we are asked for the formula for aluminum chloride, we know that it contains aluminum and chlorine, but we do not know whether they are combined as $AlCl$, Al_2Cl, $AlCl_2$, or something else. There is, however, a method for determining the subscripts that does not require us to perform an experiment for every compound, and we shall find out what this method is in the next chapter.

Self-examination

1. The electrolysis of water yields
   a. gaseous hydrogen only
   b. gaseous oxygen only
   c. both gaseous hydrogen and gaseous oxygen
   d. water vapor

2. The process of removing oxygen from combination with a metal is called
   a. oxidation
   b. reduction
   c. vaporization
   d. electrolysis

3. Graphite and diamond are different in physical properties because
   a. they are composed of different elements
   b. diamond is pure carbon while graphite contains traces of other substances
   c. their crystal structures are different
   d. their atomic weights are different

4. The element contained in the greatest number of compounds is
   a. hydrogen
   b. oxygen
   c. carbon
   d. sulfur

5. Which of the following elements does not react with oxygen to form an oxide?
   a. hydrogen
   b. carbon
   c. sulfur
   d. chlorine

6. Acids invariably contain
   a. hydrogen
   b. oxygen
   c. chlorine
   d. water

7. A characteristic of bases is that
    a. they taste sour
    b. they taste sweet
    c. they contain hydrogen with or without oxygen
    d. they contain one or more hydroxide (OH) groups per molecule

Problems

1. In what ways is the chemical behavior of sodium similar to that of hydrogen? In what ways is the chemical behavior of oxygen similar to that of chlorine?

2. Name the following acids and bases: H_2S, HNO_3, $Ca(OH)_2$, $Al(OH)_3$, $NaOH$, HF, H_2SO_4, H_3BO_3.

3. Name the following compounds: $MgCO_3$, $HgSO_4$, SiO_2, $AgNO_3$, $AgCl$, Na_3N, K_2CO_3, NiS, $Al_2(SO_4)_3$, $Zn(NO_3)_2$, UF_6.

4. Match each of the chemical compounds listed below with the appropriate formula from the list at the right.
    a. ammonia HNO_3
    b. ferrous chloride H_2O_2
    c. ferric hydroxide HCl
    d. nitric acid $FeCl_2$
    e. potassium hydroxide KOH
    f. hydrochloric acid $Fe(OH)_3$
    g. sodium oxide NH_3
    h. hydrogen peroxide Na_2O

5. Quicklime (CaO) is prepared by heating limestone ($CaCO_3$). The gas CO_2 is evolved during the reaction. Write the equation for the process, and give the chemical names of the three substances involved.

6. The rusting of iron is a complex reaction in detail, but it is essentially the oxidation of iron to form ferric oxide (Fe_2O_3). Write the equation for this reaction.

7. Name (*a*) the two oxides of phosphorus, P_2O_3 and P_2O_5; (*b*) the two chlorides of mercury, Hg_2Cl_2 and $HgCl_2$; (*c*) the two hydroxides of iron, $Fe(OH)_2$ and $Fe(OH)_3$.

8. Which of the following equations (*a*) are balanced, (*b*) show a reaction between two gases, (*c*) show a reaction involving an acid, (*d*) show the production of a colorless gas, (*e*) show reduction of an oxide?
    (1) $Zn + H_2SO_4 \text{ (soln)} \rightarrow H_2 + ZnSO_4 \text{ (soln)}$
    (2) $Al + 3O_2 \rightarrow Al_2O_3$
    (3) $H_2CO_3 \rightarrow H_2O + CO_2$

(4) $3CO + Fe_2O_3 \rightarrow 3CO_2 + 2Fe$
(5) $N_2 + H_2 \rightarrow 2NH_3$
(6) $6Na + Fe_2O_3 \rightarrow 2\ Fe + 3Na_2O$
(7) $MnO_2 + 4HCl \rightarrow MnCl_2 + 2H_2O + Cl_2$

9. When an electric current is passed through a solution of hydrogen chloride, hydrogen is liberated at one electrode and chlorine at the other. Write an equation for the reaction. Would you expect the volumes of hydrogen and chlorine liberated to be equal? Why or why not?

10. When an acetylene flame is used in welding, the intense heat is produced by the burning of acetylene gas (C_2H_2) to form carbon dioxide and water. Write the equation.

11. Write balanced equations for the following reactions:
   a. Hydrogen and oxygen combine to form water.
   b. Carbon burns in air to form carbon monoxide.
   c. Sulfur trioxide (SO_3) combines with water to form sulfuric acid.
   d. Potassium and sulfur combine to form potassium sulfide (K_2S).
   e. Barium reacts with water to liberate hydrogen.

12. Write balanced equations for the following reactions:
   a. Aluminum reacts with ferric oxide (Fe_2O_3) to form iron and aluminum oxide (Al_2O_3).
   b. Aluminum reacts with hydrochloric acid solution to liberate hydrogen and form a solution of aluminum chloride.
   c. Cesium reacts with bromine to form cesium bromide.
   d. Potassium chlorate $(KClO_3)$ is decomposed into potassium chloride (KCl) and oxygen.

CHAPTER 11 | THE PERIODIC LAW

Science progresses by seeking relationships among things and processes. Relationships can be interpreted by generalizations in the form of laws, theories, and hypotheses. Generalizations, once established, lead to a search for new relationships, and on these in turn further generalizations are based. At each stage the relationships become more fundamental and the laws and theories widen in scope. So, as scientific thought develops, explanations of the natural world becomes possible in simpler and simpler terms.

This is an old theme, but still an important one. The myriad details of scientific knowledge must not obscure for us the underlying process by which the knowledge has been obtained. The guiding motive of this process, the mainspring of the scientific method, is the search for relationships. Always, when faced with new phenomena, the scientist asks how they are related, both among themselves and to other phenomena. In what ways are they similar, in what ways dissimilar? What mathematical rules connect them?

Kepler sought relationships in the observations of Tycho Brahe on planetary motions and found the three generalizations that we call Kepler's laws. Newton sought a connection between these generalizations and Galileo's laws of falling bodies and found the law of gravitation. Rumford and Joule tried to find the relation between mechanical energy and heat; from the rule connecting these two forms of energy and similar rules for others came the law of conservation of energy. Boyle, Charles, and Gay-Lussac searched for relationships among gas volumes at various pressures and temperatures and discovered simple proportionality laws. Relationships between these laws and other regularities in gas behavior led to the kinetic theory.

When a large number of objects are under investigation, the search for relationships becomes primarily a problem of classification. Any classification implies relationships, for objects are grouped according to their similarities and differences. From a classification, other relationships and generalizations often emerge.

Thus chemistry in its beginnings faced a formidable number of different materials. Relationships among these materials finally suggested their classification into elements, compounds, and mixtures. This classification focused attention on relations among the compositions of different compounds, and from these relations Dalton built the atomic theory.

By Dalton's time chemists were convinced that the earth's materials were constructed from a handful of elementary substances, therefore from a limited number of different kinds of atoms. But the handful was a big one, and steadily growing bigger: By the middle of the nineteenth century about 60 different elements had been discovered. Was it possible that the elements themselves might be interrelated, that their atoms might show resemblances and differences which would reveal some even more fundamental principle of nature? Here again was a problem primarily of classification.

Attacked by several chemists in the 1860s, this problem was brilliantly solved by a Russian, Dmitri Mendeleev. To understand Mendeleev's work, let us inquire further into the properties of the elements, paying special heed to similarities and dissimilarities that might serve as a basis for their classification.

Metals and Nonmetals

Among the more obvious distinctions between different kinds of elements is that which divides metals from nonmetals. So generally familiar is the idea of a metal that we have used this distinction frequently without trying to make it precise. Iron, mercury, gold, aluminum, sodium, and tin are examples of metallic elements; carbon, sulfur, hydrogen, chlorine, and helium are nonmetals.

The outstanding physical properties that differentiate metals from other substances are their characteristic sheen, or metallic luster, and the ease with which they conduct heat and electricity. Instinctively we associate also the qualities of hardness and toughness with metals, but a moment's glance at the softness of gold, lead, and sodium shows that these are not general characteristics. Nonmetals in the solid state are usually brittle materials without metallic luster (graphite and one form of silicon are exceptions) and are very poor conductors of heat and electricity (graphite is an exception, but its conductivity is small compared with that of most metals). In some other physical properties nonmetals have an extreme range: in melting point, from helium ($-269°C$) to carbon (above $3500°C$), and in hardness, from diamond to soft white phosphorus.

In chemical behavior metals show considerable differences among themselves. Sodium, for example, is extremely active, whereas gold and platinum are highly resistant to chemical change. In general:

1. Metals combine with nonmetals much more readily than with one another. All metals combine directly with fluorine and chlorine, and most combine directly with oxygen. Many metals mix readily to form alloys, but definite compounds between metals are few and unstable.
2. All the more active metals react with dilute acids to liberate hydrogen, and very active metals liberate hydrogen from water.
3. Oxides of the more active metals react with water to form bases. Thus sodium oxide placed in water yields sodium hydroxide, which is a base. The reaction would be written in equation form as

$$Na_2O + H_2O \rightarrow 2NaOH$$

Nonmetals show an even greater variety of chemical properties than the metals do. Some (argon, helium, neon) form almost no compounds, whereas others (chlorine, fluorine) are highly active. In general:

1. Nonmetals (except for those like argon) combine readily with active metals, somewhat less readily with one another. Thus chlorine and fluorine react violently with active metals, but will not combine directly with oxygen. Sulfur and phosphorus, on the other hand, burn brightly in oxygen.
2. The nonmetals do not react with dilute acids. Several are attacked by bases, but the reactions do not follow a single pattern.
3. Oxides of nonmetals, if soluble, combine with water to form acids. The slightly sour taste of soda water is due to carbonic acid, formed from the dissolved oxide of carbon:

$$CO_2 + H_2O \rightarrow H_2CO_3$$

Sulfuric acid is manufactured by dissolving SO_3 in water:

$$SO_3 + H_2O \rightarrow H_2SO_4$$

The nonmetal hydrogen is unique: Although distinctly nonmetallic in its physical properties and much of its chemical behavior, some of its reactions suggest similarities with the metals. For example, hydrogen combines more readily and more violently with nonmetals than with metals, and its compounds with atom groups like SO_4, CO_3, etc., are similar in formula to metallic compounds.

We shall learn later a more sophisticated general definition of metals and nonmetals. Even this better definition, however, does not make the distinction sharp, for a few elements show properties in some measure characteristic of both groups. Metals far outnumber the nonmetals; only 20 of the 103 elements known today are considered definitely nonmetallic.

Active and Inactive Elements

Sodium we call an *active* metal, gold a very *inactive* one. Precisely what do these terms mean?

We know that sodium is tarnished by a few seconds' exposure to air, whereas a gold ring keeps its luster after years of exposure to air and perspiration. We think of the spectacular combustion of sodium in chlorine, accompanied by much heat and light energy; gold combines sluggishly with chlorine, setting free little energy. We recall that sodium liberates hydrogen rapidly from dilute acids, even from water; gold is unaffected by ordinary acids, dissolving only in a mixture of concentrated HCl and HNO_3. In reactions like these we say that sodium exhibits its greater activity.

There are a number of other criteria with whose help we can establish the relative activity of the various elements. We might measure the amount of heat liberated in similar chemical reactions undergone by various elements. Suppose, for instance, that we combine samples of gold, copper, iron, and sodium with chlorine. In each case let us use 1 mole of chlorine (35.45 g) with enough of the metal to react completely with it. We find that the amounts of energy evolved are 5.8 kcal for gold, 27.7 kcal for copper, 32.1 kcal for iron, and 98.4 kcal for sodium; the chemical activities of these metals must therefore be in that order, with gold the least active and sodium the most active.

A related method of establishing relative activity is to start with similar compounds and ask how easily they can be separated into their component elements or element groups. In the metal chlorides, we would find that gold chloride is decomposed by heating to about 300°C, copper chloride by heating to somewhat above 1000°C, iron chloride and sodium chloride only by heating to much higher temperatures. Gold chloride is said to be a relatively *unstable* compound, whereas sodium chloride is a very *stable* compound. In general, the more active an element is, the more difficult are its compounds to decompose. Relative stabilities of similar compounds, then, give us a second method for comparing activities. Roughly quantitative measurements of relative stabilities may be obtained by determinations of decomposition temperatures, or better by the amounts of energy which must be supplied to bring about decomposition.

If samples of the four metals are placed in test tubes and a dilute HCl solution is poured over them, hydrogen bubbles off rapidly in the tube containing sodium, more slowly in the tube containing iron, not at all from the copper and gold. Thus the rate at which hydrogen is evolved from dilute acids is a third and somewhat cruder method for comparing activities of metals.

For different nonmetals, a comparison of activities is more difficult than for metals, since a nonmetal that is only moderately active in reactions with metals (phosphorus, for example) may be highly active in reactions with other nonmetals. In general, however, the term "active nonmetal" applied to an element refers to its behavior in reaction with metals and metallic compounds. With this understanding, the activities of two nonmetals may be compared by methods similar to those that apply to metals: The heat liberated in their reactions with equal quantities of the same metal may be measured, or the stabilities of similar compounds may be determined. Thus chlorine is a more active nonmetal than oxygen, since it combines directly with more metals than does oxygen and since in most of its reactions with metals it liberates more energy. Sulfur is less active than oxygen, because sulfides are as a rule more easily decomposed than oxides.

By using the results of several different methods, both metals and nonmetals may be arranged in continuous series showing the order of their activities. In the following partial listing, the most active elements are at the top of each series, the least active at the bottom.

Metals	*Nonmetals*
Potassium	Fluorine
Sodium	Chlorine
Calcium	Bromine
Magnesium	Oxygen
Aluminum	Iodine
Zinc	Sulfur
Iron	
Lead	
Copper	
Mercury	
Silver	
Gold	

Families of Elements

The resemblances among some elements are so striking that these elements seem to be members of the same natural family. As examples of families of elements whose grouping together is almost inevitable to the chemist, we shall discuss a family of active nonmetals called the *halogens*, a group of active metals called the *alkali metals*, and a group of gases that undergo almost no chemical reactions whatever, called the *inert gases*.

The *halogens* consist of the highly active elements fluorine (F), chlorine (Cl), bromine (Br), and iodine (I), listed in order of increasing atomic weight. They are responsible for some of the vilest odors (*bromos* is Greek for "stink") and most brilliant colors (*chloros* is Greek for "green") to be found in the laboratory. The name *halogen* means "salt former," a token of the fact that these elements produce white, crystalline solids when they combine with many metals. Fluorine is a pale-yellow gas and chlorine a greenish-yellow gas at room temperature; bromine is a reddish-brown liquid, and iodine is a steel-gray solid. Both bromine and iodine evaporate readily, a property the chemist calls *volatility*.

What are the similarities among the halogens? For one thing, in the vapor phase all their molecules contain two atoms at ordinary temperatures: F_2, Cl_2, Br_2, I_2. Also, the compounds they form with metals have similar formulas. Here are three examples:

$$NaF \qquad ZnF_2 \qquad AlF_3$$
$$NaCl \qquad ZnCl_2 \qquad AlCl_3$$
$$NaBr \qquad ZnBr_2 \qquad AlBr_3$$
$$NaI \qquad ZnI_2 \qquad AlI_3$$

In all compounds with a specific metal, the same number of halogen atoms combine with each metal atom, though this number may vary for different metals.

All the halogens react with hydrogen to form, as the case may be, HF, HCl, HBr, or HI. These compounds can be dissolved in water to form acids, of which hydrochloric acid is a familiar example. The halogens are readily soluble in carbon tetrachloride to give solutions colored in the same way as their vapors, but they are only slightly soluble in water.

Although the halogens are all active elements, their activity declines markedly with increasing atomic weight. Fluorine is the most active of all nonmetals—so active that it is difficult to prepare, difficult to keep, dangerous to work with. Chlorine is somewhat less active; bromine and iodine, still less. All metals combine directly with fluorine and chlorine, but the less active ones are not affected by bromine and iodine. Table 11.1 lists the amounts of energy liberated when one mole of potassium (39.1 g) reacts with the various halogens to form KF, KCl, KBr, and I, respectively; these heats of formation decrease with increasing atomic weight, indicating less and less stability. Also evident in this table is a steady increase in both melting and boiling points with atomic weight. Thus the halogens constitute a group of elements with many similar properties, some of which change progressively with increasing atomic weight.

Table 11.1. Properties of the halogens.

Name	Symbol	Atomic weight	Heat of formation per mole of K, kcal	Melting point, °C	Boiling point, °C
Fluorine	F	19.00	KF, 118	−223	−187
Chlorine	Cl	35.45	KCl, 106	−102	−35
Bromine	Br	79.91	KBr, 95	−7	59
Iodine	I	126.90	KI, 80	114	184

The *alkali metals* are all soft, light, and extremely active metals. In order of increasing atomic weight they are lithium (Li), sodium (Na), potassium (K), rubidium (Rb), and cesium (Cs). Like sodium, the other alkali metals tarnish quickly in air, liberate hydrogen from water and dilute acids, combine energetically with active nonmetals to form very stable compounds, and form oxides that combine with water to make bases. Formulas of their compounds are strikingly similar:

Bromides	LiBr	NaBr	KBr	RbBr	CsBr
Sulfides	Li_2S	Na_2S	K_2S	Rb_2S	Cs_2S
Hydroxides	LiOH	NaOH	KOH	RbOH	CsOH

Among the other properties the alkali metals have in common are rather low melting points for metals: Cesium melts in a warm room, and even lithium, which has the highest melting point of the group, liquefies at only 186°C. Table 11.2 lists a few of the properties of the alkali metals; evidently their densities increase steadily with atomic weight (potassium is an exception), while their melting and boiling points decrease.

Table 11.2. Properties of the alkali metals.

Name	Symbol	Atomic weight	Density, $10^3 kg/m^3$	Melting point, °C	Boiling point, °C
Lithium	Li	6.94	0.53	186	1200
Sodium	Na	22.99	0.97	98	880
Potassium	K	39.10	0.87	62	760
Rubidium	Rb	85.47	1.53	39	700
Cesium	Cs	132.91	1.87	28	670

In general, the chemical activity of the alkali metals increases as atomic weight increases. The three heavier metals liberate so much energy in their reactions with cold water that the hydrogen produced ignites spontaneously, while from lithium and sodium, hydrogen is evolved without burning. Cesium forms the most stable compounds with chlorine and bromine; lithium, the least stable compounds. Thus, like the halogens, the alkali metals show striking similarities in their chemical and physical properties, several of which change progressively in magnitude with increasing atomic weight.

The inert gases, in marked contrast with the active halogens and alkali metals, are so inactive that they form only a handful of compounds with other elements. In fact, their atoms are so inactive that they do not even join together into molecules, like the atoms of other gaseous elements. The family of inert gases includes, once more in order of increasing atomic weight, helium (He), neon (Ne), argon (A), krypton (Kr), xenon (Xe), and radon (Rn). All the inert gases are found in small amounts in the atmosphere, with argon making up nearly 1 percent of the air and the others much less. Their scarcity and inactivity prevented their discovery until the very end of the nineteenth century. The common physical properties of the inert gases, outlined in Table 11.3, show the same general similarity and regular grada- tions with increasing atomic weight that we have found in the other groups.

Table 11.3. Properties of the inert gases.

Name	Symbol	Atomic weight	Density of liquid, 10^3 kg/m^3	Melting point, °C	Boiling point, °C
Helium	He	4.00	0.15	−272	−269
Neon	Ne	20.18	1.20	−249	−246
Argon	Ar	39.95	1.40	−189	−186
Krypton	Kr	83.80	2.16	−169	−152
Xenon	Xe	131.30	3.52	−140	−109
Radon	Rn	222	4.4	−110	−62

Valence

As we have seen, it is possible to classify elements according to whether they are active or inactive metals or active or inactive nonmetals. Further, there are apparently families of elements, all the members of each sharing certain properties that distinguish them from other families of elements. Closely related to these methods of sorting the elements into categories is a property the chemist calls *valence*. We shall describe briefly what valence is from the point of view of chemistry and why it is so useful, but for a true understand- ing of valence we must have a background in atomic structure, for which we must wait until Chap. 22. Here is another case where physics and chemistry overlap, for valence and its origin are important topics in both sciences.

We shall begin by defining the valence of a metal as follows: *The valence of a metal is equal to the number of chlorine atoms per metal atom in the formula for the chloride of that metal. The valence of a metal is labeled +*.

In terms of this definition, we can determine the valence of some of the metals we have already mentioned. The chlorides of the alkali metals, for instance, are

Lithium chloride	LiCl
Sodium chloride	NaCl
Potassium chloride	KCl
Rubidium chloride	RbCl
Cesium chloride	CsCl

The atoms of the alkali metals all combine with a single chlorine atom to form their respective chlorides, and so these metals all have the valence +1.

Barium, calcium, and magnesium, among other metals, form chlorides whose formulas are

Barium chloride	$BaCl_2$
Calcium chloride	$CaCl_2$
Magnesium chloride	$MgCl_2$

The atoms of these metals require two chlorine atoms each to form their respective chlorides, and so they all have the valence +2.

In the same way we find that aluminum and chromium have valences of +3, hafnium has the valence +4, and tantalum the valence +5. Some elements may have two or more valences, depending upon the specific circumstances surrounding the formation of their compounds; thus iron may have the valence +2, in which case its compounds are called *ferrous* [for example, ferrous chloride ($FeCl_2$)], or the valence +3, in which case its compounds are called *ferric* [for example, ferric chloride ($FeCl_3$)].

For nonmetals, valence is defined as follows: *The valence of a nonmetal is equal to the number of hydrogen atoms per nonmetal atom in the formula for the hydrogen compound of that nonmetal. The valence of a nonmetal is labeled −.*

The halogens, which form

Hydrogen fluoride	HF
Hydrogen chloride	HCl
Hydrogen bromide	HBr
Hydrogen iodide	HI

when combined with hydrogen, all have the valence −1. Oxygen, which forms the compound

| Water | H_2O |

with hydrogen, has the valence −2. Nitrogen, which forms the compound

| Ammonia | NH_3 |

with hydrogen, has the valence −3.

The inert gases, which form no compounds whatever, stand in a class by themselves, with the valence zero.

How Valence Is Applied

In formulas of simple compounds, *the total number of positive and negative valences must be equal.* This rule follows from the two definitions just given. In Na_2O, each sodium atom has a valence of +1, giving a total positive valence of 2, and the single oxygen atom supplies an equal negative valence of 2. In $AlBr_3$, the Al supplies a total positive valence of 3, and the three Br atoms (the valence of each is −1) supply an equal negative valence. By use of this rule, the valence of an unfamiliar element can be determined if the formula of any one of its simple compounds is known. Thus, if we know that the rare metal scandium forms the fluoride ScF_3, we need no further information about its chemical behavior to assign it a valence of $+3$, since a positive valence of 3 is necessary to equal the negative valence of 3 supplied by three fluorine atoms. Since scandium has a valence of 3, we should expect the formula of its chloride to be $ScCl_3$, its oxide to be Sc_2O_3, and so on. The idea of valence, therefore, supplies the information necessary to write the formula of a compound with correct subscripts when the name of the compound is given.

Formulas of more complex compounds can be written if the idea of valence is extended to atom groups. Since the nitrate group (NO_3) appears in the compound HNO_3, the group as a whole may be assigned a valence of -1, just as Br is assigned a valence of -1 from the formula HBr. Similarly, the formula H_2SO_4 suggests a valence of -2 for the sulfate group, the formula H_2CO_3 a valence of -2 for the carbonate group, the formula HOH (or H_2O) a valence of -1 for the hydroxide group. Corresponding to these valences we find the compounds $NaNO_3$, Na_2SO_4, Na_2CO_3, $NaOH$, $Ca(OH)_2$, $CaSO_4$, $Al_2(SO_4)_3$, $Al(NO_3)_2$, etc.

The importance of valence in classification is apparent from the constant valences in the three families of similar elements discussed: $+1$ for the alkali metals, -1 for the halogens, zero for the inert gases. Evidently, a characteristic valence links together elements of similar properties. As a basis for a general classification of the elements, however, valence has two drawbacks: (1) Some elements of very dissimilar properties have the same valence; for instance, the inactive metal silver shows the same valence as the alkali metals. (2) Some elements have two or more different valences; thus copper forms the two chlorides CuCl and $CuCl_2$, and iron, the two chlorides $FeCl_2$ and $FeCl_3$. We shall find that valence is indeed useful in the general classification, provided that these drawbacks are given due weight.

The concept of valence will be broadened later to include compounds of nonmetals with one another as well as their compounds with metals.

The Periodic Table

The periodic table of the elements is another of those great intellectual achievements that cannot be separated from the name of the man responsible for it. The planetary laws bring to mind Kepler; the laws of motion, Newton; the atomic theory, Dalton. The Russian Dmitri Ivanovich Mendeleev is similarly associated with the periodic table.

Mendeleev, who was born in Siberia, was for many years professor of chemistry at the University of St. Petersburg. He devoted himself to government service as well as to scientific work, although his outspoken liberal ideas were frequently embarrassing to the tsarist regime. Mendeleev was a gifted teacher, an able experimenter, but above all a dreamer, a scientific visionary. If some of his speculations seem fantastic, for one vision at least chemistry owes him a great debt, the vision that gave him the key to the classification of the elements.

The fact that some elements have strikingly similar properties was, of course, known long before Mendeleev's time. The grouping of elements according to valence became possible after 1860, when acceptance of Avogadro's hypothesis cleared away the difficulties in determining atomic weights and assigning formulas. What Mendeleev saw was that valence and other properties were related to atomic weight. In this vision he was not alone, for a few of his contemporaries reached the same conclusion independently; but Mendeleev was the first to apply it to all the known elements and to predict from it the existence of elements then unknown.

Following Mendeleev, but using our modern list of elements (Table 9.1) rather than the limited number that he knew, let us write down the elements in order of increasing atomic weight. First is hydrogen; then the inert gas helium; then the alkali metal lithium; then a rare metal called beryllium, less active than lithium, with a valence of $+2$; then boron, a relatively inactive nonmetal, which forms a chloride BCl_3; then carbon, a nonmetal that forms both CCl_4 and CH_4; then nitrogen, another nonmetal; then oxygen, a more active nonmetal; and fluorine, most active of all nonmetals. From lithium to fluorine is a complete transition from a highly active metal to a highly active nonmetal and a change in valence through positive values from $+1$ to $+4$, then through negative values from -4 to -1. After fluorine comes neon, another inert gas like helium; then sodium, an alkali metal like lithium. To suggest these resemblances, we break off the rows of elements at helium and fluorine and start new rows with lithium and sodium (Table 11.4). In the seven elements beyond neon, we find again a transition from active metals to active nonmetals and a change in valence like that of the first two rows.

After chlorine, in order of atomic weights, comes potassium, then argon, then calcium. Ending the third row with potassium would put this active metal under the inert gases helium and neon, and argon would go beneath sodium and lithium. To avoid this obvious discrepancy, we deliberately reverse the order for once, bringing argon before potassium.

After calcium, in the fourth row, more difficulties appear. Scandium, the next element, has the same valence as aluminum, but differs in other important properties. Titanium (Ti) is even less like carbon and silicon. Then follow 10 metals (including iron, copper, zinc), quite similar among themselves but differing conspicuously from the nonmetals at the end of the first three rows. Only after the 10 metals do three relatives of these nonmetals appear, arsenic (As), selenium (Se), and bromine. Thus, between the first inert gas (He) and the second (Ne) is a sequence of 8 elements; between neon and argon is another sequence of 8; but between argon and krypton the sequence includes 18. Beyond krypton is a second sequence of 18, including again a dozen metals of doubtful relationships. From xenon to the last inert gas, radon, is a yet more complex sequence of 32 elements.

Although the interval between similar elements changes in this peculiar manner, with a few reversals of order (for example, K and A), nevertheless this arrangement of elements does show a strikingly regular repetition of properties. *If the elements are listed in the (approximate) order of their atomic weights, elements with similar properties recur at definite intervals.* This is one way of stating Mendeleev's *periodic law.* A tabular arrangement, like Table 11.4, showing this recurrence of properties, is called a *periodic table.*

Most periodic tables show similar elements in vertical rows, called *columns,* or *groups,* of elements. The horizontal rows, containing elements with widely different properties, are called *periods.* Across each period is a more or less steady transition from an active metal to less active metals and weakly active nonmetals to highly active nonmetals and finally to an inert gas. Within each column there is also a steady change in properties, but much less rapid and less conspicuous than within the periods. Thus increasing atomic weight brings increasing activity in the alkali metal family and decreasing activity among the nonmetals of the halogen family. These changes are typical: Chemical properties within each group change from top to bottom in the direction of increased metallic activity or decreased nonmetallic activity, which amounts to the same thing.

A complete periodic table should display not only these major changes in properties but also the more subtle relationships among elements in the long periods. Many ingenious arrangements of the complete table have been suggested in order to show such relationships, but for present purposes the comparatively simple form of Table 11.4 is sufficiently informative. The 8 principal groups (indicated by Roman numerals at the top) form vertical columns, as usual. The inert gases (Group VIII) are placed at the right since this arrangement has the advantage of grouping them with the other nonmetals at the right side of the table. Each of the 8-element periods (Periods 2 and 3) is broken after the second element, in order to keep the elements in columns with the most closely related elements of the long periods below. The 10 *transition elements* in each long period are metals showing considerable chemical resemblance to one another but no pronounced resemblance to elements in the major groups. Period 6 contains 32 elements altogether, but 15 of these are taken out and placed in the box below the table; these *rare-earth metals* resemble one another very closely, so much so that their separation is a matter of extreme difficulty, and hence they are all lumped together in the spot (marked by an asterisk) below yttrium (Y). A similar group of closely related elements (the *actinide metals*) appears in the same position in Period 7, and these elements are shown with the rare earths in the box below the table. The position of the nonmetal hydrogen in Group I with the very active alkali metals seems odd but can be partly justified on the basis that the usual valence both of hydrogen and of the alkali metals is +1.

Relationships shown by the periodic table are rather vague in spots, but

Table 11.4. The periodic table of the elements.

The number above the symbol of each element is its atomic weight, and the number below the symbol is its atomic number. The elements whose atomic weights are given in parenthesis do not occur in nature, but have been prepared artificially in nuclear reactions. The atomic weight in such a case is the mass number of the most long-lived radioactive isotope of the element.

Period	I	II	III	IV	V	VI	VII	VIII
1	1.00 H 1							4.00 He 2
2	6.94 Li 3	9.01 Be 4	10.82 B 5	12.01 C 6	14.01 N 7	16.00 O 8	19.00 F 9	20.18 Ne 10
3	22.99 Na 11	24.31 Mg 12	26.98 Al 13	28.09 Si 14	30.98 P 15	32.07 S 16	35.46 Cl 17	39.94 Ar 18
4	39.10 K 19	40.08 Ca 20	44.96 Sc 21	47.90 Ti 22	50.94 V 23	52.00 Cr 24	54.94 Mn 25	55.85 Fe 26 / 58.93 Co 27 / 58.71 Ni 28
			63.54 Cu 29	65.37 Zn 30	69.72 Ga 31	72.59 Ge 32	74.92 As 33	78.96 Se 34 / 79.91 Br 35 / 83.8 Kr 36
5	85.47 Rb 37	87.62 Sr 38	88.91 Y 39	91.22 Zr 40	92.91 Nb 41	95.94 Mo 42	(99) Tc 43	101.1 Ru 44 / 102.91 Rh 45 / 106.4 Pd 46
			107.87 Ag 47	112.40 Cd 48	114.82 In 49	118.69 Sn 50	121.76 Sb 51	127.61 Te 52 / 126.90 I 53 / 131.30 Xe 54
6	132.91 Cs 55	137.34 Ba 56	*57–71	178.49 Hf 72	180.95 Ta 73	183.85 W 74	186.2 Re 75	190.2 Os 76 / 192.2 Ir 77 / 195.09 Pt 78
			196.97 Au 79	200.59 Hg 80	204.37 Tl 81	207.19 Pb 82	208.98 Bi 83	210 Po 84 / (210) At 85 / (222) Rn 86
7	(223) Fr 87	226.05 Ra 88	†89–103					

*Rare earths														
138.91 La 57	140.12 Ce 58	104.91 Pr 59	144.24 Nd 60	(147) Pm 61	150.35 Sm 62	151.96 Eu 63	157.25 Gd 64	158.92 Tb 65	162.50 Dy 66	164.93 Ho 67	167.26 Er 68	168.93 Tm 69	173.04 Yb 70	174.97 Lu 71

†Actinides														
(227) Ac 89	232.04 Th 90	(231) Pa 91	238.03 U 92	(237) Np 93	(242) Pu 94	(243) Am 95	(245) Cm 96	(249) Bk 97	(249) Cf 98	(253) Es 99	(255) Fm 100	(256) Md 101	(253) No 102	(257) Lw 103

on the whole the table brings together similar elements with great **accuracy**. Mendeleev's achievement seems all the more remarkable if we recall that in 1869, when the periodic law was discovered, only 63 elements were known. This meant that Mendeleev had to leave many gaps in his table of elements in order to make similar elements fall one under the other. Sure of the correctness of his classification, he predicted boldly that these gaps represented undiscovered elements. Further, from the position of each gap, from the properties of the elements around it, and from his knowledge of the variation of these properties across the periods and down the columns, he ventured to guess at the properties of the unknown elements. His guesses included not only predictions about the valence and general chemical activity, but precise numerical values for densities, melting points, etc. As the unknown elements were discovered one by one and as their properties were found to check Mendeleev's predictions with uncanny accuracy, the correctness and usefulness of the periodic classification became firmly established. Perhaps its greatest triumph came at the end of the century, when the inert gases were discovered: Here were six new elements whose existence Mendeleev could not have predicted, but they fitted perfectly, as one more family of similar elements, into the periodic table.

Today all gaps in the table have been filled. The usefulness of the periodic law in predicting new elements is past, but its usefulness in coordinating chemical knowledge is as great today as it was in Mendeleev's time. A chemist need not learn in detail the properties of all the elements, or even of a large proportion of them; if he knows thoroughly the chemical behavior of a few elements and if he knows how properties vary in the periods and groups of the periodic table, then for any other element he need only glance at its position in the table to infer its chief physical and chemical characteristics.

And the periodic table has a deeper significance. Like any successful classification, it not only shows the relationships on which it was based, but suggests further relationships. It exhibits complex relations among different elements; these must mean complex relations among different kinds of atoms. Differences and similarities of various sorts among atoms inevitably suggest that the atoms must have *structure*, must have parts whose form and arrangement are responsible for the differences and similarities. In the search for the structure of Dalton's indivisible atoms, the periodic law plays at once the roles of guide and arbiter, pointing out how the various structures must be related and serving as a check on any theory devised to picture them.

Self-examination

1. Of the following metals, the one least stable when exposed to air is
    a. sodium
    b. copper
    c. lead
    d. mercury

2. Of the following nonmetals, the one not a halogen is
    a. chlorine
    b. bromine
    c. sulfur
    d. iodine

3. Every simple chemical compound
    a. is either an acid or a base
    b. contains the same number of positive and negative valences
    c. is a member of the periodic table
    d. contains at least one hydrogen atom

4. The periodic table of the elements does *not*
    a. permit us to make accurate guesses of the properties of undiscovered elements
    b. reveal regularities in the occurrence of elements with similar properties
    c. include the inert gases
    d. tell us the arrangement of the atoms in a molecule

5. Atoms of two different elements
    a. may form no compounds together
    b. can form only one compound together
    c. can always form more than one compound together
    d. must have the same valence if they are to form a compound together

6. An important characteristic property of metals is
    a. their hardness
    b. their ability to conduct electricity readily
    c. their ability to form oxides
    d. the stability of their compounds

7. The nonmetal whose chemical behavior is most like that of typical metals is
    a. hydrogen
    b. helium
    c. chlorine
    d. carbon

8. The alkali metals all have valences of
    a. +2
    b. +1
    c. 0
    d. −1

Problems

1. Sodium never occurs in nature as the free element, and platinum seldom occurs in combination. How are these observations related to the chemical activities of the two metals?

2. From what physical and chemical characteristics of iron do we conclude that it is a metal? From what physical and chemical characteristics of sulfur do we conclude that it is a nonmetal?

3. From the following formulas, determine the valences of the underlined elements: $\underline{Cd}O$, $\underline{As}H_3$, $\underline{U}O_2$, $\underline{Cr}Cl_3$, $\underline{Pb}(OH)_2$, $\underline{Ni}(NO_3)_2$, $Na_2\underline{Si}O_3$.

4. What are the valences of the underlined atom groups in the formulas that follow? $Na_2\underline{SiO_3}$, $K_2\underline{CrO_4}$, $\underline{NH_4}Cl$, $Cu(\underline{NH_3})_4SO_4$.

5. The element astatine (At), which appears at the bottom of the halogen column in the periodic table, has been prepared artificially in minute amounts but has not been found in nature. Using the periodic law and your knowledge of the halogens, predict the properties of this element, as follows:
   a. At room temperature, is it solid, liquid, or gaseous?
   b. How many atoms does a molecule of its vapor contain?
   c. Is it very soluble, moderately soluble, or slightly soluble in water?
   d. What is the formula of its compound with hydrogen?
   e. What are the formulas for its compounds with potassium and calcium?
   f. What is its approximate atomic weight?
   g. Is its compound with potassium more or less stable than potassium iodide?

6. The following metals are listed in order of increasing chemical activity: potassium, sodium, calcium, magnesium. How does this order agree with their positions in the periodic table? Where would you place cesium in the above list?

7. Write formulas for aluminum oxide, magnesium iodide, lithium carbonate, calcium sulfide, sodium nitride, rubidium hydroxide, potassium sulfate, and barium nitrate.

Part III

ELECTRICITY
AND MAGNETISM

CHAPTER 12 | ELECTRICITY

The kinetic theory assumes that all matter is made up of tiny moving particles. In gases, the particles are far apart and attract each other only to a negligible extent; in liquids, the attraction between them is great enough to keep the particles close together but not to prevent their moving about; in solids, the particles are held so firmly that their motion is restricted to vibrations about fixed positions. An increase in temperature leads to the faster motion of the particles, and so to a tendency for them to disperse in spite of their mutual attractions. In terms of these particles and the simple forces between them, such diverse phenomena as boiling, freezing, the expansion of gases, and the flow of liquids find reasonable explanation. Thus the kinetic theory introduces order and simplicity into the apparently complex behavior of ordinary materials.

Like Newton's picture of the solar system, the kinetic theory is a *mechanical* explanation, an explanation depending on the motion of objects that exert simple forces on each other. In the solar system the objects are planets and satellites; in ordinary matter, they are molecules. So successful were these two applications of mechanical ideas that nineteenth-century scientists looked eagerly for similar explanations in other fields. Some physicists ventured to predict that presently all natural phenomena would be interpreted by means of particles and forces acting between them—not only other phenomena in physics, but chemical reactions and even biological processes. Attainment of such a goal would satisfy the philosophical urge to find an underlying simplicity and order throughout the universe and, in the practical world, would make possible the prediction and control of all manner of processes desirable for human welfare.

But in the nineteenth century that goal was still distant. In chemical processes certain basic principles had been recognized—that all matter is made up of a limited number of elements, that each element consists of tiny particles, that the particles or atoms of different elements are somehow related by the periodic law—but these principles provided no basis for a mechanical explanation. Little was known about the motions of atoms, and the forces which bound them together in molecules remained a subject for speculation. Moreover, the intricate relationships among different atoms brought out by the periodic law seemed to hint that these were not simple particles, but particles which themselves must have complex structures.

Similarly other branches of physics, in particular those concerned with light, electricity, and magnetism, did not lend themselves readily to mechanical interpretation. These subjects had been under investigation since the time of Galileo, but rapid progress came only in the nineteenth century. Attempts to apply mechanical ideas were successful only to a minor extent, a situation still true; a more sophisticated and subtle approach is needed.

In the chapters to follow we shall take up the study of electromagnetic phenomena. With this information in hand we shall cross the threshold that divides "classical" from "modern" physical science and, after exploring the atom and its nucleus, go on to obtain new insights into the world of chemistry. The next few chapters, then, do not represent any real change in the continuity of our exploration of nature. In fact, it is in a way remarkable that we have so far been able to proceed without referring to electricity and magnetism, since these related phenomena are among the chief factors all the way from the minute realm of the atom to the immense realm of the nebulae (which are "island universes" of stars). Electricity and magnetism also have very practical applications, of course; it is hard to conceive of our modern civilization without electric lights, electric motors, electrical communication. We shall find much to interest us in this branch of physics.

Electric Charge

Comb your hair with a hard rubber comb on a day when the air is dry; you will find that your hair crackles, and its loose ends are attracted by the comb. If you stand before a mirror in a darkened room when you do this, you will see tiny sparks jump from the comb to your hair. An even more striking effect of this kind takes place when a rubber rod is rubbed vigorously with a piece of cat's fur. The rod not only produces sizable sparks but also is able to attract and pick up small bits of paper and cloth.

The first recorded investigator of this behavior was Thales of Miletus, a Greek philosopher who lived about 600 B.C. Lacking rubber, Thales experimented with amber, in his language *electron*. We immortalize his work by saying that amber (or hard rubber) rubbed with fur possesses an *electric charge*, by which we mean simply that it is capable of producing a spark and attracting small light objects.

Let us examine the behavior of electric charges more carefully. We begin by suspending a small pith ball from a silk thread, to serve as an indicator of charges in its vicinity. If touched with a rubber rod that has been stroked with fur, the pith ball jerks violently away and, thereafter, is strongly repelled whenever the rod is brought near (Fig. 12.1). We assume that the pith ball had no electric charge at the beginning of the experiment; at the instant of contact with the rod the ball acquired some of the charge on the rod and in this charged condition is repelled by the rod.

Now we bring near the same pith ball a glass rod that has been rubbed with silk. The ball is no longer repelled, but strongly attracted (Fig. 12.1). With the ball in this condition, therefore, the charge of the rubber rod repels it and the glass rod attracts it. Next we try the experiment in reverse and charge a second pith ball by touching it with the glass rod. It bounds away, evidently repelled. But the charged rubber rod attracts this second ball strongly.

We can draw only one conclusion: The charges on the two rods are somehow different. Furthermore, the kind of charge on one rod attracts the kind on the other, but each rod repels an object that has some of its own kind of charge. More simply, *like charges repel each other, unlike charges attract each other*.

Comprehensive experiments show that all electric charges that can be produced fall into one or the other of the two types described above; that is, they behave as though they originated on a rubber rod rubbed with fur or

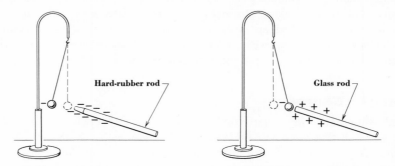

Fig. 12.1 *A pith ball touched by a rubber rod that has been stroked with cat fur is repelled by the rod. When a glass rod that has been stroked with silk cloth is brought near, however, the pith ball is attracted to it. Performing the experiment in the reverse order has the same effect; hence the conclusion that like charges repel each other, unlike charges attract each other.*

else on a glass rod rubbed with silk, regardless of their actual origin. Benja-min Franklin suggested names for these two basic kinds of electricity. He called the charge produced on a rubber rod rubbed with fur *negative charge;* the charge produced on a glass rod rubbed with silk *positive charge.* These definitions are the ones we follow today.

We have concentrated our attention on the positive charge of the glass, the negative charge of the rubber. However, we do not produce a positive charge alone by rubbing glass with silk or a negative charge alone by stroking rubber with fur. If the fur used with the rubber is brought near a positively charged pith ball, the ball is repelled; if the fur is brought near a negatively charged ball, the ball is attracted. Thus the fur must have a positive charge. Similarly, the silk used with the glass has a negative charge. In general, when electricity is produced by contact between two dissimilar objects, one acquires a positive charge and the other a negative charge, the distribution of charge depending on the nature of the two substances used.

Conductors and Insulators

Although pith balls are very convenient for simple experiments in electricity, they are hardly quantitative tools for the physicist. Somewhat better is an *electroscope,* a device consisting of two leaves of thin metal foil suspended from a metal support inside a glass-walled box (Fig. 12.2). A charge of either kind applied to the metal support spreads itself over the leaves; charged with the same kind of electricity, they fly apart, the distance apart depending roughly on the amount of the charge.

Let us use the electroscope to study the motion of electric charges from one place to another. Our experiments have already shown that charges can move. For example, when a pith ball was touched with an electrified rubber rod, part of the charge on the rod went over to the ball. Suppose

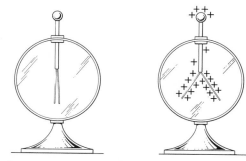

Fig. 12.2   An electroscope. *When the electroscope is uncharged its leaves hang freely, but when it is charged they fly apart because of their mutual repulsion.*

that we place an electroscope a foot or so from a charged object, say a large metal sphere, and that we connect the sphere and the metal of the electroscope with rods or wires of different materials (Fig. 12.3). If a copper wire is laid between them, the leaves of the electroscope fly apart at once. With about equal readiness a charge is transferred from sphere to electroscope by wires of other metals. But if connection is made with a dry glass rod or a silk thread or a piece of dry wood, the electroscope is scarcely affected. In other words, the ability of electric charge to pass from sphere to electroscope depends on the nature of the material making the connection. Materials like iron or copper, which carry charge readily, we call *conductors*. Materials like glass or dry wood or hard rubber, through which charges move with difficulty, we call *insulators*.

A perfect conductor would be a substance along which charges could pass with no resistance to their motion, and a perfect insulator would be a substance through which no electric charge could be forced. No substance of either type is known. We find good conductors like copper and good insulators like rubber and silk, but these fall far short of perfection. Between good conductors and good insulators can be listed a great variety of substances along which charges move with more or less difficulty. A few of these intermediate substances may be considered either insulators or conductors, depending on circumstances; there is no sharp line between the two.

Ordinary air is a very poor conductor. If two strong opposite charges are brought close together, however, the air between them may momentarily become a good conductor. The air molecules become violently agitated, in a manner we shall describe later, and the charges are able to leap across the gap. This type of sudden discharge is an *electric spark*. After the spark, unless the two charges are continuously renewed, the air reverts quickly to its normal nonconducting state.

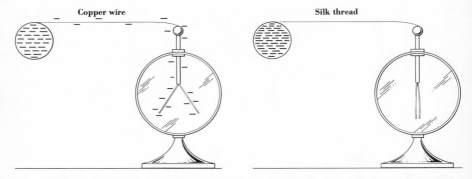

Fig. 12.3 *Copper wire is able to conduct an electric charge readily from one place to another, while silk thread cannot. Copper is an example of a* conductor, *and silk an example of an* insulator.

The conductivity of pure water is extremely small. But traces of dissolved impurities increase the conductivity enormously; since most water we use in daily life is somewhat impure, we usually think of it as a fair conductor. On humid days solids exposed to the atmosphere become coated with an invisible film of water, which makes even good insulators capable of conducting charges appreciably. Experiments with electric charges are difficult in humid weather, since the water films on insulators enable charges to leak away from pith balls and electroscopes; even in dry weather, experiments are improved if insulating materials are heated or rubbed with alcohol to remove adhering water molecules.

The earth as a whole, at least that part of it beneath the outer dry soil, is a fairly good conductor. Hence, if a charged object is connected with the earth by a piece of metal, the charge is conducted away from the object to the earth. This convenient method of removing the charge from an object is called *grounding* the object. You ground your radio by attaching the appropriate wire to a gas or water pipe (which is connected to other pipes below the surface), thereby giving electric charges in the radio a path to the ground. Ground connections for radios or lightning rods must be carefully made, using metal all the way, but for rough experiments with small electric charges the connection is sufficiently good if a person simply touches a charged object with his finger. The charge travels through his body, through the floor or the walls of the building, to water pipes or directly to the ground.

The human body is not a good conductor—a fortunate circumstance, for otherwise we should be shocked more frequently and more severely. But charges can easily be produced in the laboratory that can be very painful if allowed to move through the body to the ground. When properly insulated from the ground, however, say by standing on a plate of glass or on a platform supported by glass or rubber insulators, a person can be given a considerable charge, large enough to make separate hairs stand out away from each other and to make tiny sparks jump from his finger tips, without any unpleasant sensation. The charge is dangerous only when it can actually move through the body.

The readiness of charges to move to the ground, either through the air or through solid supports, makes exact experimentation difficult. Small charges tend to leak off slowly; even a pith ball, hung from a silk thread in dry air, will not maintain a charge indefinitely. Larger charges may find their way to the ground by sparking unless sufficient insulation is provided.

Thus far we have said nothing about the actual nature of the electric charge. What really happens in a conductor when we say that a charge is moving from one point to another? Modern physics can answer this question fairly satisfactorily, and we shall study its answer in succeeding chapters. But the men who developed our knowledge of electricity to the point where an answer was possible worked with only a hazy notion of what electricity in motion actually was. Something moved from one object to another. The only remotely comparable motion in their experience was the motion of substances like liquids and gases. So, quite naturally, they called electricity a "fluid."

At first two kinds of electric fluid were assumed. Benjamin Franklin proposed an alternative explanation: that there is only one kind of fluid (positive), that all objects normally possess a certain amount of the fluid, and that a positive charge represents an excess of fluid and a negative charge a deficiency. Practical electricians to this day use Franklin's hypothesis, regarding electric currents as a movement of positive "juice" from one place to another. In the two centuries since Franklin's time, however, we have learned that the nature of electricity is actually not this simple. Charges are made up of tiny particles rather than a continuous fluid, and the particles may be of many different kinds, both positive and negative. The most familiar kind of electricity in motion, the kind that flows in wires and operates our lights and heaters and household gadgets, consists largely of tiny negative particles called *electrons*. The electricity that moves through gases and liquids and the electric charges that accumulate on pith balls and electroscopes may involve particles with both positive and negative signs. Movement of the tiny particles may still be likened to the movement of a fluid, and for many purposes this picture remains a useful one; but details of the movement are much more complicated than Franklin imagined.

Coulomb's Law

Before proceeding to the modern treatment of electricity, let us study electric charges quantitatively in an experiment that requires no knowledge of their properties except that they attract and repel one another. The repulsive force between a rubber rod stroked with fur and a negatively charged pith ball evidently depends on two things: how close the pith ball is to the rod and how much charge each possesses. The influence of these two factors can be shown by noting (1) that the pith ball is not affected by the rod when it is some distance away but is increasingly repelled the closer the rod is brought, and (2) that an increased charge produced by more rapid stroking of the rod with fur makes the repulsion stronger (Fig. 12.4). A third factor is involved which we shall neglect, the influence of the air between the two charges. If the air were replaced by some other gas or a liquid or were removed altogether, the repulsive force would be different.

The repulsive force between two objects of like sign is greater the smaller the distance between them. If the two objects are 2 cm apart, the force between them is one-fourth as great as if they are 1 cm apart and four times as great as when they are 4 cm apart (these relationships are exact only when the objects are very small compared with the distance between them). In other words, doubling the distance between the objects quarters the force

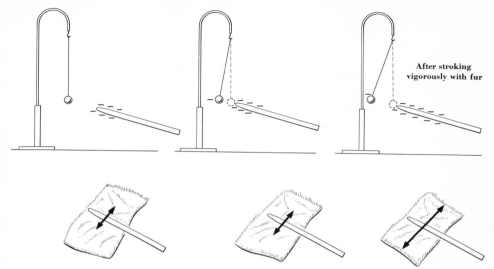

Fig. 12.4 *When a rubber rod that has been stroked with fur is brought near a negatively charged pith ball, the force on the ball is greater when the rod is held close to it and also greater when the rod has been vigorously stroked.*

between them, tripling the distance decreases the force ninefold, and so forth. Between force and distance there is evidently an inverse relationship: *As the distance increases, the force decreases as its square.*

We have not yet specified any way of determining the amount of charge on an object. One way of doing this requires two insulated spheres of the same size and composition. We give one of them a charge, any charge we please; the amount does not matter. Then we bring them in contact and make the reasonable assumption that the charge distributes itself equally over the two. By separating them we provide ourselves with two charges known to be equal. Now we bring one sphere near to a third charged object, say at a distance of 1 m, and measure the force between them. Next we put the two spheres together at the same distance from the third object, and again measure the force. We find that the force is just twice as great (Fig. 12.5). It looks as if the force is directly proportional to amount of charge; we can verify this by obtaining other spheres identical with the first two, giving them all equal charges by letting them come in contact, and testing their effect in various combinations on the third object. Also, we could duplicate the third object and see how doubling its charge affects the force. We should find that *the force is proportional to each of the charges.*

Now we are in a position to state in mathematical terms exactly how the force between two charges depends upon the magnitudes of the charges and upon the distance between them. We have already used the symbols F

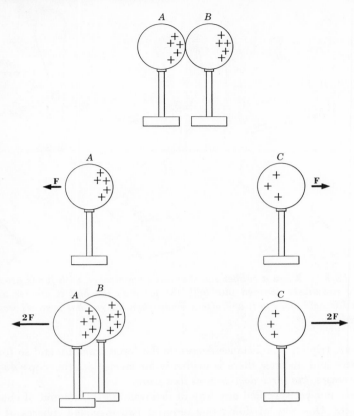

Fig. 12.5 *The force between charged bodies is proportional to the product of the charges.*

for force and d for distance; electric charges are usually denoted by the letter q, and if we have more than one, we distinguish them by calling one of them q_1, another q_2, and so on. On the basis of the experiments described in the preceding paragraphs, the force between two charges of magnitudes q_1 and q_2 that are separated by the distance d is

$$F = K \frac{q_1 q_2}{d^2} \qquad (12.1)$$

where K is a constant of proportionality whose numerical value depends upon the units in which we measure the charges. Equation (12.1), called *Coulomb's law,* is a shorthand way of expressing the fact that the force between the two charges q_1 and q_2 depends directly upon the magnitudes of q_1 and q_2 and inversely on the square of the distance d between them. The larger the charge values, the greater the force, and the larger the separation, the smaller the force.   When the charges have the same sign—both positive or both negative—the force is repulsive, tending to push the charges apart, and when the charges have opposite signs—one positive and the other negative—the force is attractive, tending to pull the charges together.

The modern unit of charge is the *coulomb*, named in honor of Charles Coulomb (1736–1806), who developed the above equation.   With q_1 and q_2 expressed in coulombs, the constant K is almost exactly 9×10^9 newton-m^2/ coul^2.   Thus we may rewrite Coulomb's law

$$F = 9 \times 10^9 \, \frac{q_1 q_2}{d^2} \qquad\qquad (12.2)$$

where the force F is expressed in *newtons* and the distance d in *meters*, the metric units for these quantities.

Coulomb's law for the force between charges is one of the fundamental laws of physics, in the same category as Newton's law of gravitation.   The latter, as we know, is written in mathematical form as

$$F = G \, \frac{m_1 m_2}{d^2}$$

Coulomb's law and the law of gravitation are remarkably similar, but they have one important difference: Gravitational forces are always attractive, tending to draw the objects involved together, but electric forces may be either attractive or repulsive.

Let us elaborate a significant consequence of this last fact.   Because one lump of matter always attracts another lump, however feebly, matter in the universe as a general rule tends to assemble into large masses.   Even though dispersive forces of various kinds exist, they must contend with this steady attraction; the stars and planets, which modern theories indicate to have condensed from originally diffuse matter, bear witness to this cosmic herd instinct.   And, on a terrestrial scale, we can pile up as large a pyramid as we like with rather primitive means.   To collect a significant electric charge of either sign, however, is far more of a feat.   Charges of opposite sign attract each other strongly, so it is hard to separate neutral matter into differently charged portions.   And charges of the same sign repel each other, so even if the charge separation is performed a little at a time, the assembly of charges of one sign is difficult to manage.

To sum up the above argument, we might say that a system of neutral particles is most stable (that is, has a minimum potential energy) when the particles make up a single solid body, while a system of electric charges is most stable when charges of opposite sign pair off to cancel each other out. Hence, on a cosmic scale, gravitational forces are significant and electric ones are not; no single charge can be very great before it attracts others of opposite sign and starts to be torn apart by internal repulsion.   On an atomic scale, however, the reverse is true.   The masses of subatomic particles are too small for them to interact gravitationally to any appreciable extent, while their electric charges, though minute, are still enough for electric forces to exert marked effects.

The hydrogen atom serves to illustrate the above statement. As we shall learn, it consists of two particles, a *proton* (mass 1.7×10^{-27} kg, charge $+1.6 \times 10^{-19}$ coul) and an *electron* (mass 9.1×10^{-31} kg, charge -1.6×10^{-19} coul), whose mean separation is 5.3×10^{-11} m. The gravitational force of attraction between the proton and electron is

$$
\begin{aligned}
F_{\text{grav}} &= G \frac{m_p m_e}{r^2} \\
&= \frac{6.7 \times 10^{-11} \text{ newton-m}^2/\text{kg}^2 \times 1.7 \times 10^{-27} \text{ kg} \times 9.1 \times 10^{-31} \text{ kg}}{(5.3 \times 10^{-11} \text{ m})^2} \\
&= 3.7 \times 10^{-47} \text{ newton}
\end{aligned}
$$

The electric force of attraction is

$$
\begin{aligned}
F_{\text{elec}} &= K \frac{q_p q_e}{r^2} \\
&= \frac{9 \times 10^9 \text{ newton-m}^2/\text{coul}^2 \times 1.6 \times 10^{-19} \text{ coul} \times 1.6 \times 10^{-19} \text{ coul}}{(5.3 \times 10^{-11} \text{ m})^2} \\
&= 8.1 \times 10^{-8} \text{ newton}
\end{aligned}
$$

which is more than 10^{39} times greater! Clearly, gravitational effects are negligible within atoms as compared with electrical effects.

Fields of Force

We are so familiar with gravitational, electric, and magnetic forces that they do not excite astonishment, yet if we really examine their natures, it is hard to repress a feeling of wonder. Unlike other common forces, they act upon other objects without actual contact being made across the intervening space. We cannot move a book from a table by merely waving our hand at it; a golf ball will not move from its tee, however violent our exertions, until the golf club actually strikes it. But a charged pith ball does not wait until a charged glass rod touches it, but somehow "senses" the presence of the rod while it is still some distance away. Remove the air, place rod and ball in the most perfect vacuum attainable, and the force is not diminished. The two react on each other without benefit of anything that our senses can detect. For the pith ball the region near the rod is somehow different from other space, since in this space it is impelled to move. Near any electric charge is such a region of altered space. A magnet, also, though in a different way, changes the space around it, so that material of the proper sort is acted on by a force, and as we know, every mass causes around it an alteration in space that re-sults in an attractive force on any other masses in the vicinity.

What precisely is meant by an "alteration in space," and how do the various kinds of such alterations differ from one another? Is there any relationship among these various kinds of alteration; that is, are gravitational, electric, and magnetic forces in some way connected? These questions, which occur very naturally, have troubled scientists for many centuries. The chief source of difficulty has been the inability of most people's imaginations to conceive of what we call space—which we regard as emptiness, the complete absence of matter—as being capable of being altered. After all, how can *nothing* be altered?

But the facts of the matter are that as long as we are able to express mathematically just how forces act without the participating bodies actually touching one another (as we have already done in Newton's law of gravitation and Coulomb's law of electric forces and as we shall do in Chap. 14 for magnetic forces), we have no real need for a mental image of what is happening. To be sure, it is always helpful to be able to visualize what is going on in a physical process, but if we are honest, we must admit that most of our mental pictures are surely not accurate. Consider a bat striking a ball: Both bat and ball are made up of individual particles rather far apart from one another—just how do these particles interact when the ball is struck by the bat? Why do not the particles of the ball and bat, which have so much space in between, simply mesh together into a single object? When this problem is analyzed in detail, we find that it is the action of these peculiar electric and magnetic forces on the molecular level that produces the observed transfer of energy and momentum from the bat to the ball. But as long as we can describe phenomena quantitatively in terms of mathematical equations, we have as much information about these phenomena as we need. Mental pictures, however desirable, are not really required by the working scientist.

The region of altered space around a mass, an electric charge, or a magnet is called a *field of force*. Strictly speaking, a field of force extends to infinite distances in all directions, since a mass, a charge, or a magnet presumably exerts a force everywhere in the universe. But practically, the force becomes negligible at a relatively short distance from the exciting object, and by its field of force we ordinarily mean the space immediately adjacent to the object, the space in which its force is perceptible.

The *electric field intensity* **E** at any point in space is so defined as to equal numerically the force that it would exert on a positive charge of 1 coul located there. If a charge q is at that point, the force **F** it experiences is given by

$$\mathbf{F} = q\mathbf{E} \tag{12.3}$$

Electric field intensity is a vector quantity with both magnitude and direction; the direction of **E**, as we can see from the above equation, is that of the force on a positive charge. The units of electric field intensity are newtons per coulomb.

Lines of Force

Fields of force are recognized by the tendency of appropriate bodies in them to move; accordingly, we define their intensities in terms of forces. Let us now try to describe a field pictorially in terms of the ideal behavior of a small test particle (a mass in a gravitational field, a charge in an electric field) in it, neglecting such perturbations as friction, air resistance, and so on. For example, we might want to envision the electric field about a positively charged metal sphere. If we put a negative charge in the field, it will move in a straight line toward the sphere, while a positive charge will move away from the sphere. The paths in either case are straight lines radiating out from the center of the sphere (Fig. 12.6). Conventionally, we consider the direction of motion of a *positive* charge and indicate this motion by placing outward-pointing arrows on the lines. A negatively charged sphere will have a field of the same shape, but its lines will be directed inward.

Consider now the field near two adjacent charges, one positive and the other negative. Here again we inquire into how a small charge will move. Between the charges it will move directly from the positive one toward the negative one; off to one side, repelled by one and attracted by the other, it will move in a curved path (Fig. 12.7).

Fields of magnetic or gravitational force may be similarly described. The lines used to describe a field—gravitational, magnetic, or electric—are called *lines of force*. Although purely fictitious, lines of force enable us to visualize how an object will tend to move in any path of a field. Where many lines are close together, the field is strong; where they spread apart, the field is weak. Note that lines of force cannot cross or branch and can end only on one of the exciting objects or at infinity.

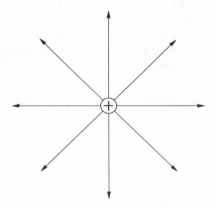

Fig. 12.6   *The lines of force about an isolated positive charge are radial lines whose direction is outward from the charge.*

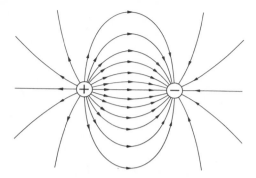

Fig. 12.7   Lines of force around nearby electric charges. *Each line of force represents the path that would be taken by a positive charge.*

But convenient as lines of force are in the study of electricity and magnetism, they are purely descriptive. They tell us what will happen in the field, but not what the field is or exactly how it affects the properties of empty space.

Self-examination

1. The modern unit of electric charge is the
    a. electron volt
    b. coulomb
    c. newton per square meter
    d. ion

2. An electroscope is a device
    a. for generating electric charge
    b. for producing sparks
    c. for determining the magnitude of a charge
    d. that magnifies electrons so that they are visible

3. A positive electric charge
    a. attracts other positive charges
    b. repels other positive charges
    c. does not interact with other positive charges but only with negative ones
    d. consists of an excess of electrons

4. A positive and a negative charge are initially 4 cm apart. When they are moved closer together so that they are now only 1 cm apart, the force between them is
    a. 4 times smaller than before

    b. 4 times larger than before

    c. 8 times larger than before

    d. 16 times larger than before

5. An electron is placed a certain distance from a positive charge, and the force of attraction between them is measured. Another electron is brought up and placed next to the first electron. The force on the positive charge

    a. does not change

    b. is half as large as before

    c. is twice as large as before

    d. is four times as large as before

6. Coulomb's law for the force between electric charges most closely resembles

    a. the law of conservation of energy

    b. Newton's second law of motion

    c. Newton's law of gravitation

    d. the law of conservation of mass

7. An electric current consists of

    a. a succession of tiny sparks

    b. a flow of electrically charged fluid

    c. a flow of electrically charged particles

    d. a flow of atoms or molecules

8. Lines of force are

    a. invisible elastic strands that connect positive and negative charges

    b. the strings used to support pith balls in electrostatic experiments

    c. imaginary lines used to represent the paths that might be taken by particles moving freely in a field of force

    d. applicable solely to electric fields

Problems

1. Describe simple experiments that demonstrate that there are two kinds of electricity and no more.

2. Describe what happens when a positively charged electroscope is touched with

    a. a rubber rod that has been stroked with fur

    b. a glass rod that has been rubbed with silk

3. How could you charge an electroscope negatively with only the help of a positively charged object?

4. In the eighteenth century both heat and electricity were thought to be weightless fluids. To what extent is this still a useful notion? What experimental evidence in each case indicates that this hypothesis is inadequate?

5. Compare the gravitational attraction between two electrons a distance 10^{-10} m apart with their electrostatic repulsion. Which type of force would you expect to be most important in atomic phenomena?

6. A charge of $+3 \times 10^{-9}$ coul is located 0.5 m from a charge of -5×10^{-9} coul. What is the magnitude and direction of the force between them?

7. Two small spheres are given identical positive charges. When they are 1 cm apart the repulsive force between them is 0.002 newton. What would the force be if
   a. the distance is increased to 3 cm?
   b. one charge is doubled?
   c. both charges are tripled?
   d. one charge is doubled and the distance is increased to 2 cm?

8. Explain why lines of force can never cross one another.

9. List the similarities and differences between electric and gravitational fields.

10. How do we know that the force holding the earth in its orbit about the sun is not an electric force, since both gravitational and electric forces vary inversely with the square of the distance between centers of force?

11. (*a*) A metal sphere with a charge of $+1 \times 10^{-5}$ coul is 10 cm from another metal sphere with a charge of -2×10^{-5} coul. Find the magnitude of the attractive force between the spheres. (*b*) The two spheres are brought in contact and again separated by 10 cm. Find the magnitude of the new force between the spheres.

12. Find the electric field intensity 40 cm from a charge of $+7 \times 10^{-6}$ coul.

13. A particle of mass 10^{-6} kg is suspended in equilibrium by an electric field of 9.8 newtons/coul intensity. Find the magnitude of the charge on the particle.

14. (*a*) Find the force acting on a particle of charge 10^{-5} coul when it is in an electric field of intensity 50 newtons/coul. (*b*) If the particle is released from rest in this field, what will its kinetic energy be after it has traveled 1 m?

CHAPTER 13 | ELECTRICITY AND MATTER

On the gross level of our personal experience, matter and electric charge both are continuous, apparently capable of being subdivided into smaller and smaller bits without limit. As we have learned, the contrary is true of matter: There is another level, beyond the direct reach of our senses, where matter would be revealed as aggregates of atoms, distinct building blocks which cannot be further fragmented by ordinary means. Electric charge, too, has a microscopic structure, whose basic unit, both positive and negative, is 1.6×10^{-19} coul, a quantity known familiarly to scientists as e. This charge always appears associated with specific particles, notably the electron ($q = -e$) and the proton ($q = +e$), and all charges are multiples of this fundamental quantity. In this chapter we shall be introduced to the evidence for e and to some of the electrical phenomena in matter that are consequences of the quantization of charge.

Cathode Rays

In the repertory of physics demonstrations, few experiments are more spectacular than an exhibition of cathode rays. On the lecture table is a long glass tube, with a small metal disk sealed into each end (Fig. 13.1). A side tube is connected with a vacuum pump. The room is darkened, and the experimenter throws a switch, giving one metal disk a strong positive charge, the other a strong negative charge. Nothing is visible yet except a faint glow at each end of the tube, since too much air separates the charges for a spark to jump between them. Now the vacuum pump is turned on, slowly reducing the air pressure in the tube. Suddenly a bright discharge leaps between the metal disks, like a long spark but wider and more diffuse, at first branching, irregular, dancing from side to side. Widening as the air pressure falls, the discharge becomes a wavering, purplish column filling the tube completely. Now the pressure has dropped to less than 1 mm of mercury (less than a thousandth of normal atmospheric pressure): The purple column breaks near one end, the dark gap grows wider, and soon the tube is once more nearly invisible. Still the pump pulls traces of air from the tube, reducing its pressure to 0.001 mm or less. Now at last, on the walls of the tube opposite the negative disk, appears a greenish glow, faint at first, but spreading and brightening until much of the glass is softly luminous. The interior of the tube remains dark, but the green radiance of the glass shows that the tube is filled with the invisible and once-mysterious *cathode rays*.

Electric discharges in tubes of this sort attracted the serious attention of physicists in the 1870s, but not until 1897 was the green glow of the glass at very low pressures explained. Discovery of the true nature of cathode rays we owe to many workers, in this country and in Europe, but one name stands out above the rest, that of the great English physicist J. J. Thomson. With Thomson's work on cathode rays begins that extraordinary scientific development we call *modern physics*.

The Electron

The two metal disks of the evacuated tube are called its *electrodes,* a general term applied to any pair of adjacent conductors on which unlike charges are maintained. The negative electrode is named the *cathode;* the positive one, the *anode.* Cathode rays are so named because they stream from the negative metal plate. We can demonstrate that they originate in the cathode by using a tube equipped with an opaque object that can be set before the negative electrode; the object is silhouetted sharply against the green glow at the far end of the tube (Fig. 13.2), showing that the invisible rays in this direction have been blocked off.

Opinion was divided in the early days of cathode-ray experimentation,

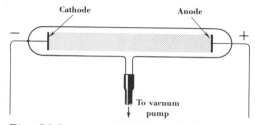

Fig. 13.1   *A cathode-ray discharge tube.*

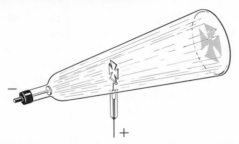

**Fig. 13.2   A cathode-ray discharge tube with an obstruction in
the path of the rays.** *This experiment demonstrates that the rays originate in the cathode, or negative terminal, of the tube.*

one group maintaining that the radiation was a form of invisible light; the
other group, that the radiation consisted of material particles.   Experiments
designed to settle the issue brought out many properties of the mysterious
rays.   Under their influence not only glass but many other substances glow
softly, or *fluoresce*.   Experiments showing that obstacles in the path of the
rays produce sharp shadows proved that the radiation travels approximately
in straight lines.   The rays can be focused on a point by using a cathode
with a concave surface, somewhat as light is focused by a concave mirror.
A piece of platinum placed at the point where the rays converge quickly
becomes red hot, proving that the cathode radiation carries considerable
energy.   All these properties could be explained satisfactorily either by supposing that the rays consisted of particles or by supposing that they were
akin to ordinary light.

     But other experiments favored the particle hypothesis.   Most convincing
were experiments showing that the rays carry an electric charge.   One way
to show this is to make a tube with a second pair of metal disks sealed into
its side, so that the cathode rays must pass between them (Fig. 13.3).   When

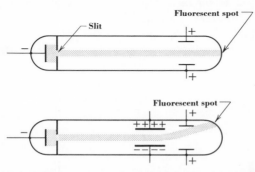

**Fig. 13.3   A beam of cathode rays is repelled by a negative charge and
attracted by a positive one, evidence that these rays consist of negatively
charged particles.**

these disks are given opposite charges, the greenish fluorescence caused by the rays moves from its position at the end of the tube to a spot on the side, as if the rays had been deflected. The direction of the deflection indicates that the rays are repelled by the negative charge and attracted by the positive charge, in other words, that the rays themselves are negatively charged. No radiation like light has ever been found to carry a charge, so this property is good evidence that cathode rays consist of moving particles. These tiny particles, each possessing a minute charge of negative electricity, are *electrons.*

The early years of this century saw an extensive program of careful experiments to measure the properties of the electron. The British physicist J. J. Thomson was able to determine accurately the ratio q/m between the charge and mass of individual electrons by observing the deflection of a beam of electrons in an ingenious combination of electric and magnetic fields. His figure was

$$\frac{q}{m} = 1.76 \times 10^{11} \text{ coul/kg}$$

a relatively high one: A gram of electrons placed 1 cm away from another gram would be repelled by a force of over 10^{26} tons! This information firmly established the particle nature of cathode rays, since electrons have mass, but it did not, by itself, demonstrate that all electrons are alike.

The final step in the "discovery" of the electron was taken by an American, Robert A. Millikan, in his famous oil-drop experiment. As shown in Fig. 13.4, Millikan sprayed a mist of fine oil drops between a pair of electrodes. Friction between the drops and the atomizer nozzle caused many of the drops to become electrically charged. Connecting the plates to a battery charged them oppositely, producing a uniform electric field E. Then, adjusting the magnitude and direction of this field, the electric force

$$F = qE \tag{13.1}$$

that it exerts on an oil drop carrying the charge q could be made to precisely counterbalance the weight of the drop,

$$W = Mg \tag{13.2}$$

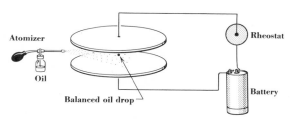

Fig. 13.4   The Millikan oil-drop experiment. *The rheostat makes it possible to vary the electric field between the plates.*

When this happened, that particular drop was stationary, while others would drift up or down, depending upon their mass and charge. For the stationary drop,

$$W = F$$
$$Mg = qE$$

and the drop's charge is

$$q = \frac{Mg}{E} \qquad\qquad (13.3)$$

Since the mass M of the drop could be determined by independent means and both g and E were known, q could be found.

Millikan obtained several different values for q, but in every case they were multiples of the single charge

$$e = 1.60 \times 10^{-19} \text{ coul}$$

and no smaller charge has ever been found. Thus e is the basic unit of electric charge.

Since Thomson had shown that the charge-to-mass ratio q/m of electrons is always 1.76×10^{11} coul/kg, the constancy of e meant that all electrons are indeed identical. The mass of the electron is, since $q = e$,

$$m = \frac{e}{q/m} = \frac{1.60 \times 10^{-19} \text{ coul}}{1.76 \times 10^{11} \text{ coul/kg}}$$
$$= 9.1 \times 10^{-31} \text{ kg}$$

This mass is only about 1/1,800 of that of the hydrogen atom. Because they are so light and so highly charged, it is easy to accelerate electrons to very high speeds. In almost all devices employing electron streams (for instance, television picture tubes) the electron velocities are very close to the velocity of light—186,000 mi/sec.

Electrical Properties of Matter

All ordinary matter contains electrons, but most of the time it is electrically neutral. This suggests that the negative charge of the electrons is balanced by positive charges somewhere within the atoms. It is possible to isolate the positive charges, to set them free as electrons are set free in a cathode-ray tube, but the experiments are more difficult. The nature of the positive charges will occupy us later on (Chap. 19), but for the moment we must get acquainted with the more accessible and more readily movable electrons.

In simple, everyday applications of electricity, where we are dealing with the movement of electricity in metals—electricity in wires, in light bulbs, in heaters, in electric motors—electrons play a role similar to that which Franklin imagined for his positive electric fluid. Franklin thought that a positively charged object had an excess of fluid; a negatively charged object, a deficiency. Today we should say, rather, that a positive charge indicates a deficiency of electrons and a negative charge an excess.

A solid conductor, in terms of electrons, is a substance whose electrons are relatively free to move; an insulator is a substance whose electrons are firmly bound in their atoms. If a copper wire is placed between a negatively charged sphere and an electroscope, some of the movable electrons in the wire, repelled by the negative charge, move into the electroscope and give it a negative charge. Some of the excess electrons on the sphere, so to speak, crowd into one end of the wire, pushing before them the movable electrons of the wire so that some at the other end spill over onto the electroscope. If silk thread is used in place of wire, its electrons, although repelled by the charge, are so firmly fixed in their atoms that almost none move to the electroscope (Fig. 13.5). A positive charge on the sphere would draw electrons out of the wire or out of any piece of metal connected to it. Thus electrons move easily along a metal away from a negative charge or toward a positive charge, which is what we mean by saying that all metals are conductors.

Conduction of electricity through gases and liquids—in a cathode-ray tube, a fluorescent light, or the acid of a storage battery—is somewhat more complicated, and the simple analogy with Franklin's electric fluid breaks down. Electricity moves through most gases and liquids, not as a simple flow of electrons but, at least in part, as a movement of charged atoms and molecules called *ions*. An atom or molecule gains a positive charge (becomes a positive ion) if it loses one or more electrons, and it gains a negative charge (becomes a negative ion) by attaching to itself electrons in excess of its normal number. The process of forming ions, or *ionization*, may take place in a number of ways. A gas like ordinary air becomes ionized when X rays, ultraviolet light, or radiation from a radioactive material passes through it, when an electric spark is produced, or even when a flame burns in it. Air molecules are sufficiently disturbed by these processes so that electrons

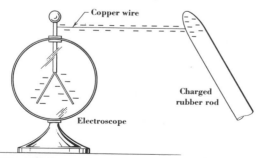

Fig. 13.5 *Electric current is a flow of electrons; hence substances whose electrons are relatively free to move are conductors, while those whose electrons are tightly bound in place are insulators. Copper, like other metals, is a good conductor.*

are ripped off some of them; the electrons thus set free may attach themselves to adjacent molecules, so both positive and negative ions are formed (Fig. 13.6). Ordinarily, the ions last no more than a few seconds, because movement of the gas molecules brings oppositely charged ions together and the electrons redistribute themselves to give neutral particles. Liquids, in contrast with gases, may contain positive and negative ions that persist indefinitely; the ions may be formed when the liquid itself is formed or when other substances are dissolved in it.

Electricity can move through a gas or liquid (at ordinary pressures and temperatures and at moderate voltages) only if ions are present. The flow of electricity is a movement of ions in two directions, positive ions moving toward the cathodes and negative ions (plus electrons in the case of gases) toward the anode, as in Fig. 13.7. When no ions are present, gases and liquids are excellent insulators, as is shown by the fact that oppositely charged spheres may be placed close to each other in air without any discharge occurring. If the charges are made large enough, however, they are capable themselves of ionizing some of the gas molecules nearby; then a current is possible, and we say that a spark jumps between them. If the air pressure is reduced, as it is in a cathode-ray tube, ions can travel farther and the discharge can jump over a longer gap. The light produced in a spark or in the glowing column of a cathode-ray tube is due to the violent disturbance pro-

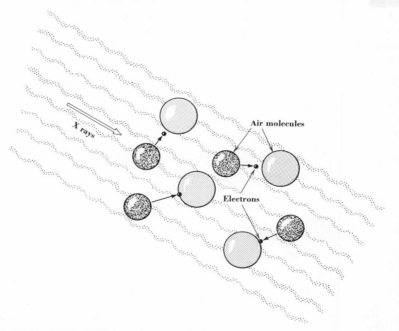

Fig. 13.6   Ionization of air.

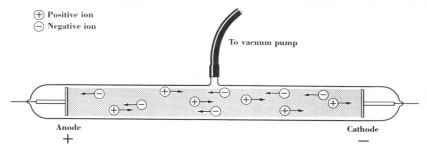

Fig. 13.7   *The flow of electricity in a gas consists of the motion of positive charges to the cathode and of negative charges to the anode.*

duced when fast-moving ions collide with other molecules. Cathode rays themselves consist of electrons knocked out of the cathode when it is struck by positive ions.

The simple experiments with which we began our study of electricity—stroking a rubber rod with fur or a glass rod with silk—probably involve movement of both ions and electrons. Contact between rubber and fur apparently permits electrons to move from the fur to the rubber, making the rod negative and leaving the fur positive. But both substances are nonconductors, so we should not expect electrons to move in great numbers. Probably the separation of charge is accomplished in part by a movement of ions, chiefly ions in films of water and air on their surfaces. Thus the complete explanation of these elementary experiments becomes very complicated. For most purposes, however, an explanation in terms of electrons is adequate. In discussions to follow, when we are considering movements of electricity in solids, we shall speak only of moving electrons; for nonconductors this represents an oversimplification, but not a serious one, unless we are concerned with intimate details of the movement.

To summarize, all matter contains both electrons and positive charges. Flow of electricity in solids is largely a movement of electrons alone, ease of movement in a given solid determining how good a conductor it is. A negative charge on a solid object is a concentration of electrons in excess of the normal number its atoms contain; a positive charge is a deficiency of electrons. In most liquids and gases conduction of electricity takes place by the movement in two directions of much larger particles called ions, which are atoms or molecules containing either an excess or a deficiency of electrons. These generalizations have many exceptions, for free electrons can move through some fluids and ions can move along the surfaces of some solids. But the rules apply to so many processes that we shall find them frequently useful, and they serve as a good illustration of how effectively the discovery of electrons has brought order into the study of electrical phenomena.

Induction

We are now in a position to consider a question that we have managed to avoid thus far. One sign that a body possesses an electric charge is that it causes other objects to move toward it. A charged rubber rod readily attracts a pith ball; but the ball was not itself charged originally, and so it is not clear where the attractive force comes from that pulls it to the rod.

The explanation is not difficult if we think in terms of electrons. When the rod, given its usual negative charge by stroking with a piece of fur, is brought near the pith ball, electrons in the ball, repelled by the negative charge, move as far away as they can, which is to the far side of the ball (Fig. 13.8). The side of the ball near the rod is left with a positive charge, and the ball is accordingly attracted to the rubber. If the rod is removed without actually touching the ball, the disturbed electrons resume their normal positions and the ball is unchanged. But if contact is made, some of the rod's electrons flow onto the ball, giving the ball as a whole a negative charge and causing the violent repulsion we have observed before.

The + and − charges on opposite sides of the pith ball, produced without actual contact with another charge, we call *induced charges*. The induced charges are temporary, disappearing as soon as the negative rod is

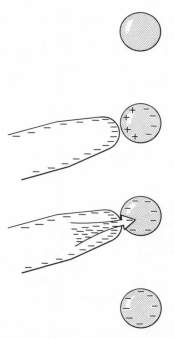

Fig. 13.8   *A charged rod attracts an uncharged object by first causing a separation of charge within the object.*

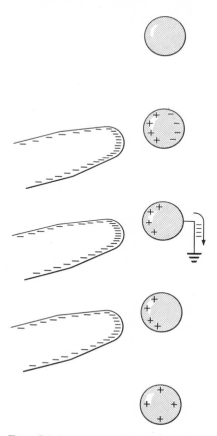

Fig. 13.9   Charging an object by induction.

removed.   But a permanent charge may be fixed on the ball by induction, provided that the ball is grounded while the rubber rod is near (Fig. 13.9). Grounding the ball (say, by touching it) makes it and the earth temporarily part of a single huge conductor; in this conductor the negative rod drives electrons as far away as possible, that is, from the ball down into the earth. If now the ground connection is broken while the rod is still held nearby, the electrons have no means of returning to the ball, and the ball therefore has a positive charge that will remain when the rod is taken away.   In the same fashion a negative charge may be given to another pith ball: Hold near it a positively charged glass rod; ground the ball, letting electrons attracted by the rod flow up from the ground into the ball; break the ground connection and remove the rod, thus leaving the excess electrons stranded on the ball.   Note that the induced charge on the ball is always opposite in sign to the original charge.

In general, any object with a negative charge induces positive charges on all objects near it, simply because it repels away from itself the movable negative charges in these objects. Insulated objects near the negative charge will have a concentration of positive electricity on the side toward the charge, a concentration of negative electricity on the opposite side. Grounded objects will have lost some of their electrons to the earth. The amount of the induced charge on any object depends on the size and shape of the object and on its nearness to the negative charge. In similar fashion a positive charge induces negative charges on objects in its immediate vicinity.

Electric Current

Until now we have been concerned primarily with stationary electric charges. These charges sometimes moved from one place to another—from rubber rod to pith ball, along a wire to an electroscope—but our principal interest was in the causes and results of the motion of charges, not in the motion itself. Further, in the cases we considered, the motion took place in a very short period of time, nearly instantaneously as far as we were concerned. Static electricity is interesting enough in itself, but it is not the kind of electricity that lights our lamps, runs our motors, and permits us to talk to people many miles away. The electricity of everyday use is in the form of electric current—electric charges in continuous motion. There is no fundamental difference, of course, between a moving charge and a charge at rest, but as we shall see, the fact that the former is in motion gives it properties not shared by its stationary twin.

We shall start with the simple type of current produced when a wire is connected between the terminals of a battery. A battery is a device for maintaining a positive charge on one terminal and a negative charge on the other. This is accomplished by a chemical reaction in the battery, chemical energy being continuously transformed into electric energy whenever the battery is in use. Connecting a wire between the terminals provides a path for the excess electrons at the negative electrode to move toward the positive electrode. This flow of electrons tends to cancel out the two charges, but chemical processes in the battery build up the charges as fast as they are depleted. Thus the current in the wire consists of a movement of electrons from one end to the other. Note that we do not say, "The electrons carry the current" or "The motion of electrons produces a current"; the moving electrons *are* the current.

Suppose the wire is cut and its free ends are attached to a switch; then by closing and opening the switch, we can start or stop the current at will. The current flows whenever a continuous conducting path is provided between the electrodes and stops whenever the path is broken. When the conducting path is complete (that is, when the switch is closed), we say the circuit is *closed;* when the path is interrupted, we say the circuit is *open* (Fig. 13.10).

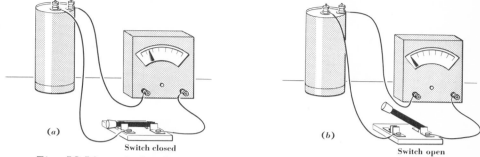

Fig. 13.10   *A closed circuit is one in which there is a complete conducting path; an open circuit is one in which there is an interruption in the conducting path.*

Given a battery, a switch, and wires of different sizes and materials, let us examine electric currents in some detail. First of all, how do we know when there is an electric current present? A wire looks the same whether the circuit is closed or open; how can we tell whether electrons are moving along it?

One way in which a current may betray its presence is by the spark produced if a small air gap is left somewhere in the circuit, for instance if the wire is detached from one terminal and its end held near, but not touching, the terminal. A large gap would break the circuit, but a spark will jump readily across a small air space.

Another easily detectable effect of the passage of electrons is the heating produced. The amount of heating for a given flow of electrons depends greatly on the wire used: Small wires become hotter than large ones; wires of certain metals, like tungsten and iron, become much hotter than silver or copper wires of similar size. The heating is explained by the resistance the wires offer to the movement of electrons along them, much as the heat due to friction is explained by resistance to mechanical movement. We take advantage of the heating effect of currents in a multitude of common electrical devices. Electric-light bulbs are an example, with a slender tungsten filament being made hot enough to emit light.

Every conductor exhibits a certain amount of resistance to the flow of electric current. Before we can examine the way in which the current in an electric circuit is affected by the resistance present, we must consider current itself from a quantitative point of view.

In a number of ways the flow of electricity along a wire is analogous to the flow of water in a pipe. The analogy is often helpful because we can visualize water much more readily than electrons. When we wish to describe the rate at which water is moving through a pipe, we might express the flow in terms of, say, gallons per second. If 1.5 gallons of water pass through a given pipe each second, the flow is 1.5 gallons per second (gal/sec). The quantitative description of electric current is very similar. Quantity of electric charge is measured in coulombs, as quantity of water is measured in gallons, and a natural way of referring to the flow of charge in a wire is in terms of the number of coulombs per second going past a given point in the wire, just as a natural way of referring to the flow of water is in terms of gallons per second. This unit of electric current is called the *ampere* (amp), after the French physicist André Marie Ampère; that is,

$$1 \text{ amp} = \frac{1 \text{ coul}}{1 \text{ sec}}$$

Ohm's Law

Suppose that a gallon of water is poised at the brink of a waterfall. We say that it possesses here a certain potential energy, since it is capable of moving under gravitational attraction. When it drops to the base of the fall, its potential energy decreases. The work obtainable from the gallon of water during its fall is equal to this decrease in potential energy. Now consider a coulomb of negative charge on the negative terminal of a battery. It is capable of moving under the repulsion of adjacent negative charges and the attraction of charges on the other terminal. We say, therefore, that it possesses a certain potential energy by reason of its position on the negative electrode. When it has moved along a wire to the positive terminal, its potential energy is smaller, since here it can no longer move spontaneously. The amount of work the coulomb can perform in flowing from the negative to the positive terminal is measured by its decrease in potential energy. This decrease in potential energy brought about by the motion of 1 coul from the negative to the positive terminal is a quantity called the *potential difference* between the two terminals. It is a quantity analogous to difference of elevation in the case of water. We measure difference of elevation in feet; we measure difference of potential in *volts* (named for the Italian physicist Alessandro Volta).

When 1 coul of charge travels through 1 volt of potential difference, this work that it does is equal to 1 joule. (As we recall from Chap. 4, the joule is the unit of both work and energy in the metric system.) Because the volt is defined in this way, it is easy to make transitions from mechanical to electrical quantities.

A widely used unit of energy in atomic physics is the *electron volt*, which is the amount of energy gained by an electron that is accelerated by a potential difference of 1 volt. The abbreviation for electron volt is *ev*. Since the charge on the electron is 1.6×10^{-19} coul,

$$1 \text{ ev} = 1.6 \times 10^{-19} \text{ coul} \times 1 \text{ volt}$$
$$= 1.6 \times 10^{-19} \text{ joule}$$

The electron volt is a very small unit, and frequently its multiples the *Mev* and the *Bev* are used, where

$$1 \text{ Mev} = 1 \text{ million ev} = 10^6 \text{ ev} = 1.6 \times 10^{-13} \text{ joule}$$
$$1 \text{ Bev} = 1 \text{ billion ev} = 10^9 \text{ ev} = 1.6 \times 10^{-10} \text{ joule}$$

The maximum difference of potential between the terminals of an ordinary storage battery is about 6 volts; of a dry cell, about 1.5 volts. Every coulomb of electricity at the negative terminal of the storage battery, therefore, is capable of doing four times as much work as a coulomb at the negative electrode of a dry cell, just as a gallon of water at the brink of a waterfall 600 ft high is capable of doing four times as much work as a gallon at the brink of a 150-ft fall. If a storage battery and a dry cell are connected in exactly similar circuits, the battery will push four times as many electrons around its circuit in a given time as the dry cell, giving a current four times as great. Very crudely, we may speak of the potential difference between two points as the amount of "push" effective in moving charges between the points.

If a circuit is set up so that different voltages can be applied to the ends of the same piece of wire and if the temperature of the wire is maintained constant, it is found experimentally that the current flowing in the wire is proportional to the potential difference over a wide range of values of the latter. The greater the voltage of the battery across the wire, the more current flows. This generalization is called *Ohm's law*, after its discoverer, the German physicist Georg Simon Ohm (1787–1854).

Evidently there is some property of the wire that opposes the flow of current. The more current we want, the more potential difference we must apply. This property is called *resistance*, and as we have said, it is closely related to friction. A large current requires a large potential difference; moving a heavy box across a room requires more force than moving a light box.

According to Ohm's law, the current in a circuit, usually denoted by the letter i, is proportional to the potential difference, denoted by V, across the circuit. Clearly, the more the resistance, the less the current, so that, if we write R for resistance, Ohm's law may be expressed in the form

$$i = \frac{V}{R}$$

When i is in amperes and V in volts, the unit of R is the *ohm*; that is,

$$1 \text{ amp} = \frac{1 \text{ volt}}{1 \text{ ohm}}$$

The great usefulness of Ohm's law is that, once we know the resistance R of a given electric circuit, we can determine immediately how much potential difference V is needed to cause a given amount of current i to flow.

Or, given the potential difference and resistance, we can compute the current.

Let us see how Ohm's law can be applied in a practical situation. A typical automobile has a 12-volt battery whose capacity is 60 ampere-hours (amp-hr), which means that it can provide a current of 60 amp for 1 hr, or 6 amp for 10 hr, or 1 amp for 60 hr, etc., before it becomes "dead." How long can such an automobile have its headlights, of total resistance 4 ohms, left on without the engine running (which would recharge the battery) before the battery runs down? To solve the problem we first calculate the current, which is

$$i = \frac{V}{R} = \frac{12 \text{ volts}}{4 \text{ ohms}} = 3 \text{ amp}$$

Since the battery's capacity is 60 amp-hr, the lights can be left on for 20 hr before the battery runs down.

Ohm's law can also be used to find the resistance of an electrical appliance when its voltage and current ratings are known. An electric toaster draws a current of 4 amp when it is plugged into a 120-volt supply line. To find its resistance, we rewrite Ohm's law in the form

$$R = \frac{V}{i}$$

and substitute the values given:

$$R = \frac{V}{i} = \frac{120 \text{ volts}}{4 \text{ amp}} = 30 \text{ ohms}$$

The resistance of the toaster is 30 ohms.

Electric Power

Electric energy is so very useful because it is readily converted into other kinds of energy. Electric energy in the form of electric current is converted into radiant energy in a light bulb, into chemical energy when a storage battery is charged, into mechanical energy in an electric motor, into heat energy in an electric oven. In each case the current performs work on whichever device it passes through, and the device then transforms this work into another kind of energy. A very important quantity in any discussion of electric current is therefore the rate at which a current is doing work, in other words, the *power* of the current.

Earlier in this chapter we learned that when 1 coul of charge is pushed through a circuit by a potential difference of 1 volt, the amount of work done is equal to 1 joule. In general, then,

$$\text{Electrical work} = \text{charge} \times \text{potential difference}$$
$$W = qV$$

where W is expressed in joules, q in coulombs, and V in volts. Power P is defined as the rate at which work is being done; so

$$\text{Power (watts)} = \frac{\text{work (joules)}}{\text{time (sec)}}$$

$$P = \frac{W}{t}$$

If we substitute for W its electrical equivalent qV, we find that

$$P = \frac{W}{t} = \frac{qV}{t}$$

But, by definition,

$$\text{Current (amp)} = \frac{\text{charge (coul)}}{\text{time (sec)}}$$

or, in symbols,

$$i = \frac{q}{t}$$

This means that we are able to express electric power as

$$P = \frac{q}{t}V$$
$$= iV$$

Power (watts) = current (amp) × potential difference (volts)

Now we can see why nearly all electrical appliances are rated in terms of *watts*: This designation expresses the rate at which the appliance uses electric energy. A 60-watt light bulb requires twice the power of a 30-watt light bulb and one-tenth the power of a 600-watt electric fan. Because

$$P = iV$$

we can readily determine the current requirements of an appliance that is rated in watts when it is connected across the power main whose voltage is specified. A 60-watt bulb connected across a 120-volt power line needs a current of

$$i = \frac{P}{V}$$
$$= \frac{60 \text{ watts}}{120 \text{ volts}} = \frac{1}{2} \text{ amp}$$

Electric fuses are designed to protect a power line by blowing out, and thereby opening the circuit, whenever an unsafe amount of current passes through them. The fuses normally used in homes are rated at 15 amp. Since the power-line voltage is 120 volts, the greatest power that the line can provide without blowing the fuse is

$$P = iV$$
$$= 15 \text{ amp} \times 120 \text{ volts} = 1,800 \text{ watts}$$

Self-examination

1. Cathode rays are
   a. streams of cathodes
   b. the green light rays seen near certain electrical devices
   c. moving charges of either sign
   d. moving electrons

2. When an electron is removed from an atom or molecule, the atom or molecule becomes
   a. a negative ion
   b. a positive ion
   c. a cathode
   d. an anode

3. Which of the following statements is correct?
   a. Electrons carry electric current.
   b. The motion of electrons produces an electric current.
   c. Moving electrons constitute an electric current.
   d. Electric currents are carried by conductors and insulators only.

4. Match each of the electrical quantities listed below with the appropriate unit from the list on the right:
   a. resistance   volt
   b. current   ampere
   c. potential difference ohm
   d. power   watt

5. The current in a 40-watt 120-volt electric-light bulb is
   a. ⅓ amp
   b. 3 amp
   c. 80 amp
   d. 4,800 amp

6. A billion electrons are added to a small object. Its charge is
   a. 1.6×10^{-10} coul
   b. 1.6×10^{-28} coul
   c. -1.6×10^{-10} coul
   d. -1.6×10^{-28} coul

7. The electron volt is a unit of
   a. potential difference
   b. charge
   c. energy
   d. momentum

8. The potential difference between a certain thundercloud and the ground is 4×10^6 volts. A lightning stroke occurs during which 80 coul of charge is transferred between the cloud and the ground. The energy dissipated during the lightning stroke is
   a. 5×10^{-6} joule
   b. 2×10^5 joules
   c. 3.2×10^7 joules
   d. 3.2×10^8 joules

Problems

1. Contact between road and tires often produces an appreciable electric charge in the body of an automobile or truck. Enough charge may accumulate to produce a spark. Trucks carrying gasoline or other inflammable materials usually have metal chains attached to their frames which touch the road. How does this chain prevent dangerous sparks?

2. A person can be electrocuted while taking a bath if he touches a poorly insulated light switch. Why is the electric shock he receives under these conditions so much more dangerous than usual?

3. Name five good conductors of electricity and five good insulators. How well do these substances conduct heat? What general relationship between the ability to conduct heat and the ability to conduct electricity could you infer from this information?

4. Explain in terms of electrons why the production of electricity by friction always yields equal amounts of positive and negative electricity.

5. How is the movement of electricity through air different from its movement through a copper wire?

6. What properties of cathode rays demonstrate that they are streams of particles rather than a wave phenomenon like light?

7. How many electrons must be added to a pith ball to give it a charge of -1 coul? What would be the total mass of these electrons? Why is it unlikely that this would ever be done?

8. If a 75-watt light bulb is connected to a 120-volt power line,
   a. how much current flows through it?
   b. what is the resistance of the bulb?
   c. how much power does the bulb consume?

9. How many coulombs of electric current pass through an electrical appliance in 20 min if the current through the appliance is 0.4 amp? If the potential difference across the appliance is 120 volts, how much power does it consume? How much energy in joules does it draw from the circuit in 20 min?

10. If your home has a 120-volt power line, how much power in watts can you draw from the line before a 30-amp fuse will burn out? How many 100-watt light bulbs can you put in the circuit before the fuse will burn out?

11. A hot-water heater employs a 2,000-watt resistance element. If all the heat from the resistance element is absorbed by the water in the heater, how much water per hour can be warmed from 10 to 70°C?

12. If electricity costs 3 cents per kilowatthour, how much does it cost to warm a kilogram of water from 10 to 70°C in the heater of Prob. 11?

13. How many electrons per second flow past a point in a wire carrying a current of 2 amp?

14. A power rating of 1 hp is equivalent to 746 watts. How much current does a ¼-hp electric motor require when it is operated at 120 volts?

15. Find the speed of an electron whose energy is 26 ev.

16. Find the energy (in electron volts) of an electron whose speed is 10^6 m/sec.

CHAPTER 14 | MAGNETISM

While it is not immediately obvious, there is an intimate relationship between electricity and magnetism. By the middle of the nineteenth century the chief features of this relationship were understood, and they not only furnished the basis for the industrial utilization of electricity, but also led directly to the discovery of the electromagnetic nature of light. Before we begin to explore the connection between electricity and magnetism, which is one of the most significant of all physics, we shall inquire into magnetism and magnetic phenomena in order to have a background from which to work.

Magnets

Ordinary magnets are familiar to everybody. The simplest kind consists of a bar of iron that has been magnetized in one of a variety of ways, say by having been stroked by another magnet. A magnetized bar of iron is recognized, of course, by its ability to attract and hold other pieces of iron. Another property, illustrated by the familiar compass needle, is its tendency when freely suspended to turn so that one end points north and the other south. We call the north-pointing end the *north pole* of the magnet, the south-pointing end, the *south pole*. Here, near the ends, the greater part of the magnetization is concentrated, as can easily be shown by testing the attraction of various parts of the bar for small iron nails. If two magnets are brought near to each other, the two poles are found to behave quite differently. Laid end to end so that the two north poles are near together, the magnets repel each other;

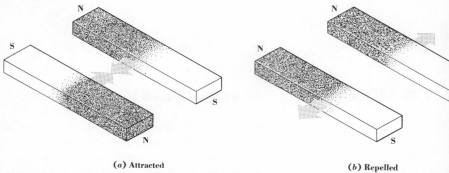

(a) Attracted (b) Repelled

Fig. 14.1 *Like magnetic poles repel each other; unlike magnetic poles attract.*

if a north pole is brought near a south pole, the two attract each other (Fig. 14.1). We may formulate a simple rule analogous to that for electric charges: *Like magnetic poles repel each other; unlike poles attract.*

It would be convenient for experimental purposes if we could isolate a single north pole unencumbered by the south pole at the other end of the magnet. Seemingly, isolation of the north pole should not be difficult; we need only saw the magnet in half. Unfortunately this method will not work. The resulting half magnets have each a north pole and a south pole, two new poles appearing where the middle of the former magnet was, as shown in Fig. 14.2. We may cut the resulting magnets in two again, with the same results, and continue as long as we have tools fine enough for the cutting; still each magnet that we prepare, however small, will have a north pole and a south pole. *There is no such thing as a single free magnetic pole.*

Since a magnet can be cut into smaller and smaller fragments indefinitely, each fragment acting as a small magnet, we may reasonably assume that magnetism is a property of the smallest particles of a substance. Presumably each particle of iron (or any other material that can be magnetized) behaves as if it had a north pole and a south pole. In ordinary iron the particles are haphazardly arranged, and adjacent north and south poles neutralize each other's effect. When the iron is magnetized, we imagine that many or all of the particles are aligned with their north poles in the same direction, so that the strengths of all the tiny magnets are added together (Fig. 14.3).

The ultimate magnetic particles in iron have been identified as the iron atoms themselves. The magnetic properties of an atom are determined by the behavior within it of the electrons it contains. The units that line up when a bar of iron is magnetized are usually microscopic "domains" containing many atoms in more or less uniform alignment.

The metal iron is distinguished from most other substances by its ability

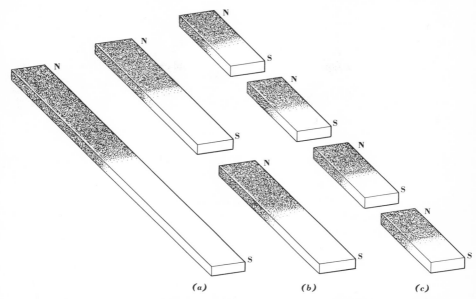

Fig. 14.2 *Cutting a magnet in half produces two other magnets. There is no such thing as a single free magnetic pole.*

to be strongly magnetized. Certain alloys, or mixtures, of other metals are also strongly magnetic; the metals cobalt and nickel, certain compounds of iron, and liquid oxygen are less magnetic. With delicate instruments, in fact, all substances can be shown to be very faintly magnetic. Some are attracted to a magnet, as iron is; most are very slightly repelled.

Let us try an experiment with magnets analogous to the electrical experiment with conductors and insulators. We place a magnet a foot or so from an unmagnetized piece of iron and connect the two by various materials, but no substance is found to carry the magnetism from the original magnet to the unmagnetized iron except a third piece of iron (or a magnetic alloy).

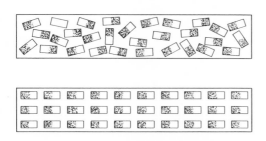

Fig. 14.3 *In an unmagnetized iron bar the tiny magnetic particles of iron are arranged at random, while in a magnetized bar they are aligned.*

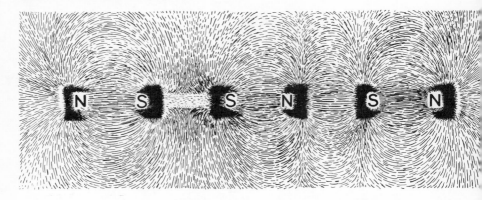

Fig. 14.4 *Patterns formed by iron filings sprinkled near three bar magnets. The filings align themselves in the direction of the lines of force passing through them.*

If iron is used for the connection, the unmagnetized piece becomes temporarily able to attract small nails or filings, but all or nearly all its magnetism vanishes when the connection is severed. Meanwhile, the strength of the original magnet remains practically unimpaired; that is, when a magnet touches a piece of iron, its magnetism in effect extends along the iron, but is not conducted permanently through it in the sense in which an electric charge is carried through a conductor.

Since magnets exert forces on one another that act even though the magnets themselves are not in actual contact, we can speak of the *magnetic field* of a single magnet even though there is no other magnet nearby for it to attract or repel. In Chap. 12 we discussed briefly the method of describing fields of force in terms of imaginary *lines of force* whose direction

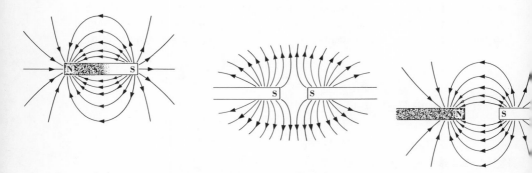

Fig. 14.5 *Lines of force around magnets. These lines of force were obtained by calculation and may be compared with the patterns of iron filings near bar magnets.*

at any point is the same as the direction in which a test body would move if placed at that point.   In the case of a gravitational field the test body is a particle; in the case of an electric field it is a small charge.   Lines of force are also helpful in describing magnetic fields, particularly because they are easily exhibited with the help of iron filings.   An iron filing, just like a compass needle, tends to line up in a magnetic field along the direction of the field.   If we scatter iron filings on a card placed over a magnet and shake the card slightly, the filings form into a pattern indicative of the configuration of the magnetic field.   The accompanying illustration (Fig. 14.4) shows the patterns obtained near bar magnets in various combinations, and Fig. 14.5 shows the patterns for the same magnets obtained by calculation; they are clearly very similar.

Magnetic Fields of Electric Currents

Perhaps unfamiliar to us as sources of magnetic field are electric currents, yet every current is surrounded by such a field.   To repeat a famous experiment first performed in 1820 by the Danish physicist Hans Christian Oersted, let us connect a horizontal wire to a battery and hold beneath the wire a small compass needle (Fig. 14.6); the needle swings into a position at right angles to the wire.   Place the compass just above the wire; the needle swings completely around until it is again perpendicular to the wire but pointing in the opposite direction.   We can use iron filings to determine the magnetic field pattern around a wire carrying a current.   When we do this, as in Fig. 14.7, we find that the lines of force near the wire consist of concentric circles.   The direction of the lines of force (that is, the direction in which

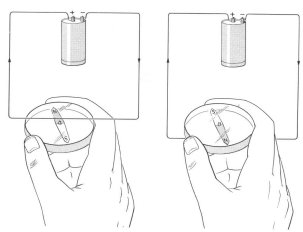

Fig. 14.6   Oersted's experiment, showing that a magnetic field surrounds every electric current. *The field direction above the wire is opposite to that below the wire.*

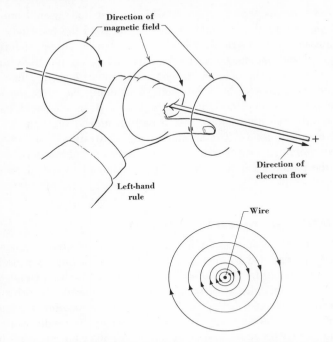

Fig. 14.7   Magnetic lines of force around a wire carrying an electric current. *The direction of the lines may be found by placing the thumb of the left hand in the direction of electron flow; the curled fingers then point in the direction of the lines of force. In the lower diagram the current flows up from the paper.*

the N pole of the compass points) depends on the direction of flow of electrons through the wire; when one is reversed, the other reverses also. In any particular case the direction of the field can be found by encircling the wire with the fingers of the *left hand,* so that the extended thumb points along the wire *in the direction in which the electrons move;* then the finger tips point in the direction of the field.

If we think in terms of a hypothetical positive current, as engineers do, the above rule must be stated as a right-hand rule. Grasp the wire in the right hand with the thumb pointing in the direction of the hypothetical positive current, and the fingers will point in the direction of the magnetic field. The two rules, of course, give identical results. The confusion here goes back to Franklin's unfortunate guess that the electricity moving in wires was positive electricity. In either way of thinking, the current and the field are perpendicular to each other.

A magnetic field and the current that produces it are related in a rather involved way, and we shall not go into the details here. However, a few specific items are worth knowing. In Chap. 12 we learned that the electric field intensity **E** at a point is defined in terms of the force it exerts on a unit electric charge at that point. The corresponding definition of the *magnetic induction* (symbol **B**, a vector quantity) at a point is in terms of the force the magnetic field exerts on a unit length of wire carrying a unit current perpendicular to the field. The unit of magnetic induction is the *weber per square meter*. In order to give an idea of the magnitude of this unit, we note that the magnetic induction of the earth's magnetic field is about 3×10^{-5} weber/m² at sea level; the magnetic induction near a typical permanent magnet is about 1 weber/m²; and the strongest electromagnets can produce fields whose magnetic induction is as much as 100 webers/m².

Oersted's discovery was the first positive proof that a connection exists between electricity and magnetism; it was also the first demonstration of the principle on which the electric motor is based. Magnetism and electricity are related, but magnetic poles and electric charges *at rest* have no effect on one another. This is an important fact. A magnet is completely uninfluenced by a stationary electric charge near it, and vice versa.

Although electric charges at rest do not affect a magnet, in motion they produce a magnetic field. There is no simple explanation of this phenomenon. Oersted's experiment is a fundamental one, like the experiments that enable us to define positive and negative charges. We simply accept, as one of the basic properties of electric charges, the fact that, when they are in motion, they are surrounded by magnetic fields as well as by electric fields.

When a current passes through a wire bent into a circle, the resulting magnetic field, shown in Fig. 14.8, is exactly the same as that produced by a bar magnet. One end of the loop acts as a north pole, the other as a south pole; if suitably suspended, the loop swings to a north-south position. A current loop attracts pieces of iron just as a bar magnet does.

When several wires that all carry currents in the same direction are placed side by side, as in Fig. 14.9, the magnetic fields of the individual wires

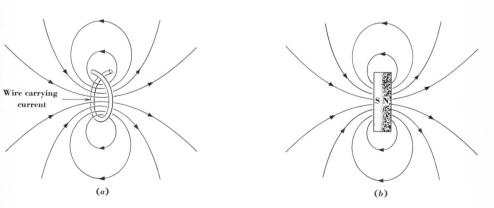

Wire carrying current

(a)   (b)

Fig. 14.8   *The magnetic field of a loop of electric current is the same as that of a bar magnet.*

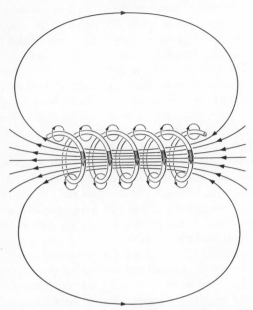

Fig. 14.9 *The magnetic field of a coil is like that of a single loop but is stronger.*

add together to give a resultant magnetic field. This combined field is just like that of a single wire with a current in it equal to the sum of all the separate currents. This effect is often employed to increase the magnetic field of a current loop. Instead of one loop, many loops of wire are wound into a coil, and the resulting magnetic field is as many times stronger than the field of one turn as there are turns in the coil: A coil with 50 turns produces a field 50 times greater than a coil with just one turn. The magnetic strength of the coil is enormously increased if a rod of soft iron is placed inside it (Fig. 14.10). This combination of coil and iron core is called an *electromagnet*. An electromagnet exerts magnetic force only when current flows through its turns, and so its action can be turned on and off. Also, by using many turns and a sufficient amount of current, it can be made far more powerful than a permanent magnet of similar size. These two properties make electromagnets among the most widely employed devices in the technical world. They range in size from the tiny coils in telephone receivers to the huge coils that load and unload scrap iron.

Galvanometers and Motors

Let us look briefly into the very similar mechanisms of galvanometers, which are used to measure electric currents, and electric motors, which are used to convert electric energy into mechanical energy.

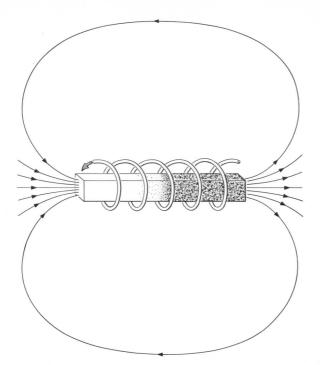

Fig. 14.10   *An electromagnet consists of a coil with an iron core, which considerably enhances the magnetic field produced.*

Suppose that a horizontal wire connected to a battery is suspended as in Fig. 14.11, so that it is free to move from side to side; and suppose that the N pole of a strong bar magnet is placed directly beneath it. This setup is the reverse of Oersted's experiment: Oersted placed a movable magnet near a wire fixed in position; here we have a movable wire near a fixed magnet. We might predict, from Oersted's results and Newton's third law of motion, that in this case the wire will move. It fulfills the prediction, jumping out quickly to one side as soon as the circuit is closed. The direction of its motion is perpendicular to the lines of force of the bar magnet's field. Whether it jumps to one side or the other depends on the direction of flow of electrons in the wire and on which pole of the magnet is used.

The push that a magnetic field exerts on a wire carrying a current is often called the *motor effect*, since the running of an electric motor depends on this force. Keep in mind the nature of the force: It is not attraction or repulsion, but a *sidewise push*. The wire does not move toward the magnet or away from it, but perpendicular to its field.

The motor effect can be demonstrated with a cathode-ray discharge tube. In this tube (Fig. 14.12) we have an electric current reduced to bare essentials: a flow of electrons, unencumbered by a wire, moving across a vacuum

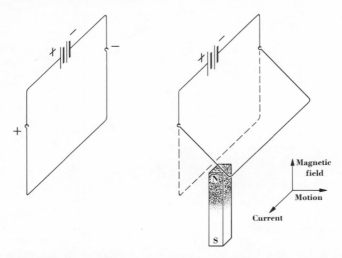

Fig. 14.11   The motor effect. *The wire moves to one side in a direction perpendicular to both the magnetic field and the current.*

away from the cathode. By placing a fluorescent screen at the end of the tube, we can make the invisible electrons leave a trace of their movements as a bright line. If now we bring near the side of a tube so equipped one end of a bar magnet or place the tube between the poles of a horseshoe magnet, the line bends either upward or downward; that is, the swiftly moving electrons are pushed in a direction at right angles to the magnetic field and so are forced out of their accustomed straight path. Since the amount of deflection depends, among other things, on the speed, mass, and charge of the electrons, experiments of this sort give physicists valuable information about these tiny particles.

Suppose that a small coil is suspended between the poles of a horseshoe

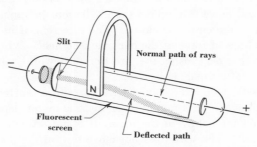

Fig. 14.12   Deflection of cathode rays in a magnetic field. *The deflection is perpendicular to the directions of both the magnetic field and the electron movement.*

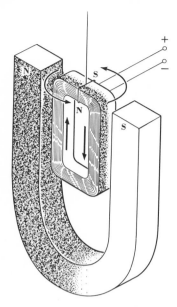

Fig. 14.13   *Principle of the galvanometer.* *When a current passes through the coil, it rotates so that its N pole is close to the S pole of the magnet and its S pole close to the N pole of the magnet.*

magnet (Fig. 14.13).   It hangs limp until a current is passed through it; then it snaps into a position such that its N pole is as near as possible to the S pole of the horseshoe, its S pole near the N pole of the horseshoe.   The thread suspending the coil resists somewhat the coil's turning, and the coil comes to rest at an intermediate position.   How far the coil turns toward a direct alignment with the magnet depends on two things: the resistance of the thread to twisting and the strength of the coil's N and S poles.   The magnetic strength of the coil depends in turn on the amount of current passing through it.   Hence, for a given supporting thread, the angle through which the coil turns is a measure of the strength of the electric current applied to it. Devices built so that this angle can be measured accurately are our most convenient instruments for detecting and measuring electric currents.   They are called *galvanometers* (after the Italian scientist Luigi Galvani).   The ordinary direct-current *voltmeters* and *ammeters* used by electricians are galvanometers of this type adapted for special purposes.

A galvanometer has nearly all the essential parts of a simple electric motor.   In a motor the coil must be supported on an axle rather than by a delicate thread, and some device must be used for changing the direction of current through the coil every time it aligns itself with the magnet.   Changing the current reverses the poles of the coil, so that every time it swings into and a little past the position of alignment, it receives a new impulse to turn into the opposite position. Thus its motion becomes continuous. The device used for automatically changing the current direction is called a *commutator;* it may often be seen on the axle of a motor as a copper sleeve divided into two or more segments.

Practical electric motors are not built on quite so simple a pattern. There are many designs, adapted to different uses and different kinds of electric currents. Ordinarily electromagnets are employed rather than the simple permanent magnet of a galvanometer. In some motors the coil is fixed in position, and the magnet or magnets rotate about it. Some motors, built for alternating rather than direct current, do not need commutators. But regardless of design, motors without exception utilize in their operation the force between a magnet and an electric current in its vicinity.

Electromagnetic Induction

Energy in any of its usual forms can be converted directly into electric energy. The battery is a device for changing chemical energy into electric energy. Instruments called thermocouples, used in the measurement of temperature, convert heat directly into electric energy. Even radiant energy can produce small electric currents, as we shall see later.

But the electric energy that is supplied so copiously to our homes and factories comes neither from light nor from heat nor from chemical reactions, but from mechanical energy. The great dynamos in power plants that supply electricity to cities utilize water power or steam engines. Isolated farms may have small generators operated by gasoline or diesel motors or, more rarely, by wind power. In all cases the energy that is turned directly into electricity is the mechanical energy of moving machinery.

Commercial generators utilize a principle somewhat different from that used in galvanometers and electric motors. The story goes back to some famous observations by the English physicist Michael Faraday. Intrigued by the researches of Ampère and Oersted on the magnetic fields around electric currents, Faraday reasoned that, if a current can produce a magnetic field, then somehow a magnet should be capable of generating an electric current. Now a wire placed in a magnetic field and connected to a galvanometer shows no sign of a current. But *if the wire or the magnet is moving*, Faraday discovered, *a current is produced*. As long as the wire continues to cut across lines of force in the magnetic field, the current persists; when the motion stops, the current stops. Because it is produced by motion in the presence of a magnetic field, without any direct contact with electric charges, this sort of current is called an *induced current*. The entire phenomenon is known as *electromagnetic induction*.

Let us repeat Faraday's experiment in very simple form. Suppose that the copper wire of Fig. 14.14 is moved back and forth across the lines of force of the bar magnet. The galvanometer will indicate a current flowing first in one direction, then in the other. Note that the wire is held approximately at right angles to the lines of force; thus the motion of electrons along the wire is at right angles to the magnetic field. The direction along the wire in which the induced current will flow depends on the direction of its motion and the direction of the lines of force; reverse the direction of motion, or use the opposite magnetic pole, and the current is reversed. The strength of the current depends on the rapidity of movement and on the strength of the field.

This phenomenon, sometimes called the *dynamo effect*, is related to the motor effect. A motor runs because electrons flowing along a wire are pushed sidewise in a magnetic field. In Faraday's experiment we again cause electrons to move through a magnetic field, but this time by moving the wire as a whole. The electrons are pushed sidewise as before and, in response to the push, move along the wire as an electric current.

To intensify the induced current produced by moving a conductor near a magnet, commercial dynamos employ a large coil rather than a single wire and several electromagnets instead of a bar magnet. Turned rapidly between the electromagnets by steam engine or water turbine, wires of the coil cut lines of force first in one direction, then in the other. Operation of the dynamo is illustrated in simplified form in Fig. 14.15, where a coil is shown turning between two magnets. Evidently during half a revolution each side of

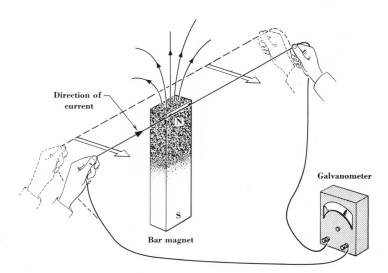

Fig. 14.14 **The dynamo effect.** *The direction of the induced current is perpendicular both to the magnetic lines of force and to the direction in which the wire is moving. No current is induced when the wire is at rest.*

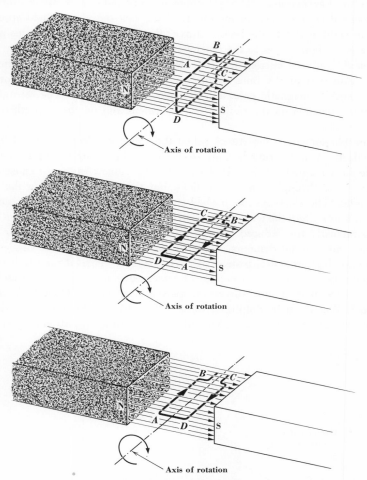

Fig. 14.15 *An alternating-current dynamo. As the loop rotates, current is induced in it first in one direction and then in the other. No current flows at those times when the loop is moving parallel to the magnetic field.*

the coil cuts the field in one direction; then during the other half revolution it cuts the field in the opposite direction. Hence the induced current flows alternately one way and the other. We call such a current an *alternating current.*

Currents produced by batteries, thermocouples, and similar devices are one-way, or *direct*, currents, flowing steadily in one direction unless we arbitrarily change the connections. In alternating currents electrons move first one way, then the other, not from one end of the circuit to the other but back and forth over short-distances. In the 60-cycle current that we ordinarily use in our homes, electrons change their direction of motion 120 times each second.

By using commutators similar to the commutators used on direct-current motors, dynamos can be constructed to produce direct current, but alternating current is usually produced because it is more economical for transmission over long distances. In most household appliances, such as lights and heaters, the direction of the current is immaterial, and alternating current works quite as efficiently as direct.

The Transformer

To generate an induced current requires that magnetic lines of force be made to move across a conductor. Two ways of accomplishing this motion have been mentioned: The wire may be moved past a magnet, or the wire may be held stationary while the magnet moves. We come now to a third, less obvious, method, which involves no visible motion at all.

Suppose that coil *A* in Fig. 14.16 is connected to a switch and a battery, coil *B* to a galvanometer. When the switch is closed, a current flows through *A*, building up a magnetic field around it. The current and field do not start instantaneously; during a tiny fraction of a second the current increases from zero to its normal value, and its magnetic influence expands from a weak field close to the wire to a strong field perceptible at some distance. We may

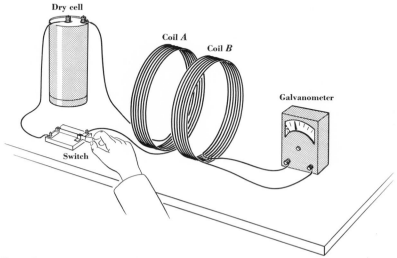

Fig. 14.16 *A simple transformer.* *Momentary currents are detected by the galvanometer when the current in coil A is started or stopped.*

imagine the circular lines of force expanding, moving outward across the wires of coil *B*. This motion of the lines across coil *B* produces in it a momentary current, recorded by a sharp deflection of the galvanometer needle. Once the current in *A* reaches its normal, steady value, the field becomes stationary and the induced current in *B* stops. Now suppose the switch is opened; in another small fraction of a second the current in *A* drops to zero, and its magnetic field collapses back around the coil. Again lines of force cut across *B*, and the galvanometer responds with another deflection, this time in the opposite direction since the motion of the lines of force has changed. Thus starting and stopping the current in *A* has the same effect as moving a magnet in and out of *B*. An induced current is generated whenever the switch is opened or closed.

Suppose that *A* is connected, not to a battery, but to a 60-cycle alternating current. Now we need no switch; automatically, 120 times each second, the current comes to a complete stop and starts off again in the other direction. Its magnetic field expands and contracts at the same rate, and the lines of force cutting *B* first in one direction, then the other, induce an alternating current similar to that in *A*. An ordinary galvanometer will not respond to these rapid alterations, but an instrument built to measure alternating currents will show the induced current readily.

Thus an alternating current in one coil will produce an alternating current in a second coil, even though a considerable distance separates them. However, to generate an induced current most efficiently, the two coils should be close together and wound on a core of soft iron. Such a combination of two coils and an iron core constitutes a *transformer*. The coil into which electricity is fed from an outside source is the primary coil; that in which an induced current is generated is the secondary coil.

Transformers are useful because the voltage of the induced current can be made any desired multiple or fraction of the primary voltage by suitable winding of the coils. If the number of turns of wire in the secondary coil is the same as the number of turns in the primary, the induced voltage is the same as the primary voltage. If the secondary has twice as many turns, its voltage is twice that of the primary; if it has one-third as many turns, its voltage is one-third that of the primary; and so on. Thus, by using a suitably designed transformer, we may secure any desired voltage, high or low, from a given alternating current.

Terrestrial Magnetism

A fascinating example of interrelationships in science is the origin of the earth's magnetic field. Let us briefly examine this field and its origin on the basis of what we have learned in this chapter.

Although the earliest description of the compass and its use in navigation that we have was published by Alexander Neckham in 1180, there is little doubt that knowledge of the compass was widespread even further back in antiquity.   Until 1600, however, it was believed that this phenomenon had its origin in an attractive force exerted by Polaris, the North Star, on magnetized needles.   In that year, Sir William Gilbert, physician to Elizabeth I, wrote of experiments he had performed with spherical pieces of lodestone, a naturally magnetized mineral.   By comparing the direction of the magnetic force on a test iron needle at various positions near the lodestone sphere with similar measurements made over the earth's surface by explorers, Gilbert concluded that the earth behaves like a giant magnet: "magnus magnes ipse est globus terrestris."

Today a great deal is known about geomagnetism, and an equally substantial amount is still beyond our grasp.   Essentially, the information we have is confined to the magnetic field at the earth's surface and a short distance above it.   From this information we can deduce that the magnetic field originates within the earth and that the field must be very strong in the interior.   But the big problem of how the field is generated has had only a partial solution so far.

Nearly all the magnetic field at the earth's surface is equivalent to the field that would be produced by an ordinary bar magnet (or *dipole*) of enormous power located a few hundred miles from the center of the earth and tilted 11° from the direction of the earth's axis (Fig. 14.17).   No such magnet can possibly exist, since iron loses its magnetic properties above about 1400°C, and temperatures exceeding this figure are present in all but

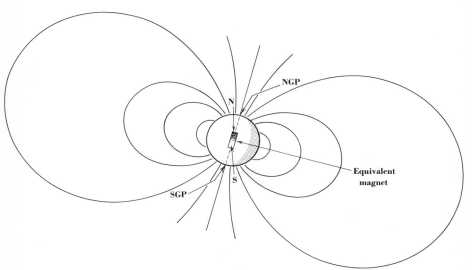

Fig. 14.17   *The earth's magnetic field is approximately that which would be produced by an imaginary bar magnet located within the earth. The positions of the geomagnetic poles (NGP and SGP) are indicated.*

the top 15 miles of the earth. However, this dipole is a useful fiction for making computations and serves as a definite target for theories of the origin of the earth's magnetism to aim at. The points at which the magnetic axis intersects the earth's surface are called the *geomagnetic poles* and are indicated in Fig. 14.17.

Besides this dipole magnetic field there are irregularities of various kinds also present in the magnetic field of the earth. Some of them are due to local deposits of iron ore, and magnetic prospecting is a well-developed tool for investigating geological structures as well as for simply looking for iron. Other anomalies come from within the earth and, in a sense, represent malfunctioning in the operation of the geomagnetic dynamo. The net result is that compasses point to slightly different "magnetic poles" in different regions around the world, and these variations must be indicated on navigation charts. It is true that a spot called a *dip pole* has been located in each hemisphere at which a compass needle, if suspended freely, would point straight down, and these dip poles are popularly called the *magnetic poles*.

Apart from its very existence, the most intriguing aspect of the earth's magnetism lies in the changes it has experienced in the past. That such changes occur was discovered quite early in the game, when Henry Gellibrand noticed in 1634 that the direction to which a compass needle pointed in London seemed to vary from year to year. From 1576, the earliest date for which appropriate records exist, a compass in London would have gone from 8° east of true north all the way over to 24° west in 1823, whereupon it would have begun meandering back until now it is about 8° west. Magnetic records for Paris, starting in 1617, exhibit similar wandering. From these data it would seem that the geomagnetic axis is moving around within the earth so that it makes a complete circle in about 500 years. But when records for other parts of the globe are examined, this conclusion is less attractive; these compass variations are probably local affairs not shared by the entire planet.

The strength of the geomagnetic field itself has been measured for over a century and in that period has dropped by about 6 per cent. This decrease is definitely not a local anomaly, since the measurements from which it is derived were obtained all over the world. The immediate conclusion that we can draw is that the field must originate in the liquid iron core of the earth, where physical changes can take place rapidly (a century is a very brief interval on a geological time scale), and not in the mantle (the outermost 1,800 miles of the earth), whose solid nature inhibits any but long-term phenomena. Although this does no more than reinforce our assumption that the earth's magnetism arises in the core because of the possibility of electric currents there, it is comforting to have such corroboration. Quite apart from these small but precisely known magnetic variations of the recent past, evidence has been found for changes of a spectacular nature that occurred much further back in the history of the earth.

From the earliest times it has been known that certain rocks are naturally magnetized, but it has been possible only recently to interpret the data so as to yield information about the magnetic field that existed when and where the rocks were formed. In studying fossil magnetism the procedure is to cut a specimen from a geological formation of known age, marking its orientation, and then, in the laboratory, to determine the direction in which it is magnetized. By comparing this direction with the orientation the specimen had in its parent rock, the local direction of the geomagnetic field (that is, the direction in which a compass needle would point) at the time the rock was formed can be found. And these directions often differ considerably from the direction of the present magnetic field.

Primary in the interpretation of fossil magnetism is the hypothesis that the geomagnetic and geographic poles have never been far apart. From a theoretical standpoint, as we shall see, this is a necessary consequence of the generation of the magnetic field in the liquid core; experimentally, there are indications that the present 11° angle between the geomagnetic axis and the rotational axis is unusually large and that this angle has averaged half this amount or less in the past.

Going on the assumption that the geomagnetic and geographic poles have always roughly coincided, the fossil-magnetism studies show that the earth's crust has shifted radically with respect to its interior. Figure 14.18 is a map of the world showing the tracks made by the North and South Poles in the past 500 million years. Three billion years ago the North Pole was somewhere in mid-Pacific and from there migrated via Japan and Siberia

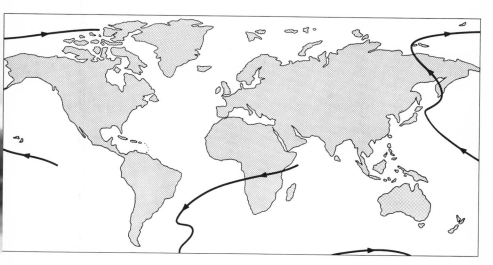

Fig. 14.18   The "wandering" of the North and South Poles in the past 500 million years according to magnetic data.

to its present position; the South Pole, meanwhile, moved across Africa and down the South Atlantic Ocean. We must beware of taking this particular map too seriously, but since climatic and magnetic data independently point to polar wandering of the kind shown, it must be somewhere near the truth.

A startling discovery in fossil magnetism is that the earth's magnetic field has reversed itself innumerable times. In numerous locations rock specimens of different ages exhibit opposite magnetic polarities, and it seems that the only explanation is that the earth's field has reversed itself more than once during the period of formation of the various rocks. These reversals do not represent an incessant sliding of the earth's crust over the mantle. Instead, each time, the geomagnetic field probably dropped to zero in a period of several thousand years and shortly was resurrected with the opposite polarity. Then, after a longer interval of from a hundred thousand to a few million years, the field reversed itself once more. Apparently these flip-flops are a regular feature of the dynamo within the earth's core and represent one more problem for those who have the temerity to try to explain such a dynamo.

Origin of the Earth's Magnetic Field

Finally, we come to the origin of the earth's magnetism. The most successful approach is based upon the quite new science of hydromagnetism. (New as it is, it has already undergone a change of name from the more cumbersome magnetohydrodynamics.) We must not be fooled into thinking that magnetic water is involved; rather, hydromagnetism treats of the interactions between magnetic and fluid dynamic effects, interactions that take place only in gases and liquids that are good conductors of electricity. Accordingly, hydromagnetism is concerned principally with such astrophysical phenomena as sunspots and galactic structure, but finds application also in the liquid iron core of the earth. (We might remark, as an aside, that hydromagnetic principles are being applied to the generation of thermonuclear power, which, when perfected, will represent almost as great a jump in technology as the first utilization of fire.)

One of the basic principles of physics is that all magnetic fields arise from electric currents. Conversely, all currents are surrounded by magnetic fields. When a coil of wire that is free to rotate is placed in a magnetic field, passing the proper current through it will cause its resultant magnetic field and the external magnetic field to exert forces on each other so as to turn the coil. This is the mechanism behind the electric motor, which operates through the agency of magnetic forces.

There is also a reciprocal effect: When a wire or other conductor of electricity is subjected to a changing magnetic field, a current is induced in it. If we rotate a coil of wire in a magnetic field, then, we have a generator of electric current.

Now let us connect an electric motor and a generator together, electrically and mechanically. At first glance it appears that the combination will go on forever, once we have given it an initial push, with the generator supplying power to the motor, which in turn rotates the generator to produce more power. Unfortunately this cannot actually occur because of the inevitable presence of friction, resistance in the connecting wires, and similar agencies of power loss. However, given a small external energy source sufficient to make up the power dissipated in friction, there is no reason why the motor generator should not continue indefinitely. And in the vicinity of the combination, we should encounter a magnetic field resulting from the various currents.

In essence, most theories of the earth's magnetism invoke a mechanism of this kind, in which there is a coupling of mechanical, electrical, and magnetic phenomena. The required auxiliary energy is presumably supplied by the solid central core in the form of heat, which then produces convective motions in the liquid iron much as a hot radiator produces convective motions in the surrounding air. There is no agreement on the manner in which the heat itself is produced: Some authorities feel that it comes from radio-

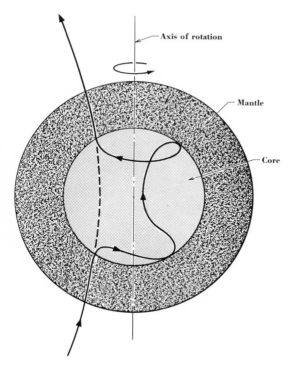

Fig. 14.19 *Formation of loops of magnetic lines of force within the earth's core, according to one theory of the origin of the geomagnetic field.* Energy is fed into the field through the formation of these loops, which in turn regenerate the external geomagnetic field.

active materials there, while others argue for chemical processes and crystallization as the answer. In any event the required heat is not large, and no one doubts that enough is present.

The chain of events in the core that leads to the observed geomagnetic field seems to be something like the following. Magnetic lines of force that exist initially are dragged around by the fluid motion so that they form closed loops, like parallels of latitude (Fig. 14.19). These loops cannot be detected outside the core but are believed to be very numerous there. It is in the formation of the loops that energy is fed into the magnetic field, since work must be done by the fluid motions in the core in stretching the original lines of force into their new shapes. Portions of the loops are then twisted by the combination of convection and the effect of the rotation into smaller loops that lie in meridional planes (a meridional plane corresponds to a thin orange segment). These loops then coalesce into the dipole—or bar-magnet—field we perceive at the earth's surface, and the cycle starts over.

Of course, the true picture is much more involved, but at least the mechanism described can take care of the main features of the observed field. There is no difficulty in explaining the alignment of the magnetic and rotational axes, since the symmetry of motion imposed by the spinning earth must be reflected in the field generated as a result of the spin. Further, reversals in the external dipole field can occur as a result of rather minor changes in the pattern of fluid currents in the core. And, most important, the feedback between the two systems of lines of force, the dipole and the internal closed loops, is self-regulating, so that the external field remains fairly constant in the intervals between reversals.

Self-examination

1. A magnetic field exerts no force on
   a. an electric current
   b. an unmagnetized iron bar
   c. a stationary electric charge
   d. a magnet

2. A device that does *not* rely upon the relationships between electric currents and magnetic fields is the
   a. electric motor
   b. generator
   c. galvanometer
   d. thermocouple

3. Electromagnetic induction is involved in
   a. the charging of a storage battery
   b. the production of a current by relative motion between a magnet and a wire

c. the charging of an electroscope without actually touching it with a charged rod

d. the operation of an electric motor

4. In a transformer, the immediate cause of the induced alternating current in the secondary coil is
   a. a varying magnetic field
   b. a varying electric field
   c. the iron core of the transformer
   d. a motion of the primary coil

5. A compass needle tends to
   a. line up at right angles to the lines of force of a magnetic field
   b. line up parallel with the lines of force of a magnetic field
   c. rotate slowly in a constant magnetic field
   d. point only toward the North Pole

6. A strong magnet
   a. attracts all substances
   b. attracts only iron and iron alloys and repels nothing
   c. attracts iron and iron alloys and repels other substances
   d. attracts some substances and repels others

7. The magnetic field of a bar magnet resembles most closely the magnetic field of
   a. a straight wire carrying a direct current
   b. a straight wire carrying an alternating current
   c. a wire loop carrying a direct current
   d. a wire loop carrying an alternating current

8. The earth's magnetic field
   a. varies in direction but not magnitude
   b. varies in magnitude but not direction
   c. varies in both magnitude and direction
   d. is centered exactly about the center of the earth

9. A charged particle moves through a steady magnetic field. The effect of the field is to change the particle's
   a. speed
   b. direction of motion
   c. acceleration
   d. energy

10. A dynamo is said to "generate electricity." What it actually does is act as a source of
    a. electric charge
    b. electrons
    c. magnetism
    d. potential difference

Problems

1. What kind of observations would you have to make in order to prepare a map showing the lines of force of the earth's magnetic field?

2. In what fundamental respect are the motor effect and the dynamo effect similar?

3. Would you expect to find direct or alternating current in
   a. the filament of a light bulb in your home?
   b. the filament of a light bulb in an automobile?
   c. the secondary coil of a transformer?

4. Given a coil of wire and a small light bulb, how can you tell whether the current in another coil is direct or alternating without touching the second coil or its connecting wires?

5. A long coil is suspended by a thread at its midpoint between the poles of a strong magnet. What (if anything) happens when a direct current is sent through the coil? When an alternating current is sent through the coil?

6. A transformer has a primary coil with 1,000 turns and a secondary coil with 200 turns. If the primary voltage is 660, what is the secondary voltage? What primary current is required if 1,000 watts is to be drawn from the secondary?

7. All atoms contain moving electrons. What connection would you suspect between this fact and the fact that all atoms exhibit magnetic properties?

8. What are the similarities and differences between galvanometers and simple direct-current motors?

9. What provides the energy required to "power" the dynamo mechanism that causes the earth's magnetic field?

10. Why is a piece of iron attracted to either pole of a magnet?

11. When a wire loop is rotated in a magnetic field, the direction of the current induced in the loop reverses itself twice per rotation. Why?

12. The shaft of a dynamo is much easier to turn when the dynamo is not connected to an outside circuit than when such a connection is made. Why?

13. An electric motor requires more current when it is started than when it is running continuously. Why?

Part IV

WAVES AND PARTICLES

CHAPTER 15 | ELECTROMAGNETIC WAVES

We are so accustomed to light—which is, after all, what we see with—that we seldom stop to wonder about its true nature. But something enters our eyes when we experience the sensation of vision, and it is by no means obvious just what that something is. The search for an explanation for light and its effects in terms of known physical principles was pursued for several centuries, but not until the essentials of electricity and magnetism were known was a satisfactory explanation found. It seems odd that light should be related to electrical and magnetic phenomena, and the discovery of the details of this relationship is one of the most noteworthy of all physical science.

Faraday and Maxwell

Let us begin with a little history. Michael Faraday, the son of a blacksmith, was apprenticed to a bookbinder in his youth, and schooled himself in chemistry and physics from the books he was learning to bind. At the age of twenty-one he obtained the humble position of bottle washer for Sir Humphry Davy at that chemist's great laboratory in the Royal Institution of London. Within twenty years the blacksmith's son succeeded Davy as head of the Institution. During those twenty years Faraday's experiments, particularly in chemistry, had won him wide acclaim in scientific circles. To the later years of his life belong the more famous investigations into electricity and magnetism that we discussed briefly in the last chapter. Never adept at mathematics, Faraday is remembered as one of physical science's greatest experimental geniuses. Like many of us, he felt the necessity of working with real, tangible things, such as the coils and magnets of his laboratory. To make real the electric and magnetic forces that he could not see or feel, Faraday invented *lines of force*—lines which do not exist, which give at best a crude picture of fields of force, but which students ever since have found useful in their early attempts to visualize the abstractions of electricity.

James Clerk Maxwell was born into an old and distinguished Scottish family in 1831, when Faraday was forty years old. Given the best education that England could provide, Maxwell became a precocious scientist. At fifteen he published his first paper; at twenty-five he was made professor of physics and astronomy at Cambridge. Maxwell was gifted with extraordinary mathematical ability; for him fields of force could be better expressed by equations than in terms of Faraday's lines. With his complicated equations, based largely on Faraday's experiments, Maxwell at length not only expressed the interconnections between electricity and magnetism but formulated a theory of light as well.

Many a moral could be drawn from the lives of these two men, so different in talent and in training, who stand out above the host of nineteenth-century scientists who were seeking an explanation for the mysterious phenomena of electricity. Their work is an especially good illustration of the progress of science from experiment to broad generalization. Sometimes experimental ability and theoretical insight are combined in the same person, but more often we find these faculties in different men. As Faraday's work paved the way for Maxwell, so the experiments of Lavoisier lay behind Dalton's atomic theory, the observations of Tycho Brahe behind Kepler's laws of planetary behavior, Galileo's experiments with falling bodies behind Newton's laws of motion.

Electromagnetic Waves

One of the startling results of Maxwell's calculations was the prediction that an electric charge moving with a changing velocity (in other words, an *accelerated* charge) would generate combined electrical and magnetic disturbances capable of traveling long distances through empty space. These disturbances are called *electromagnetic waves*. Such waves are difficult to visualize because they represent periodic changes in fields which are themselves difficult to imagine.

To get some idea of what is involved, we shall consider the three electrons A, B, and C of Fig. 15.1. These electrons are confined to wires so that they can move only up and down. Let us set electron A to vibrating up and down as though attached to an oscillating spring—something that is not hard to do in an actual experiment. As it goes up and down, this electron is alternately moving faster and slower. Now an accelerating electric charge is

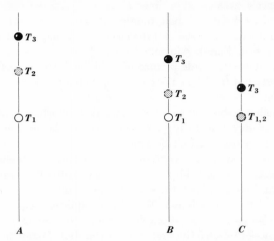

Fig. 15.1 *The electrons B and C are affected at different times by changes in the electric and magnetic fields because of the motion of the electron A.*

accompanied by a magnetic field that spreads out away from it, the magnetic lines of force sweeping over adjacent charges and causing them to move. When the charge slows down, the magnetic lines move in the opposite direction as the field shrinks back around it, and adjacent charges are impelled to reverse their motion. Hence the electrons *B* and *C* will move back and forth along their wires as the magnetic field around *A* builds up and dies down. In effect, the wires at *B* and *C* are similar to the secondary coils of a transformer, and alternating currents are induced in them by an alternating current in the wire in which electron *A* is moving.

In a transformer the secondary coil or coils are placed as close as possible to the primary to secure maximum efficiency. In the present experiment we are concerned with a different problem: Suppose that *B* and *C* are at a distance from *A*; then how long does it take for a motion in *A* to produce a response in *B* and *C*? Will *C* move at the same time as *B*, or later, because it is farther from *A*? Does the magnetic field build up and die down instantaneously or over a measurable period of time? Maxwell was the first to answer these questions satisfactorily. He showed that changes in the field around *A* are *not* instantaneous in all parts, in other words that *B* would start to move before *C*. The disturbance caused by *A*'s back-and-forth motion travels outward from *A* with the same speed as that of light, 186,000 mi/sec (3×10^8 m/sec), according to Maxwell's calculations.

During its motion *A* is surrounded not only by a magnetic field but by its electric field as well. The electric field travels with it as it moves back and forth, so that *B* and *C* are affected by moving electric lines of force in addition to lines of the magnetic field. Naïvely, we may think of the electric lines of force about A as long, straight ropes extending outward in all directions; when A moves, a kink travels outward along each rope, much as a kink will travel along a real rope if it is jerked at one end. Maxwell's equations predict that the "kinks," or the disturbances in the electric field, will travel outward from A with exactly the same speed as the magnetic disturbances and that their effect on B and C will be added to the magnetic effects.

Maxwell was led to the discovery of electromagnetic waves by an argument based on the symmetry of nature. We know that a changing magnetic field can give rise to a current in a suitable conductor, from which we conclude that such a field has an electric field associated with it. Maxwell proposed the converse, that a changing electric field aways has a magnetic field associated with it whose strength is proportional to the rate of change of the electric field. The mathematical formulation of this hypothesis is a persuasive one, but it must nevertheless meet the test of experiment. The weak electric fields produced by electromagnetic induction are easy to detect because metals offer so little resistance to the flow of charges. There is no such thing as a magnetic current, and it is accordingly very difficult to measure the feeble magnetic fields Maxwell proposed. However, if Maxwell was right, then electromagnetic waves must exist in which changing electric and magnetic fields are coupled together by both electromagnetic induction and the converse mechanism that he proposed. During Maxwell's lifetime electromagnetic waves remained a theoretical prediction. Finally, in 1887, the German physicist Heinrich Hertz showed experimentally that electromagnetic waves exist and behave exactly as Maxwell expected them to.

Waves

Let us consider exactly what is meant by a *wave* before going on to explore the properties of the electromagnetic variety. If we stand on an ocean beach, watching the waves roll in and break one after the other, we are impressed with the ceaseless motion toward the shore. At first we might guess that masses of water are moving bodily shoreward, carrying along pebbles and shells and bits of driftwood. A few minutes' observation, however, convinces us that this cannot be true, for between the breakers water rushes out to sea, and there is no accumulation of water on the shore. The overall motion seems to be merely an endless back-and-forth movement. We can see the details of the motion better if we move out beyond the breakers, say at the end of a pier or in a boat; now if we fix our attention on a floating cork or piece of seaweed, we find that its actual position changes very little. As the crest of each wave passes, the cork rises and appears to move shoreward; in the following trough it drops and moves an equal distance backward. On the whole its path is approximately circular, and we can guess that adjacent water particles must follow similar circular paths.

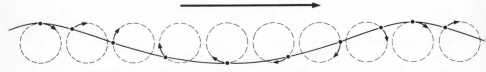

Fig. 15.2   Nature of a water wave in deep water. Each particle performs a periodic motion in a small circle, and because successive particles reach the top of their circles at slightly later times, their combination appears as a series of crests and troughs moving along the surface of the water.

The illusion of an overall movement toward the shore is explained by the fact that each particle of water performs its circular motion a trifle later than the last, as if the motion of one particle caused the next to move, and this one imparted its motion to another, so that the impulse was transmitted shoreward.   In other words, each particle has a periodic motion in a circle, and a regular succession of these periodic motions, each a little later than the last, gives the illusion of bodily movement toward shore (Fig. 15.2).

What does move shoreward is *energy*.   Most water waves at sea are produced by wind, and it is energy from the wind far out at sea that is transmitted by means of wave motion to the shore.   All familiar wave motions have this same characteristic: By a succession of periodic motions of individual particles, they accomplish a transfer of energy from place to place, but produce no bodily movement of matter in the direction of the waves.

Surface waves on water are the most familiar, but among the most complex, of the wave motions that a physicist must unravel.   Much simpler are the waves set up in a taut rope by a succession of jerks at one end (Fig. 15.3).   Obviously, the rope as a whole does not change position, but waves in the rope carry energy from the hand to the point of attachment.   If we fix our attention on one small segment of the rope, we will note that it moves up, then down, then up again as each wave passes, and that this motion is transmitted from one segment to the next down the length of the rope.   In other words, the motion of particles here is mostly perpendicular to the motion of the wave itself.   Such waves are called *transverse*.   Electro-

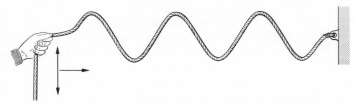

Fig. 15.3   Transverse waves. The waves travel along the rope, whose individual particles move back and forth perpendicular to the rope.

magnetic waves are transverse in that they consist of electrical and magnetic disturbances that are perpendicular to the direction in which the wave as a whole is moving through space.

Another type of wave can be illustrated by a long coiled spring suspended vertically (Fig. 15.4). If the bottom end of the spring is moved up and down, a series of *compressions* and *rarefactions* moves up the spring, compressions being places where the loops of the spring are pressed together and rarefactions places where they are stretched apart. Any one loop simply moves up and down, transmitting its motion to the next in line, and the regular succession of up-and-down movements gives rise to the compressions and

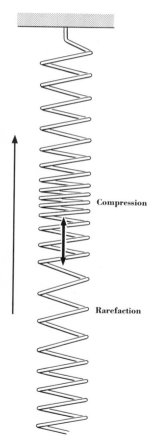

Compression

Rarefaction

Fig. 15.4   Longitudinal waves. *A coil of steel wire is suspended from above and momentarily compressed at the lower end, which causes regions of compression and rarefaction to move up the spring. The particles of the spring move back and forth parallel to the spring.*

rarefactions.   A similar motion would be produced in a line of people, each with his hands on his neighbor's shoulders, if someone were to push and pull alternately at one end of the line; the back-and-forth motion would be transmitted from one person to the next down the line.   Waves of this kind, in which the motion of individual units is along the same line that the wave itself travels, are called *longitudinal*.   Sound consists of longitudinal waves, with air molecules executing the back-and-forth motion (Fig. 15.5).

Water waves, on the basis of these definitions, could be described as having both transverse and longitudinal characteristics inasmuch as each particle moves partly horizontally, in the direction of the waves, and partly vertically, at right angles to the waves.

Describing Waves

All waves can be represented by a curve like that in Fig. 15.6.   The resemblance to transverse wave motion is easiest to see; in fact, the curve is an idealized picture of continuous waves in a rope like that of Fig. 15.3.   As the wave moves to the right, each point on the curve can be thought of as moving up or down along a path whose extremes are the heights of the high point and low point of the curve, just as any small segment of the rope would move. The resemblance to longitudinal waves is not so obvious.   Here we should

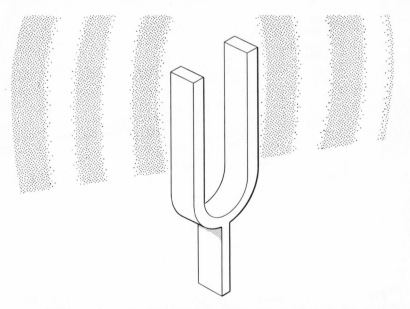

Fig. 15.5   Sound waves produced by a tuning fork.   *Alternate regions of compression and rarefaction move outward from the vibrating tines of the fork.*

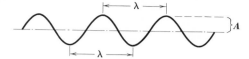

Fig. 15.6 *Describing a wave. The wavelength is λ, and the amplitude is A.*

s⌄y simply that high points of the curve represent maximum displacements of individual particles in one direction; low points, maximum displacements in the other direction.

A representation like Fig. 15.6 permits us to assign numbers to certain characteristics of a wave so that we can compare different waves quantitatively. The distance from crest to crest (or from trough to trough) is called the *wavelength,* usually symbolized by the Greek letter λ (lambda). The *speed* of the waves v is the rate at which each crest appears to move, and the *frequency f* is the number of crests that pass a given point each second. Now the number of waves that pass per second multiplied by the length of each wave should give the speed with which the waves travel; if 10 waves, each 2 ft long, pass in a second, then each wave must travel 20 ft during that second. In other words, frequency f times wavelength λ gives speed v:

$$v = \lambda f \tag{15.1}$$

This is a general relationship that applies to waves of all kinds. For example, big water waves on the open sea sometimes have wavelengths as great as 1,000 ft; they travel at roughly 70 ft/sec, so their frequency would be 0.07 sec^{-1}. As another example, sound in air travels at 1,100 ft/sec; the tone of middle C has a frequency of 261 vibrations per second and hence a wavelength of 4.2 ft. The tiny waves of visible light can be treated in exactly the same way: Red light has a speed of 3×10^8 m/sec, a wavelength of 7.5×10^{-7} m, and therefore a frequency of 4×10^{14} waves per second.

The *amplitude* of a wave refers to the heights of the crests and troughs. It would be represented by A in Fig. 15.6, and is defined in general as half the length of the path over which each particle moves. The amount of energy carried by waves evidently depends on their amplitude and their frequency, in other words, on the violence of the waves and the number of waves per second. It turns out that the energy is proportional to the square of each of these quantities.

Another characteristic of waves is called *waveform.* So far we have considered only waves produced by simple back-and-forth or up-and-down motions of particles, but the motions are commonly much more complicated. Such complications would be represented in a diagram like Fig. 15.6 by irregularities in the smooth waveform, irregularities like those shown in the lower diagram of Fig. 15.7. This kind of complication often results when

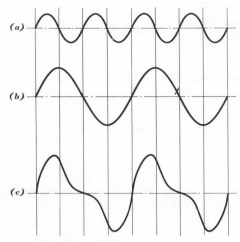

Fig. 15.7 *Complex wave at c is equivalent to a combination of two simple waves,* a *and* b, *traveling over the same path.*

two (or more) kinds of vibrational motion are imposed on the same material simultaneously, say when two people try to jerk the same stretched rope at different rates. Two simple wave motions may add together to give more complex motion, as Fig. 15.7 shows, and likewise a complex waveform can be analyzed into a combination of simple motions. In acoustics the waveform of a sound is what accounts for its "quality" or "timbre," while the frequency of a sound is called its "pitch."

Types of Electromagnetic Waves

Heinrich Hertz was not aware of the commercial possibilities of his experimental production of electromagnetic waves, and it remained for the Italian inventor Guglielmo Marconi to develop what we now call radio. Radio transmission is accomplished by means of electromagnetic waves produced by electrons oscillating hundreds of thousands to millions of times per second in the antenna of the sending station. When these waves strike the antenna of a receiving station, they cause the electrons there to vibrate in unison with those of the transmitter. By means of electronic devices of various kinds the receiver can be *tuned* so that it responds to a specific frequency of electromagnetic waves only, and thus, since each transmitter operates on a different frequency, a receiver can pick up the signals sent out by whatever station it wishes. The original current set up by the radio waves is very feeble, but it can be amplified in the receiver so that its variations are strong enough to produce sounds in a loudspeaker.

Radio waves are particularly useful because they have the property of being reflected from layers of ionized gas high in the earth's atmosphere. If it were not for this property, the direct reception of radio programs would be limited to short distances, for electromagnetic waves travel in straight lines and would be shielded from more distant receivers by the curvature of the earth. Since, however, the waves can bounce repeatedly between the upper atmosphere and the earth's surface, transmission is possible for long distances, even to the opposite side of the earth (Fig. 15.8).

In recent times methods have been found of generating electric currents with more rapid oscillations, and hence of producing electromagnetic waves of higher frequency (shorter wavelength). Frequencies of ordinary radio waves extend up to more than 10^6 oscillations per second, and those of waves used in short-wave broadcasting up to 3×10^7; waves with frequencies in the range from 3×10^7 to 3×10^{10} have found widespread use in television and radar. These shorter, high-frequency waves are not able to bounce back from ionized layers in the atmosphere, so direct reception of television is limited by the horizon. On the other hand, such waves are especially useful because they can be channeled easily into beams in particular directions and because the beams are reflected by solid objects like ships and airplanes; this is the principle behind radar detection.

Electromagnetic waves have been produced by causing charges to oscillate more than a million million times a second, and the limit has probably not yet been reached. But Maxwell's theory did not stop with predicting waves of these various frequencies; it went on to propose that *light itself is a*

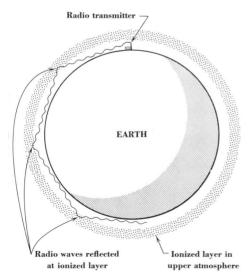

Fig. 15.8   *Long waves used in radio transmission are reflected back to the earth's surface from layers of ions in the upper atmosphere.*

form of electromagnetic wave motion. It was known before Maxwell's time that light showed characteristics of wave motion, but his work gave the first intimation that light, electricity, and magnetism were closely related. How close the relationship is and how intimately all three are connected with the innermost structure of matter, physicists have learned only during the present century.

Not only light but also many other kinds of radiation have been shown to consist of electromagnetic waves. Infrared radiation has wavelengths longer than those of visible light, and ultraviolet radiation has shorter wavelengths. Still shorter are the electromagnetic waves of X rays, and shorter yet the waves of gamma radiation from radium. The electromagnetic nature of all these radiations is shown only indirectly, but the demonstration that they are similar in nature to radio waves is beyond all doubt. Electromagnetic waves thus include an enormous range of frequencies and wavelengths, from radio waves a few miles in length, with frequencies less than 100,000 sec^{-1}, to waves

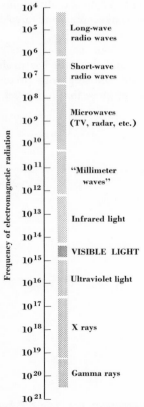

Fig. 15.9   The electromagnetic spectrum.

of gamma radiation less than 10^{-10} cm long and having frequencies greater than 10^{20} sec^{-1} (Fig. 15.9). Waves in various parts of this range have particular characteristics, but all have many properties in common, notably a speed in vacuum of 186,000 mi/sec (3×10^8 m/sec).

The Speed of Light

If light consists of electromagnetic waves that transport energy from one place to another, it should be possible to detect its motion and to measure its speed. However, this turns out to be a matter of great difficulty in practice. We switch on a lamp, and instantly the room is filled with light; there is no impression of anything spreading out from the lamp to the walls. We say that light comes to the earth from the sun, but nothing seems to move; we are simply bathed in a sea of solar luminosity. If we try to measure how fast light travels by arranging to have a distant light turned on at a specified time and then noting its arrival with a stop watch, we find no detectable lag between the turning on of the light and the time it reaches our eyes (an experiment first tried by Galileo). Evidently light moves so very rapidly that measurement of its speed requires more than simple experiments.

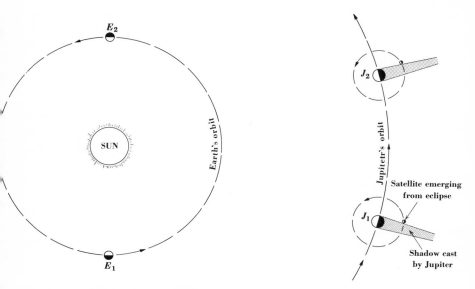

Fig. 15.10   Romer's measurement of the speed of light. *When the earth is at* E_1 *its distance from Jupiter is decreasing and the eclipses of the satellite occur earlier than predicted. Six months later, with the earth at* E_2 *and Jupiter at* J_2, *the distance is increasing and the eclipses occur later than predicted.*

The first measurement of the speed of light happened almost by accident. A contemporary of Isaac Newton, the Danish astronomer Olaf Romer, was making a careful study of the times when Jupiter eclipsed one of its satellites, in the hope that a table of these times would be useful to navigators in determining longitude at sea. Romer predicted the exact times of these eclipses, based upon the constant 42.5-hr period of satellite rotation, and then compared the figures with observations. He found that the predicted times were about 22 min in error after 6 months had elapsed, but the discrepancy disappeared after a year. Apparently the satellite decreased in speed when the earth was moving away from Jupiter so as to be "late" for its eclipse when the earth was farthest distant, and increased in speed in the next half of the earth's orbital circuit to be on time again when the earth was near Jupiter. Romer correctly supposed that the time differences were due to the difference in the paths which light from Jupiter had to follow to reach the earth (Fig. 15.10) ; as the earth circles the sun away from Jupiter, light takes longer and longer to reach us, while this time decreases as the earth approaches Jupiter on its return. Romer's estimate of the speed of light was not very accurate since neither the exact time delay nor the diameter of the earth's orbit was known correctly in those days, but modern figures give the same value as more direct measurements. Today it is known that the maximum apparent retardation of an eclipse of a Jovian satellite is just about 1,000 sec, and the earth's orbit has a diameter of twice the 93-million-mile sun-earth distance, or 186 million miles. Hence the speed of light, symbol c, is given by

$$c = \frac{\text{distance}}{\text{time}} = \frac{186,000,000 \text{ miles}}{1,000 \text{ sec}}$$
$$= 186,000 \text{ mi/sec}$$

The metric equivalent of this speed is 3×10^8 m/sec.

Accurate laboratory measurements of the speed of light became possible only in the mid-nineteenth century. The first successful attempt, by the French physicist Fizeau in 1849, was made by using a rapidly moving toothed wheel to interrupt a narrow beam of light (Fig. 15.11). The light was reflected from a mirror placed about 5 miles away, and the reflected beam was observed through the same toothed wheel. As long as the wheel turned slowly, the light passing through any gap between two teeth could reach the mirror, be reflected, and return through the same gap, so that the mirror would be visible to an observer behind the wheel. If, however, the wheel was going faster, the light originally passing through a gap would return to the wheel in time to strike the following tooth; thus it would be blocked off, and the mirror could no longer be seen through the wheel. When the wheel's speed was increased still further, the light reappeared, this time passing through the gap following the one it went through on the outward journey. The speed of the wheel gave the time needed for a tooth to move into the position of the adjacent gap. In this tiny fraction of a second the light had

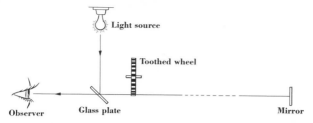

Fig. 15.11 *Fizeau's method of determining the speed of light.*
A beam of light is directed onto a partly silvered glass plate, which reflects part of the beam through the edge of a toothed wheel to a distant mirror. The mirror reflects the light back along the same path, and part of it is transmitted to the observer through the lightly silvered glass. When the wheel is turned rapidly, light moving through a gap in the wheel is reflected from the mirror in time to meet the adjacent tooth on its return journey, so that no light reaches the observer.

traversed a distance of about 10 miles, and these two figures provided the necessary data for computing the speed of light.

Fizeau's method was improved the following year by his colleague Foucault, with the introduction of a rotating mirror in place of the toothed wheel. This procedure was greatly refined by the American physicist Michelson in a long series of experiments which gave a very accurate figure for the speed of light. In recent years other methods have been devised for checking Michelson's results. Today the accepted figure for the speed of light in vacuum is

$$c = 2.998 \times 10^8 \text{ m/sec}$$

For most purposes it is sufficiently accurate to let $c = 3 \times 10^8$ m/sec.

The Doppler Effect

We all know that sounds produced by vehicles moving toward us seem higher-pitched than usual, whereas sounds produced by vehicles receding from us seem lower-pitched than usual. Anybody who has listened to the whistle of a train as it approaches and then leaves a station, or to the siren of a fire engine as it passes by at high speed, is aware of these apparent changes in frequency, called the *Doppler effect*. A similar effect occurs in light waves, and is one of the techniques by which astronomers detect and measure stellar motions. Stars emit light which contains only certain characteristic wavelengths; when a star moves either toward or away from the earth, these wavelengths are, respectively, shorter or longer than usual. From the amount of the shift it is possible to calculate the speed with which the star is approaching or receding.

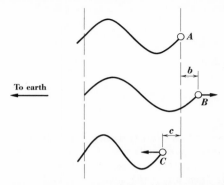

Fig. 15.12   The Doppler effect in starlight. *Star* A *is stationary; star* B *is receding from the earth; star* C *is approaching the earth. Distance* b *shows how far* B *has moved during the emission of a single light wave, hence how much the wavelength is increased. Distance* c *shows the decrease in wavelength due to approach.*

Let us see how the Doppler effect comes about. Imagine a star emitting light of only one wavelength. If the star is receding, it moves a short distance away from us between the emission of each wave and the next (Fig. 15.12). Thus each wave starts from a point a little more distant than the last, and the distance between waves appears to be a little greater than it would be if the star were motionless. Now a greater distance between waves, or a longer wavelength, means a slight change in color toward the red. So if the star were at first motionless and then started to recede, the single line in its spectrum would shift toward the red end, the amount of shift depending on the rate of motion. Similar reasoning applies to an approaching star: The wavelength of its light would be shortened because the star moves a short distance toward us between each wave and the next.

In the radiation from a star all wavelengths are shifted by the same amount in one direction or the other. This shift records only motion of approach or recession; motion of a star across the line of sight causes no change in the wavelengths it emits.

Self-examination

1. The distance from crest to crest of any wave is called its
    a. frequency
    b. wavelength
    c. speed
    d. amplitude

2. Which of the following does *not* consist of electromagnetic waves?
   a. X rays
   b. radar waves
   c. sound waves
   d. infrared waves

3. Electromagnetic waves transport
   a. electric charge
   b. alternating current
   c. energy
   d. wavelength

4. The scientist whose theoretical work showed that light is an electromagnetic phenomenon was
   a. Faraday
   b. Maxwell
   c. Hertz
   d. Marconi

5. A boat at anchor is rocked by waves whose crests are 100 ft apart and whose velocity is 25 ft/sec. These waves reach the boat once every
   a. 2,500 sec
   b. 75 sec
   c. 4 sec
   d. 0.25 sec

6. Maxwell based his theory of electromagnetic waves on the hypothesis that a changing electric field gives rise to
   a. an electric current
   b. a stream of electrons
   c. a magnetic field
   d. longitudinal waves

7. Of the following properties of a wave, the one that is independent of the others is its
   a. velocity
   b. amplitude
   c. wavelength
   d. frequency

8. A kilocycle is equal to 10^3 cycles. What is the wavelength of the electromagnetic waves sent out by a radio station whose frequency is 660 kc/sec?
   a. 2.2×10^{-3} m
   b. 4.55×10^2 m
   c. 4.55×10^3 m
   d. 1.98×10^{14} m

Problems

1. We say that light is a transverse wave. What is it that varies at right angles to the direction in which a light wave travels?

2. The light-year is an astronomical unit of length equal to the distance light travels in a year. What is the length of a light-year in miles?

3. What is the wavelength of radio waves whose frequency is 500 kc/sec? 1,500 kc/sec? 10 mc/sec? (1 kc = 10^3 cycles; 1 mc = 10^6 cycles.)

4. The speed of sound waves in water is approximately 4,700 ft/sec. If an echo-sounding device on a ship measures an interval of 3 sec between the emission of a sound pulse and the reception of its echo from the sea bottom, how deep is the water?

5. Why do the electromagnetic waves set up by the alternating-current power lines in your home not produce disturbances in your radio and television receivers?

6. A certain groove in a phonograph record travels past the needle at a speed of 40 cm/sec. The frequency of the sound that is produced is 3,000 cycles/sec. Find the wavelength of the wavy indentations of the groove.

7. It is desired to repeat Fizeau's determination of the speed of light using a mirror 7 miles from the light source. If the toothed wheel has 100 teeth, how fast must it turn for light leaving through one gap to return through the next gap?

CHAPTER 16 | *OPTICS*

Much of the behavior of light can be understood without reference to its electromagnetic nature. Such phenomena as reflection, refraction, dispersion, and interference are common to all kinds of waves, and because of this universality the study of optics has value well outside the domain of lenses and mirrors. To give but two examples, the analysis of earthquake waves has provided detailed information on the earth's interior, and, as we shall see in Chap. 18, the notion of "matter waves" has turned out to be extremely fruitful in understanding atomic structure.

Light Rays

Early in life we learn that light travels in straight lines. As direct evidence we might point to the sharp shadows cast by objects illuminated by small light sources and to the straight beams produced when light from small holes penetrates the recesses of a dusty basement. Actually, our entire physical orientation to the world about us, our sense of the location of things in space, depends on *assuming* that light follows straight-line paths. In everyday life we use this property to define straightness, rather than Euclid's definition about "the shortest distance between two points"; if we want to know whether a given line is straight or not, we sight along it instead of trying to determine whether it is the shortest of all possible lines between its end points.

Just as familiar, however, is the fact that light does not always follow straight lines. We see most objects by *reflected* light, light that has been turned abruptly on striking a surface. The distorted appearance of objects seen through a glass of water, through glass objects of irregular shape, or through the heated air rising above a flame, all testify to the ability of light to turn from a straight path. In these cases we say that the light is bent, or *refracted,* and we note that this occurs when light moves through transparent materials having different densities.

Although we recognize, with the intellectual part of our minds, that light can be reflected and refracted, our eyes are so accustomed to finding light traveling along straight paths that we are often deceived about the true positions of objects. When you look in a mirror, for example, you actually see light that has traveled in a broken path to the mirror and back again, but your eyes tell you that the light has followed a straight path from your image behind the mirror. When you look at someone standing in shallow water, his legs appear foreshortened; actually, light coming from water into air is bent, but your eyes refuse to believe this is happening and give you the illusion of foreshortening.

A good deal can be learned about the behavior of light and our reactions to it simply from a study of the paths that light follows in various situations. Since light appears to travel in straight paths, we can represent its motion by geometrically straight lines called *rays*. In nature there are no such things as rays, for light sources and light beams always have finite size. But rays are a convenient abstraction, and we can visualize what we mean by thinking of a narrow pencil of light in a darkened room.

Note that, in making this abstraction, we exclude many familiar properties of light—its heating effect and its color, for example. Nor does this abstraction imply any hypothesis about the nature of light; we could suppose that it consisted of particles or waves or even streams of continuous fluid, and rays would still be convenient for describing its behavior. As a matter of fact, in using rays we do not even need to know which way light moves; the first man to investigate these phenomena carefully, the Greek geometer Euclid, thought that something traveled from the eye to the object seen rather than vice versa, but this faulty hypothesis did not invalidate his conclusions. Rays of light are a beautiful example of how far we can go in science by using a simple idealized model having no actual counterpart in nature and by ignoring those aspects of a phenomenon with which we are not at the moment concerned.

Reflection

When you look at yourself in a mirror, light from all parts of your body (this is reflected light, of course, but we may treat it as if it originated in your body) is reflected from the mirror back to your eyes (Fig. 16.1). Light from your foot, for example, follows the path $CC'E$; your eyes, looking along the ray $C'E$ and unconsciously projecting it in a straight line, see your foot

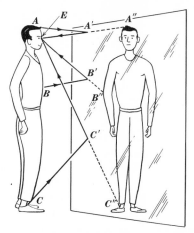

Fig. 16.1 *Formation of an image in a plane mirror. The image appears to be behind the mirror because we instinctively respond to light as though it travels in straight lines.*

at the proper distance but apparently behind the mirror at C''. A ray from the top of your head is reflected at A' and your eyes see the point A as if it were behind the mirror at A''. Rays from other points of your body are similarly reflected, and in this manner a complete *image* is formed behind the mirror.

The fact that the image is a perfect replica of your body (provided the glass of the mirror has no imperfections) means that each ray must be reflected from the mirror at the same angle as the angle of approach; in other words, the angle made by CC' with the mirror must equal the angle made by $C'E$. This property of rays is expressed by the statement that *the angle of incidence equals the angle of reflection.* In order to make this rule applicable to curved as well as plane surfaces, the angles are usually measured from a perpendicular to the surface (Fig. 16.2) rather than from the surface itself.

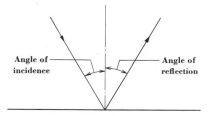

Fig. 16.2 *When light is reflected, the angle of incidence equals the angle of reflection.*

Why do we not see images of ourselves in walls and furniture as well as in mirrors? This is simply a question of the relative roughness of surfaces. Rays of light are reflected from walls just as they are from mirrors, but the reflected rays are scattered in all directions by the many surface irregularities. We see the wall by the scattered light reflected from it.

Refraction

Next, consider what happens when light reaches your eyes from an object under water. If you look obliquely through a water surface at a stone lying on the bottom, the stone appears to be lying at a higher point than it actually is (Fig. 16.3). This is a restatement of the familiar observation that water depths are deceiving, that a body of water is always deeper than it appears to be. Another aspect of the same phenomenon is the apparent shortening of a friend's body when he is standing in water and you look at him from the side. The explanation depends on the bending, or *refraction*, of light as it moves from water into air: A ray of light from the stone in Fig. 16.3 follows the broken path *ABE* to your eye, but your eye deceives you by telling your brain that the segment *BE* is part of the straight-line path originating at *A'*.

Note that rays of light from under water are bent *toward* the water surface as they emerge into air. A ray starting in air and going obliquely into water would follow the same path in reverse, as can be shown experimentally by letting a slender pencil of light fall on the surface of slightly turbid water in a darkened room. We may generalize the behavior of light during refraction by saying that rays going obliquely from one medium into another are bent away from a perpendicular to the surface if the second medium is less dense than the first, toward the perpendicular if the second medium is more dense (Fig. 16.4). Light moving from air into glass, for

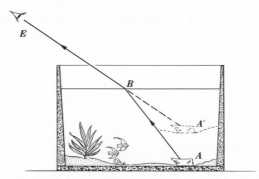

Fig. 16.3   *Light is refracted when it travels obliquely from one medium to another; here the effect of refraction is to make the water appear shallower than it actually is.*

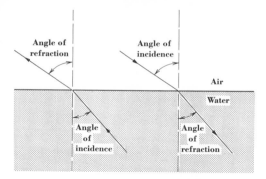

Fig. 16.4 *Light rays are bent away from the perpendicular when they leave a dense medium, and are bent toward the perpendicular when they enter a dense medium. The paths taken by light rays are always reversible.*

example, is bent toward the perpendicular; light moving from glass into air or from glass into water is bent away from the perpendicular.

The phenomenon of refraction occurs whenever light passes from one medium into another in which its speed is different. Figure 16.5 shows two rays of light, I and II, that are part of a beam of light going from air into a glass plate. Ray I reaches the glass first, at point A; at this time ray II is at A'. After some time interval t ray II enters the glass at B', ray I

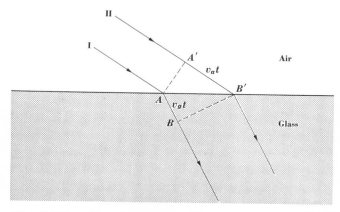

Fig. 16.5 *The phenomenon of refraction occurs whenever light passes from one medium into another in which its speed is different. Here two rays of light, I and II, pass from air, in which their speed is v_a, to glass, in which their speed is v_g. Because v_g is less than v_a, A'B' is longer than AB, and the beam of which I and II are part changes in direction when it enters the glass.*

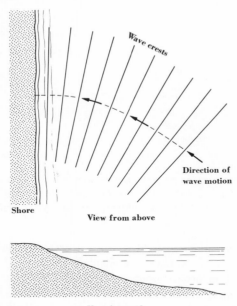

Shore

View from above

View from side

Fig. 16.6   Refraction of water waves. *Waves approaching shore obliquely are turned because they move more slowly in shallow water near shore.*

having meanwhile proceeded to *B*. The distance *A'B'* is equal to $v_a t$, where v_a is the speed of light in air, and the distance *AB* is equal to $v_g t$, where v_g is the speed of light in glass. Since light travels more slowly in glass than in air, *AB* is less than *A'B'*, and the two rays again proceed parallel to each other but in a direction different from their original one.

Water waves approaching a sloping beach provide a conspicuous illustration of refraction. No matter what direction the wind may be blowing from, the direction of motion of waves near shore is practically at right angles to the shore (Fig. 16.6). Further out in open water the direction of motion may be oblique, but the waves turn as they move in so that their crests become parallel with the shoreline. The explanation is straightforward. As a wave moves obliquely shoreward, its near-shore end encounters shallow water where friction with the bottom slows it down. More and more of the wave is slowed as it continues to move, and the slowing becomes more pronounced as the water gets shallower. As a result the whole wavefront swings around until it is moving almost directly shoreward. The wave has turned because part of it is forced to move more slowly than the remainder. Physically, this kind of refraction is no different in origin from that exhibited by light waves.

Color

Useful as the ray hypothesis is, light is obviously far too complex a phenomenon to be understood entirely in terms of so simple a concept. One of the prominent aspects of light with which the hypothesis of rays cannot give much help is color.

If white light is used in experiments with lenses, colors appear annoyingly as fringes that tend to blur the outlines of images. Similar color fringes appear in field glasses and telescopes, unless the lenses are specially constructed to eliminate this effect. Something in the process of refraction through glass seems to produce color, and we can make the colors especially strong by using a prism instead of a lens. In this case white light appears to spread itself out into a rainbow band of color, or *spectrum*, the colors showing the familiar sequence from red through orange and yellow to green, blue, and violet. If we use our accustomed method of representation by rays, we draw a single ray for the incident white light and a succession of rays for the refracted colors (Fig. 16.7).

We interpret this experiment today by saying that white light contains a variety of wavelengths, each of which evokes a different response by the eye so as to give the sensation of a particular color, and that the prism separates these wavelengths into different paths. The prism accomplishes the separation by refracting light of different wavelengths through different angles, red light showing the least refraction and violet the most. When the experiment was first studied intensively nearly 300 years ago by Isaac Newton, none of these conclusions was obvious. Colors were thought to be *qualities* that light could assume under various conditions; one color could supposedly be changed to another, and white light was considered no different from the rest. Only by a long series of careful experiments was Newton able to establish the permanence of the different colors and their relation to white light, concepts that now seem to us so easy and so reasonable because we have grown up with them in our intellectual background.

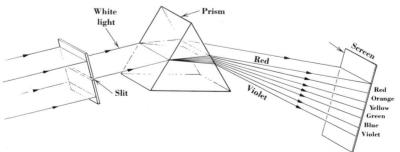

Fig. 16.7 *Formation of a spectrum by the refraction of white light in a glass prism.* The different colors blend into one another smoothly.

Detailed analysis of the colors present in any kind of light is accomplished by means of a *spectroscope,* an instrument that has played a central role in the development of modern physics and astronomy. The simplest form of spectroscope consists of a prism placed between two cylindrical tubes (Fig. 16.8). One of the tubes has a narrow slit at one end through which the light to be examined is admitted. The light is spread out into its separate colors by the prism and then passes down the second tube to the eyepiece. The tubes also contain a system of lenses that focuses an image of the slit on the eyepiece, so that each separate color appears as an image of the slit. If all colors are present, the slit images overlap and the spectrum is a continuous rainbow. If only a few colors are present, the spectrum consists of a few bright lines.

Any solid or liquid material, or any gas if sufficiently compressed, when it is heated until it glows brightly, gives out light of all colors. At lower temperatures the most intense radiation is at the red end of the spectrum ("red heat"); as the temperature rises, the greatest intensity shifts to the middle of the spectrum, and the light appears white ("white heat"); at still higher temperatures the light becomes bluish. Because of this relation between color and temperature, astronomers can estimate the temperatures of stars from the intensity of various parts of their spectra.

Luminous gases at low or moderate pressures ordinarily produce light of only a few colors to yield spectra consisting of a few bright lines. These are *discontinuous spectra,* contrasted with the *continuous,* rainbowlike spectra of heated solids. Thus the sodium-vapor lights used to illuminate foggy roads give a spectrum restricted largely to two lines close together in the orange-yellow section; the neon lights that adorn our city streets have a spectrum consisting of a few lines near the red end.

Colors of objects that we see by reflected light depend on the kind of light falling on them and on their composition. If an object can reflect red light but absorbs other colors, it will appear red in sunlight; if it reflects chiefly green light, it will appear green in sunlight; and so on. Most objects reflect or absorb more than one color, and the color we see is a combination

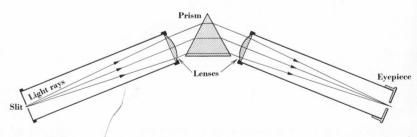

Fig. 16.8 A spectroscope, showing the arrangement of slit, prism, and lenses.

of those that are reflected.   Obviously, an object can reflect a certain color only if that color is present in the light falling on it; thus, in sodium light, a red or green object will appear black.   The ghastly hues that even the most carefully made-up complexions assume under sodium or mercury light are due simply to the absence in these lights of the colors that skin and cosmetics normally reflect.

Some colors have a different origin.   The blue of the sky, for example, is due to scattering of the sun's light by molecules and dust particles in the atmosphere.   Blue light is scattered more effectively than red; hence the sky, which we see only by scattered light, has an excess of blue, and the sun itself is a little more yellowish or reddish than it would appear if we had no atmosphere.   At sunrise or sunset, when the sun's light must traverse great thicknesses of dust-laden air, the scattering of its blue light is more pronounced, and the sun is often a brilliant red.

Interference

The phenomena of reflection, refraction, and color can all be explained by any one of several hypotheses about the nature of light.   Historically, two famous hypotheses were formulated toward the end of the seventeenth century, the *corpuscular* hypothesis of Newton and the *wave* hypothesis proposed by Newton's great Dutch contemporary, Christian Huygens.   According to the corpuscular idea, light consists of tiny particles (corpuscles) moving very rapidly, like a stream of bullets from a machine gun.   Light is reflected because these bullets bounce back from surfaces they strike, and it is refracted because the bullets are attracted more by one substance than by another. Colors are explained by supposing that each color has its own particular kind of particle.   In the wave hypothesis, on the other hand, light is assumed to consist of periodic vibrations traveling outward from the light source, like ripples on a pond produced when a falling pebble disturbs the surface.   Color is explained by assuming that each color has a particular wavelength.

Each hypothesis provides a good explanation for many properties of light, but each has serious drawbacks.   Newton's particles must be assumed weightless, or nearly so, because an object may absorb light indefinitely without growing heavier, and furthermore the particles must travel enormously faster than do other material objects.   The wave hypothesis, on the other hand, faces the difficulty that light travels readily across empty space; if light consists of periodic vibrations, what is it that vibrates?   Huygens' answer was to assume that all space is filled with a weightless, elastic medium called ether, whose vibrations affect our eyes as light.

In the seventeenth century experimental means were not available for making a decision between the two hypotheses.   It is one of the ironies of history that Newton made the first careful study of the phenomenon of interference that later on was to prove his ideas wrong.

Interference refers to the adding together of two or more waves of the same kind that pass by the same point in space at the same time. A simple demonstration of interference is shown in Fig. 16.9. If waves are started along the stretched strings *AC* and *BC* by shaking them at the ends *A* and *B*, the single string *CD* will be affected by both. Each portion of *CD* must respond to two different impulses at the same time, and its motion will therefore be determined by the sum of the effects of the two original waves. When *A* and *B* are shaken in unison, the waves add together, so that in *CD* the crests are twice as high and the troughs twice as deep as in *AC* and *BC*. This situation is called *constructive* interference. On the other hand, if *A* and *B* are shaken just out of step with each other, wave crests in *AC* will arrive at *C* just when troughs get there from *BC*. As a result, crest matches trough, the wave impulses cancel each other out, and *CD* remains stationary. This situation is called *destructive* interference. As another possibility, if *A* is

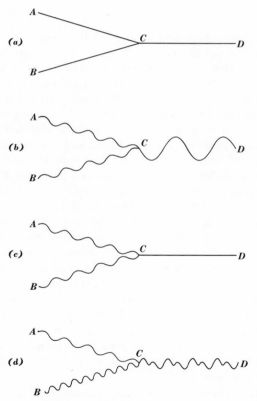

Fig. 16.9   *(a) Waves started along stretched strings* AC *and* BC *will interfere at* C. *(b) Constructive interference. (c) Destructive interference. (d) A mixture of constructive and destructive interference.*

shaken less strongly than but twice as rapidly as *B*, the two waves add together to give a complex waveform (Fig. 16.9*d*). The variations are endless, and the resulting waveforms depend upon the amplitudes, wavelengths, and timing of the incoming waves.

The interference of water waves is shown by ripples in Fig. 16.10. Ripples spreading out from the vibrating rods affect the same water particles: In some directions crests from one source arrive at the same time as crests from the other source, and ripples are reinforced, while between these regions of prominent motion are narrow lanes where the water is quiet, representing directions in which crests from one source arrive together with troughs from the other, so that the wave motions cancel.

The interference of light is readily exhibited by shining light obliquely on a soap film (Fig. 16.11) or a film of air between two glass plates (Fig. 16.12). The results are clearest if we use light of only one color, say the yellow light of a sodium-vapor lamp; a thin film in this kind of light shows a succession of yellow and black bands, in lines or circles or irregular figures.

Newton recognized that such bands must somehow be produced by re-

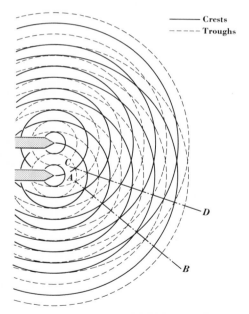

————— Crests
— — — — Troughs

Fig. 16.10   *Interference of water waves.* Ripples are spreading out across the surface of a shallow tank from the two sources shown at the left of the drawing. In some directions (for example AB) the ripples reinforce each other and waves are prominent. In other directions (for example CD) the ripples are out of step and destroy each other, so that waves are small or absent.

Fig. 16.11   Interference bands produced by reflections of light from a soap film. The film is stretched across a loop of wire.

flection and refraction at the surfaces of the film, but in order to explain them in detail he was forced into the awkward assumption that the light particles were "put into fits of easy reflexion and easy transmission" by vibrations set up by the action of the particles on the material of the film. The wave hypothesis gives a much more direct and reasonable explanation, as illustrated by Fig. 16.13. This drawing shows a greatly enlarged cross section of a part of the film. Light falling on the film is reflected twice, once from the upper surface and once from the lower surface. Light rays from the two reflections travel upward along nearly the same path, and their waves interfere. At some places on the film wave crests in the reflected rays are out of step, so that one cancels the effect of the other, while at other places wave crests are in step and reinforce each other. Where cancellations occur, the film appears black because no light propagates; where reinforcement occurs, it is bright yellow. What effect interference will have at any point on the film depends on the thickness of the film at that point, since the thickness determines how far one reflected ray lags behind the other.

When white light is used instead of monochromatic light, the reflected rays of one color will be in step at a given point while rays of other colors

 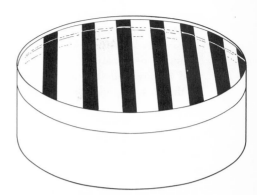

Fig. 16.12   Interference of light by reflection from thin air films. *In each drawing the two glass plates are touching at one edge, very slightly separated at the opposite edge, leaving a wedge-shaped film of air between them. Light reflected from one surface of the film interferes with light reflected from the other surface. In the right-hand drawing the surfaces are optically plane, while in the left-hand drawing they are somewhat uneven.*

will not.   Hence, rather than white and black bands, the film shows a succession of brilliant colors.   These are the rainbow effects we see so often in bubbles and in oil films on water.

Interference is a particularly important property of wave motion, because it can often be used to test whether an unknown form of radiation consists of waves or of streams of tiny particles.   In the case of light, the phenomenon of interference gives a clear verdict in favor of the wave hy-

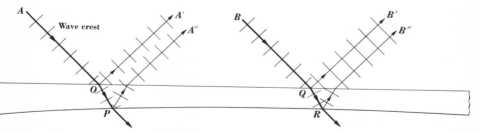

Fig. 16.13   Cross section of soap film in Fig. 16.11, greatly enlarged. *AO and BQ are two rays of monochromatic light falling on the film. AO is reflected in the two rays OA' and PA'', and BQ is reflected in the rays QB' and RB''. In each case the reflected rays interfere. OA' and PA'' cancel each other because their waves are out of step, while QB' and RB'' reinforce each other.*

pothesis. This hypothesis was not generally accepted until early in the nineteenth century, when Thomas Young established the interference of light beyond all doubt with experiments involving light from a single source passing through two pinholes close together. In the meantime the corpuscular theory, backed by Newton's great name, had been considered correct. After Young's demonstration the superiority of Huygens' ideas seemed evident, and through all the nineteenth century waves in the "ether" were regarded as the only possible explanation of light.

Newton was wrong, but he was not so far wrong as nineteenth-century physicists believed. In the present century, as we shall see in Chap. 18, the corpuscular theory has in a sense been resurrected, but in a transfigured form that Newton would scarcely recognize.

Light as an Electromagnetic Wave

Maxwell's great accomplishment was to specify very precisely the nature of light waves. The waves themselves had been shown to exist with the help of a variety of interference experiments, but Maxwell went on to demonstrate that they must consist of periodic changes in electric and magnetic fields. The electromagnetic waves of Maxwell's theory have all the essential properties found in light waves.

It is possible to measure in a direct way how long the waves of light are. Red light turns out to have a wavelength of 0.00007 cm, and violet light about half as much. If these numbers and the speed of light are substituted in the equation $v = \lambda f$, the frequencies of vibration can be calculated. They turn out to be prodigious, ranging from 4×10^{14} to 8×10^{14} vibrations per second. If these vibrations are produced by oscillating electric charges, like the longer electromagnetic waves of radio and television, then somewhere in a luminous material charges must be moving back and forth at these unimaginable rates. Maxwell had no way of knowing what these moving charges might be, but today we can identify them with the electrons inside atoms and molecules.

To be able to describe light waves as disturbances in electric and magnetic fields and to specify precisely their wavelengths and frequencies is certainly most satisfying. On the philosophical side it enables us to explain the behavior of light and to correlate light with electricity and magnetism. On the practical side it makes possible predictions about how light can be used and controlled. Yet it is still hard to believe that light can move across empty space, both through the best vacuum we can prepare in our laboratories and through the still better vacuum between the stars.

We can assume, as early scientists did, that light travels as vibrations in an ether. But this is not wholly satisfactory, because the ether must be assumed to have strange and seemingly contradictory properties. Maxwell, himself convinced that the assumption of ether was necessary, pinpointed the difficulty by identifying light with disturbances in fields. The fields may themselves be described as "strains" in the ether which cause magnets or electric charges in the fields to move. This brings us back to the problem we met in our first discussion of electric forces in Chap. 12, the problem of explaining how such forces can act across empty space. Thus Maxwell introduced a measure of simplicity by replacing two difficulties with one: The propagation of light involves the same fundamental question as the existence of electric and magnetic fields.

In modern times the concept of the ether has been abandoned because efforts to detect it experimentally have been uniformly unsuccessful (Chap. 17). The idea lingers on in such expressions as "ether waves" for radio waves or programs coming "over the ether," but scientists no longer use the term seriously. We speak now, rather, of light waves traveling through empty space and of electric and magnetic fields as disturbances in space. On the face of it there seems little difference between *waves in ether* and *waves in space;* we have merely replaced one mysterious word with another. The point is that we need not ascribe specific properties to empty space, as we do to a supposed substance like ether; the disadvantage is that we leave open the essential mystery of how wave motion is possible without a medium for the waves to travel in. We confine ourselves to describing the waves and their effects as accurately as possible, granting that the waves exist because we know what they can do. This is always the physicist's pragmatic viewpoint; to go beyond what can be measured into pure speculation is not the job of the scientist.

Self-examination

1. Light waves
   a. require air or another gas to travel through
   b. require ether to travel through
   c. require electric and magnetic fields to travel through
   d. can travel through a perfect vacuum

2. The term *refraction* refers to
   a. the bending of light rays when they strike a mirror
   b. the bending of light rays when they enter a different medium
   c. the fact that white light is made up of many colors
   d. the fact that light travels in straight lines in a uniform medium

3. A spectroscope
   a. spreads a beam of light out into its component colors
   b. is a device for examining the rainbow
   c. is a telescope modified to examine colored stars
   d. mixes colors to produce any desired hue

4. The light emitted by a luminous object comes from
   a. the ether in its atoms
   b. glowing electrons in its atoms
   c. moving electrons in its atoms
   d. combustion on the atomic level

5. The red light emitted by a neon sign comes from
   a. a metal wire inside the glass tubing, which is heated until red hot by a current passing through it
   b. a luminous red liquid inside the glass tubing
   c. a luminous gas at low pressure inside the glass tubing
   d. the oxidation of neon within the glass tubing

6. When we see a tree, the light that reaches our eyes
   a. has undergone interference in passing through the tree
   b. has been decomposed into a spectrum by the tree
   c. has been reflected by the tree
   d. has been refracted by the tree

7. The property of light waves that leads to the phenomenon of color is their
   a. velocity
   b. amplitude
   c. quality
   d. wavelength

8. A phenomenon that can only be explained if light consists of waves is
   a. reflection
   b. refraction
   c. interference
   d. the ether

Problems

1. Devise an experiment to show that light is a form of energy.

2. What is the height of the smallest mirror in which you could see yourself at full length?   Use a diagram to explain your answer.

3. Why is light sometimes spoken of in terms of rays and sometimes in terms of waves?

4. Some stars appear red, some yellow, and some blue.   Which has the highest temperature?   Which the lowest?

5. When a fish looks up through the water surface at an object in the air, will the object appear to be its normal size and distance above the water?   Use a

diagram to explain your answer, and assume that the fish's eye, like the human eye, is accustomed to interpreting light rays as straight lines.

6. What color would red cloth appear if it were illuminated by light from
   a. the sun?
   b. a neon sign?
   c. a sodium-vapor lamp?

7. Why do large bodies of water appear bluish? How would the sky appear to an astronaut above the earth's atmosphere during the day? During the night?

8. Compare the histories of phlogiston and ether. Why was each introduced, and what led to its abandonment?

9. When a beam of white light passes perpendicularly through a flat pane of glass, it is not dispersed into a spectrum. Why not?

10. The period of daylight is increased by a small amount because of the refraction of sunlight by the earth's atmosphere. Show how this effect comes about with the help of a diagram.

11. A diamond shows flashes of color when held in white light. Why? If the diamond were exposed to red light, what would happen?

CHAPTER 17 | RELATIVITY

All physical science is ultimately concerned with measurement, and the theory of relativity is no more than an analysis of how measurements depend upon the observer as well as upon what is observed. From relativity emerges a new mechanics in which there are intimate relationships between space and time, mass and energy. Without these relationships it would be impossible to understand the microscopic world within the atom, whose elucidation is the central problem of modern physics.

What Is Relativity?

To approach the meaning of relativity, let us begin with a simple experiment. Suppose that you are on a moving train and that I am observing you from the station platform. You proceed to roll two balls along a level table, one toward the front end of the car and the other toward the rear, and both of us measure the speed of each ball. Your results will indicate that the balls are moving with the same speed, say 20 mi/hr. But to me their speeds will seem very different. The ball that you rolled forward would have not only the speed given it by your arm but, in addition, the speed of the train; if the train's speed is 20 mi/hr, I should see the ball moving $20 + 20 = 40$ mi/hr. The second ball would appear to me motionless, for you have given it just enough speed backward to overcome the train's motion forward. The speed of each ball is evidently *relative* to the position of an observer; relative to your position, both speeds are 20 mi/hr; relative to mine, they are 40 and 0 mi/hr respectively.

All this is obvious enough. A moving observer always views the motions of other objects differently from a stationary observer, since his own motion is added to other motions. But now we face the awkward question: Which is correct, your measurement of the ball's speed or mine? You might well concede that my measurements show the "real" motion, since I am standing still while you are obviously moving. But why should measurements from a station platform be any more valid than measurements from a moving train? Perhaps the "real" motion of the balls could only be seen by an observer on the sun, who would add to your observations not only the speed of the train but the speed of the earth as it rotates and moves in its orbit. Yet the sun itself is moving with respect to the stars, so why should an observer there be any more correct than one of us? We might refer the problem to an observer at the center of our galaxy, but even he would admit that he is moving with respect to other galaxies. We are driven to conclude that there is no "real" motion of the balls—or, better, that the motion seen by any observer is just as "real" as that seen by any other. Motion has no meaning unless it is referred to an observer; if an object is alone in a universe of empty space, there is no possible way of determining whether it is in motion or not.

If you were to try a variety of simple experiments in your moving railroad car while I looked on, we should find that your observations and mine were in good agreement. In other words, the ordinary laws of physics hold as well on the moving car as on the station platform. No experiment gives us any basis for concluding that your measurements are any more correct than mine, nor mine than yours. Einstein phrased this result in general terms: *All laws of nature are the same in all systems of reference moving relative to one another at uniform speed.*

This statement leads to no difficulty until we try experiments that involve the speed of light. Let us first try an experiment with another form of wave motion, sound. Suppose that you stand in the middle of the moving car and say something. If we both had means of determining when the sound of your voice reached the two ends of the car, you would find that the sound moved in each direction with its normal speed, about 1,100 ft/sec, and that sound waves reached the two ends at the same instant. I should find, of course, that the sound waves moving forward were traveling somewhat faster than normal because of the train's motion and that those moving backward were somewhat slower. I should agree with you, however, that sound waves reach the two ends simultaneously, since the front end of the car is moving away from the source of the sound and the rear end toward the source just fast enough to make up for the differences in speed. There is nothing new here, since the motion of sound waves is exactly analogous to the motion of the two balls.

Now suppose that you switch on a light source in the middle of the car. If we undertake the difficult measurement of the speed of light toward the front and rear of the car, would you again expect to find equal speeds in the two opposite directions? Should I expect to find one speed increased and the other decreased by the train's motion? These are subtle questions, difficult to answer before trying the experiment. Our results for sound waves depended on the fact that the air molecules that transmitted the sound were being carried along by the train. Now light is not transmitted by any material particles but consists of changes in an electromagnetic field in empty space. When we try the experiment, we find, amazingly, that both of us get the *same* figure for the speed of light in the two directions. Neither motion of the light source nor motion of the observer seems to affect the speed of light at all.

Our hypothetical experiment was actually of enormous significance in the history of physics. During most of the nineteenth century light was thought to consist of wave motion in a hypothetical ether, just as sound is wave motion in air or in other materials. Belief in an ether became untenable when measurements showed that the speed of light was not influenced by the direction in which the light moved or by the speed of its source.

Einstein generalized this strange property of light in the statement that *the speed of light in vacuum is the same in all systems of reference moving uniformly relative to one another*. This statement and the one above are the foundation for the *special theory of relativity,* which Einstein published in 1905.

Consequences of Special Relativity

Let us examine some of the remarkable consequences of the two postulates of special relativity. From inside the moving railroad car you can see light traveling with equal speed from a source in the middle toward the two ends, and you find that light waves reach the two ends simultaneously. From outside the car, I also see light traveling in opposite directions with the same speed. But while the light is traveling, I see the rear end of the car approaching the backward-moving light waves and the front end of the car receding from the forward-moving waves. Hence I report that light reaches the rear end before it reaches the front end. Two events that are simultaneous from your point of view seem from my point of view to be separated by a short interval of time. At the instant when you find that each light ray is striking an end of the car, I find that one ray has already struck and the other has not yet arrived.

Again we ask, which observation is correct? And again the answer must be, both are correct. Like velocity, the concept of simultaneity is relative to the motion of the observer. This means a revision in our notions of past, present, and future; an event which seems to be happening now from my point of view may be an event of the past to a second observer and may still be in the future of a third. Our different conclusions about the same event depend simply on our motions relative to each other.

Let us try another experiment. Suppose that we point a flashlight upward and switch it on momentarily. We may imagine its light, a short train of electromagnetic waves, traveling rapidly outward into space. Suppose that, just as the light is flashed, you set out in the same direction in a rocket, at a speed, say, of 180,000 mi/sec, while I remain on the ground. If we both measure the speed of the retreating waves, we must both get 186,000 mi/sec, since motion of the observer does not affect the speed of light. But how is this possible? We are both using the same kind of clocks to measure time and the same sort of meter sticks to measure distance. How can you possibly maintain that the light flash is moving away from you at 186,000 mi/sec, when to me it is perfectly obvious that your rocket is moving nearly as fast?

Our measurements can both be right only if your motion has somehow changed the characteristics of your measuring instruments. The changes required are a decrease in the length of your meter stick and a slowing down of your clock: If your meter stick is shortened, then the distances you measure will seem longer than they should be, and if your clock runs slow, the times you measure will be abnormally short. If the changes are large enough, your measurement of 186,000 mi/sec for a speed that to me seems only 6,000 mi/sec becomes understandable. You, of course, would not be aware of the changes; your meter stick and your clock would seem perfectly normal. You would conclude, in fact, that my instruments had been altered in the same way, so that my measurements were peculiar rather than yours.

The shortening of a meter stick at high velocities means that *length* also must be relative to the motion of the observer. The change in length is only in the direction of the relative motion; the meter stick on your rocket would appear to me to have its normal length if you turned it sidewise to your motion, but to shrink when you turned it into the line of motion.

The equations governing the variation of time intervals and length with relative velocity were found by Einstein to be

$$t = \frac{t_0}{\sqrt{1 - v^2/c^2}} \qquad\qquad (17.1)$$

and $\qquad L = L_0 \sqrt{1 - v^2/c^2} \qquad\qquad (17.2)$

where $\qquad t_0$ and $L_0 =$ time interval and length measured when clock and object are at rest

$\qquad t$ and $L =$ time interval and length measured by an observer who is stationary with respect to moving clock or object

$\qquad v$ and $c =$ relative speed and speed of light, respectively

A striking illustration of both the time dilation of Eq. (17.1) and the length contraction of Eq. (17.2) occurs in the decay of unstable particles called *mu mesons.* For the moment our interest lies in the fact that a mu meson decays into an electron an average of 2×10^{-6} sec after it comes into being. Now mu mesons are created high in the atmosphere by fast cosmic-ray particles arriving at the earth from space and reach sea level in profusion. Such mesons have a typical speed of 2.994×10^8 m/sec, which is 0.998 of the velocity of light c. But in $t_0 = 2 \times 10^{-6}$ sec, the meson lifetime, they can travel a distance of only

$$L = vt_0$$
$$= 2.994 \times 10^8 \text{ m/sec} \times 2 \times 10^{-6} \text{ sec}$$
$$= 600 \text{ m}$$

while they are actually created at altitudes more than ten times greater than this!

We can resolve the meson paradox by using the results of the special theory of relativity. Let us examine the problem from the frame of reference of the meson, in which its lifetime is 2×10^{-6} sec. While the meson lifetime is unaffected by the motion, its distance to the ground appears shortened by the factor

$$\frac{L}{L_0} = \sqrt{1 - v^2/c^2}$$

That is, while we, on the ground, measure the altitude at which the meson is produced as L_0, the meson "sees" it as L. If we let L be 600 m, the maximum distance the meson can go *in its own frame of reference* at the speed $0.998c$ before decaying, we find that the corresponding distance L_0 *in our reference frame* is

$$L_0 = \frac{L}{\sqrt{1 - v^2/c^2}}$$
$$= \frac{600}{\sqrt{1 - (0.998c)^2/c^2}} \text{ m}$$
$$= \frac{600}{\sqrt{1 - 0.996}} \text{ m}$$
$$= \frac{600}{0.063} \text{ m}$$
$$= 9,500 \text{ m}$$

Hence, despite its brief life span, it is possible for the meson to reach the ground from quite respectable altitudes.

Now let us examine the problem from the frame of reference of an observer on the ground. From the ground the altitude at which the meson is produced is L_0, but its lifetime *in our reference frame* has been extended because of the relative motion to the value

$$t = \frac{t_0}{\sqrt{1 - v^2/c^2}}$$

$$= \frac{2 \times 10^{-6}}{\sqrt{1 - (0.998c)^2/c^2}} \; \text{sec}$$

$$= \frac{2 \times 10^{-6}}{0.063} \; \text{sec}$$

$$= 31.7 \times 10^{-6} \; \text{sec}$$

almost sixteen times greater than when it is at rest with respect to us. In 31.7×10^{-6} sec a meson whose speed is $0.998c$ can travel a distance

$$L_0 = vt$$

$$= 2.994 \times 10^8 \; \text{m/sec} \times 31.7 \times 10^{-6} \; \text{sec}$$

$$= 9{,}500 \; \text{m}$$

the same distance we found before. *The two points of view give identical results.*

The Relativity of Mass

We have seen that such fundamental physical quantities as length and time have meaning only when the particular reference frame in which they are measured is specified. Given this frame, we may compute what the values of these quantities would be if measured in other reference frames in motion relative to the specified frame by applying the proper transformation equations. An event in time and space—a collision between two bodies, for instance—will have a different appearance in different frames of reference. However, according to the postulates of special relativity, the laws of motion arrived at by observing events of this kind must have the same form in all frames of reference. It is this requirement that led to the prediction of the relativity of mass, which was subsequently confirmed by experiment.

If m_0 is the mass of an object as measured when it is at rest with respect to an observer, its mass m as measured when it is moving at the speed v with respect to an observer is

$$m = \frac{m_0}{\sqrt{1 - v^2/c^2}} \qquad\qquad (17.3)$$

The mass of a body moving at the speed v relative to an observer is larger than its mass when at rest relative to the observer by the factor $1/\sqrt{1 - v^2/c^2}$. This mass increase is reciprocal, just like the relativistic length contraction. As seen from the earth, a rocket ship in flight is shorter than its twin still on the ground and its mass is greater. To somebody on the rocket ship in flight, the ship on the ground also appears shorter and to have a greater mass.

Relativistic mass increases are significant only at speeds approaching that of light (Fig. 17.1). At a speed one-tenth that of light the mass increases amount to only 0.5 percent, but this increase is over 100 percent at a speed nine-tenths that of light. Only atomic particles such as electrons, protons, mesons, and so on, have sufficiently high speeds for relativistic effects to be measurable, and in dealing with these particles the "ordinary" laws of physics cannot be used. Historically, the first confirmation of Eq. (17.3) was the discovery by Bucherer in 1908 that the ratio e/m of the electron's charge to its mass was smaller for fast electrons than for slow ones; this equation, like the others of special relativity, has been verified by so many experiments that it is recognized as one of the basic formulas of physics.

As an example, let us calculate the mass of an electron whose speed is 99 percent of the speed of light. The rest mass of an electron is

$$m_0 = 9.1 \times 10^{-31} \text{ kg}$$

When $v = 0.99c$, the electron mass m is

$$
\begin{aligned}
m &= \frac{m_0}{\sqrt{1 - v^2/c^2}} \\
&= \frac{9.1 \times 10^{-31}}{\sqrt{1 - (0.99c)^2/c^2}} \\
&= \frac{9.1 \times 10^{-31}}{\sqrt{1 - 0.98}} \\
&= \frac{9.1 \times 10^{-31}}{0.14} \\
&= 65 \times 10^{-31} \text{ kg}
\end{aligned}
$$

which is over seven times its rest mass.

The Cerenkov Effect

The relativity of mass places a limit on the speed a body can have relative to an observer. As the body's speed v approaches the speed of light c, the ratio v^2/c^2 approaches 1 and the quantity $\sqrt{1 - v^2/c^2}$ approaches 0. Hence the mass m of the body, given by Eq. (17.3), approaches infinity as v approaches c. The relative speed v therefore must be less than c. An infinite force would be needed to accelerate a body to a speed at which its mass is infinite, and there are neither infinite forces nor infinite masses in the universe.

The speed of light c in special relativity is the *speed of light in free space*, 3×10^8 m/sec. In all material media, such as water, glass, or air, visible light travels more slowly than this, and atomic particles are capable of moving with higher speeds in such media than the speed of light *in them—* though never faster than the speed of light in free space. When an electrically

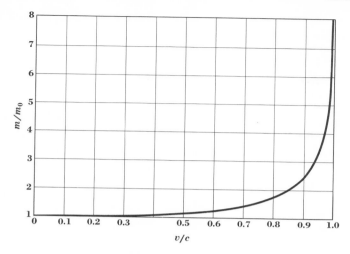

Fig. 17.1 The relativity of mass. *The quantity* m_0 *is the mass of an object when it is at rest with respect to an observer and* m *is its mass as measured when it is moving at the speed* v *with respect to the observer. The velocity of light is* c.

charged particle moves through a substance at a speed exceeding that of light in the substance, a cone of light waves is emitted in a process roughly similar to that in which a ship produces a bow wave as it moves through the water at a speed greater than that of water waves. These light waves are known as *Cerenkov radiation*.

Mass and Energy

The most famous relationship Einstein obtained from the postulates of special relativity concerns mass and energy. This relationship can be derived directly from the definition of the kinetic energy (KE) of a moving body as the work done in bringing it from rest to its state of motion by taking into account the variation of mass with speed. When this is done, the result is

$$KE = mc^2 - m_0c^2 \tag{17.4}$$

Equation (17.4) states that the kinetic energy of a body is equal to the increase in its mass consequent upon its relative motion multiplied by the square of the speed of light.

Equation (17.4) may be rewritten

$$mc^2 = KE + m_0c^2 \tag{17.5}$$

If we interpret mc^2 as the *total energy E* of the body, it follows that, when the body is at rest and KE = 0, it nevertheless possesses the energy m_0c^2.

Accordingly m_0c^2 is called the *rest energy* E_0 of a body whose mass at rest is m_0. Equation (17.5) therefore becomes

$$E = E_0 + KE \qquad\qquad (17.6)$$

where $\qquad E = mc^2 \qquad\qquad\qquad\qquad (17.7)$

and $\qquad E_0 = m_0c^2 \qquad\qquad\qquad\qquad (17.8)$

In addition to its kinetic, potential, electromagnetic, thermal, and other familiar guises, then, energy can manifest itself as mass. The conversion factor between the unit of mass (kilogram) and the unit of energy (joule) is c^2, so 1 kg of matter has an energy content of 9×10^{16} joules. Even a minute bit of matter represents a vast amount of energy, and, in fact, the conversion of matter into energy is the source of the power liberated in all the exothermic reactions of physics and chemistry.

Since mass and energy are not independent entities, the separate conservation principles of energy and mass are properly a single one, the principle of conservation of mass energy. Mass *can* be created or destroyed, but only if an equivalent amount of energy simultaneously vanishes or comes into being, and vice versa.

When the relative speed v is small compared with c, the formula for kinetic energy must reduce to the $\frac{1}{2}m_0v^2$ we are familiar with and which experiment shows to be correct at low speeds. Let us investigate this important point. The binominal theorem of algebra states that, if some quantity x is much smaller than 1,

$$(1 \pm x)^n \approx 1 \pm nx$$

The relativistic equation for kinetic energy is

$$KE = mc^2 - m_0c^2$$
$$= \frac{m_0c^2}{\sqrt{1 - v^2/c^2}} - m_0c^2$$

Expanding the first term of this equation with the help of the above formula, with v^2/c^2 much less than 1 since v is much less than c,

$$KE = (1 + \tfrac{1}{2}v^2/c^2)\, m_0c^2 - m_0c^2$$
$$= \tfrac{1}{2}m_0v^2$$

Hence at low speeds the relativistic expression for the kinetic energy of a moving particle reduces to the classical one. The total energy of such a particle is

$$E = m_0c^2 + \tfrac{1}{2}mv^2$$

In the above calculation relativity has precisely the same results as ordinary mechanics at low speeds, where we know that the latter agree with experiment. It is nevertheless important to keep in mind that, so far as is known, the correct formulation of mechanics has its basis in relativity, with classical mechanics no more than an approximation correct only under certain circumstances.

Velocity Addition

One of the postulates of special relativity states that the speed of light c in free space has the same value for all observers, regardless of their relative motion. But "common sense" tells us that, if we throw a ball forward at 50 ft/sec from a car moving at 80 ft/sec, the ball's speed relative to the ground is 130 ft/sec, the sum of the two speeds. Hence we should expect that a ray of light emitted in a frame of reference in the direction of its motion at velocity v relative to another frame will have a speed of $c + v$ as measured by somebody in the latter, contradicting the above postulate. "Common sense" is no more reliable as a guide in science than it is elsewhere, and we must turn to the special theory of relativity for the correct scheme of velocity addition.

The relativistic formula for velocity addition states that

$$V_0 = \frac{V + v}{1 + vV/c^2} \qquad (17.9)$$

where V_0 is the velocity of a moving body as measured in a certain frame of reference and V is its velocity as measured in another frame of reference whose own speed is v relative to the first (Fig. 17.2). (This formula is valid only when V_0, V, and v are in parallel directions.) If $V = c$, that is, if a ray of light is emitted in the "moving" frame in the same direction as its own motion, an observer in the "stationary" frame will measure the velocity

$$\begin{aligned} V_0 &= \frac{V + v}{1 + vV/c^2} \\ &= \frac{c + v}{1 + vc/c^2} \\ &= \frac{c\,(c + v)}{c + v} \\ &= c \end{aligned}$$

Both observers determine the same value for the speed of light, as they must according to the first postulate of relativity.

The relativistic velocity transformation has other peculiar consequences. For instance, we might imagine wishing to pass a spaceship whose speed with respect to the earth is $0.9c$ at a relative speed of $0.5c$. According to

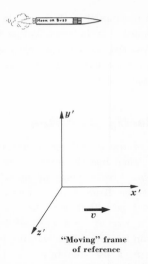

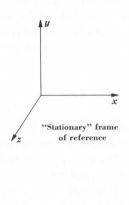

"Stationary" frame
of reference

"Moving" frame
of reference

Fig. 17.2 *An observer in the "stationary" frame of reference finds the rocket speed to be* V_0 *and an observer in the "moving" frame finds it to be* V. *The relationships among* v, V_0, *and* V *are given by Eq. (17.9).*

conventional mechanics, our required speed relative to the earth would have to be $1.4c$, more than the velocity of light. According to Eq. (17.9), however, with $V = 0.5c$ and $v = 0.9c$, the necessary speed is only

$$V_0 = \frac{V + v}{1 + vV/c^2}$$

$$= \frac{0.5c + 0.9c}{1 + \dfrac{(0.9c)(0.5c)}{c^2}}$$

$$= 0.9655c$$

which is less than c. We need go less than 10 percent faster than a spaceship traveling at $0.9c$ in order to pass it at a relative speed of $0.5c$.

General Theory of Relativity

The special theory of relativity is an attempt to generalize the equations describing natural laws so that they will apply to the experiments of observers moving uniformly with respect to one another, regardless of their speed. A more difficult undertaking is embodied in the *general theory of relativity*, which Einstein published in 1915. Here his problem was to modify the equations for natural laws so that they would apply to any part of space, no matter how that part of space might be moving with respect to an observer. The special theory refers only to uniform motion, whereas the general theory includes accelerated and rotational motion as well.

A simple example will show something of the increased complexity that accelerated motion introduces. Suppose that you had lived all your life in a large box falling freely toward the earth from somewhere far out in space. The box and everything within it would be moving with uniform acceleration, the speed increasing steadily as it approached the earth. Since you would be moving with the box, you would not be conscious of any gravitational pull toward the earth; your feet would not press down on the floor, and if you tried to let a ball drop, it would hang motionless in mid-air. Obviously, from my position on solid earth I should see things in your box very differently from you. If I watched you drop a ball, I should say that the ball approached the earth with a steadily accelerated motion; you would say that the ball remained motionless with respect to your box. I should say that the ball was impelled downward by a force; you would say that you find no evidence of any force whatever. One of us sees accelerated motion and the action of a force; the other sees no motion and no force. Einstein would tell us that we were both right, as usual. Not only motion, but force as well, is relative to our points of view.

Thus an extension of relativistic ideas to accelerated motion involves a new description of gravitation. In this description Einstein dispenses with a mysterious gravitational force associated with matter, substituting a complex curvature in space-time near every material object, the distortion being greatest near large masses. Such a curvature can be treated mathematically, but it is almost impossible to visualize in any terms that our minds can grasp. The important thing is that Einstein refers the motion of objects near large masses to a *structure* in the surrounding space rather than to a force in the ordinary sense.

Einstein's picture of gravitation as a distortion in space-time does not in any sense mean that Newton was "wrong." Einstein simply reexamined the whole problem from a new and broader point of view and suggested a different formulation. Einstein's equations give the same results as Newton's for all ordinary masses, suggesting slightly different results only for very strong gravitational fields, like that near the sun. Three predictions from the theory for strong fields—slight irregularities in the orbit of Mercury, the deflection of starlight passing close to the sun, and displacements of lines in the spectra of very dense stars—have been verified by observation, suggesting that the theory does actually give a truer description than Newton's for gravitational effects near large masses.

Einstein's great contribution to physical science is perhaps less the theory of relativity itself than his demonstration that ordinary ideas of time, distance, and mass are unreliable guides to relative motion and that ordinary ideas about gravitation require conceptual revision. The theory of relativity suggests how these ideas should be expressed.

Self-examination

1. When we measure the velocity and acceleration of an object, the figures we obtain
    a. refer to the motion of the object relative to the coordinates of four-dimensional space-time
    b. are the same as those all other observers would find
    c. refer only to the motion of the object relative to us
    d. are always constant

2. The mass of an object moving with respect to us is
    a. greater than its rest mass when it is moving toward us and less than its rest mass when it is moving away from us
    b. less than its rest mass when it is moving toward us and more when it is moving away from us
    c. always greater than its rest mass
    d. always less than its rest mass

3. Which of the following quantities is always the same to all observers?
    a. length
    b. mass
    c. the velocity of an object
    d. the velocity of light

4. An electron is traveling through the ocean. Its maximum speed is the speed of
    a. water waves
    b. sound waves in water
    c. light waves in water
    d. light waves in vacuum

5. The symbol c in the formula $E = mc^2$ represents
    a. the charge of the particle
    b. the velocity of the particle
    c. the velocity of the observer
    d. the velocity of light

6. Newton's laws of motion are
    a. correct for velocities up to the velocity of light
    b. correct for velocities exceeding the velocity of light
    c. approximately correct for all velocities
    d. approximately correct for velocities much smaller than the velocity of light

7. An observer wishes to determine the absolute speed of his motion through space.
    a. It is impossible for him to do so.
    b. He can find it by measuring the apparent speed of light.
    c. He can find it by measuring his speed relative to the ether.
    d. He can find it by comparing measurements made by another observer.

Problems

1. State the two postulates of the special theory of relativity. Were experiments necessary to verify these postulates, or do we accept them because they were stated by Einstein?

2. Calculate the mass of a 1-g object when it is traveling at 10 percent of the speed of light. Make the same calculation for speeds of 90 and 99 percent of the speed of light.

3. What is the velocity of an electron whose kinetic energy is 10^{-16} joule? 10^{-13} joule? What is its mass when it has these kinetic energies?

4. Approximately 4×10^9 kg of matter is converted into energy in the sun per second. Express the power output of the sun in watts.

5. An astronaut 6 ft tall on earth is lying along the axis of a spaceship whose speed is 2.7×10^8 m/sec relative to the earth. An observer on the earth measures his height. What value does the observer find?

6. What would the speed of a spaceship have to be in order that each day on the ship correspond to 2 days on the earth?

7. An observer is situated in a windowless laboratory. Can he determine whether the earth: (*a*) Is traveling through space with a constant velocity? (*b*) Is traveling through space with a constant acceleration? (*c*) Is rotating?

8. Approximately 1.3×10^3 kcal of chemical energy is released when 1 kg of dynamite explodes. What fraction of the total energy of the dynamite is this?

CHAPTER 18 | WAVES AND PARTICLES

To most of us there is nothing mysterious or ambiguous about the concepts of *particle* and *wave*. A stone dropped into a lake and the ripples that spread out from its point of impact apparently have in common only the ability to carry energy and momentum from one place to another. Classical physics, which describes scientifically the "physical reality" of our sense impressions, treats particles and waves as separate aspects of that reality. The mechanics of particles and the optics of waves are, by tradition, independent subjects, each with its own chain of experiments and hypotheses. But the physical reality we experience has its roots in phenomena that occur in the microscopic world of atoms and molecules, electrons and nuclei, and in this world there are neither particles nor waves in our sense of these terms. We regard electrons as particles because they possess charge and mass and behave according to the laws of particle mechanics in such familiar devices as television picture tubes. However, there is as much evidence in favor of interpreting a moving electron as a wave manifestation as there is in favor of interpreting it as a particle manifestation. We regard electromagnetic waves as waves because under suitable circumstances they exhibit such characteristic wave behavior as interference. However, under other circumstances electromagnetic waves behave as though they consist of streams of particles. Together with the theory of special relativity, the wave-particle duality is central to an understanding of modern physics, and we shall explore its meaning in this chapter.

The Photoelectric Effect

Late in the nineteenth century a series of experiments were performed which revealed that electrons are emitted from a metal surface when light of sufficiently high frequency falls on it (Fig. 18.1). For most metals ultraviolet light is necessary for electron emission to occur, but very active metals, such as potassium and cesium, respond to visible light as well. The emission of electrons by a substance being irradiated with light is known as the *photoelectric effect.*

Evidently electromagnetic waves can concentrate their energy on single electrons, setting them free from the positive charge of their parent atoms. In itself this observation does not seem surprising; as a mechanical analogy, we can think of pebbles dislodged from a beach by water waves. Light waves also carry energy, and some of the energy absorbed by the metal may somehow concentrate on individual electrons and give them enough kinetic energy to escape. When we look more closely at the data, however, we find that the photoelectric effect can hardly be interpreted so simply.

One of the features of the photoelectric effect that particularly puzzled its discoverers is that the maximum energy of the emitted electrons (called *photoelectrons*) is independent of the intensity of the light. A strong light beam yields more photoelectrons than a weak one of the same frequency, but the maximum electron energy is the same. If water waves followed the same rule, pebbles would move out from shore with the same average speed no matter how strong or how weak the waves might be; the number of pebbles would change with the strength of the waves, but not the violence of their

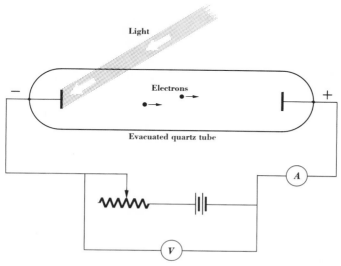

Fig. 18.1 *Experimental observation of the photoelectric effect.*

motion. Also, within the limits of experimental accuracy, there is no time lag between the arrival of light at a metal surface and the emission of photo-electrons. These observations cannot be understood from the electromagnetic theory of light, which predicts that the electron energy should vary with the intensity of the light and that, under the conditions of the actual experiments, an average of nearly a year would be required for enough energy to be absorbed by an individual electron to accumulate the energy needed for escape.

Equally odd from the point of view of the wave theory is the fact that the maximum photoelectron energy depends upon the *frequency* of the light employed. At frequencies below a certain critical frequency characteristic of each particular metal, no electrons whatever are emitted. Above this threshold frequency the photoelectrons have a range of energies from zero to a certain maximum value, and this maximum energy increases linearly with increasing frequency. High frequencies result in high maximum photo-electron energies, low frequencies in low maximum photoelectron energies. Thus a faint blue light produces electrons with more energy than those produced by a bright red light, although the latter yields a greater number of them.

The Quantum Theory of Light

The electromagnetic theory of light, one of the immortal achievements of the human intellect, accounts so well for such a variety of phenomena that it must contain some measure of truth. Yet this well-founded theory is completely at odds with the photoelectric effect. In 1905 Albert Einstein found that the paradox presented by the photoelectric effect could be understood by taking seriously a notion proposed five years earlier by the German theoretical physicist Max Planck. Planck was seeking to explain the characteristics of the radiation emitted by bodies hot enough to be luminous, a problem notorious at the time for its resistance to solution. He was able to derive a formula for the spectrum of this radiation (that is, the relative brightness of the various colors present) as a function of the temperature of the body that was in agreement with experiment, provided he assumed that the radiation is emitted *discontinuously* as little bursts of energy. These bursts of energy are called *quanta,* or alternatively, *photons.* Planck found that the quanta associated with a particular frequency f of light all have the same energy, and that this energy E is directly proportional to f; that is,

$$E = hf \qquad (18.1)$$

where h, today known as *Planck's constant,* has the value

$$h = 6.63 \times 10^{-34} \text{ joule-sec}$$

Planck was not altogether happy about this idea, which, though it led to agreement with certain experimental data, nevertheless was contrary to the orthodox electromagnetic theory of light. He took the position that, although light is emitted discontinuously in little bursts, it nevertheless is propagated in waves exactly as everybody thought.

Einstein, however, thought that, if light is emitted in little packets, it should travel through space and ultimately be absorbed in the same little packets. His idea fitted the experiments on the photoelectric effect perfectly. He supposed that some specific minimum amount of energy, which we might call w, is required in order to pull an electron away from a metal surface. If the frequency of the light is too low, so that E, the energy of the photons, is less than w, no photoelectrons are emitted. When E is greater than w, a photon of light striking an electron can impart to the electron enough energy for it to emerge from the metal with a certain amount of kinetic energy. Einstein's famous formula for the process is very simple:

$$hf = \text{KE} + w \qquad\qquad (18.2)$$

where $\quad hf =$ energy of a photon of light whose frequency is f

$\text{KE} =$ kinetic energy of emitted electron

$w =$ energy needed to extract the electron from the metal

The quantity w for a particular metal is known as its *work function*.

Not all photoelectrons have the same amount of kinetic energy, but come out of the metal with energies up to the KE of the above formula. This is because w is the work that must be done to take an electron through the metal surface from just beneath it, and more work is required when the electron originates deeper in the metal.

The validity of the above interpretation of the photoelectric effect is confirmed by studies of *thermionic emission*. For centuries it has been known that the presence of a very hot object increases the electrical conductivity of the surrounding air, and late in the nineteenth century the reason for this phenomenon was found to be the emission of electrons from such an object. Thermionic emission makes possible the operation of the vacuum tubes so widely used in electronics, where metal filaments or specially coated electrodes at high temperature supply dense streams of electrons. The emitted electrons evidently obtain their energy from the thermal agitation of the particles constituting the metal, and we should expect that the electrons must acquire a certain minimum energy in order to escape. This minimum energy can be determined for many surfaces, and it is always almost identical with the photoelectric work function for the same surfaces. In photoelectric emission, photons of light provide the energy required by an electron to escape, while in thermionic emission heat does so; in both cases the physical processes involved in the emergence of an electron from a metal surface are the same.

Let us apply Eq. (18.2) to a specific situation. The work function of potassium is 2.0 ev. When ultraviolet light of wavelength 3,500 Å (1Å $= 1$ angstrom unit $= 10^{-10}$ m) falls on a potassium surface, what is the maximum energy in electron volts of the photoelectrons? From Eq. (18.2),

$$KE = hf - w$$

Since w is already expressed in electron volts, we need only compute the quantum energy hf of 3,500 Å light. This is

$$hf = \frac{hc}{\lambda}$$
$$= \frac{6.63 \times 10^{-34} \text{ joule-sec} \times 3 \times 10^{8} \text{ m/sec} \times 10^{10} \text{ Å/m}}{3,500 \text{ Å}}$$
$$= 5.7 \times 10^{-19} \text{ joule}$$

To convert this energy from joules to electron volts we recall that

$$1 \text{ ev} = 1.6 \times 10^{-19} \text{ joule}$$

and so
$$hf = \frac{5.7 \times 10^{-19} \text{ joule}}{1.6 \times 10^{-19} \text{ joule/ev}}$$
$$= 3.6 \text{ ev}$$

Hence the maximum photoelectron energy is

$$KE = hf - w$$
$$= 3.6 - 2.0$$
$$= 1.6 \text{ ev}$$

What Is Light?

The view that light propagates as a series of little packets of energy is directly opposed to the wave theory of light. And the latter, which provides the sole means of explaining a host of optical effects, notably diffraction and interference, is one of the most securely established of physical theories. Planck's suggestion that a hot object emits light in separate quanta led to no more than raised eyebrows among physicists in 1900 since it did not apparently conflict with the propagation of light as a wave. Einstein's suggestion in 1905 that light travels through space in the form of distinct photons, on the other hand, astonished many of his colleagues. According to the wave theory, light waves spread out from a source in the way ripples spread out on the surface of a lake when a stone falls into it. The energy carried by the light in this picture is distributed continuously throughout the wave pattern. According to the quantum theory, however, light spreads out from a source as a series of localized concentrations of energy, each sufficiently small to be capable of absorption by a single electron. Curiously, the quantum theory of light, which treats it as a strictly particle phenomenon, incorporates the light frequency *f*, a strictly wave concept.

The quantum theory of light is strikingly successful in explaining the photoelectric effect. It predicts correctly that the maximum photoelectron energy should depend upon the frequency of the incident light and not upon its intensity, contrary to what the wave theory suggests, and it is able to explain why even the feeblest light can lead to the immediate emission of photoelectrons, again contrary to the wave theory. The wave theory can give no reason why there should be a threshold frequency such that when light of lower frequency is employed, no photoelectrons are observed, no matter how strong the light beam, something that follows naturally from the quantum theory.

Which theory are we to believe? A great many physical hypotheses have had to be modified or discarded when they were found to disagree with experiment, but never before have we arrived at two totally different theories to account for a single physical phenomenon. The situation here is fundamentally different from what it is, say, in the case of relativistic versus Newtonian mechanics, where the latter turns out to be an approximation to the former. There is no way of deriving the quantum theory of light from the wave theory of light or vice versa.

In a specific event light exhibits *either* a wave or a particle nature, never both simultaneously. The same light beam that is diffracted by a suitable optical device can cause the emission of photoelectrons from a suitable surface, but these processes occur independently. The wave theory of light and the quantum theory of light complement each other. Electromagnetic waves provide the sole possible explanation for certain experiments involving light and optical phenomena, while photons provide the sole possible explanation for all the other experiments in this field. We have no alternative to regarding light as something that manifests itself as a stream of discrete photons on occasion and as a wave train the rest of the time. The "true nature" of light is no longer a meaningful concept, and we must accept both wave and quantum theories, contradictions and all, as the closest we can get to a complete description of light.

X Rays

The photoelectric effect provides convincing evidence that photons of light can transfer energy to electrons. Is the inverse process also possible? That is, can part or all of the kinetic energy of a moving electron be converted into a photon? As it happens, the inverse photoelectric effect not only does occur, but had been discovered (though not at all understood) prior to the theoretical work of Planck and Einstein.

In 1895, in his laboratory at Wurzburg, Wilhelm Roentgen accidentally observed that a screen coated with a fluorescent salt glowed every time he switched on a nearby cathode-ray tube. Roentgen knew that cathode rays themselves could not escape through the glass walls of his tube, yet, evidently, some sort of invisible radiation was falling on the screen. The radiation was strangely powerful; thick pieces of wood, glass, and even metal could be interposed between tube and screen, and still the screen glowed. At length Roentgen found that his mysterious rays would penetrate human flesh and leave a photographic record of bones beneath the flesh. With these observations Roentgen announced his discovery to the world, christening the radiations X rays after the algebraic symbol for an unknown quantity.

X rays are produced where cathode rays (which are fast electrons) stop. Rapidly moving electrons must be brought to rest suddenly; the more abruptly they are stopped, the more powerful are the resulting X rays. An X-ray tube is simply a cathode-ray tube designed to produce and to bring to a sudden stop a powerful beam of electrons. Usually the stopping is accomplished by the metal of the anode (Fig. 18.2). Crudely, we might compare the production of X rays to the stopping of a bullet by a tree; just as the bullet buries itself in the wood and gives up its kinetic energy as heat, so an electron buries itself in the anode and gives up its energy as X rays.

What are X rays? After many attempts had been made to determine their nature, in 1912 Max von Laue and his students were able to show definitely by means of an interference-type experiment that they were electromagnetic waves of extremely high frequency. X rays contain frequencies higher than those in ultraviolet light, but somewhat lower than those of the gamma rays produced by radioactive atomic nuclei.

Even the early workers with X rays noted that increasing the voltage applied to the tube—which means faster electrons striking the anode—led to the production of X rays of greater penetrating power. Experiments showed that the more penetrating X rays were of higher frequency than the

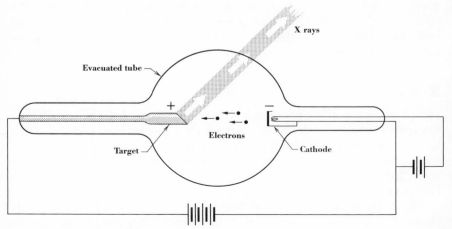

Fig. 18.2   An X-ray tube.

less penetrating ones, so it was clear that there was a direct relationship between the speed of the electrons and the frequency of the resulting X rays. Furthermore, the more intense the beam of electrons, the more intense the beam of X rays, but there was no correlation between the electron intensity and the X-ray energy; many slow electrons would produce many low-frequency X rays, and a few fast electrons would produce a few high-frequency X rays.

The quantum theory of light is in complete accord with these observations. Most of the electrons striking the target lose their kinetic energy gradually in numerous collisions, their energy merely going into heat. (It is for this reason that the targets in X-ray tubes are normally of high-melting-point metals, and an efficient means of cooling the target is often employed.) A few electrons, though, lose most or all of their energy in single collisions with target atoms, and this is the energy that is evolved as X rays. X-ray production, then, represents an inverse photoelectric effect. Instead of photon energy being transformed into electron kinetic energy, electron kinetic energy is being transformed into photon energy. The energy of an X-ray photon of frequency f is hf, and therefore the minimum kinetic energy of the electron that, in stopping, produced the X-ray photon must be equal to hf; that is,

$$KE_{min} = hf \qquad (18.3)$$

which agrees with the experimental data.

A conventional X-ray machine might have an accelerating potential of 50,000 volts. To find the highest frequency present in its radiation we use Eq. (18.3), with the result that, since $1 \text{ ev} = 1.6 \times 10^{-19}$ joule,

$$f = \frac{KE}{h}$$
$$= \frac{5 \times 10^4 \text{ ev} \times 1.6 \times 10^{-19} \text{ joule/ev}}{6.63 \times 10^{-34} \text{ joule-sec}}$$
$$= 1.2 \times 10^{19} \text{ sec}^{-1}$$
$$= 1.2 \times 10^{19} \text{ cycles/sec}$$

The corresponding wavelength is

$$\lambda = \frac{c}{f}$$
$$= \frac{3 \times 10^8 \text{ m/sec}}{1.2 \times 10^{19} \text{ sec}^{-1}}$$
$$= 2.5 \times 10^{-11} \text{ m} = 0.25 \text{ Å}$$

The Compton Effect

A further triumph for the quantum theory of light came in 1923. The American physicist Arthur H. Compton noticed that, when a beam of X rays passed through a gas, some of the X rays were scattered off to the side. The

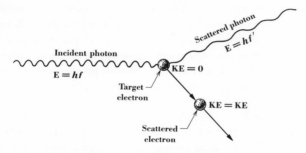

Fig. 18.3   The Compton effect.

scattered X rays were found to be of lower frequency than the original beam!
Now the quantum theory of light postulates that photons behave like particles
except for the absence of any rest mass. If this is true, then it should be
possible for us to treat collisions between photons and, say, electrons in the
same manner as billiard-ball collisions are treated in elementary mechanics.
Figure 18.3 shows how such a collision might be represented, with an X-ray
photon striking an electron and being scattered away from its original direction of motion, while the electron receives an impulse and begins to move.
When this happens the photon must give up some of its energy to the electron,
just as in any other collision. If the electron energy after the collision is
KE, then, from the law of conservation of energy,

$$\text{Loss in photon energy} = \text{gain in electron energy}$$

$$hf - hf' = \text{KE} \qquad\qquad (18.4)$$

where f is the initial frequency of the X ray and f' is its frequency after
having been scattered. Compton was able to verify his idea through careful
measurements, and subsequently received a Nobel prize for this work.

Matter Waves

The distinction between particles and waves, a distinction that seems so
obvious in our everyday world, becomes hazy in the world of the very small
when we learn that light has aspects of both waves and particles. The distinction grows still more troublesome when we find that bona fide material
particles—things like electrons, protons, and alpha particles, whose particle
nature we have "proved"—sometimes act just like waves. In retrospect it
may seem odd that two decades passed between the 1905 discovery of the
particle properties of waves and the speculation that the converse might also
be true. However, it is one thing to suggest a revolutionary hypothesis to
explain otherwise mysterious data and quite another to advance an equally
revolutionary hypothesis in the absence of a strong experimental mandate.

The latter is what Louis de Broglie did in 1924 when he proposed that matter possesses wave as well as particle characteristics. So different was the intellectual climate at the time from that prevailing at the turn of the century that de Broglie's notion soon received respectful attention, while the earlier quantum theory of light of Planck and Einstein created hardly any stir despite its striking empirical support.

Although it is hard enough to believe that light sometimes behaves as if it had wave properties and sometimes as if it had particle properties, it is harder still to accept the idea that a particle can sometimes behave as if it were a wave. Yet de Broglie's hypothesis could not be ignored, for in the next few years a number of experiments were performed with beams of fast electrons that demonstrated that moving particles do have dual characters. The wavelengths involved are too short to be significant in the large-scale world to which our senses respond, but in the atomic world that lies beneath what we see, the wave nature of particles and the particle nature of waves are of the utmost importance.

According to the quantum theory of light, the momentum of a photon whose wavelength is λ is h/λ, where h is Planck's constant. Drawing upon an intuitive feeling for symmetry in nature, de Broglie asserted that this relationship is a completely general one that applies to material particles as well as to photons. The momentum of a particle of mass m and velocity v is mv, and consequently its *de Broglie wavelength* is

$$\lambda = \frac{h}{mv} \qquad\qquad (18.5)$$

There is nothing imaginary about these *matter waves*. They are perfectly real, just as light waves or sound waves are. Shortly after their discovery, in fact, they were used for a practical purpose similar to a use we often make of light waves: to illuminate objects in a microscope. The difficulty with light waves for microscopic work is that they are too long; the magnifying power of a microscope is limited by the fact that objects cannot be distinguished unless they are somewhat larger than the waves of light reflected from them. Smaller waves, like the waves of ultraviolet radiation or X rays, would improve the performance of a microscope, but to find materials for lenses that will both transmit and refract these radiations has proved difficult. Electron waves are an excellent solution to this problem, for they have wavelengths similar to those of X rays and at the same time carry a charge, which permits them to be controlled by electric and magnetic fields. To construct an electron microscope, then, we must let a beam of electrons pass through an object, then direct it through a system of electric and magnetic fields that act like lenses in focusing the beam, and finally let it fall on a fluorescent screen or photographic plate so that the image may become visible. The electron microscope is today a standard research instrument.

Not only electrons but all other particles can be shown to behave like waves under suitable circumstances. All matter may be said to consist of waves just as correctly as it is said to consist of particles. For many aspects of the behavior of small particles their wave nature provides a better explanation than their particle nature in fact, as we shall see in subsequent chapters. As in the case of electromagnetic waves, the wave and particle aspects of moving bodies can never be simultaneously observed, so that we cannot determine which is the "correct" description. All we can say is that sometimes a moving body exhibits wave properties and at other times it exhibits particle properties.

The Uncertainty Principle

Well, then, what *is* an electron? It has mass, and so we have spoken of it as a particle in the sense of being a very tiny object that obeys the same laws of motion as the larger objects around us. When it is moving it exhibits certain properties that lie exclusively in the domain of waves. To us the two are mutually exclusive: A wave is a wave; a particle is a particle. How can we determine the true nature of the electron? Or, perhaps, is the the question itself meaningless, because we are trying to use models based on ordinary experience to describe entities so small that we have only indirect evidence of them? To put it another way, just because we do not find things that sometimes seem like waves and at other times like particles in everyday life, we might not be justified in assuming that such dual personalities are not truly characteristic of electrons, protons, neutrons, and the like.

One of the basic difficulties in trying to understand electrons is that we cannot experiment with them without disturbing them. If we experiment with a rubber ball, we can observe the ball by means of light reflected from it, and the light has no appreciable effect on our experiments. With the electron, because of its small size, this is no longer true: Every attempt to observe it introduces a disturbance.

A hypothetical experiment will make this difficulty clear. Suppose we could construct a microscope powerful enough to see an electron. We cannot use ordinary light to illuminate the electron on the stage of this microscope: Ordinary light has a wavelength about a hundred million times the diameter of the electron, and a microscope will show details only down to a size near the wavelength of the light employed. But perhaps we can arrange to use some sort of high-frequency gamma rays, with wavelengths about the same as the electron's diameter. These rays would not be visible to our eyes, but we might design an appropriate device that would respond to them.

We therefore arrange to get an electron on the stage of our microscope, and we illuminate it by turning on the gamma-ray light. Expectantly, we peer down the microscope tube. We see a momentary flash, and then the field is blank; our electron has disappeared. Then we recall that gamma rays of short wavelength are photons of very high energy. At least one of these photons must be reflected from the electron in order for us to see it, but when the electron is struck by the photon, it recoils out of the microscope field (Fig. 18.4). Evidently, if the electron is to stay in our field of view, we shall have to be content with gamma rays of longer wavelength and lower energy. Making this change to longer waves, we again look down the micro-scope tube. Now the electron moves more slowly, so that we can actually see it; but we see it only as a hazy blur, because, with longer waves, our microscope loses its power to show details clearly. No matter how we alter the microscope, we cannot improve matters. It is impossible to obtain a clear look at the electron without disturbing it.

In the first of our experiments we tried to see the electron as a distinct image in a definite spot, and the electron moved rapidly out of our field of view. In the second experiment we kept it in the field long enough to see it, but we did not locate it as a clearly defined image. These disappointing results, together with results of other experiments, both hypothetical and real, are summarized in the *uncertainty principle*, first stated by the German physicist Werner Heisenberg. *It is impossible to determine simultaneously the position and velocity of any particle.* We can get rough values for both position and velocity, but if we try to get the position more accurately, the measurement of velocity becomes very inaccurate, and if we try to determine the velocity precisely, the position becomes uncertain. The indeterminate-ness is due not to faulty experimental technique, but to the impossibility of observing particles without disturbing them.

The uncertainty relation makes it impossible to decide experimentally whether the electron is a wave or a particle. Either a particle disturbed by the process of observing it or a tiny "packet" of waves would show the necessary indeterminateness of position and velocity. Is the electron a wave or a particle? We find this question, posed at the beginning of this section,

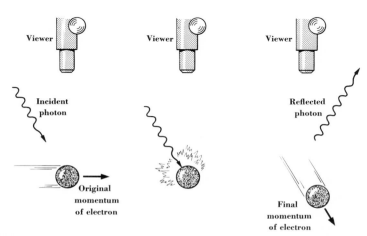

Fig. 18.4 *An electron cannot be observed without changing its mo-mentum.*

to be meaningless in the sense that no experiment can be devised to give us an answer.

The clearest picture we can get of an electron is to regard it as a particle and to think of the associated waves as "waves of probability." According to the uncertainty principle, if we know anything at all about the velocity of an electron, we cannot know its position exactly, but we can express its position as a probability of its being in any particular spot. Not only the present position but future positions and velocities of the electron may be expressed as probabilities. We cannot say just where an electron will be 2 sec hence or how fast it will be moving, but we can say that it will more probably be in one place than another and that its speed will be more likely to have one value than another.

The uncertainty principle can be expressed in a quantitative way. If we write the uncertainty in a particle's position as Δx and the uncertainty in its momentum as Δmv,

$$\Delta x \, \Delta mv \geqslant \frac{h}{2\pi} \qquad\qquad (18.6)$$

where h is Planck's constant and the sign $\geqslant$ means "greater than or equal to." Planck's constant h is so minute—only 6.63×10^{-34} joule-sec—that the limitations imposed by the uncertainty principle are significant only in the realm of the atom. On this microscopic scale, however, there are many phenomena that can be understood only in terms of this principle.

As an example, let us ask whether electrons are present in atomic nuclei. A typical nucleus might be 10^{-15} m in radius. For an electron to be confined within such a nucleus, the uncertainty in its position may not exceed 10^{-15} m. The corresponding uncertainty in the electron's momentum is

$$\begin{aligned} \Delta mv &\geqslant \frac{h}{2\pi \, \Delta x} \\ &\geqslant \frac{6.63 \times 10^{-34} \text{ joule-sec}}{2\pi \times 10^{-15} \text{ m}} \\ &\geqslant 1.1 \times 10^{-19} \text{ kg-m/sec} \end{aligned}$$

If this is the uncertainty in the electron's momentum, the momentum itself must be at least comparable in magnitude. An electron whose momentum is 1.1×10^{-19} kg-m/sec has a kinetic energy of over 200 Mev. (The energy of so fast an electron must be computed according to the formulas of relativity, since its mass is many times its rest mass m_0.) Experiments indicate that the electrons associated even with unstable atoms never have more than about 1 percent of this considerable energy, and we conclude that electrons cannot be present within nuclei.

Let us now ask how much energy an electron must have to be confined to an atom. The hydrogen atom is about 5×10^{-11} m in radius, so that the uncertainty in the position of its electron may not exceed this figure. The corresponding momentum uncertainty is

$$\Delta mv = 2.2 \times 10^{-24} \text{ kg-m/sec}$$

An electron whose momentum is of this order of magnitude is nonrelativistic in behavior, and its kinetic energy is

$$
\begin{aligned}
KE &= \frac{(mv)^2}{2m} \\
&= \frac{(2.2 \times 10^{-24} \text{ kg-m/sec})^2}{2 \times 9.1 \times 10^{-31} \text{ kg}} \\
&= 2.7 \times 10^{-18} \text{ joule}
\end{aligned}
$$

or about 17 ev. This is of the same order of magnitude as the actual electron energy in the hydrogen atom.

The uncertainty principle thus brings an essential unpredictability into physics. The behavior of large objects like stones or rifle bullets can be described in terms of definite laws. Knowing the position and speed of a falling stone, we can predict accurately where it will be at future times by using the law of falling bodies. We are confident in our predictions, because all falling stones of our experience have behaved similarly. Stones and other objects of everyday life obey the principle of *causality*, that similar events always follow similar causes. But electrons (and other submicroscopic particles) are different; we cannot make accurate predictions about an electron's future motion, and we cannot be sure that two electrons with roughly similar positions and velocities will behave at all alike. The principle of causality, expressing our faith in the uniformity of natural processes, does not hold for electrons.

Other particles besides electrons are affected by the uncertainty principle, which means that their motions likewise can be expressed only as probabilities. Since the objects of everyday life are made up of particles, we might conjecture that even their behavior should be a matter of probability rather than of fixed laws. There is a chance, for example, that this book will some-day defy gravity and rise straight up in the air. But for objects this large—in fact, even for objects the size of molecules—the relevant probabilities are so great as to be practically certainties. The likelihood that this book will continue to obey gravity is so great that we might wait a trillion years without seeing any sign of deviation. Only for electrons and other particles of similar size is there appreciable chance for differences from expected behavior.

All this long discussion gives us no clear picture of what the electron actually is. Something that behaves at times like a particle, at times like a wave, or something that resembles a particle but cannot definitely be located —we have only vague language like this to describe it. In future discussions we might find it convenient to think of electrons as particles, as miniature billiard balls carrying electric charges, and at other times as waves, but we must keep in the back of our minds the knowledge that neither picture tells the whole story.

Self-examination

1. When light is directed at a metal surface, the emitted electrons
   a. are called photons
   b. have random energies
   c. have energies that depend upon the intensity of the light
   d. have energies that depend upon the frequency of the light

2. According to the theories of modern physics,
   a. there is no such thing as a particle
   b. there is no such thing as a wave
   c. moving bodies behave in some respects as though they were waves and in others as though they were particles
   d. all bodies, moving or stationary, behave in some respects as though they were waves and in others as though they were particles

3. The uncertainty principle states that
   a. fast electrons are electromagnetic waves
   b. neither the position nor the velocity of an electron can ever be precisely measured
   c. the position and velocity of an electron cannot be simultaneously determined with accuracy
   d. electrons sometimes behave like particles and sometimes like waves

4. When an X-ray photon collides with an electron and bounces off, its new frequency
   a. is lower than its original frequency
   b. is the same as its original frequency
   c. is higher than its original frequency
   d. depends upon the electron's frequency

5. A beam of light is used to determine the position of an object. The maximum accuracy will be obtained if the light has a
   a. short wavelength
   b. long wavelength
   c. high speed
   d. low speed

6. The de Broglie wavelength of a body is proportional only to its
   a. mass
   b. velocity
   c. momentum
   d. energy

7. A phenomenon that cannot be understood on the basis of the quantum theory of light is
   a. the photoelectric effect
   b. the Compton effect
   c. X-ray production
   d. interference

Problems

1. List as many differences as you can between a photon and an electron.

2. Calculate the amount of energy in a photon of ultraviolet light whose frequency is 2×10^{16} cycles/sec. Do the same for a photon of radio waves whose frequency is 2×10^5 cycles/sec.

3. Calculate the de Broglie wavelengths of
   a. an electron of mass 9.1×10^{-31} kg and velocity 2×10^8 m/sec
   b. an automobile of mass 1,500 kg and velocity 30 m/sec

4. Compare the evidence for the wave nature of light with the evidence for its particle nature.

5. Explain the relationship between the photoelectric effect and the Compton effect.

6. An energy of 4×10^{-19} joule is required to remove an electron from the surface of a particular metal. What is the frequency of the light that will just dislodge photoelectrons from the surface? What is the maximum energy of photoelectrons emitted through the action of light of wavelength 2×10^{-5} cm?

7. The radiant energy reaching the earth from the sun is about 20 kcal/m²-sec. If this energy is all green light of wavelength 5.5×10^{-7} m, how many photons strike each square meter per second?

8. Find the energy of the photons in light whose wavelength is 2.5×10^{-7} m.

9. A photon whose energy is 2×10^5 ev strikes a free electron which acquires an energy of 1.5×10^5 ev in the collision. Find the frequency of the scattered photon.

10. Electrons are accelerated through potential differences of approximately 10,000 volts in television picture tubes. Find the maximum frequency of the X rays that are produced when these electrons strike the screen of the tube.

11. Give a reason why the wave aspect of light was established long before its particle aspect.

Part V

THE ATOM

CHAPTER 19 | *ATOMIC STRUCTURE*

We have now arrived at the last step before we reach what is perhaps the most remarkable achievement in all physical science, the elucidation of the structure of the atom. As we shall see in the later chapters, nearly all of what we have learned thus far about force and motion, conservation of energy, the gross properties of matter, the existence of the elements and their chemical behavior, electricity and magnetism, and electromagnetic waves is able to supply clues that help to explain the atom and its behavior. One obviously essential thing is missing: experimental evidence regarding what it is that makes atoms weigh so much. Atoms are very much heavier than electrons, the only indivisible (or *elementary*) particles whose existence we know of at this point, and this, together with the fact that the electrons we normally find in nature are negatively charged but atoms are electrically neutral, makes it difficult to believe that electrons are the sole constituent of atoms. What is the missing ingredient (or ingredients) in matter? This is the chief question that we shall consider in this chapter.

Radioactivity

In the year 1896 Henri Becquerel made a curious discovery in his laboratory in Paris. A small amount of a yellow salt containing uranium had been accidentally left for several days on a photographic plate in his darkroom; for no particular reason he developed the plate and found the silhouette of the pile of salt as a developed image. This was extraordinary—a substance that could take a photograph of itself without emitting any visible light whatever.   More of this uranium salt placed on other photographic plates produced similar behavior, no matter how carefully the plates were covered and protected from outside influences.   The uranium salt was unquestionably giving out some sort of unknown radiation, a property Bacquerel named *radioactivity*.

Experiments following his initial discovery convinced Becquerel that the part of the salt responsible for darkening his photographic plates was the element uranium.   Any compound of this metal produced a similar darkening, and the amount of darkening was roughly dependent on the amount of uranium present.   Having discovered these few facts about the new phenomenon, Becquerel turned the problem over to a young woman working in the laboratories at the Sorbonne.   Her name was Marie Curie.

The story of Madame Curie and her husband has been often told.   Early in their work on radioactivity came the surprising discovery that a piece of pitchblende, a black mineral from Bohemia, produced a darkening of photographic plates out of all proportion to its uranium content.   This suggested that the mineral contained traces of some other element far more powerful than uranium.   The Curies set themselves the forbiddingly difficult task of isolating this unknown element.   There followed two years of labor, seeking to wrest from a ton of black ore a fraction of a gram of a substance whose properties were completely unknown.   When their work was at last completed, the Curies had added not one but two new elements to the periodic table.   The first to be discovered was named polonium, after Madame Curie's native Poland; the other, more abundant element was the famous metal radium.

Radium belongs in the second group of Mendeleev's table, with calcium and barium.   Like them, it is a soft, silvery metal, tarnishing rapidly in air and dissolving in water with the evolution of hydrogen.   Unlike calcium and barium, radium shows an astonishing ability to produce the radiations Becquerel associated with uranium.   Thousands of times more active than uranium, radium and its salts not only blacken photographic plates, but, when mixed with certain compounds such as zinc sulfide, cause them to glow softly in a darkened room.

Alpha, Beta, and Gamma Rays

The radiation from radium and other radioactive elements causes fluorescence, darkens a photographic plate, and ionizes gases, and at least part of it is highly penetrating.   The harshest physical or chemical treatment cannot stop the radiation or even slow it down; whether the elements are free or combined in salts, cooled in liquid air or heated in an electric arc, their ability to radiate remains unchanged.   Spontaneously and continuously, year after year, these substances give out their peculiar rays.   Evidently, the emission is somehow associated with the atoms themselves—and with a part of each atom that is not affected by ordinary physical and chemical changes.

In electric and magnetic fields the radiation shows a complex behavior. It splits into three parts; one part is deflected to one side, a second part to the other side, and a third part continues straight through (Fig. 19.1). Before their nature was known, the three parts were labeled provisionally with the first three letters of the Greek alphabet: *Alpha rays* were those that were deflected as if they carried a positive charge; *beta rays,* those that seemed to have a negative charge; and *gamma rays,* those that passed undeflected through a field. Investigation has shown that gamma rays are electromagnetic waves shorter than X rays and that beta rays are electrons. But alpha rays, by all odds the most interesting of the three, consist of particles whose counterparts we have not met before.

Alpha particles ultimately proved to be atoms of helium. More correctly, we should say *ions* of helium—atoms that have been stripped of two electrons apiece, so that they carry a double positive charge. Seven thousand times as heavy as an electron, moving much more slowly than beta or gamma rays (only about 10,000 mi/sec), the particles of alpha rays cannot penetrate nearly so far through gases or metals; but their relatively enormous mass makes them highly destructive to atoms that get in their way. Collisions between alpha particles and other atoms, as we shall see in a later section, gave physicists their best early clues in deciphering atomic structures.

One type of alpha particle collision can be observed with astonishing simplicity. Take a watch or clock with a luminous dial into a darkened room, give your eyes time to become thoroughly accustomed to the darkness, and then look at the glowing paint through a low-power magnifying glass.

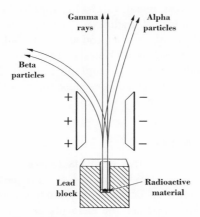

Fig. 19.1   *In the presence of an electric field, alpha particles behave as though positively charged, beta particles as though negatively charged, and gamma rays as though uncharged.*

You will find that the glow is made up of myriads of tiny flashes, like the sparks from a sky rocket, each flash lasting only a moment. In the paint is a tiny bit of some radioactive substance together with a material that emits light under its influence; each flash is the disturbance created when a single alpha particle is stopped by molecules of the luminous substance. You do not see the helium ions themselves, of course, but you see the effect that each one produces.

Radioactive Decay

The fraction of a gram of paint on your watch dial, with its incredibly small amount of actual radioactive material, has been giving off helium ions in immense numbers since the watch was made. Now it is fairly easy to show that no helium is present in the materials of the paint when it is mixed, and equally easy to show that the helium is produced just as rapidly when all the materials of the paint are removed except the infinitesimal speck of some radioactive element that it contains. *The helium is evidently being produced spontaneously from the atoms of the radioactive element.* This conclusion means that we must abandon our idea that elements are substances that cannot be broken down into simpler substances.

Naïvely, we may think of the expulsion of an alpha particle from a radium atom as a sort of minute explosion: A fragment of the atom bursts out of its interior, and part of the energy of the explosion appears as gamma radiation. The structure remaining after the explosion is no longer a radium atom; it has lost four atomic-weight units and is, accordingly, an atom of an element with altogether different chemical properties. This is the element *radon*, a gas that forms no compounds and hence is assigned to the zero group of the periodic table. Like radium, radon is intensely radioactive. Each of its atoms emits another alpha particle, becoming in the process an atom of radium A, which likewise is radioactive. Thus the explosion of a radium atom sets afoot a long series of radioactive changes.

Radium itself is the product of a series of changes starting with uranium. Table 19.1 shows this complete series of radioactive elements, from uranium through radium and radon finally to lead, which is not radioactive. Each element in the series is produced by the disintegration of the one above it and produces in its turn the one below it. Note that some of the changes take place by the emission of an alpha particle, some by emission of a beta particle. Gamma radiation does not of itself produce a change from one element to another, but appears to be energy given out following alpha or beta decay as the residual atoms reach stable configurations.

Three other disintegration series are known involving other atoms of high atomic weight. They are the *thorium* and *actinium* series, both of which occur in nature and end in lead, like the uranium series, and the *neptunium* series, which begins with an atom that must be artificially produced and ends

Table 19.1. *Radioactive transformations in the uranium series.*

Element	Mass number	Half-life	Particle emitted during transformation
Uranium	238	4.4×10^9 years	Alpha
Uranium X$_1$	234	24.5 days	Beta
Uranium X$_2$	234	1.14 min	Beta
Uranium II	234	3×10^5 years	Alpha
Ionium	230	8×10^4 years	Alpha
Radium	226	1,590 years	Alpha
Radon	222	3.82 days	Alpha
Radium A	218	3.05 min	Alpha
Radium B	214	26.8 min	Beta
Radium C	214	19.7 min	Beta
Radium C'	214	10^{-6} sec	Alpha
Radium D	210	22 years	Beta
Radium E	210	4.9 days	Beta
Polonium	210	140 days	Alpha
Lead	206		

in bismuth. Elements whose atomic weights are less than that of lead, with the seven exceptions in Table 19.2, are not naturally radioactive. Radioactive forms of the light elements, however, can be prepared by subjecting ordinary atoms to various kinds of radiation from accelerators or nuclear reactors.

After the mass number of each element in Tables 19.1 and 19.2 is its so-called *half-life*, the length of time necessary for half of any quantity of the element to disintegrate. If we start with 1 million radium atoms, after 1,600 years 500,000 of them will have changed to radon, and after another 1,600 years half the remainder will be gone (Fig. 19.2). If we used instead the feebly radioactive element uranium, we should have to wait over 4 billion years for half its atoms to disappear. If we worked with the active element

Table 19.2. *Radioactive transformations in the lighter elements.*

Element	Mass number	Half-life, years	Particle emitted during transformation
Hydrogen	3	12.5	Beta
Carbon	14	5,580	Beta
Potassium	40	1.83×10^9	Beta
Rubidium	87	6×10^{10}	Beta
Samarium	152	1×10^{12}	Alpha
Lutetium	176	2.4×10^{10}	Beta
Rhenium	187	4×10^{12}	Beta

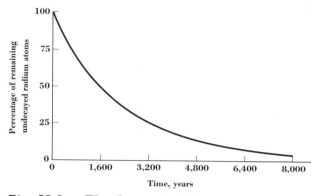

Fig. 19.2 The decay of radium. *The number of remaining unde-cayed radium atoms decreases by one-half in each 1,600-year period. This time span is accordingly known as the "half-life" of radium.*

radon, we should have to wait less than 4 days. These half-lives are about all the information we have concerning the time required for radioactive decay. We do not know how long it would take a million atoms of radium to change completely to radon, nor can we predict just how long an individual atom will last. We have only the sort of statistical information that enables a life insurance company to calculate accurately the death rate of a country's population, even though it can make no guess about when an individual will die.

Rutherford's Experiment

There are a number of ways we can trace the paths followed by atomic parti-cles after they have been emitted from a radioactive substance. The earliest way—and still a useful one—is based on the fact that water droplets tend to condense on the ions left by the passage of beta and alpha particles in a very moist atmosphere. By shining a light from the side on these droplets, we can make them gleam brightly against a dark background.

Perhaps the most astonishing thing about alpha particle tracks is that they are all extremely straight. One line on occasion does show a fork, but such occurrences are rare. The alpha particles, we remember, are travel-ing through several centimeters of ordinary air, and in this distance they should encounter many air molecules. It is true that the molecules are small compared with their distance apart, but simple calculations from the kinetic theory of gases show that an alpha particle in the course of its journey must nevertheless collide with several thousand molecules. It apparently goes right *through* the molecules. The encounters eventually slow the particle down, but they are unable to turn it from its path. Clearly, from the point of view of an alpha particle, air molecules are not very formidable obstacles.

Once in a while a track does show a deflection, usually a very sharp deflection, as if the particle had struck something hard and massive. The gas, so to speak, behaves like a soft cushion with scattered hard pellets embedded in it; collision with a pellet will turn the particle abruptly aside, but the pellets are so small and so far apart that its chance of hitting one before being slowed and stopped by the cushion is very slight. Let us see how this observation led to the modern concept of atomic structure.

Although most of the scientists of the nineteenth century accepted the idea that the chemical elements consist of atoms, they knew virtually nothing about the atoms themselves. The discovery of the electron and the realization that all atoms contain electrons provided the first important insight into atomic structure. Electrons contain negative electric charges, while atoms themselves are electrically neutral: Every atom must therefore contain enough positively charged matter to balance the negative charge of its electrons. Furthermore, electrons are thousands of times lighter than whole atoms, which suggests that the positively charged constituent of atoms is what provides them with nearly all their mass. When J. J. Thomson proposed in 1898 that atoms are uniform spheres of positively charged matter in which electrons are imbedded, his hypothesis then seemed perfectly reasonable. Thomson's plum-pudding model of the atom—so called from its resemblance to the raisin-studden delicacy—is sketched in Fig. 19.3. Despite the importance of the problem, thirteen years passed before a definite experimental test of the plum-pudding model was made. This experiment, as we shall see, compelled the abandonment of this apparently plausible model, leaving in its place a concept of atomic structure incomprehensible in the light of classical physics.

The most direct way to find out what is inside a plum pudding is to plunge a finger into it, a technique not very different from that used by Geiger and Marsden to find out what is inside an atom. In their classic experiment, performed in 1911 at the suggestion of Ernest Rutherford, they employed the fast alpha particles spontaneously emitted by certain radioactive elements as probes. Geiger and Marsden placed a sample of an alpha particle–emitting substance behind a lead screen that had a small hole in it, as in Fig. 19.4, so that a narrow beam of alpha particles was produced. This beam was directed at a thin gold foil. A movable zinc sulfide screen, which gives off a visible flash of light when struck by an alpha particle, was placed on the other side of the foil. It was anticipated that most of the alpha particles would go right through the foil, while the remainder would suffer at most slight deflections. This behavior follows from the Thomson atomic model, in which the charges within an atom are assumed to be uniformly distributed throughout its volume. If the Thomson model is correct, only weak electric forces are exerted on alpha particles passing through a thin metal foil, and their initial momenta should be enough to carry them through with only minor departures from their original paths.

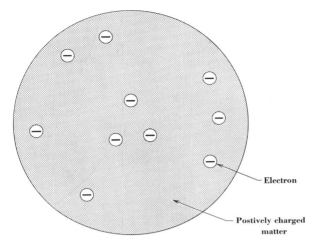

Fig. 19.3   The Thomson model of the atom. Experiment shows it to be incorrect.

What Geiger and Marsden actually found was that, while most of the alpha particles indeed emerged without deviation, some were scattered through very large angles.   A few were even scattered in the backward direction.   Since alpha particles are relatively heavy (over 7,000 times more massive than electrons) and those used in this experiment traveled at high speed, it was clear that strong forces had to be exerted upon them to cause such marked deflections.   To explain the results, Rutherford was forced to picture an atom as being composed of a tiny *nucleus,* in which its positive charge and nearly all its mass are concentrated, with its electrons some distance away (Fig. 19.5).   With an atom largely empty space, it is easy to see why most alpha particles go right through a thin foil.   However, when an alpha particle approaches a nucleus, it encounters an intense electric field, and is likely to be scattered through a considerable angle.   The atomic electrons, being so light, do not appreciably affect the motion of incident alpha particles.

Numerical estimates of electric field intensities within the Thomson and Rutherford models emphasize the difference between them.   If we assume with Thomson that the positive charge within a gold atom is evenly spread throughout its volume and we neglect the electrons completely, the electric field intensity at the atom's surface (where it is a maximum) is about 10^{13} volts/m.   On the other hand, if we assume with Rutherford that the positive charge within a gold atom is concentrated in a small nucleus at its center, the electric field intensity at the surface of the nucleus exceeds 10^{21} volts/m— a factor of 10^8 greater.   Such a strong field can deflect or even reverse the direction of an energetic alpha particle that comes near the nucleus, while

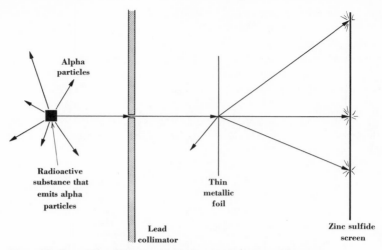

Fig. 19.4   The Rutherford scattering experiment.

the feebler field of the Thomson atom cannot.   Suppose, as a rough analogy, that a small star approaches the solar system from outer space.   With sufficient speed, the chances are excellent that it will pass through unharmed, except for a slight slowing down by the gravitational fields of sun and planets; even direct collision with a planet would not affect its motion appreciably. Only if it happened to approach closely the great central mass of the sun would its direction be radically altered.   Similarly, said Rutherford, an alpha

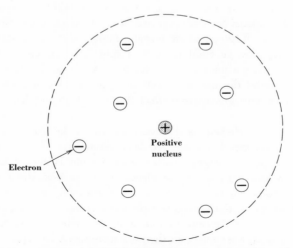

Fig. 19.5   The Rutherford model of the atom.   *This conception of atomic structure is supported by experiment.*

particle plows straight through the electric field of an atom, undeterred even by striking an electron now and then; only close approach to the heavy central core turns it aside.

Ordinary matter, then, is mostly empty space. The solid wood of a table, the steel that supports a skyscraper, the hard rock underfoot, all are but myriads of moving electric charges, isolated from one another by greater distances, comparatively, than the distance of the earth from its sister planets. If all the actual matter, all the electrons and nuclei, in our bodies could somehow be packed closely together, we should shrivel to specks just visible with a magnifying glass.

Atomic Number

Rutherford's concept of an atom as a positive nucleus surrounded by moving electrons can be used to explain many familiar observations. Since an ordinary atom is electrically neutral, the total positive charge on the nucleus must equal the negative charge of all the electrons in the electron cloud. If one of the electrons in the cloud is temporarily lost, the atom as a whole will show a positive charge; if an extra electron is temporarily added to the cloud, the atom as a whole will have a negative charge. Ions produced by high-speed particles are just such charged atoms or charged molecules that have lost or gained electrons as the particles moved through them. Ordinary positive charges on pith balls or electrodes imply a deficiency of electrons in the electron clouds of the atoms present, and negative charges imply an excess. The easy movement of electric currents through metals suggests that some electrons in the clouds of metal atoms are loosely held and can jump from one atom to the next.

Rutherford's work supplied also more precise information about the makeup of different atoms. The deflection that an alpha particle undergoes as it approaches an atomic nucleus depends on the amount of positive charge in the nucleus, so measurements of the deflection by atoms of different elements provide a means of estimating the amounts of nuclear charge. Rutherford found that all atoms of any one element have the same nuclear charge, that this charge is different for different elements, and, further, that the amount of charge increases regularly from element to element in the periodic table. The nucleus of hydrogen has a positive charge equal in magnitude to the negative charge of a single electron; the nucleus of helium has a charge equal to that of two electrons; the lithium nucleus has a charge equal to that of three electrons; and so on, up to the most complex element known to occur naturally, plutonium, whose nucleus has a positive charge equal to the negative charge of 94 electrons. *The number of unit positive charges on the atomic nuclei of an element is called the atomic number of the element.* Thus the atomic number of hydrogen is 1, of helium 2, of lithium 3, and of plutonium 94. Atomic numbers of the elements are listed in Table 11.4.

   Since in normal atoms the positive nuclear charge must be equaled by the total negative charge of the electrons in the cloud, atomic number can also be defined as the number of electrons in the uncharged atoms of an element. For example, the atomic number of phosphorus is 15; this means that the nucleus of the phosphorus atom has a positive charge of 15 and that around this nucleus is an electron cloud of 15 electrons.

   The atomic number of an element is its most fundamental property. Atoms with the same atomic number may have somewhat different weights and still show almost identical physical and chemical properties. But no change in atomic number is possible without a radical change in properties. The amount of positive charge on the nucleus of an atom serves to determine the fundamental nature of the atom and to distinguish it from all others. As an illustration of the significance of atomic numbers, Mendeleev's periodic law becomes an exact law when these numbers are used in place of atomic weights: *If the elements are arranged in order of increasing atomic number, elements with similar properties recur at regular intervals.* This statement of the law eliminates awkward exceptions that creep in when atomic weights are used instead of atomic numbers.

The Proton

Rutherford was able to go a step beyond the discovery of the atomic nucleus. In 1919 he found in a cloud-chamber photograph of alpha particles traveling through nitrogen an alpha track that ended in a peculiar way. From the end of the wide track, where the alpha particle came to a stop, a thinner track started off in a different direction. Another particle, less effective in ionizing the gas than alpha particles, evidently had come out of the collision between the alpha particle and a nitrogen atom. From the characteristics of the track, Rutherford was able to determine that the new particle had a mass about one-fourth that of an alpha particle and a positive charge equal in magnitude to that of the electron. This particle was called the *proton.*

   Now we know that an alpha particle is a helium ion with atomic weight 4. A particle with one-quarter this weight and a unit positive charge must be the same as the nucleus of the hydrogen atom, since hydrogen has atomic weight 1 and also atomic number 1. Thus *the proton is a hydrogen nucleus.* An ordinary hydrogen atom consists of a proton with a single electron revolving about it. The two particles have charges of the same magnitude (though with opposite sign), but the mass of the proton is a little over 1,800 times that of the electron (to be precise, the proton mass is 1.6724×10^{-27} kg, which is 1.0073 atomic mass units). Practically all the mass of the hydrogen atom, then, is concentrated in the proton.

   In later photographs of alpha particle tracks through substances other than nitrogen, Rutherford found occasional collisions showing the telltale thin fog tracks of protons. Since protons could be knocked out of many kinds of atoms, he guessed that these particles made up a part of all **atomic** nuclei. This guess has been amply confirmed by later work. In ordinary atoms, protons are the fundamental positive charges, as electrons are the fundamental negative charges. *The atomic number of an element is the number of protons in its nucleus.*

The Neutron

In the late 1920s, several observers reported a different kind of collision involving alpha particles and atoms of very light elements, particularly atoms of the metal beryllium (atomic weight 9). In these collisions no fog tracks of emitted particles appeared from the actual sites of the collisions, but emission of some kind of radiation was suggested by tracks that appeared to start spontaneously in other parts of the cloud chamber. Evidently, the radiation itself produced no ionization, but was capable of exciting atoms at a distance so that they would produce ionizing particles. This effect might be produced by high-energy gamma rays, and for some time this explanation was favored. Finally, in 1932, James Chadwick, working in Rutherford's laboratory, proved that the radiation consisted not of gamma rays, but of tiny *uncharged* particles that the alpha particles had knocked out of beryllium nuclei. These uncharged particles, christened *neutrons*, have approximately the same mass as protons but lack positive charge. The neutron mass is 1.6747×10^{-27} kg, which is 1.0087 atomic mass units. Because of their lack of charge and their small size, they can travel through the electron clouds of atoms without producing enough disturbance to cause appreciable ionization, but when they happen to strike a nucleus, charged particles may be emitted which cause the fog tracks observed at a distance from the original collision.

Free neutrons outside of nuclei are unstable and undergo radioactive decay into a proton and an electron each. The half-life of this beta decay is about 13 min; that is, if we start out with 100 neutrons, after 13 min, 50 of them will have turned into protons and electrons, after another 13 min, 25 of the remaining 50 neutrons will have decayed, and so on. We may legitimately think of the beta decay of a radioactive nucleus as corresponding to the conversion of one of its neutrons into a proton with the emission of an electron. Positron emission, another form of beta decay, we might think of as the conversion of a proton to a neutron with the emission of a positive electron (or *positron*); this latter process, however, does not occur in free protons outside of nuclei.

Nuclear Structure

The neutron and the proton (together often called *nucleons*) have masses about the same as the hydrogen atom and nearly 2,000 times the mass of the electron. Neutrons and protons make up almost the entire mass of an atom; the electron is so much lighter that even in the heaviest atoms the combined weight of all the electrons is only a small fraction of the weight of a single nucleon.

If ordinary nuclei consist of protons and neutrons, both of which are particles with a mass approximately equal to that of the hydrogen atom, it should follow that the weight of any nucleus is approximately an even multiple of the weight of the hydrogen nucleus. Since electrons contribute very little to an atom's mass, this means, further, that the atomic weight of any element ought to be an integral multiple of the atomic weight of hydrogen. In other words, since hydrogen has an atomic weight of approximately 1, all other atomic weights should be whole numbers or nearly so. Now it is a striking fact, as we have noted before, that atomic weights for many elements are indeed close to whole numbers; thus carbon has a weight of 12.01, fluorine 19.00, nitrogen 14.01. On the other hand, some atomic weights are conspicuously different from whole numbers; for example, chlorine 35.45, copper 63.54, magnesium 24.31. How can we possibly construct atoms with these weights out of protons and neutrons?

The answer to this dilemma is that the atoms of any one element are not necessarily all exactly alike. This suggestion had been made in the early 1900s, long before protons and neutrons were discovered, in order to account for the fact that in radioactive series the same element might be produced by different types of radioactive decay and would then show slight differences in atomic weight. It was a radical suggestion, completely at variance with Dalton's atomic theory. Convincing proof of its correctness was obtained in 1919 through some ingenious experimental work by J. J. Thomson and another Cambridge physicist, F. W. Aston. The experiment consisted in sending positively charged atoms (positive ions) at high speeds through combined electric and magnetic fields. In their passage through the fields heavy atoms were deflected somewhat less than light atoms, and the amount of the deflection provided an accurate means of determining just how heavy different atoms were. When ions of chlorine were passed through this instrument, the ions did not all form a single beam corresponding to a mass of 35.45, but instead were divided into two beams, the stronger beam corresponding to a mass of 35 and the weaker to a mass of 37. This means that natural chlorine must contain two kinds of atoms, normally mixed in constant proportions of about 77 percent of mass 35 and 23 percent of mass 37, giving the apparent atomic weight of 35.45.

Not only chlorine but many other elements are found to have atoms with slightly different weights when examined in Aston's instrument. These varieties of an element with different atomic weights are called *isotopes*. Extensive research has shown that fractional atomic weights always mean mixtures of isotopes; once the atoms are ionized and separated, each isotope proves to have an atomic weight very nearly a whole number. In other words, *all atoms have weights that are nearly integral multiples of the weight of the hydrogen atom.* This conclusion, of course, is consistent with the idea that all atomic nuclei are built wholly of neutrons and protons.

Even the element hydrogen has isotopes. Ordinary hydrogen nuclei, of .course, consist of a single proton. In addition, there is an isotope of hydrogen called *deuterium*, of atomic weight 2, whose nuclei are each composed of a proton plus a neutron, and an isotope called *tritium*, of atomic weight 3, whose nuclei are each composed of a proton plus two neutrons. Both of these heavy isotopes are found in nature, but only in relatively small amounts. So-called *heavy water* is water in which deuterium atoms instead of hydrogen atoms are present in combination with oxygen. Tritium is unstable and undergoes radioactive decay with the emission of a beta particle; the process has a half-life of about $12\frac{1}{2}$ years.

Experiments involving knocking protons and neutrons out of atoms and the existence of isotopes make it necessary for us to reexamine our definition of the chemical elements. In an earlier chapter we defined an element as a substance not decomposable into other substances, and Dalton's atomic theory assumes that all the atoms of an element are identical. But if alpha particles can change an atom of one element into an atom of another by ejecting one or more nucleons, the above definition is not valid, and Aston's discovery of isotopes renders Dalton's assumption untenable. The proper statement is that *an element is a substance all of whose atoms have the same atomic number.*

Atoms of two isotopes have the same number of protons in their nuclei but different numbers of neutrons. The light isotope of chlorine, for example, has nuclei containing 17 protons and 18 neutrons, and the heavy isotope has nuclei containing 17 protons and 20 neutrons. The electron clouds, whose structure is determined by the total positive charge on the nucleus, are practically identical. In other words, the different isotopes of an element have the same atomic number but different atomic weights. These relations are illustrated for several elements in Table 19.3.

The ordinary physical and chemical properties of an element are determined almost wholly by the electron clouds of its atoms and therefore by its atomic number. Since different isotopes have the same atomic numbers and almost identical electron structures, their properties are very nearly the same. The two isotopes of chlorine, for instance, have the same yellow color, the same suffocating odor, the same efficiency as poisons and bleaching agents, and the same readiness to combine with metals and hydrogen. Their densities, boiling points, freezing points, and rates of diffusion depend somewhat on the masses of the atoms and thus are very slightly different. The extreme similarity in properties explains why isotopes are not appreciably separated in natural processes and why chemists failed to detect them before Aston's work.

The following terms and symbols are widely used to describe a nucleus:

Z = atomic number = number of protons

N = neutron number = number of neutrons

$A = Z + N$ = mass number = total number of neutrons and protons

Table 19.3.   The isotopes of hydrogen, chlorine, and lead.

Element	Atomic number	Protons in nucleus	Neutrons in nucleus	Atomic weight	Isotope name (if any)
Hydrogen	1	1	0	1	
	1	1	1	2	Deuterium
	1	1	2	3*	Tritium
Chlorine	17	17	18	35	
	17	17	20	37	
Lead	82	82	121	203*	
	82	82	122	204*	
	82	82	123	205*	
	82	82	124	206	
	82	82	125	207	
	82	82	126	208	
	82	82	127	209*	
	82	82	128	210*	Radium D
	82	82	129	211*	Actinium B
	82	82	130	212*	Thorium B
	82	82	132	214*	Radium B

* Radioactive isotope.

The term nucleon refers to both protons and neutrons, so that the mass number A is the number of nucleons in a particular nucleus. Nuclear species (sometimes called *nuclides*) are identified according to the scheme

$$_ZX^A$$

where X is the chemical symbol of the species. Thus the arsenic isotope of mass number 75 is denoted by

$$_{33}As^{75}$$

since the atomic number of arsenic is 33. Similarly, a nucleus of ordinary hydrogen, which is a proton, is denoted by

$$_1H^1$$

Here the atomic and mass numbers are the same because no neutrons are present.

Self-examination

1. The half-life of tritium is 12½ years. If we start out with 1 g of tritium, after 25 years there will be
   a. no tritium left
   b. ¼ g of tritium left

    c. ½ g of tritium left
    d. a total of 4 g of tritium

2. The atomic number of an element is the number of
    a. protons in its nucleus
    b. neutrons in its nucleus
    c. electrons in its nucleus
    d. protons and neutrons in its nucleus

3. The atomic weight of an element is
    a. always equal to or less than its atomic number
    b. always equal to or greater than its atomic number
    c. equal to its atomic number except in the case of isotopes
    d. sometimes greater and sometimes smaller than its atomic number

4. The basic idea of the Rutherford atomic model is that the positive charge in an atom is
    a. spread uniformly throughout its volume
    b. concentrated at its center
    c. readily deflected by an incoming alpha particle
    d. the same for all atoms

5. Radioactive materials do not emit
    a. electrons
    b. protons
    c. alpha particles
    d. gamma rays

6. Uranium eventually decays into a stable isotope of
    a. radium
    b. polonium
    c. radon
    d. lead

7. After 2 hr has elapsed, one-sixteenth of the original quantity of a certain radioactive substance remains undecayed. The half-life of this substance is
    a. 15 min
    b. 30 min
    c. 45 min
    d. 60 min

8. Atoms whose nuclei contain the same numbers of protons but different numbers of neutrons are called
    a. alpha particles
    b. isotopes
    c. radioactive
    d. positrons

Problems

1. The following statements were thought to be correct in the nineteenth century. Which of them are now known to be incorrect? For those that are incorrect, indicate the experimental information that proved the statement wrong, and modify the statement appropriately so that it is in accordance with modern views.
   a. Atoms are indivisible and indestructible.
   b. Equal volumes of all gases under the same conditions of temperature and pressure contain the same number of molecules.
   c. Energy can be neither created nor destroyed.
   d. The acceleration of a body is directly proportional to the force applied to it and inversely proportional to its mass.
   e. An element is a substance that cannot be decomposed into other substances.
   f. All atoms of any one element are identical.

2. For each of the following elements, the atomic weight of whose chief isotope is given below, state (*a*) the number of protons in its nucleus, (*b*) the number of neutrons in its nucleus, and (*c*) the number of electrons surrounding its nucleus.

Element	Atomic weight	Atomic number
Oxygen	16	8
Iron	56	28
Iodine	127	53
Bismuth	209	83

3. Radium decomposes spontaneously into radon and helium. Why is radium considered an element rather than a compound of radon and helium?

4. When the nucleus of a radium atom, which has an atomic number of 88 and an atomic weight of 226, undergoes alpha decay, what happens to its atomic number and atomic weight?

5. Can you give a reason why it is so difficult to produce new isotopes in the laboratory?

6. Would you expect the gravitational attractive force between two protons in a nucleus to counterbalance their electrical repulsion? Can you calculate the ratio between the electric and gravitational forces acting between two protons?

7. What happens to the atomic number and atomic weight of a radioactive isotope when it emits
   a. a negative beta particle?
   b. a positive beta particle?
   c. a gamma ray?

8. If 1 kg of radium is sealed into a container, how much of it will remain as radium after 1,600 years?   After 4,800 years?   If the container is opened after a period of time, what gases would you expect to find inside it?

9. Alpha particle tracks through gases and thin metal foils are nearly always straight lines.   To what conclusion regarding atomic structure does this observation lead?

10. An atom of radium E emits a negative beta particle from its nucleus and thereby becomes an atom of polonium.   Would you expect polonium to be to the left or right of radium E in the periodic table?

11. We have seen instances in which introducing new concepts to rescue an old theory has proved futile.   How does the successful notion of isotopes differ from such unsuccessful notions as phlogiston?

12. Find the number of neutrons and protons in each of the following nuclei: $_3\text{Li}^6$, $_6\text{C}^{13}$, $_{15}\text{P}^{31}$, $_{40}\text{Zr}^{94}$, $_{56}\text{Ba}^{137}$.

CHAPTER 20 | THE NUCLEUS

In the previous chapter we examined some of the chief characteristics of atomic nuclei, in particular their composition. Now we shall look into such dynamic aspects of nuclei as the processes by which nuclear reactions can evolve huge amounts of energy and also glance at the profusion of "elementary particles" which nuclear research has brought to light.

Nuclear Masses

We say that atomic weights of isotopes are "very nearly" whole numbers or that the mass of a heavy atom is "very nearly" an integral multiple of the mass of a hydrogen atom. Why must we make these statements indefinite? Why should not atomic weights be *exactly* whole numbers? If we examine the matter more closely and add up the masses of the individual neutrons and protons in a complex nucleus, we find that the sum of the masses turns out to be very nearly equal to the mass of the nucleus, but *not quite*. If our ideas about the structure of the nucleus are correct, why should such discrepancies crop up?

We might very well suspect that the answer is somehow connected with the mass-energy relationship of the special theory of relativity. Let us consider a specific example. We know that a helium atom consists of two neutrons, each with an atomic mass of 1.0087, and the constituent particles of two hydrogen atoms (each a proton plus an electron), each set with an atomic mass of 1.0078. The total mass of these four particles is 4.0330. The mass of a helium atom, however, is only 4.0026, smaller by 0.0304. In other words, the mass of a helium atom is *less* by almost 0.1 percent than the combined masses of its constituent particles.

In view of the mass-energy relationship

$$E = mc^2$$

this mass discrepancy is not so outrageous as it seems. All that we need assume is that, in the process of combining to form a helium atom, the two neutrons and two hydrogen atoms evolve a certain amount of energy. This energy comes from their mass, so the total mass left in the helium atom is a little less than the original mass of the constituents. The fact that the mass of the helium nucleus is less than the masses of the individual particles that went into it is, in fact, capable of explaining in a general way another question that had plagued physicists: Why does the cluster of protons in a nucleus, all repelling one another since all are positively charged, stay together? The nucleus does not contain enough mass to form free neutrons and protons; therefore it cannot fall apart into these particles unless enough *outside* energy is imparted to it to make up for the missing mass. Thus the helium nucleus is ordinarily a very stable affair, but if we can give it energy through a collision of some kind, we might then be able to break it up.

Another example will illustrate the ideas in the preceding paragraph. When a piece of lithium is bombarded by protons, the reaction pictured in Fig. 20.1 takes place. The masses of the various particles are as follows:

H nucleus + Li nucleus → 2 He nuclei

1.0073   7.0144   2 × 4.0015

The total mass on the left side is 8.0217, that on the right side is 8.0030; 0.0187 mass unit has disappeared. This missing mass is equivalent to an energy of 17 Mev (million electron volts), to use the energy unit of nuclear physics, which we might assume to be carried off as kinetic energy by the two alpha particles. When this reaction takes place in the laboratory, careful measurements show that the energies of the alpha particles indeed add up to 17 Mev. Sometimes, as in this reaction, the energy formed when mass disappears takes the form of kinetic energy of moving particles; sometimes it appears as gamma radiation, or as both kinetic energy and gamma radiation. Whatever form the energy takes, its total amount is always found to be related to the loss in mass by Einstein's equation $E = mc^2$.

If energy surges out of nuclear reactions in such enormous quantities, why did physicists not proceed to harness atomic energy as soon as the first bombardment process was discovered? Why was there a lapse of a quarter of a century between Rutherford's pioneer experiment and the atomic bomb? The explanation lies in the low efficiency of the bombardment experiments. In all these experiments tiny "bullets" are sent in the general direction of the "target" atoms; a very few bullets score direct hits and set free momentary

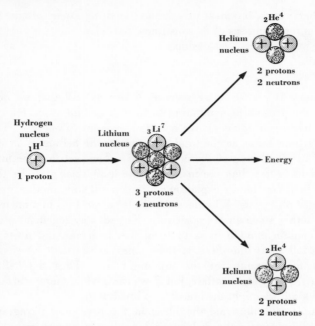

Fig. 20.1   An example of transmutation. A lithium nucleus struck by a proton yields two helium nuclei plus evolved energy. The total mass of the products is less than the total mass of the reactants; the "missing" mass appears in the form of energy.

bursts of energy, but the great majority pass through the target without encountering atomic nuclei. The reactions we have been considering are collisions between *single* atoms and *single* particles, not between large amounts of matter. Although each individual collision releases abundant energy, so many particles pass through the target without collision that the energy that must be supplied to make the particles move is far greater than the total energy produced. It is as if someone had scattered small sticks of dynamite over a hillside and we were trying to explode them by firing a machine gun at the hill from a long distance away. Once in a while one of our bullets would hit a stick and we would see a small explosion, but most of the bullets would plow harmlessly into the ground. The dynamite has an abundance of stored energy, but with this technique of releasing it we must supply more energy with our gun than we can obtain from the dynamite.

Nuclear Fission

In 1939, just before the outbreak of war, a startling announcement came from two German scientists, Otto Hahn and Lise Meitner: Atoms of the heavy metal uranium, bombarded by neutrons, split into fragments with roughly half the mass of the original atoms. This reaction was different from all other known nuclear processes in at least three important respects: (1) a heavy atom was literally split in two, whereas in other bombardment experiments only small particles were knocked out of the target atoms; (2) the energy set free was enormous even by nuclear standards, some hundreds of times greater than that produced by any other nuclear process; (3) among the products of the reaction were neutrons, the same particles that started the reaction. The third characteristic suggested an exciting possibility: Under suitable conditions, the neutrons produced from one uranium atom might cause the splitting of others, these in turn producing neutrons that would split still other atoms, the reaction thus spreading through the entire mass of uranium spontaneously—much as a forest fire spreads when the heat from one burning tree ignites others, these in burning ignite still others, and so on (Fig. 20.2). For a more exact analogy, we might suppose that the sticks of dynamite that we were trying to explode with a machine gun each contained a number of small pebbles. If we succeeded in hitting one stick, the pebbles would be scattered about and explode others, which in turn would shower their pebbles on still others, until most of the dynamite was consumed. The possibility of setting up such a *chain reaction* made it probable that

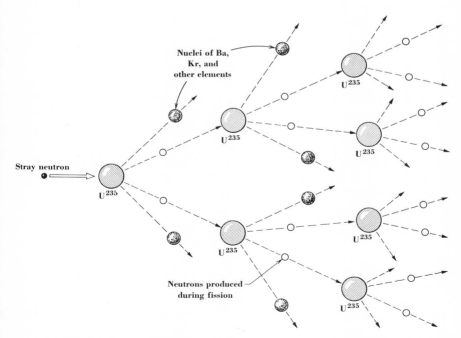

Fig. 20.2   *Sketch of a chain reaction as it might occur in pure* U^{235}.

this splitting, or *fission,* of uranium atoms would supply the long-sought key to the practical use of atomic energy.

Although Hahn's and Meitner's discovery seemed to show the possibility of utilizing atomic energy, applying it to actual production of an atomic bomb was an incredibly difficult undertaking. Industrial processes of completely new kinds had to be designed, tried out, and set up for large-scale operation. Even under the terrible urgency of wartime, it required more than four years of concerted effort by scientists, engineers, and industrialists, together with an expenditure of many millions of dollars. The same development under normal conditions would very likely have extended over a decade or longer.

One major difficulty lay in the fact that only a particular kind of uranium undergoes the fission reaction. Ordinary uranium consists of three isotopes; atoms with a weight of 238 are by far the most abundant, about 1 atom in 140 has a weight of 235 and about 1 in 16,000 a weight of 234. Only the atoms of U^{235} are fissionable by neutrons. Despite the small amount of this isotope, a chain reaction might still take place in natural uranium if a neutron could be depended on to bounce away from collisions with other atoms until it met one of the fissionable variety; unfortunately, most neutrons do not bounce, but are absorbed into U^{238} nuclei, which means that in natural uranium the chain reaction is quickly interrupted. Evidently one method of helping the chain to take place would be to separate the two isotopes. Separation of isotopes on an industrial scale had never before been attempted, but methods were devised and plants were set up to produce U^{235} in large quantities, a truly prodigious feat of engineering.

The absorption of neutrons by U^{238}, although it damps out the chain reaction in natural uranium, from another angle was a great help in releasing atomic energy. An atom of U^{238} that has absorbed a neutron becomes another isotope of uranium, U^{239}, which is unstable and quickly breaks down by emission of a beta particle into an atom of a different element, neptunium. This atom is also radioactive, its nucleus emitting another beta particle and thereby changing to an atom of plutonium. These changes may be summarized as follows:

$$n + \,_{92}U^{238} \rightarrow \,_{92}U^{239}$$
$$_{92}U^{239} \rightarrow \text{electron} + \,_{93}Np^{239}$$
$$_{93}Np^{239} \rightarrow \text{electron} + \,_{94}Pu^{239}$$

Plutonium, like U^{235}, is capable of fission when struck by neutrons. So if plutonium could be produced in quantity, it also could be used in a bomb. Now plutonium is present only in the minutest traces in natural uranium, but it seemed possible that the amount might be increased by neutron bombardment. If an increase could be brought about, the problem of separating Pu from the remaining U^{238} should be much simpler than the problem of separating U²³⁵, since plutonium is a different element and thus should be separable by ordinary chemical means. The possibility of obtaining plutonium seemed great enough to warrant a great deal of effort turned in this direction while the plants for separating isotopes were being set up.

Uranium-Graphite Reactors

The production of plutonium was brought about, not by bombardment with neutrons from an external source, but by a clever device for making the U²³⁵ chain reaction take place slowly in natural uranium. It happens that the neutrons produced in U²³⁵ fission are high-speed neutrons, which are readily absorbed by U²³⁸ atoms but which are not so effective as slow neutrons in splitting atoms of U²³⁵. Fast neutrons can be slowed down if they are passed through material consisting of light atoms that will not absorb them, like carbon atoms; their energy is gradually lost as they collide with one light nucleus after another. Now if small pieces of uranium could be scattered through a large block of graphite (pure carbon), some of the fast neutrons originating by fission in one piece should escape from the chunk, be slowed as they pass through the graphite, and thus be ready to produce fission in the U²³⁵ atoms of another piece (Fig. 20.3). This arrangement permits the chain reaction to take place in spite of the presence of U²³⁸. Of course, many neutrons are still absorbed by U²³⁸ atoms, and these atoms quickly change to plutonium. Such a uranium-graphite pile, first set up at the University of Chicago in 1942, showed by its successful operation that a controlled chain reaction was possible.

The chain reaction in natural uranium diluted with graphite liberates great quantities of energy, chiefly in the form of radiation. The reaction is not rapid enough for an effective atomic bomb, although it is an entirely practical source of energy. In the piles operated during World War II, however, energy production was incidental; the importance of the piles lay in the gradual enrichment of their uranium chunks with plutonium. By 1945, enough of both U²³⁵ and plutonium was available for the construction of bombs, and bombs were made from both materials. But difficulties were by no means ended with successful production of the fissionable elements in pure form. These strange new explosives could not be simply cut up into sticks and exploded by percussion caps, like dynamite. If a large enough mass of one of the elements were to be heaped together, it would explode by itself; there was no way to keep it from exploding, since always in the surrounding air there would be enough stray neutrons to start the chain reaction. On the other hand, a small chunk could not be exploded at all, since so many neutrons would escape from it that the chain reaction could not persist. An atomic bomb, then, must consist of small chunks of fissionable material sufficiently separated so that they will not explode, together with a device for bringing them together at the proper moment. The

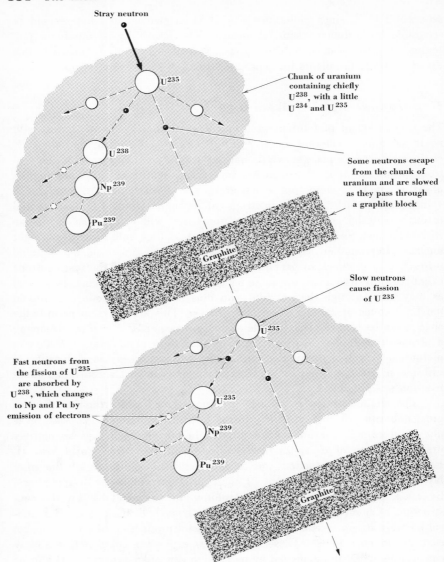

Stray neutron

U²³⁵

Chunk of uranium
containing chiefly
U²³⁸, with a little
U²³⁴ and U²³⁵

U²³⁸

Np²³⁹

Pu²³⁹

Some neutrons escape
from the chunk of
uranium and are slowed
as they pass through
a graphite block

Graphite

Slow neutrons
cause fission
of U²³⁵

U²³⁵

Fast neutrons from
the fission of U²³⁵
are absorbed by
U²³⁸, which changes
to Np and Pu by
emission of electrons

U²³⁵

Np²³⁹

Pu²³⁹

Graphite

Fig. 20.3   Principle of a uranium-graphite nuclear reactor.
Energy is evolved at each step of the process.

mechanical problem is tricky, for if the separate chunks are not brought together very rapidly, the bomb will start to explode prematurely and will fly
apart before it can do appreciable damage. It was only when this final problem was solved that the bomb was complete.

A uranium-graphite pile generates prodigious amounts of heat, and this
heat should serve as well as a coal or oil fire to make water boil and so pro-

vide power for a steam engine. Piles built for such purposes are commonly called *reactors*. Many different designs have been tried, but nearly all have three features in common: (1) a source of energy, generally uranium that has been somewhat enriched in the U^{235} isotope; (2) a *moderator*, or material to slow down fast neutrons, which is usually graphite or heavy water; and (3) a material to control the flow of neutrons by absorbing some of them, generally a rod of cadmium or boron steel that can be moved in and out of the reactor. The radiations produced by nuclear processes in the reactor are extremely dangerous, so elaborate shielding with lead or a similar material is necessary. Furthermore, automatic safety devices are essential, so that the control rods will immediately be inserted far enough to stop the reaction when anything goes wrong.

The necessity for heavy shields to prevent radiation damage has so far limited applications of atomic power to situations where weight has little importance. Stationary power plants have been built to produce electricity commercially, but in most places such plants cannot yet provide power cheaply enough to compete with electricity from coal and falling water. A few submarines are operating with nuclear engines, and such engines have been installed in surface ships. But in automobiles and airplanes, where limitation of weight is essential, the use of nuclear reactors as power sources will remain impractical until the problem of adequate but lightweight shielding has been solved.

The powerful and deadly radiation from reactors, although a serious handicap in power production, in other ways has proved very useful. The radiation consists chiefly of neutrons and gamma rays, but may contain secondary particles produced when these strike other atoms. When other substances are introduced into a reactor and subjected to this radiation, a variety of nuclear reactions is possible. In particular, many radioactive isotopes of common elements can be prepared, and these have found wide use in chemical, medical, and biological research. Some of the artificially radioactive substances have proved more effective than radium or X rays in the treatment of disease. One spectacular result of experiments with the radiation from atomic piles has been the artificial preparation of new elements —not only plutonium and neptunium, which were found in the course of work on the atomic bomb, but four elements that filled gaps in the periodic table and several additional elements heavier than plutonium.

Nuclear Fusion

Enormous as the energy production in uranium fission is, there are other nuclear processes which can give out energy in even larger amounts. One of these is the reaction of four hydrogen nuclei to produce helium, a process that actually takes place in the sun and other stars and is one of the important sources of stellar energy.

Here on the earth, 93 million miles from the sun, a surface 1 m^2 in area exposed to the vertical rays of the sun receives an average of nearly 20 kcal of heat energy per minute. Adding up all the energy received over the earth's surface gives a staggering total, although this is but a tiny fraction of the sun's total radiation. And the sun has been emitting energy at this rate for billions of years. Where does it all come from?

The answer that first suggests itself is combustion, for fire is the only familiar source of energy that seems at all comparable to the sun. But a moment's reflection shows how impossible any kind of combustion theory is. The sun is *too* hot to burn: burning implies the combination of other elements with oxygen to form compounds, but on the sun nearly all compounds are decomposed by the terrific heat. Even if burning were chemically possible, the heat obtainable from the best fuels known would be hopelessly inadequate to maintain the sun's temperature.

Solar energy must somehow be produced by processes taking place in the sun's interior. Although the interior cannot be observed directly, theoretical considerations make possible reliable estimates of conditions that exist there. Pressures must be high even at moderate depths, simply because of the weight of overlying material. Temperatures must increase rapidly toward the interior, since a continuous flow of energy is supplied to the photosphere to make good the prodigious losses by radiation. Mathematical analysis and a few reasonable assumptions lead to an estimate of 20 million degrees Celsius for the temperature and 1 billion atmospheres for the pressure near the sun's center.

It is possible to infer the properties of matter under these conditions from laboratory experiments with very small numbers of atoms. In the sun's interior, these experiments indicate, atoms of the lighter elements would have lost all their electrons, and atoms of the heavier elements would retain only their inmost electron shells. Thus matter in the sun's interior probably consists of atomic debris—free electrons in great numbers and positive nuclei surrounded by a few electrons or none at all.

These atomic fragments are in extremely rapid motion, traveling far more rapidly than gas molecules at ordinary temperatures. Such speeds mean that two atomic nuclei that collide may get close enough to each other— despite the repulsive electric force arising from their positive charges—to react, forming a single larger nucleus. When this occurs among the light elements, the new nucleus usually weighs a little bit *less* than the combined weights of the reacting nuclei. The missing mass is converted into energy in the process, according to Einstein's formula $E = mc^2$. So huge an amount of energy is evolved in nuclear reactions of this kind that it is not difficult to regard them as the source of solar energy.

The basic energy-producing reaction in the sun is the conversion of hydrogen into helium. This takes place both directly by collisions of hydrogen nuclei (protons) and indirectly by a series of steps in which carbon nuclei absorb a succession of hydrogen nuclei (Table 20.1). Each step can be duplicated on a small scale in the laboratory, and for each the energy required and the energy given out can be measured. In the sun's interior, conditions are ideal for such energy-producing collisions, not as events affecting rare, isolated atoms, like those in our laboratories, but as commonplace events occurring many times a second in every cubic centimeter of the sun's material. For the entire process by either mechanism, the energy available per helium atom corresponds to the difference in mass between four hydrogen nuclei ($4 \times 1.0073 = 4.0292$ atomic mass units) and one helium nucleus

Table 20.1. The proton-proton and carbon cycles of nuclear reactions that provide the sun's energy.

Proton-proton cycle

$_1H^1$	+	$_1H^1$	→	$_1H^2$	+	e^+	+	energy
Proton		Proton		Deuteron		Positron		

$_1H^1$	+	$_1H^2$	→	$_2He^3$	+	energy
Proton		Deuteron		Helium 3 nucleus		

$_2He^3$	+	$_2He^3$	→	$_2He^4$	+	2_1H^1	+	energy
Helium 3 nucleus		Helium 3 nucleus		Helium 4 nucleus		2 protons		

Carbon cycle

$_1H^1$	+	$_6C^{12}$	→	$_7N^{13}$	+	energy
Proton		Carbon 12 nucleus		Nitrogen 13 nucleus		

$_7N^{13}$	→	$_6C^{13}$	+	e^+	+	energy
Nitrogen 13 nucleus		Carbon 13 nucleus		Positron		

$_1H^1$	+	$_6C^{13}$	→	$_7N^{14}$	+	energy
Proton		Carbon 13 nucleus		Nitrogen 14 nucleus		

$_1H^1$	+	$_7N^{14}$	→	$_8O^{15}$	+	energy
Proton		Nitrogen 14 nucleus		Oxygen 15 nucleus		

$_8O^{15}$	→	$_7N^{15}$	+	e^+	+	energy
Oxygen 15 nucleus		Nitrogen 15 nucleus		Positron		

$_1H^1$	+	$_7N^{15}$	→	$_6C^{12}$	+	$_2He^4$	+	energy
Proton		Nitrogen 15 nucleus		Carbon 12 nucleus		Helium 4 nucleus		

* Note that in the carbon cycle the C^{12} nucleus ultimately emerges unchanged, so that it is, in effect, no more than a catalyst. N^{13} and O^{15} are both radioactive and beta-decay, respectively, into C^{13} and N^{15}, as shown, in very short time.

(4.0015 amu), or 0.0277 amu. Hence every 4 kg of helium that is formed in the sun means the liberation of very nearly

$$E = mc^2$$
$$= 0.0277 \text{ kg} \times (3 \times 10^8 \text{ m/sec})^2$$
$$= 2.5 \times 10^{15} \text{ joules}$$

About 10 million kilograms of coal would have to be burned to obtain this amount of energy!

The relative probabilities of the carbon and proton-proton cycles depend upon temperature. In the sun and stars like it, which have interior temperatures in the vicinity of 20 million degrees centigrade, one process occurs about as often as the other. On the other hand, most of the energy of hotter stars comes from the carbon cycle, and in cooler stars the proton-proton cycle predominates.

Every second the sun converts over 4 million tons of matter into energy, and its hydrogen content is such that it should be able to continue releasing energy at this rate for perhaps 30 billion years more. In fact, the amount of matter lost in all geologic history is not enough to have changed the sun's radiation appreciably, which confirms evidence that the earth's surface temperature has remained approximately constant during this period.

More feasible for duplication on the earth than the proton-proton or carbon cycles is a reaction between two nuclei of heavy hydrogen (deuterium), or even better, a reaction between deuterium and the still heavier artificial isotope of hydrogen, tritium:

$$_1H^2 + {_1}H^3 \rightarrow {_2}He^4 + {_0}n^1 + \text{energy}$$

A reaction of this sort, in which two particles unite to form a heavier particle, is often referred to as a *fusion* process, in contrast to the *fission* of uranium or plutonium. Maintaining a fusion reaction requires temperatures of several million degrees, temperatures attained on the earth during the explosion of a uranium bomb. Addition of deuterium and tritium to a uranium bomb, therefore, makes possible a still more efficient instrument of destruction, the uranium fission process serving to produce the necessary conditions for the more violent deuterium-tritium fusion. Such a bomb was exploded for the first time in 1952. The destructive capacity of a hydrogen bomb is limited only by the mechanical difficulties involved in getting its ingredients together fast enough to prevent a premature explosion.

Today laboratories throughout the world are working on means for controlling the production of energy in fusion processes. "Magnetic bottles" have been devised which employ strong magnetic fields to contain the reacting nuclei at very high temperatures, and a variety of ingenious schemes have been proposed for heating the nuclei to temperatures such that the fusion of light nuclei to form heavier ones will take place. *Thermonuclear power* is the name that has been given to the energy evolved during nuclear fusion, and it seems likely that this will be the ultimate source of power on the earth when fossil fuels such as coal and oil have been exhausted; nuclear reactors employing uranium and plutonium will almost certainly, in the long run, prove more expensive to operate than thermonuclear power plants.

Meson Theory of Nuclear Forces

At this point we know of the existence of electrons and positrons, neutrons, and protons, and it seems possible to explain the behavior of atomic nuclei without going any further. However, if we were to go into the question of what holds nuclei together in a really deep way, we should want to know something about the nature of the forces involved. Because nuclei weigh less than their component particles, they are stable, but what is it in the interactions between nucleons that leads to this loss of mass? After considering this matter in detail, the Japanese physicist Hideki Yukawa in 1935 proposed that nuclear forces arise from the constant exchange of particles (called *pi mesons*) back and forth between nearby nucleons. There were precedents for this kind of analysis: We shall see in Chap. 23 how molecules are held together by the circulation of electrons among their component atoms, and the electric forces between charges can be formally interpreted as the result of the exchange of electromagnetic quanta, of a somewhat different character from that of photons of electromagnetic radiation, between them.

According to the meson theory of nuclear forces, all nucleons consist of identical cores surrounded by a "cloud" of one or more mesons. Mesons may be neutral or carry either charge, and the sole difference between neutrons and protons is supposed to lie in the composition of their respective meson clouds. The forces that act between one neutron and another and between one proton and another are the result of the exchange of neutral mesons (designated π^0) between them. The force between a neutron and a proton is the result of the exchange of charged mesons (π^+ and π^-) between them. Thus a neutron emits a π^- meson and is converted into a proton:

$$n \rightarrow p + \pi^-$$

while the absorption of the π^- by the proton the neutron was interacting with converts it into a neutron:

$$p + \pi^- \rightarrow n$$

In the reverse process, a proton emits a π^+ meson whose absorption by a neutron converts it into a proton:

$$p \rightarrow n + \pi^+$$
$$n + \pi^+ \rightarrow p$$

Although there is no simple mathematical way of demonstrating how the exchange of particles between two bodies can lead to attractive and repulsive forces, a rough analogy may make the process intuitively meaningful.

Let us imagine two boys exchanging basketballs (Fig. 20.4). If they throw the balls at each other, they each move backward, and when they catch the balls thrown at them, their backward momentum increases further. Thus this method of exchanging the basketballs yields the same effect as a repulsive force between the boys. However, if the boys snatch the basketballs from each other's hands, the result will be equivalent to an attractive force acting between them.

It is possible to prove, by using more advanced mathematical techniques than we are using in this book, that the exchange of mesons between nucleons can indeed lead to mutually attractive forces, but a fundamental problem presents itself. If nucleons constantly emit and absorb mesons, why do we never find neutrons or protons with other than their usual masses? The answer is based upon the uncertainty principle. The laws of physics refer exclusively to experimentally measurable quantities, and the uncertainty principle limits the accuracy with which we can make certain combinations of measurements. The emission of a meson by a nucleon which does not change in mass—a clear violation of the law of conservation of energy—can occur provided that the nucleon absorbs a meson emitted by the neighboring nucleon it is interacting with so soon afterward that we cannot *even*

Repulsive force due to particle exchange

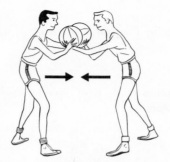

Attractive force due to particle exchange

Fig. 20.4 *Attractive and repulsive forces can both arise from particle exchange.*

in principle determine whether or not any mass change actually was involved.

A decade after Yukawa's work the pi meson was indeed discovered, and today there is no doubt that it is closely related to nuclear structure. Pi mesons may carry + or − charges equal to the charge of the electron or may be uncharged. The charged pi mesons have masses 273 times that of the electron; the uncharged ones are a little lighter.

Curiously enough, the pi meson is not a stable particle outside of a nucleus, but tends to "decay" in a fraction of a second. The charged pi mesons decay into another kind of meson called the mu meson, whose mass is 202 times that of the electron. The uncharged pi mesons decay into two gamma rays. Mu mesons are also unstable and decay after brief existences, positive mu mesons into positrons, negative mu mesons into electrons. The mass differences between pi and mu mesons and between mu mesons and electrons, of course, appear as kinetic energy of the resulting particle. All the mass of the uncharged pi meson is converted into electromagnetic energy in the two gamma rays.

Is the meson theory of nuclear forces correct? We are entitled to expect of any hypothesis that it make quantitative predictions in agreement with experiment, yet the meson theory cannot account for nuclear properties in the detailed manner that, as we shall see in the next two chapters, quantum theory can account for atomic properties. However, particles *have* been discovered whose mass and behavior are exactly in accord with meson theory; hence there can be little doubt that Yukawa was on the right track, and it is possible, perhaps likely, that an elaboration of the meson theory will prove successful.

Elementary Particles

An astonishingly large number of other unstable fundamental particles have been discovered in the past dozen years in experiments involving the bombardment of atomic nuclei with very high energy particles. Some of these new particles have only moderately short lifetimes, while others exist only for the briefest of instants. Table 20.2 lists 34 of the most prominent of the known elementary particles—only about a third of the total. The very term "elementary particle" has lost much of its meaning with the discovery of all these entities, most of which now seem to be closely related to one another though not in a simple way. The observed regularities in the properties of these particles give hope that a comprehensive theory to account for them may be forthcoming.

The electron is the only elementary particle for which a satisfactory theory is known. This theory was developed in 1928 by P. A. M. Dirac, who obtained a wave equation for a charged particle in an electromagnetic field that incorporated the results of special relativity. Perhaps its most striking result is its prediction that electrons can exist in *negative* energy states. There is nothing in the theory to prevent an electron in a positive

Table 20.2.   *Thirty-four elementary particles.*

Name	Particle	Antiparticle	Mass, in electron masses	Stability and decay	Lifetime, in seconds
Photon	γ	(γ)	0	Stable	
Neutrino	ν_e	$\overline{\nu}_e$	0	Stable	
	ν_μ	$\overline{\nu}_\mu$	0	Stable	
Electron	e^-	e^+	1	Stable	
Mu meson	μ^-	μ^+	207	Unstable; decays into electron plus two neutrinos	2.2×10^{-6}
Pi meson	π^+	π^-	273	Unstable; decays into mu meson plus neutrino	2.5×10^{-8}
	π^0	(π^0)	264	Unstable; decays into two gamma rays	10^{-16}
K meson	K^+	K^-	966	Unstable; may decay in one of six ways	1.2×10^{-3}
	$K_1{}^0$	$K_1{}^0$	974	Unstable; decays into two pi mesons	10^{-10}
	$K_2{}^0$	$K_2{}^0$	974	Unstable; may decay in one of six ways	6×10^{-8}
Proton	p^+	p^-	1,836	Stable	
Neutron	n^0	$\overline{n^0}$	1,839	Unstable in free space; decays into electron, proton, and neutrino	1.1×10^3
Lambda hyperon	Λ^0	$\overline{\Lambda^0}$	2,182	Unstable; decays into pi meson plus neutron or proton or into proton, electron, and antineutrino	2.5×10^{-10}
Sigma hyperon	Σ^+	$\overline{\Sigma^+}$	2,328	Unstable; decays into pi meson plus neutron or proton	8×10^{-11}
	Σ^-	$\overline{\Sigma^-}$	2,343	Unstable; decays into neutron plus pi meson	1.6×10^{-10}
	Σ^0	$\overline{\Sigma^0}$	2,352	Unstable; decays into lambda hyperon plus gamma ray	10^{-11}
Xi hyperon	Ξ^-	$\overline{\Xi^+}$	2,583	Unstable; decays into lambda hyperon plus pi meson	2×10^{-10}
	Ξ^0	$\overline{\Xi^0}$	2,598	Unstable; decays into lambda hyperon plus pi meson	1.5×10^{-10}

energy state from undergoing a transition to a negative energy state by radiating a photon of appropriate energy, or to prevent an electron in a negative energy state from falling to a still more negative state in the same way. Since systems always tend to evolve toward configurations of minimum energy, all the electrons in the universe should ultimately have energies of $E = -\infty$! There being no evidence that this peculiar destiny is indeed forthcoming, Dirac proposed that all negative electron energy states are normally occupied. The Pauli exclusion principle, which we shall meet in Chap. 22, prevents positive-energy electrons from undergoing transitions into any of these states. Dirac further proposed that the "sea" of negative-energy electrons is not observable directly.

While positive-energy electrons are prevented from falling into negative energy states since the latter are all occupied, the reverse process can occur. Given enough energy in some way, an electron of negative total energy can become one of positive total energy and thus become observable (Fig. 20.5). The removal of an electron from the negative-energy-electron sea leaves behind a "hole." Such a hole has interesting properties. Since it represents the absence of a particle of negative mass and kinetic energy, it behaves as though it is a particle of positive mass and kinetic energy. Moreover, a hole responds to electric and magnetic fields precisely as if it has a *positive* charge. Thus a hole has all the characteristics of an ordinary electron except that its charge is $+e$.

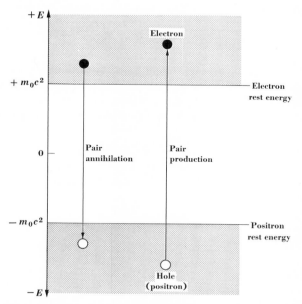

Fig. 20.5 *Pair production and annihilation according to the Dirac theory.*

While Dirac's reasoning had no obvious flaws, his notion of holes in an infinite sea of negative-energy electrons was too strange to find acceptance when proposed. In 1932, however, positive electrons were actually detected in the flux of cosmic radiation at the earth's surface, completely verifying the hole hypothesis. Positive electrons are usually called *positrons*.

The formation of a positron requires a minimum energy of $2m_0c^2$ (1.02 Mev), since this amount of energy is needed to bring an electron in a state whose energy is $-m_0c^2$ to a state whose energy is $+m_0c^2$. When a positron is formed, an electron simultaneously appears, since it is the absence of this electron from the unobservable negative-energy sea which constitutes the positron. If we wish, we can regard the process of electron-positron pair creation as one involving the materialization of matter from energy, since $2m_0c^2$ of energy disappears whenever such a pair comes into being. Any available energy in excess of $2m_0c^2$ goes into kinetic energy of the electron and positron. Experimentally, electron-positron pairs are found to be produced when gamma rays of $hf > 1.02$ Mev pass near nuclei (Fig. 20.6); the presence of the relatively heavy nuclei is required in order that momentum as well as energy be conserved in the process.

The reverse process to pair creation occurs when an electron of positive energy falls into a vacant negative energy state. Since the latter is observed as a positron, we may regard the process as one in which an electron and a positron *annihilate* each other. The simultaneous disappearance of an electron and a positron liberates $2m_0c^2$ of energy. No nucleus or other particle is needed for annihilation to take place, since the energy evolved appears as two gamma rays whose directions are such as to conserve both momentum and energy.

The positron is often spoken of as the *antiparticle* of the electron, since it is able to undergo mutual annihilation with an electron. All other known elementary particles except for the photon and the π^0 meson also have antiparticle counterparts; the photon and π^0 meson are their own antiparticles.

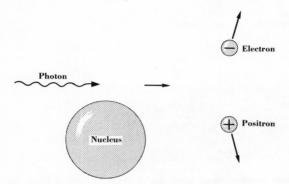

Fig. 20.6   Pair production. *The presence of a nucleus is required in order that both momentum and energy be conserved.*

The antiparticle of a particle has the same mass and lifetime if unstable, but its charge (if any) has the opposite sign.

The annihilation of a particle-antiparticle pair need not always result in a pair of photons, as it does in the case of electron-positron annihilation. When an antiproton is annihilated with a proton or neutron, for example, or an antineutron with a neutron or proton, several neutral and charged π mesons are usually produced. This is further evidence that π mesons may be regarded as quanta of the nuclear force field in the same sense that photons are quanta of the electromagnetic field.

The Neutrino

Another particle of great interest is the *neutrino*. This particle, though massless, is nevertheless able to possess energy and momentum; its existence was predicted thirty-three years before its direct experimental verification because of this peculiar combination of properties.

The electron energies observed in the beta decay of a particular nuclide are found to vary *continuously* from 0 to a maximum value KE_{max} characteristic of the nuclide. Figure 20.7 shows the energy spectrum of the electrons emitted in the beta decay of $_{83}Bi^{210}$; here $KE_{max} = 1.17$ Mev. In every case the maximum energy

$$E_{max} = m_0 c^2 + KE_{max}$$

carried off by the decay electron is equal to the energy equivalent of the mass difference between the parent and daughter nuclei. Only seldom, however, is an emitted electron found with an energy of KE_{max}.

It was suspected at one time that the "missing" energy was lost during collisions between the emitted electron and the atomic electrons surrounding the nucleus. An experiment first performed in 1927 showed that this hypothesis is not correct. In the experiment a sample of a beta-radioactive nuclide is placed in a calorimeter, and the heat evolved after a given number of decays is measured. The evolved heat divided by the number of decays gives the average energy per decay. In the case of $_{83}Bi^{210}$ the average evolved energy was found to be 0.35 Mev, which is very close to the 0.39-Mev average of the spectrum in Fig. 20.7 but far away indeed from the KE_{max} value of 1.17 Mev. The conclusion is that the observed continuous spectra represent the actual energy distributions of the electrons emitted by beta-radioactive nuclei.

In 1930 Wolfgang Pauli proposed that, if an uncharged particle of small or zero mass is emitted in beta decay together with the electron, the energy discrepancy discussed above would be removed. It was supposed that this particle, later christened the *neutrino*, carries off an energy equal to the difference between KE_{max} and the actual electron kinetic energy (the recoil nucleus carries away negligible kinetic energy) and, in so doing, has a momentum exactly balancing those of the electron and the recoiling

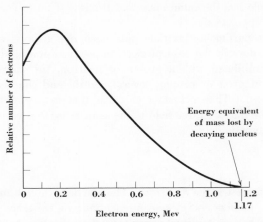

Fig. 20.7   ***Energy distribution of electrons from the beta decay of*** $_{83}\mathbf{Bi}^{210}$.

daughter nucleus.   Subsequently, it was found that there are *two* kinds of neutrino involved in beta decay, the neutrino itself (symbol ν) and the antineutrino (symbol $\bar{\nu}$).   In ordinary beta decay it is an antineutrino that is emitted:

$$n \rightarrow p + e^- + \bar{\nu}$$

Positron emission corresponds to the conversion of a nuclear proton into a neutron, a positron, and a neutrino:

$$p \rightarrow n + e^+ + \nu$$

While a neutron outside a nucleus can undergo negative beta decay into a proton because its mass is greater than that of the proton, the lighter proton cannot be transformed into a neutron except within a nucleus.

The neutrino hypothesis has turned out to be completely successful.   The neutrino mass was not expected to be more than a small fraction of the electron mass because KE_{max} is observed to be equal (within experimental error) to the value calculated from the parent-daughter mass difference; the neutrino mass is now believed to be zero.   The reason neutrinos were not experimentally detected until recently is that their interaction with matter is extremely feeble.   Lacking charge and mass, and not electromagnetic in nature as is the photon, the neutrino can pass unimpeded through vast amounts of matter.   A neutrino must pass through 1,000 *light-years* of solid iron on the average before interacting!

In 1962 it was discovered that the neutrinos emitted when charged π mesons decay into μ mesons are different from those emitted during beta decay.   The existence of these two classes of neutrino is indicated in Table 20.2 by the symbols ν_μ for the neutrino that accompanies the production of a μ meson and ν_e for the neutrino that accompanies beta decay. The corresponding antineutrinos are denoted by the same symbols with bars over them.

Self-examination

1. The only one of the following particles that does *not* decay in free space into another particle is the
   a. proton
   b. neutron
   c. pi meson
   d. mu meson

2. Stable atomic nuclei weigh
   a. less than their constituent protons and neutrons
   b. the same as their constituent protons and neutrons
   c. more than their constituent protons and neutrons
   d. sometimes more and sometimes less than their constituent protons and neutrons

3. The splitting of an atomic nucleus, such as that of U^{235}, into two or more large pieces is called
   a. beta decay
   b. fusion
   c. fission
   d. a chain reaction

4. Which of the following does *not* make use of the energy evolved when two light nuclei fuse together to make a heavier one?
   a. the generation of energy within stars
   b. proposed thermonuclear power plants
   c. hydrogen bombs
   d. nuclear reactors

5. Of the following, the one that is *not* an elementary particle is the
   a. electron
   b. proton
   c. neutron
   d. alpha particle

6. According to Yukawa's theory, nuclear forces arise through the exchange between nucleons of
   a. electrons
   b. protons
   c. neutrinos
   d. mesons

7. The physical principle that makes it possible for the law of conservation of energy to be violated under certain specific circumstances is the
   a. law of conservation of momentum
   b. uncertainty principle
   c. law of conservation of charge
   d. law of definite proportions

Problems

1. (*a*) One kg of U^{235} loses about 1 g in mass when it undergoes fission. How much energy is released when this mass disappears? (*b*) If 1 ton of TNT releases 10^6 kcal when detonated, how many tons of TNT are equivalent to a bomb containing 1 kg of U^{235}?

2. Why are magnetic fields rather than solid containers used to confine atomic nuclei at very high temperatures? Would this scheme work for electrically neutral atoms and molecules?

3. What are the differences and similarities between fusion and fission processes?

4. One atomic mass unit (amu) is equal to 1.66×10^{-27} kg, and 1 electron volt (ev) is equal to 1.60×10^{-19} joule. Find the energy equivalent of 1 amu in terms of Mev, where 1 Mev = 1 million ev.

5. The hydrogen isotope $_1H^3$ has a nuclear mass of 3.0155 amu, and the helium isotope $_2He^3$ has a nuclear mass of 3.0149 amu. Find the mass discrepancy for each nucleus in atomic mass units, and calculate the energy equivalent of this discrepancy in joules. (The proton mass is 1.0073 amu and the neutron mass is 1.0087 amu.)

6. A nucleus of $_3Li^6$ is struck by a nucleus of $_1H^2$, and a nuclear reaction occurs in which two identical nuclei are produced. State the atomic number, mass number, and chemical name of these nuclei.

7. A nucleus of $_4Be^9$ is struck by an alpha particle, and a neutron is emitted in the nuclear reaction that occurs. State the atomic number, mass number, and chemical name of the resulting nucleus.

8. In some stars three alpha particles join together in a single reaction to form a $_6C^{12}$ nucleus. The alpha particle mass is 4.0015 amu, and that of $_6C^{12}$ is 11.9967 amu; find the energy liberated in this reaction.

CHAPTER 21 | THE THEORY OF THE ATOM

It may seem odd that it is possible to discuss the arrangement of the electrons surrounding the nucleus of an atom and the structure of the nucleus itself as though they were two separate subjects, almost independent of each other. Yet this separation of our theories into two parts, one atomic and the other nuclear, seems to mirror fairly well the actual situation. Except for several minor effects, the nucleus does not respond to changes in its electron cloud, and the electrons in turn regard their parent nucleus for the most part solely as an electric charge of $+Ze$ (where Z is the number of protons in the nucleus and e is the charge on each of them) and, in their behavior, ignore the detailed structure of the nucleus. Of course, if the atomic number Z of the nucleus should change, say by radioactive alpha or beta decay, the electron cloud would change accordingly, but otherwise there is remarkably little interaction between the nucleus, apart from its electric charge, and the electrons around it.

Just as the study of the radiation from nuclei led directly to our knowledge of the nucleus, so the study of the radiation emitted by atoms was responsible for the growth of ideas about atomic structure. Most of this radiation is in the form of visible light, and the late nineteenth century saw many investigations of *atomic spectra,* as the characteristic series of wavelengths emitted by particular elements are called. Since light is an electromagnetic phenomenon that can be caused by oscillations of electrons, the discovery by J. J. Thomson that atoms contain electrons led to the speculation that atomic spectra result from electron motion within atoms. Before we go into this idea, let us first examine atomic spectra in more detail.

Spectra

We have already mentioned spectra briefly and distinguished between the rainbow bands produced when light from a glowing metal passes through a spectroscope (*continuous spectra*) and the sharp, bright lines from the light of a heated gas (*discontinuous*, or *line*, *spectra*). The continuous colored band from red to violet means that all visible wavelengths are present in the light; the discontinuous, bright-line spectrum indicates that only a few wavelengths are represented. The observed features of the radiation from heated solids can be explained on the basis of the quantum theory of light independently of the details of the radiation process itself or of the nature of the solid. From this fact it follows that, when a solid is heated to incandescence, we are witnessing the collective behavior of a great many interacting atoms rather than the characteristic behavior of the individual atoms of a particular element. At the other extreme, the atoms or molecules in a rarefied gas are so far apart on the average that their only mutual interactions occur during occasional collisions. Under these circumstances we should expect any emitted radiation to be characteristic of the individual atoms or molecules present, an expectation that is realized experimentally. When an atomic gas or vapor at somewhat less than atmospheric pressure is suitably "excited," usually by the passage of an electric current through it, the emitted radiation has a spectrum which contains certain discrete wavelengths only. An idealized laboratory arrangement for observing such atomic spectra is sketched in Fig. 21.1. Figure 21.2 shows the atomic spectra of several elements; they are called *emission line spectra*.

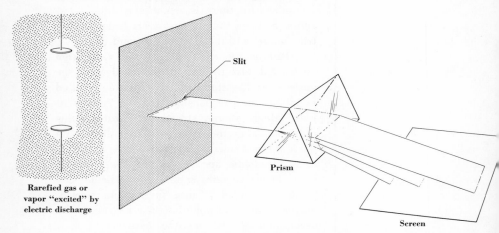

Slit

Prism

Rarefied gas or vapor "excited" by electric discharge

Screen

Fig. 21.1   An idealized spectrometer. Each wavelength produces a different image of the slit on the screen owing to dispersion in the prism.

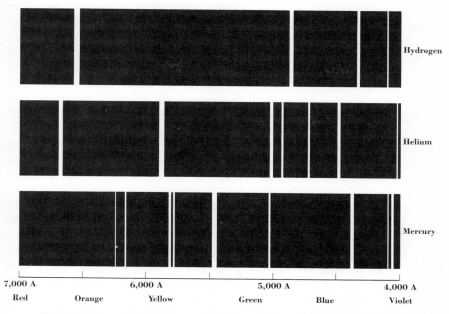

7,000 A   6,000 A   5,000 A   4,000 A

Red   Orange   Yellow   Green   Blue   Violet

Fig. 21.2 *Portions of the emission spectra of mercury, helium, and neon (1 Å = 10⁻¹⁰ m).*

Spectra of a different sort, *absorption spectra*, are produced when light from an incandescent source passes through a cool gas before entering the spectroscope. The light source alone would give a continuous spectrum, but the gas absorbs certain wavelengths out of the light that passes through it. Hence the continuous spectrum appears to be crossed by dark lines, each line representing one of the wavelengths absorbed by the gas. If the bright-line spectrum of an incandescent gas is compared with the absorption spectrum of the same gas, the dark lines in the latter are found to correspond in wavelength to a number of the bright lines in the emission spectrum. Thus a cool gas absorbs wavelengths of light that it is capable of emitting when heated to incandescence. The dark Fraunhofer lines in the solar spectrum occur because the luminous part of the sun, which radiates in a manner approximately like that of any object heated to 5800°K, is surrounded by an envelope of cooler gas which absorbs light of certain wavelengths only.

The line spectrum of each element (either its bright-line spectrum or its absorption spectrum) contains lines of certain wavelengths that are characteristic of that element. These lines can be recognized in complex spectra so that the element can be identified either in a light source or in an absorbing gas. This fact makes the spectroscope a valuable tool in chemical and metallurgical analysis; even minute traces of most elements are readily identified by the lines in their spectra.

The number, intensity, and position of the lines in the spectrum of an element vary somewhat with temperature, with pressure, with the presence of electric and magnetic fields, and with the method by which the element is made incandescent. Thus an expert can tell by examination of spectra not only what elements are present in a light source, but much about their physical condition. An astronomer, for example, can deduce from the spectrum of a star the composition of its atmosphere, whether it is approaching or receding from the earth, and what substances in its atmosphere are ionized.

In the latter part of the nineteenth century it was discovered that the wavelengths present in atomic spectra fall into definite sets called *spectral series*. The wavelengths in each series can be specified by a simple empirical formula, the formulas for the various series that comprise the complete spectrum of an element being remarkably similar. The first such spectral series was found by J. J. Balmer in 1885 in the course of a study of the visible part of the hydrogen spectrum. Figure 21.3 shows the *Balmer series*. The line with the longest wavelength is designated H_α, the next is designated H_β, and so on. As the wavelength decreases, the lines are found closer together and weaker in intensity until the *series limit* is reached, beyond which there are no further separate lines but only a faint continuous spectrum. Balmer's formula for the wavelengths of this series is

$$\text{(Balmer)} \qquad \frac{1}{\lambda} = R\left(\frac{1}{2^2} - \frac{1}{n^2}\right) \qquad n = 3, 4, 5, \ldots \qquad (21.1)$$

The quantity R, known as the *Rydberg constant*, has the value $1.097 \times 10^7 \text{ m}^{-1}$. The H_α line corresponds to $n = 3$, the H_β line to $n = 4$, and so on. The series limit corresponds to $n = \infty$, so that it occurs at a wavelength of $4/R$, in agreement with experiment.

The Balmer series contains only those wavelengths that are in the visible portion of the hydrogen spectrum. The spectral lines of hydrogen in the ultraviolet and infrared regions fall into several other series. In the ultraviolet, the Lyman series contains the wavelengths specified by the formula

$$\text{(Lyman)} \qquad \frac{1}{\lambda} = R\left(\frac{1}{1^2} - \frac{1}{n^2}\right) \qquad n = 2, 3, 4, \ldots \qquad (21.2)$$

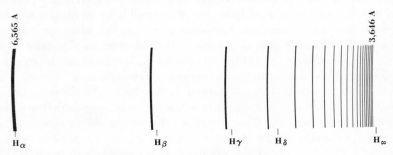

Fig. 21.3   The Balmer series of hydrogen.

In the infrared, three spectral series have been found whose component lines have the wavelengths specified by the formulas

(Paschen) $\qquad \dfrac{1}{\lambda} = R\left(\dfrac{1}{3^2} - \dfrac{1}{n^2}\right) \qquad n = 4, 5, 6, \ldots$ $\qquad\qquad$ (21.3)

(Brackett) $\qquad \dfrac{1}{\lambda} = R\left(\dfrac{1}{4^2} - \dfrac{1}{n^2}\right) \qquad n = 5, 6, 7, \ldots$ $\qquad\qquad$ (21.4)

(Pfund) $\qquad \dfrac{1}{\lambda} = R\left(\dfrac{1}{5^2} - \dfrac{1}{n^2}\right) \qquad n = 6, 7, 8, \ldots$ $\qquad\qquad$ (21.5)

The above formulas are plotted on a logarithmic scale in Fig. 21.4; the Brackett series evidently overlaps the Paschen and Pfund series. The value of R is the same in all the hydrogen spectral series.

The existence of such remarkable regularities in the hydrogen spectrum, together with similar regularities in the spectra of more complex elements,

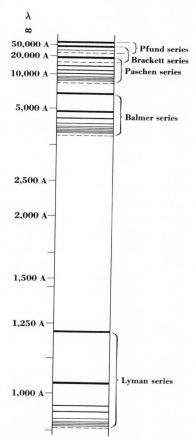

Fig. 21.4   The spectral series of hydrogen.

poses a definitive test for any theory of atomic structure. Here once more we find the familiar pattern of scientific reasoning, from observations to simple mathematical relations between the observations, and then from these relations to an inclusive theory. As Tycho Brahe's observations of the planets were correlated by Kepler's simple formulas and as these paved the way for Newton's idea of universal gravitation, so in the past hundred years observations of spectra have led to simple relations among the wavelengths of spectral lines and these in turn have led to modern concepts of atomic structure.

The Bohr Theory of the Atom

Rutherford's finding that an atom consists of a tiny, positively charged nucleus surrounded at a great distance by negatively charged electrons led immediately to the question: What keeps the electrons out there? As we know, oppositely charged particles attract, so some other force must be present to prevent the electrons from falling into the nucleus. By analogy with the planets of the solar system, where the centrifugal forces due to rotation counterbalance the gravitational force of the sun, we might suppose that the electrons within an atom are in constant motion, circling around the nucleus at just the proper speed to avoid being sucked into the nucleus.

This is not a bad notion, but there is a serious difficulty associated with it. According to Maxwell's theory, an electron so moving should emit electromagnetic radiation continuously. In giving out radiation it should continuously lose energy, its orbit should become steadily smaller, the wavelength of its radiation should grow longer, and ultimately it should collide with the nucleus. But electrons do not behave in this way, regardless of Maxwell's theory. Under ordinary conditions atoms do not emit any radiation, and when they are excited in one way or another, they emit radiation only of certain specific wavelengths, the same wavelengths that they preferentially absorb. And needless to say, atoms do not spontaneously collapse.

Niels Bohr, a Dane working in Rutherford's laboratory, applied the basic concept of the quantum theory of light—that energy comes in small packets rather than in a continuous spread—to the problem of atomic structure. He began by postulating that there were certain specific orbits in which an electron inside an atom could circle the nucleus without losing energy. Because these orbits are each a different distance from the nucleus, electrons in them have different amounts of energy. In other words, Bohr suggested that electrons within an atom can have only certain particular energy values. An electron in the innermost orbit has the least energy; an electron in an outer orbit has more. Thus each orbit may be alternatively referred to as an energy level.

The emission and absorption by atoms of only particular frequencies of light (which we observe as spectral lines) fits Bohr's atomic model perfectly. An atomic electron in some stable orbit can absorb only those **photons** of light whose energy hf will permit it to "jump" into another stable orbit farther out. Emission of radiation takes place when an electron jumps from one orbit to another of smaller energy, the difference in energy between the two orbits being equal to hf, where f is the observed frequency of the emitted light.

Figure 21.5 shows schematically the arrangement of possible orbits for the single electron in a hydrogen atom. Here the orbit pursued by the solitary electron under ordinary conditions is represented by the heavy line nearest the nucleus. The lighter lines are other possible orbits where the electron would possess greater energy than in its normal orbit, since it would then be farther from the nucleus (much as a stone at the top of a building has more potential energy than on the ground, since it is farther from the earth's center). Suppose that the electron at first is in the normal orbit. If the atom is supplied with energy—by strong heating, by an electrical discharge, or by radiation—the electron may be induced to jump to a larger orbit. This jump means that the atom has absorbed some energy. It retains the added energy as long as it remains in the excited state, that is, as long as its electron stays in the larger orbit. But the excited state is unstable, and in a small fraction of a second the electron jumps spontaneously back to its original orbit (or to another orbit smaller than the first). In this second jump radiation is emitted, the energy of the radiation representing the difference in energy between the excited and normal states of the atom. The amount of energy given out evidently depends on which of the outer orbits the electron followed in the excited state.

To gain a rough picture of the emission of radiation during an electron jump, we may imagine the electron vibrating for a moment as it subsides into the smaller orbit, much as a rubber ball will bounce repeatedly when it loses potential energy by dropping from a table to the floor. The vibrating electron sends out electromagnetic waves, just as the vibrating electrons in a radio antenna send out waves. The electron in the atom vibrates much more rapidly than those in the antenna, so its waves have far higher frequency and smaller wavelength than radio waves.

The energy, and therefore the frequency, of the radiation emitted from a hydrogen atom is determined, according to Bohr's hypothesis, by the particular jump that its electron makes. If the electron jumps from orbit 4 to orbit 1 (Fig. 21.5), the energy (and frequency) of the radiation will be greater than if it jumps from orbit 3 to orbit 1 or orbit 2 to orbit 1. Starting from orbit 4, it may return to orbit 1, not by a single leap, but by stopping at orbits 2 and 3 on the way; corresponding to these jumps will be radiations with energies (and frequencies) determined by the energy differences between orbits 4 and 3, 3 and 2, 2 and 1. Each of these several jumps gives radiation of a single frequency and will therefore be represented in the hydrogen spectrum by a single bright line. Further, the frequencies of the different lines will be simply related one to the other, since they

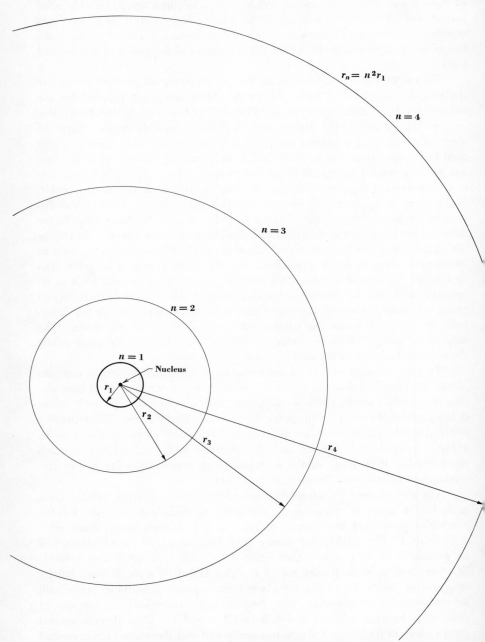

Fig. 21.5 *Electron orbits in the Bohr model of the hydrogen atom.*

correspond to different possible jumps in the same set of orbits. And the relations between the lines that Bohr predicted by this mechanism precisely matched the observed relations between lines in the spectrum of hydrogen.

Bohr's original model of the hydrogen atom presented several difficulties. It did not explain why the electron's orbital motion failed to produce radiation. It left unanswered such questions as why an electron in its jumps moved to one small orbit rather than another and why it could not revolve in other orbits than the discrete ones required by the hypothesis. Further, the model implied a radical change in orthodox ideas about the nature of energy. Nevertheless, Bohr's model found instant favor in scientific circles because of the remarkable accuracy with which it predicted the spectral-line series of hydrogen.

The Hydrogen Atom

Let us examine the Bohr theory of the hydrogen atom in a quantitative way. We must keep in mind that this theory is actually no more than an approximation to the more accurate—and also more mathematically complex—quantum-mechanical theory, but it provides a straightforward introduction to some of the notions of the latter and is worth considering for that reason.

We begin with the classical dynamics of the hydrogen atom, whose single electron makes it the simplest of all atoms. We shall assume a circular electron orbit for convenience, though it might as reasonably be assumed elliptical in shape. The centripetal force

$$F_c = \frac{mv^2}{r}$$

holding the electron in an orbit r in radius is provided by the electrostatic force

$$F_e = K \frac{e^2}{r^2}$$

between electron and nucleus. The condition for orbit stability is

$$F_c = F_e$$
$$\frac{mv^2}{r} = K \frac{e^2}{r^2}$$

so that the electron velocity v is given by

$$v = \sqrt{Ke^2/mr} \qquad\qquad (21.6)$$

The total energy E of the electron in a hydrogen atom is composed of its kinetic energy

$$KE = \frac{1}{2}mv^2$$

plus its electrostatic potential energy relative to an infinite separation of electron and nucleus, which is

$$PE = -K\frac{e^2}{r}$$

(The minus sign signifies that the force on the electron is in the $-r$ direction, that is, toward the nucleus.) Hence the total electron energy is

$$E = KE + PE$$
$$= \tfrac{1}{2}mv^2 - K\frac{e^2}{r}$$

Substituting for v from Eq. (21.6),

$$E = K\frac{e^2}{2r} - K\frac{e^2}{r}$$
$$= -K\frac{e^2}{2r} \tag{21.7}$$

The total energy of an atomic electron is negative, which is necessary if it is to be bound to the nucleus. If E were greater than zero, the electron would have too much energy to remain in a closed orbit about the nucleus.

An amount of work equal to 13.6 ev is experimentally observed to be required for the separation of a hydrogen atom into a proton and an electron; that is, the binding energy of the electron is -13.6 ev. Since 13.6 ev $= 2.2 \times 10^{-18}$ joule, we can find the orbital radius of the electron in a hydrogen atom from Eq. (21.7):

$$r = -\frac{Ke^2}{2E}$$
$$= -\frac{9 \times 10^9 \text{ newtons-m}^2/\text{coul}^2 \times (1.6 \times 10^{-19} \text{ coul})^2}{2 \times (-2.2 \times 10^{-18} \text{ joule})}$$
$$= 5.3 \times 10^{-11} \text{ m}$$

An atomic radius of this order of magnitude agrees with estimates made in other ways.

The above analysis is a straightforward application of Newton's laws of motion and Coulomb's law of electric force—both pillars of classical physics —and is in accord with the experimental observation that atoms are stable. However, it is *not* in accord with electromagnetic theory—another pillar of classical physics—which predicts that accelerated electric charges radiate energy in the form of electromagnetic waves. An electron pursuing a circular path is accelerated, and therefore should continuously lose energy until it spirals into the nucleus. Whenever they have been directly tested, the predictions of electromagnetic theory have always agreed with experiment, yet atoms do not collapse. This contradiction can mean only one thing: The laws of physics that are valid in the macroscopic world do not hold true in the microscopic world of the atom.

The reason for the failure of classical physics to yield a meaningful analysis of atomic structure is that it approaches nature exclusively in terms of the abstract concepts of "pure" particles and "pure" waves. As we learned in Chap. 18, particles and waves have many properties in common, though the smallness of Planck's constant renders the wave-particle duality imperceptible in the macroscopic world. The validity of classical physics decreases as the scale of the phenomena under study decreases, and we must make full allowance for the particle behavior of waves and the wave behavior of particles if we are to understand the atom. The Bohr atomic model, which combines classical and modern notions, accomplishes part of the latter task. (But only when the atom is considered from the point of view of quantum mechanics, which makes no compromise with intuitive notions acquired in our daily lives, does a really successful theory of the atom emerge.)

Let us examine the wave behavior of an electron in orbit around a hydrogen nucleus. The de Broglie wavelength of this electron is

$$\lambda = \frac{h}{mv} \tag{21.8}$$

where the electron speed v is that given by Eq. (21.6):

$$v = \sqrt{Ke^2/mr}$$

Hence $\quad \lambda = \dfrac{h}{e}\sqrt{r/Km} \tag{21.9}$

By substituting 5.3×10^{-11} m for the radius r of the electron orbit, we find the electron wavelength to be

$$\lambda = \frac{6.6 \times 10^{-34} \text{ joule-sec}}{1.6 \times 10^{-19} \text{ coul}} \sqrt{\frac{5.3 \times 10^{-11} \text{ m}}{9 \times 10^9 \text{ newton-m}^2/\text{coul}^2 \times 9.1 \times 10^{-31} \text{ kg}}}$$
$$= 33 \times 10^{-11} \text{ m}$$

This wavelength is exactly the same as the circumference of the electron orbit, which is

$$2\pi r = 33 \times 10^{-11} \text{ m}$$

The orbit of the electron in a hydrogen atom corresponds to one complete electron wave joined on itself (Fig. 21.6).

The fact that the electron orbit in a hydrogen atom is one electron wavelength in circumference provides us with the clue we need to construct a theory of the atom. If we consider the vibrations of a wire loop (Fig. 21.7), we find that their wavelengths always fit an integral number of times into the loop's circumference, so that each wave joins smoothly with the next. If the wire were rigid enough, these vibrations would continue indefinitely. Why are these the only vibrations possible in a wire loop? If a fractional number of wavelengths is placed around the loop, as in Fig. 21.8, destructive interference will occur as the waves travel around the loop, and the vibra-

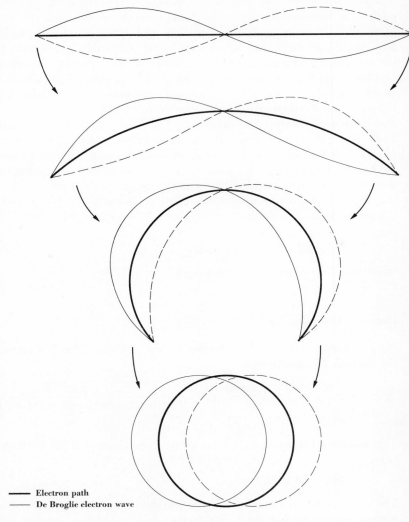

> ——— Electron path
> ——— De Broglie electron wave

Fig. 21.6   *The orbit of the electron in a hydrogen atom corresponds to a complete electron de Broglie wave joined on itself.*

tions will die out rapidly.   By regarding the behavior of electron waves in the hydrogen atom as being analogous to the vibrations of a wire loop, then, we might suppose that *an electron can circle a nucleus indefinitely without radiating energy provided that its orbit contains an integral number of de Broglie wavelengths.*

The above hypothesis is the decisive one in our understanding of the atom.   It combines both the particle and wave characters of the electron into a single statement, since the electron wavelength is computed from the orbital speed required to balance the electrostatic attraction of the nucleus. Although we can never experimentally verify these contradictory characters simultaneously, they are inseparable aspects of the natural world.

It is a simple matter to express the condition that an electron orbit contain an integral number of de Broglie wavelengths. The circumference of a circular orbit of radius r is $2\pi r$, and so we may write the condition for orbit stability as

$$n \lambda = 2\pi r_n \qquad n = 1, 2, 3, \ldots \tag{21.10}$$

where r_n is the radius of the nth orbit, that is, the one that contains n whole

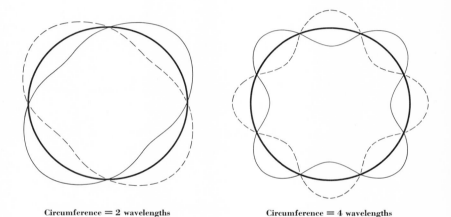

Circumference = 2 wavelengths   Circumference = 4 wavelengths

Circumference = 8 wavelengths

Fig. 21.7   *Vibrations of a wire loop.*

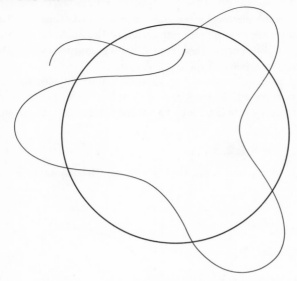

Fig. 21.8   *A fractional number of wavelengths cannot persist because destructive interference will occur.*

wavelengths. The integer n is called the *quantum number* of the orbit. Substituting for λ, the electron wavelength, from Eq. (21.9), we find

$$\frac{nh}{e}\sqrt{\frac{r_n}{Km}} = 2\pi r_n$$

and so the stable electron orbits are restricted to

$$r_n = \frac{n^2 h^2}{4\pi^2 Kme^2} \qquad n = 1, 2, 3, \ldots \qquad (21.11)$$

The orbit closest to the nucleus has the radius

$$r_1 = 5.3 \times 10^{-11} \text{ m}$$

as we found earlier. Because

$$r_n = n^2 r_1$$

the spacing between adjacent orbits increases rapidly with increasing quantum number n.

Energy Levels and Spectra

The various permitted orbits involve different electron energies. The electron energy E_n is given by Eq. (21.7) in terms of the orbit radius r_n as

$$E_n = -\frac{Ke^2}{2r_n}$$

If we substitute for r_n from Eq. (21.11), we see that

$$E_n = \frac{-2\pi^2 K^2 m e^4}{h^2} \left(\frac{1}{n^2}\right) \qquad n = 1, 2, 3, \ldots \qquad (21.12)$$

The energies E_n are called the *energy levels* of the hydrogen atom, and are plotted in Fig. 21.9. The energies are all negative, which means that the electron is bound to the nucleus. The lowest energy level E_1 is known as the *ground state* of the atom, and the higher levels E_2, E_3, E_4, and so on, are known as *excited states*. With increasing n, the corresponding energy E_n approaches closer and closer to 0; in the limit of $n = \infty$, $E_\infty = 0$, and the electron is no longer bound to the nucleus to form an atom. (A positive energy for a nucleus-electron combination means that the electron is not bound to the nucleus and has no quantum conditions to fulfill; such a combination does not constitute an atom, of course.)

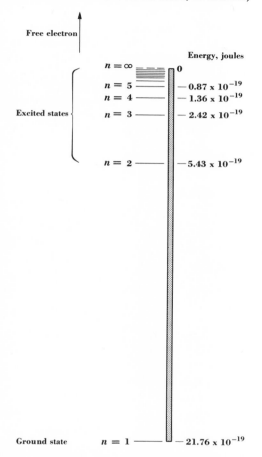

Fig. 21.9   *Energy levels of the hydrogen atom.*

It is now necessary for us to test the equations we have developed against experiment. An especially striking experimental result is that atoms exhibit line spectra in both emission and absorption. Do these spectra follow from our atomic model?

The presence of definite, discrete energy levels in the hydrogen atom suggests a connection with line spectra. We might reasonably suppose that, when an electron in an excited state drops to a lower state, the lost energy is emitted as a single photon of light. According to our model, electrons cannot exist in an atom except in certain specific energy levels. The jump of an electron from one level to another, the difference in energy between the levels being given off all at once in a photon rather than in a more gradual way, agrees with this model of the origin of spectra. If the quantum number of the initial (higher energy) state is n_i and the quantum number of the final (lower energy) state is n_f, we are proposing that

Initial energy − final energy = photon energy

$$E_i - E_f = hf \tag{21.13}$$

where f is the frequency of the photon that is emitted.

The initial and final states of a hydrogen atom that correspond to the quantum numbers n_i and n_f have, from Eq. (21.12), the respective energies

$$\text{Initial energy} = E_i = -\frac{2\pi^2 K^2 m e^4}{h^2} \left(\frac{1}{n_i^2} \right)$$

$$\text{Final energy} = E_f = -\frac{2\pi^2 K^2 m e^4}{h^2} \left(\frac{1}{n_f^2} \right)$$

Hence the energy difference between these states is

$$E_i - E_f = \frac{2\pi^2 K^2 m e^4}{h^2} \left[\left(\frac{1}{n_i^2} \right) - \left(\frac{1}{n_f^2} \right) \right]$$

$$= \frac{2\pi^2 K^2 m e^4}{h^2} \left(\frac{1}{n_f^2} - \frac{1}{n_i^2} \right)$$

The frequency f of the photon released in this transition is

$$f = \frac{E_i - E_f}{h}$$

$$= \frac{2\pi^2 K^2 m e^4}{h^3} \left(\frac{1}{n_f^2} - \frac{1}{n_i^2} \right) \tag{21.14}$$

In terms of photon wavelength λ, since in general

$$\lambda = \frac{c}{f}$$

we have $\dfrac{1}{\lambda} = \dfrac{f}{c}$

$$= \frac{2\pi^2 K^2 m e^4}{ch^3} \left(\frac{1}{n_f^2} - \frac{1}{n_i^2} \right) \tag{21.15}$$

Equation (21.15) states that the radiation emitted by excited hydrogen atoms should contain only certain specific wavelengths. These wavelengths, furthermore, fall into definite sequences that depend upon the quantum number n_f of the final energy level of the electron. Since the initial quantum number n_i must always exceed the final quantum number n_f (so that there may be an excess amount of energy to be given off as a photon), the formulas for the first five series on the basis of the above hypothesis are

$$n_f = 1: \frac{1}{\lambda} = \frac{2\pi^2 K^2 me^4}{ch^3} \left(\frac{1}{1^2} - \frac{1}{n^2} \right) \qquad n = 2, 3, 4, \ldots \qquad (21.16)$$

$$n_f = 2: \frac{1}{\lambda} = \frac{2\pi^2 K^2 me^4}{ch^3} \left(\frac{1}{2^2} - \frac{1}{n^2} \right) \qquad n = 3, 4, 5, \ldots \qquad (21.17)$$

$$n_f = 3: \frac{1}{\lambda} = \frac{2\pi^2 K^2 me^4}{ch^3} \left(\frac{1}{3^2} - \frac{1}{n^2} \right) \qquad n = 4, 5, 6, \ldots \qquad (21.18)$$

$$n_f = 4: \frac{1}{\lambda} = \frac{2\pi^2 K^2 me^4}{ch^3} \left(\frac{1}{4^2} - \frac{1}{n^2} \right) \qquad n = 5, 6, 7, \ldots \qquad (21.19)$$

$$n_f = 5: \frac{1}{\lambda} = \frac{2\pi^2 K^2 me^4}{ch^3} \left(\frac{1}{5^2} - \frac{1}{n^2} \right) \qquad n = 6, 7, 8, \ldots \qquad (21.20)$$

These sequences are identical in form with the empirical spectral series we discussed earlier. The Lyman series, Eq. (21.2), corresponds to $n_f = 1$; the Balmer series, Eq. (21.1), corresponds to $n_f = 2$; the Paschen series, Eq. (21.3), corresponds to $n_f = 3$; the Brackett series, Eq. (21.4), corresponds to $n_f = 4$; and the Pfund series, Eq. (21.5), corresponds to $n_f = 5$.

We still cannot consider our assertion that the line spectrum of hydrogen originates in electron transitions from high to low energy states as proved, however. The final step is to compare the value of the constant term in Eqs. (21.17) to (21.20) with that of the Rydberg constant R of the empirical Eqs. (21.1) to (21.5). The value of this constant term is

$$\frac{2\pi^2 K^2 me^4}{ch^3}$$

$$= \frac{2\pi^2 \times (9 \times 10^9 \text{ newton-m}^2/\text{coul}^2)^2 \times 9.1 \times 10^{-31} \text{ kg} \times (1.6 \times 10^{-19} \text{ coul})^4}{3 \times 10^8 \text{ m/sec} \times (6.6 \times 10^{-34} \text{ joule-sec})^3}$$

$$= 1.097 \times 10^7 \text{ m}^{-1}$$

which is indeed the same as R! The above theory of the hydrogen atom, which is essentially that developed by Bohr in 1913, although he did not have the de Broglie hypothesis to guide his thinking, therefore agrees both qualitatively and quantitatively with experiment. Figure 21.10 shows schematically how spectral lines are related to atomic energy levels.

Atomic Excitation

There are two principal mechanisms that can excite an atom to an energy level above its ground state, thereby enabling it to radiate. One mechanism is a collision with another particle during which part of their joint kinetic

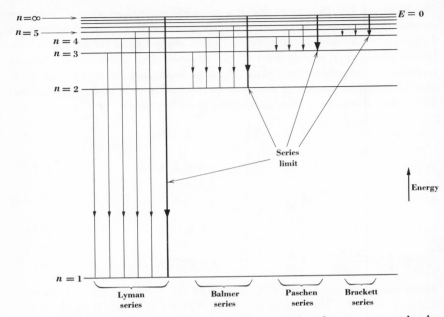

$n = \infty$

$n = 5$

$n = 4$

$n = 3$

$E = 0$

$n = 2$

Series
limit

Energy

$n = 1$

Lyman
series

Balmer
series

Paschen
series

Brackett
series

Fig. 21.10   *Spectral lines originate in transitions between energy levels.*

energy is absorbed by the atom. An atom excited in this way will return to its ground state in an average of 10^{-8} sec by emitting one or more photons. To produce an electric discharge in a rarefied gas, an electric field is established which accelerates electrons and atomic ions until their kinetic energies are sufficient to excite atoms they happen to collide with. Neon signs and mercury-vapor lamps are familiar examples of how a strong electric field applied between electrodes in a gas-filled tube leads to the emission of the characteristic spectral radiation of that gas, which happens to be reddish light in the case of neon and bluish light in the case of mercury vapor.

A different excitation mechanism is involved when an atom absorbs a photon of light whose energy is just the right amount to raise the atom to a higher energy level. For example, a photon of wavelength 6.565×10^{-7} m is emitted when a hydrogen atom in the $n = 3$ state drops to the $n = 2$ state; the absorption of a photon of wavelength 6.565×10^{-7} m by a hydrogen atom initially in the $n = 2$ state will therefore bring it up to the $n = 3$ state. This process accounts for the origin of absorption spectra. When white light, which contains all wavelengths, is passed through hydrogen gas, photons of those wavelengths that correspond to transitions between energy levels are absorbed. The resulting excited hydrogen atoms reradiate their excitation energy almost at once, but these secondary photons come off in random directions with only a few in the same direction as the original beam of white light. The dark lines in an absorption spectrum are therefore never completely black, but only seem so by contrast with the bright background. We expect the lines in the absorption spectrum of any element to have counterparts in its emission spectrum, then, which agrees with observation.

Atomic spectra are not the only means of investigating the presence of discrete energy levels within atoms. A series of experiments based on the first of the above excitation mechanisms was performed by Franck and Hertz starting in 1914. These experiments provided a very direct demonstration that atomic levels do indeed exist and furthermore that these levels are the same as those suggested by observations of line spectra. Franck and Hertz bombarded the vapors of various elements with electrons of known energy. They used an apparatus like that shown in Fig. 21.11. A small potential difference V_0 is maintained between the grid and collecting plate so that only electrons having energies greater than a certain minimum contribute to the current i through the galvanometer. As the accelerating potential V is increased, more and more electrons arrive at the plate and i rises (Fig. 21.12). If kinetic energy is conserved in a collision between an electron and one of the atoms in the vapor, the electron merely bounces off in a direction different from its original one. Because an atom is so much heavier than an electron, the latter loses almost no kinetic energy in the process. However, after a certain critical electron energy is reached, the plate current drops abruptly. The interpretation of this effect is that an electron colliding with one of the atoms gives up some or all of its kinetic energy in exciting the atom to an energy level above its ground state. (Such a collision is called *inelastic,* in contrast to an *elastic* collision in which kinetic energy is conserved.) The critical electron energy corresponds to the excitation energy of the atom. Then, as the accelerating potential V is raised further, the plate current again increases, since the electrons now have sufficient energy left after experiencing an inelastic collision to reach the plate. Eventually, another sharp drop in plate current i occurs, which in some cases arises from the excitation of a higher energy level. As Fig. 21.12 indicates, a series of critical potentials for a particular atomic species is obtained in this way. The highest potentials, of course, result from several inelastic collisions and are multiples of the lower ones.

To check the interpretation of critical potentials as being due to discrete atomic energy levels, Franck and Hertz observed the emission spectra

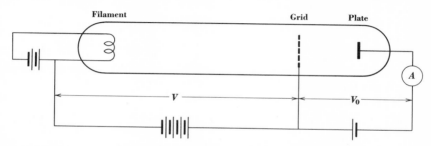

Fig. 21.11 *Apparatus for the Franck-Hertz experiment.*

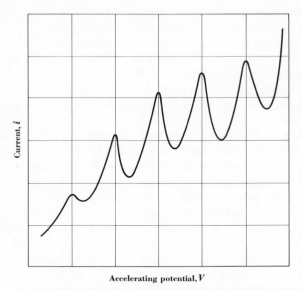

Accelerating potential, V

Fig. 21.12   Results of the Franck-Hertz experiment, showing critical potentials.

of vapors during electron bombardment. In the case of mercury vapor, for example, they found that a minimum electron energy of 4.9 ev was required to excite the 2,536 Å spectral line of mercury—and a photon of 2,536 Å light has an energy of just 4.9 ev! The Franck-Hertz experiments were performed shortly after Bohr announced his theory of the hydrogen atom, and they provided independent confirmation of his basic ideas.

Self-examination

1. The wavelengths of light emitted by the excited atoms of a particular element that make up its bright-line spectrum
   a. are different from the wavelengths in its dark-line spectrum
   b. are characteristic of the element involved
   c. come from the nuclei of the atoms
   d. are evenly distributed throughout the entire visible spectrum

2. In the Bohr model of the atom, the electrons revolve around the nucleus of an atom so as to
   a. emit spectral lines
   b. produce X rays
   c. form energy levels that depend upon their speeds only
   d. keep from falling into the nucleus

3. An atom emits a photon when one of its orbital electrons
   a. jumps from a higher to a lower energy level
   b. jumps from a lower to a higher energy level
   c. is removed by the photoelectric effect
   d. is struck by an X ray

4. Which of the following types of radiation are not emitted by the electronic structures of atoms?
   a. ultraviolet light
   b. visible light
   c. X rays
   d. gamma rays

5. According to the Bohr model of the atom, an electron in a stable orbit
   a. radiates electromagnetic energy continuously
   b. emits only spectral lines
   c. remains there forever
   d. can jump to another orbit if given enough energy

6. An electron can rotate in an orbit around an atomic nucleus without radiation energy provided that the orbit
   a. is far enough away from the nucleus
   b. is less than a de Broglie wavelength in circumference
   c. is an integral number of de Broglie wavelengths in circumference
   d. is a perfect circle

7. A neon sign does not produce
   a. a line spectrum
   b. an emission spectrum
   c. an absorption spectrum
   d. photons

Problems

1. What kind of spectrum would you expect to observe if you used a spectroscope to analyze: (a) light from the sun; (b) light from the tungsten filament of a light bulb; (c) light from a sodium-vapor highway lamp; (d) light from an electric-light bulb that has passed through cool sodium vapor?

2. In terms of the Bohr theory, explain why the hydrogen spectrum contains many lines, even though the hydrogen atom has only a single electron.

3. Why is the Bohr theory incompatible with the uncertainty principle?

4. On the basis of the Bohr model of the atom, explain why the dark (absorp-

tion) lines in the spectrum of hydrogen have the same wavelengths as the bright (emission) lines of the same element.

5. The earth has a mass of 6×10^{24} kg, and it circles the sun at 3×10^4 m/sec in an orbit 1.5×10^{11} m in radius. How many earth de Broglie wavelengths fit into this orbit?

6. Calculate the speed of the electron in the innermost $(n = 1)$ Bohr orbit of a hydrogen atom. Is this speed great enough for the relativistic mass change to be appreciable?

7. How much energy is required to remove the electron from a hydrogen atom when it is in the $n = 3$ state? The $n = 5$ state?

8. A beam of electromagnetic radiation that contains all wavelengths passes through a tube containing hydrogen gas. The hydrogen atoms are all in their ground states initially. What spectral series will be present in the absorption spectrum that results?

9. A proton and an electron, both initially at rest and far away from each other, combine all at once to form a hydrogen atom in its ground state. Find the wavelength of the photon that would be created in this hypothetical event.

10. Of the following transitions in a hydrogen atom (a) which emits the photon of highest frequency, (b) which emits the photon of lowest frequency, and (c) which absorbs the photon of highest frequency? $n = 1$ to $n = 2$, $n = 2$ to $n = 1$, $n = 2$ to $n = 6$, $n = 6$ to $n = 2$.

CHAPTER 22 | COMPLEX ATOMS

The Bohr theory of the atom we discussed in the previous chapter is able to account for certain experimental data in a convincing manner, but it has a number of severe limitations. While the Bohr theory correctly predicts the spectral series of hydrogen, it is incapable of being extended to treat the spectra of complex atoms having two or more electrons each; it can give no explanation of why certain spectral lines are more intense than others (that is, why certain transitions between energy levels have greater probabilities of occurrence); and it cannot account for the observation that many spectral lines actually consist of several separate lines whose wavelengths differ slightly. And, perhaps most important, it does not permit us to obtain what a really successful theory of the atom should make possible: an understanding of how individual atoms interact with one another to endow macroscopic aggregates of matter with the physical and chemical properties we observe.

The above objections to the Bohr theory are not put forward in an unfriendly way, for it was one of those seminal achievements that transform scientific thought, but rather to emphasize that an approach to atomic phenomena of greater generality is required. Such an approach was developed in 1925–1926 by Erwin Schrödinger, Werner Heisenberg, and others, under the apt name of *quantum mechanics*. By the early 1930s the application of quantum mechanics to problems involving nuclei, atoms, molecules, and matter in the solid state made it possible to understand a vast body of otherwise puzzling data and—a vital attribute of any theory—led to predictions of remarkable accuracy.

Quantum Mechanics

The fundamental difference between Newtonian mechanics and quantum mechanics lies in what it is that they describe. Newtonian mechanics is concerned with the motion of a particle under the influence of applied forces, and it takes for granted that such quantities as the particle's position, mass, velocity, acceleration, etc., can be measured. This assumption is, of course, completely valid in our everyday experience, and Newtonian mechanics provides the "correct" explanation for the behavior of moving bodies in the sense that the values it predicts for observable magnitudes agree with the measured values of those magnitudes.

Quantum mechanics, too, consists of relationships between observable magnitudes, but the uncertainty principle radically alters the definition of "observable magnitude" in the atomic realm. According to the uncertainty principle, the position and momentum of a particle cannot be accurately measured at the same time, while in Newtonian mechanics both are assumed to have definite, ascertainable values at every instant. The quantities whose relationships quantum mechanics explores are *probabilities*. Instead of asserting, for example, that the radius of the electron's orbit in a ground-state hydrogen atom is always exactly 5.3×10^{-11} m, quantum mechanics states that this is the *most probable* radius; if we conduct a suitable experiment, most trials will yield a different value, either larger or smaller, but the value most likely to be found will be 5.3×10^{-11} m.

Thus in quantum mechanics there is no attempt to force nature into the arbitrary molds of our personal experience. The theory is completely abstract instead of being based on a more or less mechanical model, and its only contact with reality is through observable quantities. That is, we can measure the mass of the electron and its electric charge, we can measure the frequencies of spectral lines emitted by excited atoms, and so on, and the theory must be able to relate them all. But we *cannot* measure the diameter of an electron's orbit or watch it jump from one orbit to another, and these notions, therefore, are not incorporated in the theory. The quantum-mechanical theory of the atom starts with Schrödinger's equation, a formula which requires a background in advanced mathematics to understand. The procedure is to substitute into Schrödinger's equation certain facts about the atom under consideration, such as the number of protons in its nucleus, the mass and charge of the electron, etc., and then to solve the resulting equation for the *wave function* of whichever electrons we are concerned with. From this wave function can be calculated the probability density of the electron, which is the likelihood that it will be found in any specific place whose coordinates we know. Because of the mathematical properties of Schrödinger's equation, a classification of atomic electrons in terms of energy levels follows naturally. This classification is the analogue of our previous picture of stable orbits, but it has a much more secure theoretical background and can be extended to cover many more situations accurately than can the simpler Bohr theory.

Quantum mechanics represents a complete abandonment of the traditional approach to physics in which models capable of being visualized are the starting points of theories. But although quantum mechanics does not provide any glimpses into the inner world of the atom, it does tell us almost everything we need to know about the measurable properties of atoms. And close inspection reveals a striking fact: *Newtonian mechanics is no more than an approximate version of quantum mechanics.* The certainties proclaimed by Newtonian mechanics are illusory, and their agreement with experiment is a consequence of the fact that macroscopic bodies consist of so many individual atoms that departures from average behavior are unnoticeable. Instead of two sets of physical principles, one for the macroscopic universe and one for the microscopic universe, there is only a single set, and quantum mechanics represents our best effort to date at formulating it.

Quantum Numbers

The quantum-mechanical theory of the atom reveals that *three* quantum numbers, n, l, and m_l, are needed to specify the physical state of an atomic electron. It is interesting to consider the interpretation of the hydrogen-atom quantum numbers in terms of the classical model of the atom. This model, as we saw in the previous chapter, corresponds exactly to planetary motion in the solar system, except that the inverse-square force holding the electron to the nucleus is electrical rather than gravitational. Two quantities are *conserved*—that is, maintain a constant value at all times—in planetary motion, as Newton was able to show from Kepler's three empirical laws: These are the total energy and the angular momentum of each planet. Classically the total energy can have any value whatever, but it must, of course, be negative if the planet is to be trapped permanently in the solar system. In the quantum-mechanical theory of the hydrogen atom the electron energy is also a constant, but while it may have any positive value whatever the *only* negative values (corresponding to a stable atom) it can have are specified by the formula

$$E_n = - \frac{2\pi^2 K^2 m e^4}{h^2} \left(\frac{1}{n^2} \right) \qquad (22.1)$$

(This is the same energy formula obtained from the Bohr theory.) The theory of planetary motion can also be worked out from Schrödinger's equation, and it yields an energy restriction identical in form with Eq. (22.1). However, the total quantum number n for any of the planets turns out to be so immense that the separation of permitted energy levels is far too small to be observable. For this reason classical physics provides an adequate description of planetary motion, but it fails within the atom. The total quantum number n refers to the quantization of electron energy in the hydrogen atom.

Quantum mechanics shows that the angular momentum of an atomic electron is also both quantized and conserved. (Angular momentum is the rotational analogue of linear momentum.) The angular momentum L of a particle of mass m and speed v that travels in a circular orbit of radius r is given by

$$L = mvr \qquad (22.2)$$

According to quantum mechanics, the possible values of L are restricted to

$$L = \sqrt{l(l+1)}\frac{h}{2\pi} \qquad (22.3)$$

where l, the orbital quantum number of an electron whose total quantum number is n, can be zero or any integer up to $n-1$. That is,

$$l = 0, 1, 2, 3, \ldots, (n-1)$$

In macroscopic planetary motion, once again, the quantum number describing angular momentum is so large that the separation into discrete angular momentum states cannot be experimentally observed. For example, an electron (or, for that matter, any other body) whose orbital quantum number is 2 has the angular momentum

$$L = \sqrt{2(2+1)}\frac{h}{2\pi}$$
$$= \sqrt{6}\frac{h}{2\pi}$$
$$= 2.6 \times 10^{-34} \text{ joule-sec}$$

By contrast the orbital angular momentum of the earth is 2.7×10^{40} joule-sec!

The orbital quantum number l determines the *magnitude* of the electron's angular momentum. However, angular momentum, like linear momentum, is a vector quantity, and so to describe it completely requires that its *direction* be specified as well as its magnitude. (The vector **L** is perpendicular to the plane in which the rotational motion takes place, and its sense is given by the right-hand rule: When the fingers of the right hand point in the direction of the motion, the thumb is in the direction of **L**. See Fig. 22.1.) What possible significance can a direction in space have for a hydrogen atom? The answer becomes clear when we reflect that an electron revolving about a nucleus is a minute current loop and has a magnetic field like that of a tiny bar magnet. In an external magnetic field **B** a bar magnet has an amount of energy that depends both upon how strong it is and upon its orientation with respect to the field. It is therefore not surprising to learn that the *direction* of **L** is also quantized with respect to an external magnetic field.

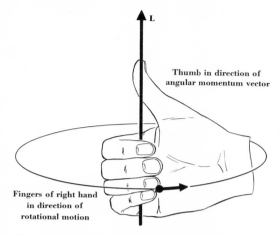

Thumb in direction of
angular momentum vector

Fingers of right hand
in direction of
rotational motion

Fig. 22.1   Right-hand rule for angular momentum.

The magnetic quantum number m_l specifies the direction of **L** by determining the projection of **L** in the field direction. If we let the magnetic field direction be parallel to the z axis, the projection of **L** in this direction is

$$L_z = m_l \frac{h}{2\pi} \qquad (22.4)$$

The possible values of m_l for a given value of l range from $+l$ to 0 to $-l$, so that the number of possible orientations of the angular momentum vector **L** in a magnetic field is $2l + 1$. When $l = 0$, L_z can have only the single value of 0, which means that **L** is perpendicular to **B**; when $l = 1$, L_z may be $-h/2\pi$, 0, or $-h/2\pi$; when $l = 2$, L_z may be $2h/2\pi$ $h/2\pi$, 0, $-h/2\pi$, or $-2h/2\pi$, and so on. We note that **L** can never be aligned exactly parallel or antiparallel to **B**, since L_z is always smaller than the magnitude $\sqrt{l(l+1)}$ $h/2\pi$ of the total angular momentum. The space quantization of the orbital angular momentum of the hydrogen atom is shown in Fig. 22.2. We must regard an atom characterized by a certain value of m_l as standing ready to assume a certain orientation of its angular momentum **L** relative to an external magnetic field, in the event it finds itself in such a field.

In a magnetic field, then, the energy of a particular atomic state depends upon the value of m_l as well as upon that of n. A state of total quantum number n breaks up into several substates when the atom is in a magnetic field, and their energies are slightly more or slightly less than the energy of the state in the absence of the field. This phenomenon is one of the effects that leads to a "splitting" of individual spectral lines into separate lines when atoms radiate in a magnetic field, with the spacing of the lines dependent upon the magnitude of the field. The splitting of spectral lines by a magnetic

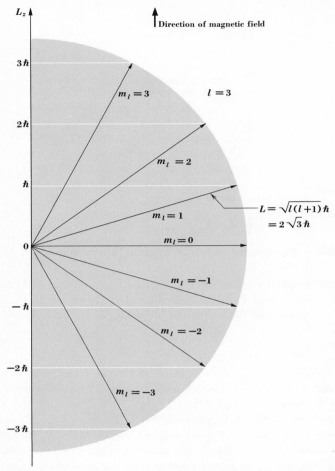

Fig. 22.2 **Space quantization of orbital angular momentum in the hydrogen atom.** *Only certain directions are possible relative to an external magnetic field.*

field is called the *Zeeman effect* after the Dutch physicist Zeeman, who first observed it in 1890. The Zeeman effect is a vivid confirmation of space quantization.

Electron Spin

Despite the accuracy with which the quantum theory accounts for certain of the properties of the hydrogen atom, and despite the elegance and essential simplicity of this theory, it cannot approach a complete description of this atom nor of other atoms without the further hypothesis of electron spin and the exclusion principle associated with it. In the remainder of this chapter we shall be introduced to the role of electron spin in atomic phenomena and to why the exclusion principle is the key to understanding the structures of complex atomic systems.

Let us begin by citing two of the most conspicuous shortcomings of the theory developed in the preceding chapter. The first is the experimental fact that many spectral lines actually consist of two separate lines that are very close together. An example of this *fine structure* is the first line of the Balmer series of hydrogen, which arises from transitions between the $n = 3$ and $n = 2$ levels in hydrogen atoms. Here the theoretical prediction is for a single line of wavelength 5,628 Å, while in reality there are two lines 1.4 Å apart—a small effect, but a conspicuous failure for the theory.

The second major discrepancy between the simple quantum theory of the atom and the experimental data occurs in the Zeeman effect, which we briefly mentioned above. There we saw that a hydrogen atom of magnetic quantum number m_l has an energy in a magnetic field that depends upon the value of m_l. Quantum mechanics shows that m_l can change by $+1$ or -1 or not at all in a transition between different atomic energency levels, so that the spectral lines of excited atoms in a magnetic field should each be split into three components at most. While the normal Zeeman effect is indeed observed in the spectra of a few elements under certain circumstances, more often it is not: Four, six, or even more components may appear, and even when three components are present, their spacing may not agree with the theory (Fig. 22.3).

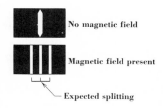

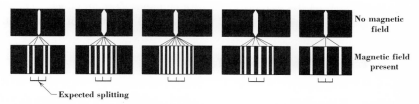

Fig. 22.3   *Normal and anomalous Zeeman effects in various spectral lines.*

In an effort to account for both fine structure in spectral lines and the anomalous Zeeman effect, S. A. Goudsmit and G. E. Uhlenbeck proposed in 1925 that the electron possesses an intrinsic angular momentum called *spin* independent of any orbital angular momentum it might have, and, associated with this angular momentum, a certain magnetic moment. What Goudsmit and Uhlenbeck had in mind was a classical picture of an electron as a charged sphere spinning on its axis. The rotation involves angular momentum and, because the electron is negatively charged, it has a magnetic moment. The notion of electron spin proved to be successful in explaining not only fine structure and the anomalous Zeeman effect, but a wide variety of other atomic effects as well. Of course, the idea that electrons are spinning charged spheres is hardly in accord with quantum mechanics, but in 1928 P. A. M. Dirac was able to show, on the basis of a relativistic quantum-theoretical treatment, that particles having the charge and mass of the electron must have just the behavior attributed to them by Goudsmit and Uhlenbeck.

The spin angular momentum of an electron is restricted to the single value

$$L_s = \frac{\sqrt{3}\,h}{4\pi}$$

but the spin magnetic quantum number m_s can have the two values $m_s = +\frac{1}{2}$ and $m_s = -\frac{1}{2}$, corresponding to two possible orientations of the spin vector in a magnetic field.

The fine structure doubling of spectral lines may be explained on the basis of a magnetic interaction between the spins and orbital motions of atomic electrons. This spin-orbit coupling can be understood in terms of a straightforward classical model. An electron revolving about a proton finds itself in a magnetic field because, in its own frame of reference, the proton is circling about *it*. This magnetic field then acts upon the electron's own spin magnetic moment to produce a kind of internal Zeeman effect. Depending upon the orientation of its spin vector, the energy of an electron in a given atomic quantum state will be higher or lower than its energy in the absence of spin-orbit coupling. The result is the splitting of quantum states into two separate substates and consequently the splitting of spectral lines into two component lines. The existence of electron spin also makes it possible to understand the various kinds of anomalous Zeeman effect. The theory of the latter is somewhat involved, however, and we shall not consider it.

The Exclusion Principle

In the normal configuration of a hydrogen atom, the electron is in its lowest quantum state. What are the normal configurations of more complex atoms? Are all 92 electrons of a uranium atom in the same quantum state, to be envisioned perhaps as circling the nucleus crowded together in a single Bohr orbit? Many lines of evidence make this hypothesis unlikely. An example is the great difference in chemical behavior exhibited by certain elements whose atomic structures differ by just one electron: For instance, the elements having atomic numbers 9, 10, and 11 are respectively the halogen gas fluorine, the inert gas neon, and the alkali metal sodium. Since the electronic structure of an atom controls its interactions with other atoms, it would be hard to understand why the chemical properties of the elements should change so abruptly with a small change in atomic number if all the electrons in an atom were to exist together in the same quantum state.

In 1925 Wolfgand Pauli discovered the fundamental principle that governs the electronic configurations of atoms having more than one electron. His *exclusion principle* states that *no two electrons in an atom can exist in the same quantum state.* Each electron in an atom must have a different set of quantum numbers n, l, m_l, m_s. Pauli was led to this conclusion from a study of atomic spectra. It is possible to determine the various states of an atom from its spectrum, and the quantum numbers of these states can be inferred. In the spectra of every element but hydrogen a number of lines are *missing* that correspond to transitions to and from states having certain combinations of quantum numbers. Thus no transitions are observed in helium to or from the ground-state configuration in which the spins of both electrons are in the same direction to give a total spin of 1, although transitions *are* observed to and from the other ground-state configuration in which the spins are in opposite directions to give a total spin of 0. In the absent state the quantum numbers of *both* electrons would be $n = 1$, $l = 0$, $m_l = 0$, $m_s = \frac{1}{2}$, while in the state known to exist, one of the electrons has $m_s = \frac{1}{2}$ and the other $m_s = -\frac{1}{2}$. Pauli showed that every unobserved atomic state involves two or more electrons with identical quantum numbers, and the exclusion principle is a statement of this empirical finding.

Electron Configurations

A system of particles is stable when its total energy is a minimum. In the case of a complex atom, the exclusion principle prevents all the various electrons from occupying the lowest quantum state. Before we look into how these two basic rules determine the actual electronic structures of complex atoms, let us examine the variation of electron energy with quantum state.

While the several electrons in a complex atom certainly interact directly with one another, as evidenced by the role of the exclusion principle in governing their behavior, it is not a bad approximation to consider each electron as though it exists in a constant mean force field. For a given electron this field is the electric field of the nuclear charge Ze, decreased by the partial shielding of those other electrons that are closer to the nucleus. All the electrons that have the same total quantum number n are, on the average, roughly the same distance from the nucleus. These electrons therefore interact with virtually the same electric field and have similar energies. It is conventional to speak of such electrons as occupying the same atomic *shell*.

The energy of an electron in a particular shell also depends to a certain extent upon its orbital quantum number l, though this dependence is not as great as that upon n. In a complex atom the degree to which the full nuclear charge is shielded from a given electron by intervening shells of other electrons varies with the "orbit" corresponding to its most probable location. When l is large, the equivalent orbit is roughly circular, while when l is small, the equivalent orbit is elliptical. An electron of small l therefore is more likely to be found near the nucleus (where it is poorly shielded by the other electrons) than one of higher l, which results in a lower total energy (that is, higher binding energy) for it. The electrons in each shell accordingly increase in energy with increasing l.

Electrons that share a certain value of l in a shell are said to occupy the same *subshell*. All the electrons in a subshell have almost identical energies, since the dependence of electron energy upon m_l and m_s is comparatively minor.

It is customary to specify angular momentum states by a letter, with s corresponding to $l = 0$, p to $l = 1$, and so on, according to the following scheme:

$$l = 0 \ 1 \ 2 \ 3 \ 4 \ 5 \ 6 \ 7 \cdots$$
$$s \ \ p \ \ d \ \ f \ \ g \ \ h \ \ i \ \ j \cdots$$

The combination of the total quantum number with the letter that represents orbital angular momentum provides a convenient and widely used notation for atomic states. In this notation a state in which $n = 2$, $l = 0$ is a 2s state, for example, and one in which $n = 4$, $l = 2$ is a 4p state. Table 22.1 gives the designations of atomic states through $n = 6$, $l = 5$.

The occupancy of the various subshells in an atom is usually expressed with the help of the above notation. A superscript after the letter indicates the number of electrons in that subshell. For example, the electron configuration of sodium is written

$$1s^2 2s^2 2p^6 3s^1$$

which means that the 1s ($n = 1$, $l = 0$) and 2s ($n = 2$, $l = 0$) subshells contain two electrons each, the 2p ($n = 2$, $l = 1$) subshell contains six electrons, and the 3s ($n = 3$, $l = 0$) subshell contains one electron.

The Periodic Table

The concept of electron shells and subshells fits perfectly into the pattern of the periodic table, which turns out to mirror the atomic structures of the elements. Let us see how this pattern arises.

The exclusion principle places definite limits on the number of electrons

Table 22.1. **The symbolic designation of atomic states.**

	s	p	d	f	g	h
	$l=0$	$l=1$	$l=2$	$l=3$	$l=4$	$l=5$
$n=1$	1s					
$n=2$	2s	2p				
$n=3$	3s	3p	3d			
$n=4$	4s	4p	4d	4f		
$n=5$	5s	5p	5d	5f	5g	
$n=6$	6s	6p	6d	6f	6g	6h

that can occupy a given subshell. A subshell is characterized by a certain total quantum number n and orbital quantum number l, where l is less than n. There are $2l+1$ different values of the magnetic quantum number m_l for any l and two possible values of the spin magnetic quantum number m_s ($+\frac{1}{2}$ and $-\frac{1}{2}$) for any m_l. Hence each subshell can contain a maximum of $2(2l+1)$ electrons, and each shell, a maximum of $2n^2$ electrons. A shell or subshell containing its full quota of electrons is said to be *closed*. A closed s subshell ($l=0$) holds 2 electrons; a closed p subshell ($l=1$), 6 electrons; a closed d subshell ($l=2$), 10 electrons; and so on.

The total orbital and spin angular momenta of the electrons in a closed subshell are zero, and their effective charge distributions are perfectly symmetric. The electrons in a closed shell are all tightly bound, since the positive nuclear charge is large relative to the negative charge of the inner shielding electrons. Thus an atom containing only closed shells has its charge uniformly distributed, so it does not attract other electrons, and its electrons cannot be readily detached. Such atoms we expect to be passive chemically, like the inert gases—and the inert gases all turn out to have closed-shell electron configurations!

Those atoms with but a single electron in their outermost shells tend to lose this electron, which is relatively far from the nucleus and is shielded by the inner electrons from all but an effective nuclear charge of $+e$. Hydrogen and the alkali metals are in this category and accordingly have valences of $+1$. Atoms whose outer shells lack a single electron of being closed tend to acquire such an electron through the attraction of the imperfectly shielded strong nuclear charge, which accounts for the chemical behavior of the halogens. In this manner the similarities of the members of the various groups of the periodic table may be accounted for.

Table 22.2 shows the electron configurations of the elements. The explanation for the structure of the transition elements evidently lies in the tighter binding of s electrons than d or f electrons in complex atoms, which we discussed in the previous section. The first element to exhibit this effect is potassium, whose outermost electron is in a $4s$ instead of a $3d$ substate.

Table 22.2. Electron configurations of the elements. *The first column lists the atomic numbers of the elements and the second their chemical symbols.*

		1s	2s	2p	3s	3p	3d	4s	4p	4d	4f	5s	5p	5d	5f	6s	6p	6d	7s
																Quantum state			
1	H	1																	
2	He	2																	
3	Li	2	1																
4	Be	2	2																
5	B	2	2	1															
6	C	2	2	2															
7	N	2	2	3															
8	O	2	2	4															
9	F	2	2	5															
10	Ne	2	2	6															
11	Na	2	2	6	1														
12	Mg	2	2	6	2														
13	Al	2	2	6	2	1													
14	Si	2	2	6	2	2													
15	P	2	2	6	2	3													
16	S	2	2	6	2	4													
17	Cl	2	2	6	2	5													
18	A	2	2	6	2	6													
19	K	2	2	6	2	6		1											
20	Ca	2	2	6	2	6		2											
21	Sc	2	2	6	2	6	1	2											
22	Ti	2	2	6	2	6	2	2											
23	V	2	2	6	2	6	3	2											
24	Cr	2	2	6	2	6	5	1											
25	Mn	2	2	6	2	6	5	2											
26	Fe	2	2	6	2	6	6	2											
27	Co	2	2	6	2	6	7	2											
28	Ni	2	2	6	2	6	8	2											
29	Cu	2	2	6	2	6	10	1											
30	Zn	2	2	6	2	6	10	2											
31	Ga	2	2	6	2	6	10	2	1										
32	Ge	2	2	6	2	6	10	2	2										
33	As	2	2	6	2	6	10	2	3										
34	Se	2	2	6	2	6	10	2	4										
35	Br	2	2	6	2	6	10	2	5										
36	Kr	2	2	6	2	6	10	2	6										
37	Rb	2	2	6	2	6	10	2	6			1							
38	Sr	2	2	6	2	6	10	2	6			2							
39	Y	2	2	6	2	6	10	2	6	1		2							
40	Zr	2	2	6	2	6	10	2	6	2		2							
41	Nb	2	2	6	2	6	10	2	6	4		1							
42	Mo	2	2	6	2	6	10	2	6	5		1							
43	Tc	2	2	6	2	6	10	2	6	5		2							
44	Ru	2	2	6	2	6	10	2	6	7		1							
45	Rh	2	2	6	2	6	10	2	6	8		1							
46	Pd	2	2	6	2	6	10	2	6	10									

Table 22.2. *Electron configurations of the elements (continued).*

Quantum state

		1s	2s	2p	3s	3p	3d	4s	4p	4d	4f	5s	5p	5d	5f	6s	6p	6d	7s
47	Ag	2	2	6	2	6	10	2	6	10		1							
48	Cd	2	2	6	2	6	10	2	6	10		2							
49	In	2	2	6	2	6	10	2	6	10		2	1						
50	Sn	2	2	6	2	6	10	2	6	10		2	2						
51	Sb	2	2	6	2	6	10	2	6	10		2	3						
52	Te	2	2	6	2	6	10	2	6	10		2	4						
53	I	2	2	6	2	6	10	2	6	10		2	5						
54	Xe	2	2	6	2	6	10	2	6	10		2	6						
55	Cs	2	2	6	2	6	10	2	6	10		2	6			1			
56	Ba	2	2	6	2	6	10	2	6	10		2	6			2			
57	La	2	2	6	2	6	10	2	6	10		2	6	1		2			
58	Ce	2	2	6	2	6	10	2	6	10	2	2	6			2			
59	Pr	2	2	6	2	6	10	2	6	10	3	2	6			2			
60	Nd	2	2	6	2	6	10	2	6	10	4	2	6			2			
61	Pm	2	2	6	2	6	10	2	6	10	5	2	6			2			
62	Sm	2	2	6	2	6	10	2	6	10	6	2	6			2			
63	Eu	2	2	6	2	6	10	2	6	10	7	2	6			2			
64	Gd	2	2	6	2	6	10	2	6	10	7	2	6	1		2			
65	Tb	2	2	6	2	6	10	2	6	10	9	2	6			2			
66	Dy	2	2	6	2	6	10	2	6	10	10	2	6			2			
67	Ho	2	2	6	2	6	10	2	6	10	11	2	6			2			
68	Er	2	2	6	2	6	10	2	6	10	12	2	6			2			
69	Tm	2	2	6	2	6	10	2	6	10	13	2	6			2			
70	Yb	2	2	6	2	6	10	2	6	10	14	2	6			2			
71	Lu	2	2	6	2	6	10	2	6	10	14	2	6	1		2			
72	Hf	2	2	6	2	6	10	2	6	10	14	2	6	2		2			
73	Ta	2	2	6	2	6	10	2	6	10	14	2	6	3		2			
74	W	2	2	6	2	6	10	2	6	10	14	2	6	4		2			
75	Re	2	2	6	2	6	10	2	6	10	14	2	6	5		2			
76	Os	2	2	6	2	6	10	2	6	10	14	2	6	6		2			
77	Ir	2	2	6	2	6	10	2	6	10	14	2	6	7		2			
78	Pt	2	2	6	2	6	10	2	6	10	14	2	6	9		1			
79	Au	2	2	6	2	6	10	2	6	16	14	2	6	10		1			
80	Hg	2	2	6	2	6	10	2	6	10	14	2	6	10		2			
81	Tl	2	2	6	2	6	10	2	6	10	14	2	6	10		2	1		
82	Pb	2	2	6	2	6	10	2	6	10	14	2	6	10		2	2		
83	Bi	2	2	6	2	6	10	2	6	10	14	2	6	10		2	3		
84	Po	2	2	6	2	6	10	2	6	10	14	2	6	10		2	4		
85	At	2	2	6	2	6	10	2	6	10	14	2	6	10		2	5		
86	Rn	2	2	6	2	6	10	2	6	10	14	2	6	10		2	6		
87	Fr	2	2	6	2	6	10	2	6	10	14	2	6	10		2	6		1
88	Ra	2	2	6	2	6	10	2	6	10	14	2	6	10		2	6		2
89	Ac	2	2	6	2	6	10	2	6	10	14	2	6	10		2	6	1	2
90	Th	2	2	6	2	6	10	2	6	10	14	2	6	10		2	6	2	2
91	Pa	2	2	6	2	6	10	2	6	10	14	2	6	10	2	2	6	1	2
92	U	2	2	6	2	6	10	2	6	10	14	2	6	10	3	2	6	1	2
93	Np	2	2	6	2	6	10	2	6	10	14	2	6	10	4	2	6	1	2

Table 22.2. Electron configurations of the elements (continued).

Quantum state

		1s	2s	2p	3s	3p	3d	4s	4p	4d	4f	5s	5p	5d	5f	6s	6p	6d	7s
94	Pu	2	2	6	2	6	10	2	6	10	14	2	6	10	5	2	6	1	2
95	Am	2	2	6	2	6	10	2	6	10	14	2	6	10	6	2	6	1	2
96	Cm	2	2	6	2	6	10	2	6	10	14	2	6	10	7	2	6	1	2
97	Bk	2	2	6	2	6	10	2	6	10	14	2	6	10	8	2	6	1	2
98	Cf	2	2	6	2	6	10	2	6	10	14	2	6	10	10	2	6		2
99	E	2	2	6	2	6	10	2	6	10	14	2	6	10	11	2	6		2
100	Fm	2	2	6	2	6	10	2	6	10	14	2	6	10	12	2	6		2
101	Md	2	2	6	2	6	10	2	6	10	14	2	6	10	13	2	6		2
102	No	2	2	6	2	6	10	2	6	10	14	2	6	10	14	2	6		2
103	Lw	2	2	6	2	6	10	2	6	10	14	2	6	10	14	2	6	1	2

The difference in binding energy between $3d$ and $4s$ electrons is not very great, as can be seen in the configurations of chromium and copper. In both of these elements an additional $3d$ electron is present at the expense of a vacancy in the $4s$ subshell.

The ferromagnetism of iron, cobalt, and nickel is related to the partial occupancy of their $3d$ subshells, whose electrons do not pair off so that their spins cancel out. In iron, for example, five of the six $3d$ electrons have parallel spins, and each iron atom has a large resultant magnetic moment.

The order in which electron subshells are filled in atoms is

$1s$, $2s$, $2p$, $3s$, $3p$, $4s$, $3d$, $4p$, $5s$, $4d$, $5p$, $6s$, $4f$, $5d$, $6p$, $7s$, $6d$

as we can see from Table 22.2 The remarkable similarities in chemical behavior among the lanthanides and actinides are easy to understand on the basis of this sequence. All the lanthanides have the same $5s^2 5p^6 6s^2$ configurations, but have incomplete $4f$ subshells. The addition of $4f$ electrons has virtually no effect on the chemical properties of the lanthanide elements, which are determined by the outer electrons. Similarly, all the actinides have $6s^2 6p^6 7s^2$ configurations and differ only in the numbers of their $5f$ and $6d$ electrons.

While we have sketched the origins of only a few of the chemical and physical properties of the elements in terms of their electron configurations, many more can be quantitatively understood by similar reasoning.

Self-examination

1. The quantum-mechanical theory of the atom is
   a. based upon a mechanical model of the atom
   b. a theory that restricts itself to physical quantities that can be measured directly

c. less accurate than the Bohr theory of the atom

d. impossible to reconcile with Newton's laws of motion

2. According to the Pauli principle,

   a. four different quantum numbers are needed to describe each electron in an atom

   b. no more than one electron in an atom can have the same set of quantum numbers

   c. eight electrons occupy each energy level

   d. electrons move in elliptical as well as circular orbits

3. The Zeeman effect refers to

   a. the splitting of spectral lines in a magnetic field

   b. electron spin

   c. the existence of the magnetic quantum number

   d. the origin of the periodic table

4. The quantum number that does not refer to the orbit of an atomic electron is the

   a. total quantum number n

   b. orbital quantum number l

   c. magnetic quantum number m_l

   d. spin magnetic quantum number m_s

5. The two electrons in a helium atom

   a. occupy different shells

   b. occupy different subshells of the same shell

   c. have different spin quantum numbers

   d. have the same spin quantum number

6. An alkali metal atom

   a. has one electron in its outer shell

   b. has two electrons in its outer shell

   c. has a filled outer shell

   d. lacks one electron of having a filled outer shell

7. A halogen atom

   a. has one electron in its outer shell

   b. has two electrons in its outer shell

   c. has a filled outer shell

   d. lacks one electron of having a filled outer shell

8. An inert gas atom

   a. has one electron in its outer shell

   b. has two electrons in its outer shell

   c. has a filled outer shell

   d. lacks one electron of having a filled outer shell

Problems

1. The Bohr theory permits us to visualize the structure of the atom, whereas quantum mechanics is very complex and concerned with such ideas as wave functions and probabilities. What reasons would lead to the replacement of the Bohr theory by quantum mechanics?

2. What is the number of electrons in the outermost shells of the elements in Group II of the periodic table?

3. How many elements would there be if atoms having filled electron shells up to and including $n = 6$ were able to exist?

4. Chemists refer to each quantum state of given n, l, and m_l as an *orbital*. How many electrons can occupy each orbital?

Part VI

ATOMS IN COMBINATION

CHAPTER 23 | THE CHEMICAL BOND

What is the nature of the forces that bind atoms together to form molecules? This question, of fundamental importance to the chemist, is hardly less important to the physicist, whose notions of atomic structure cannot be correct unless they provide a satisfactory answer. As we shall see, the modern theory of the atom, with its discovery that closed subshells represent stable electronic configurations, provides the essential clue to understanding chemical phenomena. Atoms with incomplete outer electron subshells can achieve stability by gaining or losing electrons, which takes place in the formation of a molecule either by the transfer of electrons from one atom to another or by the sharing of electrons between atoms. In the former case the resulting bond is called *ionic,* and in the latter case it is called *covalent.* In most molecules the actual bond is a mixture of the two, with one of them predominant.

Chemical bonds do not always result in the formation of individual molecules. Strictly speaking, a molecule is the smallest electrically neutral aggregate of atoms that is held together strongly enough to be experimentally observable as a unit. Thus the particles that constitute water vapor each consist of two hydrogen atoms and an oxygen atom, and we are entitled to regard them as molecules. On the other hand, the crystals of rock salt (NaCl) are aggregates of sodium and chlorine atoms which, though invariably arranged in a certain order, do not pair off into individual molecules of one sodium and one chlorine atom. While there are always equal numbers of Na and Cl atoms in rock salt, so that the formula NaCl correctly represents its composition, these atoms do not form molecules together. However, they do interact in a very specific way, namely through an ionic bond between adjacent Na and Cl atoms, and it is the properties of this bond that make NaCl just as legitimate a compound as H_2O despite the absence of individual NaCl molecules.

Electron Transfer

The simplest example of a chemical reaction involving electron transfer is the combination of a metal and a nonmetal. For a specific case, let us consider the burning of sodium in chlorine to give sodium chloride. From Table 22.2 it is evident that an Na atom can attain a stable structure most simply by getting rid of its lone outer electron. A Cl atom, on the other hand, can secure a stable outer shell most easily by adding one electron to the seven already present. Thus Na and Cl are perfect mates; one has an electron to lose, the other an electron to gain. In the process of combination, an electron may be thought of as being transferred from Na to Cl (Fig. 23.1).

The great stability of the resulting closed electron shells within both reacting atoms is indicated by the large amount of energy in the form of heat and light given out when this reaction takes place. The combination NaCl is extremely unreactive since each of its constituent atoms has a stable electronic structure. To break it apart—which means to return the electron to Na, destroying both stable eight-electron structures—requires the expenditure of the same considerable amount of energy that the combination set free.

The Na atom in the compound, shorn of its electron, is no longer a normal atom, since it consists of a nucleus with 11 positive charges and only 10 electrons. The structure as a whole therefore has a positive charge; it is called a *sodium ion*, with the symbol Na^+. The Cl atom has one electron in excess of its normal number and so is charged negatively; this structure is called a *chlorine ion* (or *chloride ion*), Cl^-. The solid salt NaCl has a crystalline structure made up of alternate sodium and chloride ions (Fig. 23.2).

The fundamental characteristic of all metal atoms is their tendency to lose their outer electrons, like sodium in the above example. Nonmetal atoms,

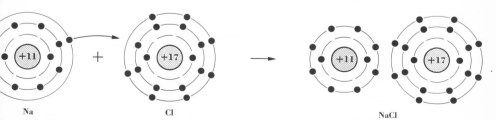

Na   Cl   NaCl

Fig. 23.1 *Sodium and chlorine combine chemically by the transfer of electrons from sodium atoms to chlorine atoms.*

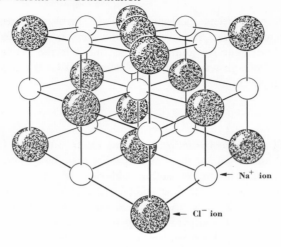

Fig. 23.2   The crystal lattice of solid NaCl.

on the other hand, tend to gain electrons, so as to fill in gaps in their outer shells. In most reactions of this sort a metal loses all its outer electrons, and a nonmetal fills all the gaps in its structure. Thus, when sodium combines with sulfur, each S atom has two spaces to fill (Table 22.2), but each Na atom has only one electron to give; hence two Na atoms are required for each S atom, and the resulting compound is Na₂S. When calcium combines with oxygen, each Ca atom contributes two electrons to each O atom, and the formula of the compound is CaO.

Compounds formed by electron transfer are called *ionic compounds*. In addition to simple compounds like NaCl, Na₂S, and CaO, ionic compounds include substances with more complex formulas like Na₂SO₄, KNO₃, and CaCO₃ in which electrons from the metal atoms have been transferred to nonmetal atom groups (SO₄, NO₃, CO₃) instead of to single nonmetal atoms. Ionic compounds in general contain a metal and one or more nonmetals, and their crystal structures are made up of alternate positive and negative ions. Most of them are crystalline solids with high melting points, as might be expected since melting involves a separation of the ions. Another important characteristic of ionic compounds that we shall discuss presently is their ability in the molten state or in solution to conduct electricity.

Chemical Activity

Since metals are characterized by the tendency of their atoms to give up outer electrons to other atoms, we may describe an active metal as a metal whose atoms give up their electrons comparatively readily. Thus magnesium is a more active metal than platinum because the magnesium atom loses its outer electrons more readily than the platinum atom does. Similarly we may describe an active nonmetal as a nonmetal whose atoms readily take electrons from metal atoms to complete their outer shells. Thus chlorine reacts more violently with metals than iodine does because its atoms have a greater attraction for the outer electrons of metal atoms.

When we first discussed the periodic table in Chap. 11, we saw that elements within each horizontal row and each vertical column show a progressive change in metallic or nonmetallic activity. In a horizontal row properties change from those of an active metal (alkali group) at one side to those of an active nonmetal (halogen group) at the other. The change takes place through a series of progressively less active metals and then a series of progressively more active nonmetals. In the vertical columns there is a much less striking change, tending as a rule toward more active metals (and less active nonmetals) at the bottom of the table. Can we find an explanation for these progressive changes in properties in terms of atomic structure? And, a related problem, can we correlate chemical activity with the strengths of chemical bonds, as exhibited by the exceptional stability of compounds composed of active elements? The notions of ionization energy and electron affinity make it possible to answer these questions quantitatively.

The *ionization energy* of an atom is the energy needed to remove one of its electrons and is therefore a measure of how tightly bound its outermost electrons are. The smaller its ionization energy, the more readily a metal atom can contribute an electron to an ionic bond and the more chemically active that metal is.

Table 23.1 shows the ionization energies of the elements in Group I and Period 2 of the periodic table. An atom of any of the alkali metals of Group I has a single s electron outside a closed subshell. The electrons in the inner shells partially shield the outer electron from the nuclear charge $+Ze$, so that the effective charge holding the outer electron to the atom is just $+e$ rather than $+Ze$ (Fig. 23.3). Relatively little work must be done to detach an electron from such an atom, and the alkali metals form positive ions readily. The larger the atom, the farther the outer electron is from the nucleus and the weaker is the electrostatic force on it, which is why the ionization energy decreases as we go down Group I. Potassium, for example, has 18 electrons inside the orbit of the outermost electron, but sodium has only 10. This means that the potassium atom is larger and that its outer electron is farther from the positive charge on the nucleus. Hence potassium atoms should lose their outer electrons more easily than sodium atoms. This checks with the experimental fact that potassium is a more active metal than sodium.

The increase in ionization energy from left to right across any period is accounted for by the increase in nuclear charge while the number of inner shielding electrons stays constant. There are two electrons in the common inner shell of Period 2 elements, and the effective nuclear charge acting on the outer electrons of these atoms is therefore reduced by two electron

Table 23.1. **Some ionization energies, in electron volts.**

	I	II	III	IV	V	VI	VII	VIII
1								
2	Li 5.4	Be 9.3	B 8.3	C 11.3	N 14.5	O 13.6	F 17.4	Ne 21.6
3	Na 5.1							
4	K 4.3							
5	Rb 4.2							
6	Cs 3.9							

charges. The outer electron in a lithium atom is held to the atom by an effective charge of $+e$, while each outer electron in beryllium, boron, carbon, etc. atoms is held to its parent atom by effective charges of $+2e$, $+3e$, $+4e$, etc. Hence a lithium atom loses its outer electron more easily than a beryllium atom, a boron atom loses its outer electron more easily than a carbon atom, and so on. The anomalously high ionization energies of beryllium and nitrogen are explained by the additional stability exhibited by filled subshells (the 2s subshell of beryllium is complete) and half-filled subshells (the 2p subshell of nitrogen is half-filled).

At the other extreme from alkali metal atoms, which tend to lose their outermost electrons, are halogen atoms, which tend to complete their outer subshells by picking up an additional electron each. The *electron affinity* of an atom is defined as the energy released when an electron is added to it. The greater the electron affinity, the more tightly bound is the added electron, and the more chemically active that nonmetal is in its role as an electron acceptor. Table 23.2 shows the electron affinities of the halogens. In general, electron affinities decrease going down any group of the periodic table and increase going from left to right across any period. The experimental

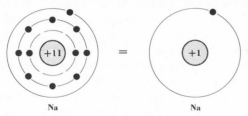

Na   Na

Fig. 23.3 **Electron shielding.**

determination of electron affinities is quite difficult, and those for only a few elements are accurately known.

The Ionic Bond

An ionic bond between two atoms can exist when one of them has a low ionization energy, and hence a tendency to become a positive ion, while the other has a high electron affinity, and hence a tendency to become a negative ion. Sodium, with an ionization energy of 5.1 ev, is an example of the former, and chlorine, with an electron affinity of 3.8 ev, is an example of the latter. When an Na^+ ion and a Cl^- ion are in the same vicinity and are free to move, the attractive electrostatic force between them brings them together. The condition that a stable unit of NaCl result is simply that the total energy of the system of the two ions be less than the total energy of a system of two atoms of the same elements; otherwise the surplus electron on the Cl^- ion would transfer to the Na^+ ion, and the neutral Na and Cl atoms would no longer be bound together. Let us see how this criterion is met by NaCl.

We begin with an Na atom and a Cl atom infinitely far apart. We expend 5.1 ev of work to remove the outer electron from the Na atom, leaving it an Na^+ ion; that is,

$$Na + 5.1 \, ev \rightarrow Na^+ + e^- \tag{23.1}$$

When this electron is brought to the Cl atom, the latter absorbs it to complete its outer electron subshell and thereby becomes a Cl^- ion. Since the electron affinity of chlorine is 3.8 ev, signifying that this amount of work must be done to liberate the odd electron from a Cl^- ion, the formation of Cl^- *evolves* 3.8 ev of energy. Hence

$$Cl + e^- \rightarrow Cl^- + 3.8 \, ev \tag{23.2}$$

The net result of these two events is the sum of Eqs. (23.1) and (23.2),

$$Na + Cl + 1.3 \, ev \rightarrow Na^+ + Cl^- \tag{23.3}$$

Our net expenditure of energy to form Na^+ and Cl^- ions from Na and Cl atoms has been only 1.3 ev.

Now we permit the electrostatic attraction between the Na^+ and Cl^- ions to bring them together, let us say to 4×10^{-10} m of each other. The energy

Table 23.2.   Electron affinities of the halogens in electron volts.

Fluorine	3.6
Chlorine	3.8
Bromine	3.5
Iodine	3.2

given off when this occurs is equal to the potential energy of the system of a $+e$ charge that distance from a $-e$ charge. This energy is -3.6 ev. Schematically,

$$Na^+ + Cl^- \rightarrow Na^+ + Cl^- + 3.6 \text{ ev} \qquad (23.4)$$
$$\underleftrightarrow{\hspace{1.2cm}}_{\infty} \quad \underleftrightarrow{\hspace{1.8cm}}_{4 \times 10^{-10} \text{ m}}$$

If we shift an electron from an Na atom to an infinitely distant Cl atom and allow the resulting ions to come together, then the entire process gives off an energy of $3.6 - 1.3 = 2.3$ ev:

$$Na + Cl \rightarrow Na^+ + Cl^- + 2.3 \text{ ev} \qquad (23.5)$$
$$\underleftrightarrow{\hspace{1.2cm}}_{\infty} \quad \underleftrightarrow{\hspace{1.8cm}}_{4 \times 10^{-10} \text{ m}}$$

Evidently an Na^+Cl^- combination with this interatomic spacing formed by the electrostatic attraction of Na^+ and Cl^- ions is stable, since 2.3 ev of work must be done on such a molecule in order to separate it into Na and Cl atoms.

We may well ask what stops the two ions from continuing to approach each other until their electron structures mesh together. It is easy to see that, if such a meshing were to take place, the positively charged nuclei of the ions would no longer be completely shielded by their surrounding electrons and would simply repel each other electrostatically. There is another phenomenon that is even more effective in keeping the ions apart. According to the Pauli exclusion principle, no two electrons in the same atomic system can exist in the same quantum state. If the electron structures of Na^+ and Cl^- overlap, they constitute a single atomic system rather than separate, independent systems. If such a system is to obey the exclusion principle, some electrons will have to go to higher quantum states than they would otherwise occupy. These states have more energy than those corresponding to the normal electron configuration of the ions, and so the total energy of an Na^+Cl^- unit increases when the Na^+ and Cl^- ions approach each other too closely.

An increasing potential energy when two bodies are brought together means that the force between them is repulsive, just as a decreasing potential energy under the same circumstances means an attractive force. (The gravitational potential energy of an object decreases the closer it is to the earth, for instance.) Figure 23.4 contains a curve showing how the potential energy V of the system of an Na^+ ion and a Cl^- ion varies with separation distance r. At $r = \infty$, an infinite separation, $V = +1.3$ ev. When the ions are closer together, the attractive electrostatic force between them takes effect and the potential energy drops. Finally, when they are about 4×10^{-10} m apart, their electron structures begin to interact, a repulsive force comes into play, and the potential energy starts to rise. The minimum in the potential energy curve occurs at $r = 2.4 \times 10^{-10}$ m, where $V = -4.2$ ev. At this separation distance the mutually attractive and repulsive forces on the ions exactly bal-

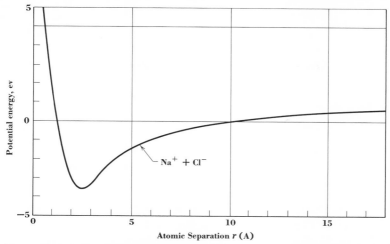

Fig. 23.4 *Variation of the potential energy of the system Na*⁺* and Cl⁻ with their distance apart.*

ance, and the system is in equilibrium. To *dissociate* an NaCl molecule into Na and Cl atoms thus requires an energy of 4.2 ev.

Electron Sharing

The theory of the ionic bond between atoms of opposite valence is unable to cope with such molecules as H_2 or Cl_2, whose constituent atoms are identical. Pure ionic binding involves the transfer of one or more electrons from those atoms in a molecule with positive valences to those with negative valences, and the resulting electrostatic forces are responsible for the stability of the molecule. In *covalent binding,* on the other hand, electrons may be thought of as being *shared* by the atoms composing a molecule. In the course of circulating among these atoms, the electrons spend more of their time between atoms than on the outside of the molecule, which leads to a net attractive electrostatic force that holds the molecule together (Fig. 23.5). In some molecules more than one pair of electrons is shared; for instance, N_2 has three shared pairs, as shown in Fig. 23.6.

Most important of the compounds formed by electron sharing are the so-called *organic compounds,* compounds of the element carbon (Chap. 28). The carbon atom has four outer electrons, which can be shared with other atoms to form a stable ring of eight.

Substances whose atoms are joined by shared electron pairs are called *covalent substances.* In general, they are nonmetallic elements or compounds of one nonmetal with another, although some compounds of metals belong to this class. Since a pair of electrons shared between two atoms remains at

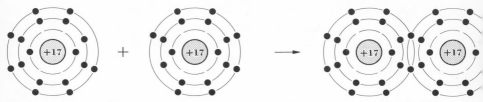

Fig. 23.5   *A pair of electrons is shared by the chlorine atoms in a chlorine molecule.*

approximately the same distance from each atomic nucleus, neither atom acquires an electric charge; hence the crystals of covalent compounds are made up of atoms or molecules rather than ions.   In general, covalent substances are poor conductors of electricity.

The distinction between covalent and ionic compounds is not sharp.   In both kinds one or more electrons are held between two atoms; the distinction depends on whether the electrons are held chiefly by one atom (ionic) or equally by the two atoms (covalent).   Some covalent compounds have an intermediate character: The electrons are somewhat closer to one atom than to the other.   Two examples are HCl and H_2O:

$$H \quad :Cl \qquad\qquad H \quad :\underset{..}{O}$$
$$H$$

These substances are called *polar* covalent compounds, because one part of the molecule is relatively negative and another part positive.   All gradations can be found between symmetric covalent molecules at one extreme, through polar covalent molecules, to ionic compounds at the other extreme.   For example,

Covalent	Cl	: Cl
Polar covalent	H	: Cl
Ionic	Na	:Cl

In covalent compounds the valence of an element is defined as the number of electron pairs that each of its atoms shares with other atoms.   Positive and negative valences are not always distinguished, since electron pairs are shared between adjacent atoms instead of being strongly attracted to one or the other.   For example, carbon has a valence of 4 in either CH_4 or $CHCl_3$, H has a valence of 1, and Cl has a valence of 1.   In SO_2, sulfur has a valence of 4 and oxygen of 2, since each sulfur atom shares four electron pairs and each oxygen atom shares two.

An important aspect of the covalent bond is that the electrons involved must have opposite spins.   When this is true, they are not affected by the Pauli exclusion principle, since their spin magnetic quantum numbers m_s are different.   Shared by both atoms, the electrons are between them more often **than** they are on the outside, and the resulting concentration of negative charge between the two positive nuclei keeps the latter together. When the atomic electrons have like spins, however, the exclusion principle tends to keep them away from the region between the nuclei where there is a common field of force and both cannot simultaneously be present in their lowest energy states. Hence these electrons spend on the average more time on the outside of the pair of nuclei, where they act to pull the nuclei apart in addition to permitting the nuclei themselves to repel each other (Fig. 23.7). Binding is impossible in this situation.

Valence

We have seen that two H atoms can combine to form an H_2 molecule, and indeed hydrogen molecules in nature always consist of two H atoms. Let us now look into how the exclusion principle prevents molecules such as He_2 and H_3 from existing while permitting such other molecules as H_2O to be stable.

Every He atom in its ground state has a $1s$ electron of each spin, $m_s = +\frac{1}{2}$ and $m_s = -\frac{1}{2}$. If it is to join with another He atom by exchanging electrons, each atom will have two electrons with the same spin for part of the time as the electrons circulate between them; that is, one atom will have both electron spins up and the other will have both spins down. The exclusion principle, of course, prohibits two $1s$ electrons in an atom from having the same spins, which is manifested by a repulsion between He atoms. Hence the He_2 molecule cannot exist. A similar argument holds in the case of H_3. An H_2 molecule contains two $1s$ electrons whose spins are antiparallel. Should another H atom approach whose electron spin is, say, up, the resulting molecule would have two spins up and one down, and this is impossible

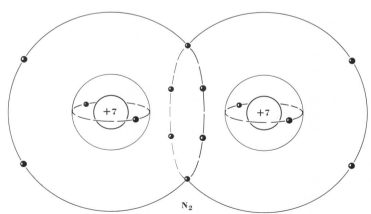

Fig. 23.6 *Three pairs of electrons are shared by the nitrogen atoms in a nitrogen molecule.*

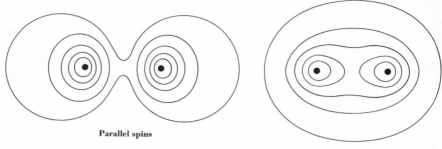

Parallel spins

Antiparallel spins

**Fig. 23.7   *Contours of electron probability for two adjacent
hydrogen atoms whose electron spins are parallel and antiparallel.***
*A repulsive force is present in the former situation, an attractive one in
the latter.*

if all three electrons are to be in 1s states.   Hence the existing H_2 molecule
repels the additional H atom.   The exclusion-principle argument does not
apply if one of the three electrons in H_3 is in an excited state.   All such states
are of higher energy than the 1s state, however, and the resulting configuration therefore has more energy than $H_2 + H$ and so will decay rapidly to
$H_2 + H$.

The water molecule H_2O achieves stability because the O atom lacks two
2p electrons of having a completed outer electron shell.   This lack is remedied
when the O atom forms covalent bonds with two H atoms so that the latter's
electrons are shared by the O atom without violating the exclusion principle.
The H_2O structure has less energy than the separate atoms because of the
electron affinity of O, and so is favored.

Evidently the interatomic forces that lead to chemical bonds, covalent
as well as ionic, exhibit *saturation:* An atom joins with only a limited number
of other atoms.   The chemist describes saturation in terms of valence.   An
atom that has only a few electrons in its outermost subshell tends to combine
with one or more other atoms whose outermost subshells lack a total of the
same number of electrons.   An atom that donates n electrons to a bond is
said to have a valence of $+n$, while one that receives m electrons from a bond
is said to have a valance of $-m$.   Hence metals have positive valences, nonmetals negative valences: The valence of a metal is the number of electrons
in the outer shell of each of its atoms, while the valence of a nonmetal is the
number of electrons needed to complete its outer shell.

For stability, the total numbers of positive and negative valences in a
molecule must be equal.   Thus H has a valence of $+1$ and O a valence of -2,
and H_2O has a net valence of $1 + 1 - 2 = 0$.   In the case of H_2, we may
think of one H atom as having a valence of $+1$ and the other of -1.   Atoms
such as carbon, which form bonds by sharing four electrons, may be regarded

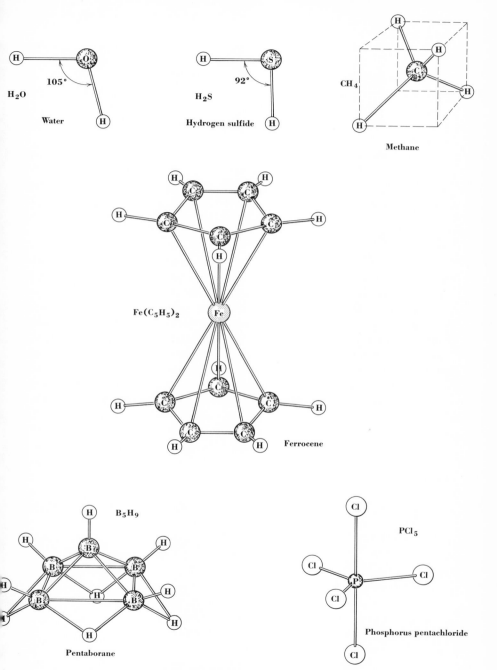

Fig. 23.8 *Directed bonds in complex molecules.*

as having valences of either +4 or −4, depending upon the atoms they combine with. For example, in CH_4 (methane) carbon has a valence of −4, while in CO_2 (carbon dioxide) its valence is +4. To be sure, in both cases the bonds are largely covalent and electrons circulate between the atoms of each molecule instead of being transferred as in purely ionic bonds. For this reason positive and negative valences are often not distinguished in covalent compounds. In this case the valence of an element in such a compound is just the number of electron pairs which each of its atoms shares with other atoms.

Since the number of electrons in the outer shell of an atom determines its normal valence, these outer electrons are often called *valence electrons.* Thus H has one valence electron, C has four valence electrons, Cl has seven, Ca has two, and so on.

Directed Bonds

The likelihood of finding a particular electron near its parent nucleus depends both upon the distance from the nucleus and upon direction. The electron probabilities that can be computed from the quantum theory of the atom are not symmetric, but instead show "lobes" of high probability in certain directions for electrons in certain quantum states. Covalent binding occurs when the appropriate probability lobes of adjacent atoms overlap. When an atom combines with two or more other atoms, the latter are therefore generally "attached" at specific places on the atoms corresponding to the lobes of greatest magnitude, instead of being located at random or in some universal configuration. Figure 23.8 shows some examples of directed bonds in complex molecules.

Self-examination

1. The most important factor in determining the chemical behavior of an atom is its
   a. nuclear structure
   b. electron structure
   c. atomic weight
   d. solubility

2. In a covalent compound
   a. electrons are transferred from one atom to another
   b. only atoms with the same valence are present
   c. there must be at least one carbon atom
   d. adjacent atoms share electron pairs

3. An atom that loses its outer electron or electrons readily is
   a. an active metal
   b. an active nonmetal
   c. an inactive metal
   d. an inactive nonmetal

4. The energy that must be expended in order to remove an electron from an atom is called
   a. electron affinity
   b. ionization energy
   c. valence
   d. heat of vaporization

5. Hydrogen atoms are held together to form hydrogen molecules by
   a. ionic binding
   b. covalent binding
   c. electron spin
   d. polar molecules

6. The chief cause of the repulsive force that keeps atoms from meshing together despite any attractive forces that may be present is
   a. electrostatic repulsion between the electrons
   b. the uncertainty principle
   c. the exclusion principle
   d. conservation of energy

7. The notion of valence is a way of describing the fact that an atom can join together with
   a. a limited number of other atoms
   b. an unlimited number of other atoms
   c. only metal atoms
   d. only nonmetal atoms

Problems

1. Illustrate with electronic diagrams (*a*) the reaction between a lithium atom and a fluorine atom and (*b*) the reaction between a magnesium atom and a sulfur atom. Would you expect lithium fluoride and magnesium sulfide to be ionic or covalent compounds?

2. What part of the atom is chiefly involved in each of the following processes?
   a. the burning of charcoal
   b. radioactive disintegration
   c. the production of X rays
   d. the ionization of air

e. the emission of spectral lines

f. the explosion of a hydrogen bomb

g. the rusting of iron

3. Electrons are much more readily liberated from metals than from nonmetals when irradiated with visible or ultraviolet light. Can you explain why this is true? From metals of what group would you expect electrons to be liberated most easily?

4. The rare element selenium has the following arrangement of electrons: 2 in the first shell, 8 in the second, 18 in the third, and 6 in the fourth. Would you expect selenium to be a metal or a nonmetal? What would its normal valence be? To what group in the periodic table would it belong?

5. What is the difference in atomic structure between the two isotopes of chlorine? How would you account for the great chemical similarity of the two isotopes?

6. Would you expect magnesium or calcium to be the more active metal? Explain your answer in terms of atomic structure.

7. Lithium is directly below hydrogen in the periodic table, yet lithium atoms do not join together to form Li_2 molecules the way hydrogen atoms do. Why not?

8. Which of the following compounds do you expect to be ionic and which covalent? IBr, NO_2, SiF_4, Na_2S, CCl_4, $RbCl$, Ca_3N_2.

CHAPTER 24 | THE SOLID STATE

A solid consists of atoms packed closely together, and their proximity is responsible for the characteristic properties of this state of matter. Most solids are crystalline in nature or nearly so, though a few, such as glass, have no definite ordered structures. The ionic and covalent bonds that are involved in the formation of molecules have important counterparts in the solid state. In addition there are the *van der Waals* and *metallic bonds* that provide the cohesive forces in, respectively, molecular crystals and metals. All these bonds are electrostatic in origin, so that the chief distinctions among them lie in the distribution of electrons around the atoms and molecules whose regular arrangement constitutes a crystal lattice. After a discussion of the various kinds of crystal structures found in solids we shall look into the behavior of the electrons in them, a study that will permit us to understand how so remarkable a phenomenon as electric conduction in metals arises.

Crystal Structure

A valuable method for determining crystal structure is based upon the use of X rays. As we know, X rays consist of electromagnetic waves of short wavelength and considerable penetrating power. When a beam of X rays is directed at a crystal, it is observed that, while most of them simply pass right through, some are scattered at certain specific angles that vary with the wavelength of the X rays and with the type of crystal (Fig. 24.1). This phenomenon is an interference effect and, originally employed

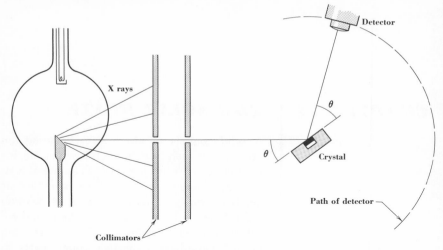

X rays

Detector

θ

Crystal

θ

Path of detector

Collimators

Fig. 24.1   X-ray-scattering experiment.

to verify the wave nature of X rays, is today widely used to study the arrangements of atoms in crystals.

Figure 24.2 shows a narrow beam of X rays that fall obliquely on one face of a crystal. The atoms in the crystal, because of their regular arrangement, can be thought of as lying in a series of parallel planes, and a portion of the X-ray beam is reflected by each of the planes. This situation corresponds very closely to that of Fig. 16.13, where the light waves reflected by two surfaces that are close together reinforce each other in certain directions and cancel each other in intermediate directions through the process of interference. The scattering of X rays by crystals was first analyzed in a similar way by W. L. Bragg in 1912. He considered a beam of X rays striking two successive atomic planes a distance d apart at an angle θ, as in Fig. 24.2. The rays are reflected by both planes at the same angle θ, but ray II must travel $d \sin \theta$ farther than ray I before it is reflected by the inner plane and then another $d \sin \theta$ before it emerges. Hence the total path difference between rays I and II is $2d \sin \theta$. If this difference is exactly one X-ray wavelength λ (or *any* whole number of wavelengths 2λ, 3λ, 4λ, etc.), both rays will be in step after reflection and can be detected. However, if the path difference is not a whole number of wavelengths, the reflected rays will be out of step and will cancel each other out. Thus the condition for a reflected ray to emerge is

Path difference = whole number of wavelengths

$$2d \sin \theta = n\lambda \qquad n = 1, 2, 3, \ldots \qquad (24.1)$$

If we know the wavelength λ of the X rays in an experimental beam, then, we can ascertain the angles θ at which the scattered rays emerge from a crystal under study and solve the above equation for the atomic spacing d.

Variations of Bragg's method have been devised which have been used to determine the exact arrangements of atoms in crystals with more complex lattices than the simple one of Fig. 24.2.

It is possible to calculate Avogadro's number N_0 from a knowledge of the spacing of the atoms in a particular crystal together with the density of that crystal. To do this we note that

$$N_0 = \text{atomic density} \times \frac{1}{\text{atoms/molecule}} \times \text{molecular weight} \times \frac{1}{\text{density}}$$

$$\frac{\text{Molecules}}{\text{Mole}} = \frac{\text{atoms}}{\text{cm}^3} \times \frac{1}{\text{atoms/molecule}} \times \frac{\text{grams}}{\text{mole}} \times \frac{1}{\text{grams/cm}^3} \qquad (24.2)$$

The atomic density of a crystal is the number of atoms per unit volume (usually per cubic centimeter) it contains. Each atom can be regarded as occupying a cube d long on each side, where d is the distance between adjacent atoms. The atomic density of a crystal is therefore equal to the number of times a volume of d^3 can fit into a unit volume, so that

$$\text{Atomic density} = \frac{1}{d^3} \qquad (24.3)$$

Let us obtain N_0 from the data for rock salt (NaCl) crystals, whose density is 2.17 g/cm³ and in which X-ray scattering has shown that $d = 2.82 \times 10^{-8}$ cm. The atomic density in solid NaCl is

$$\text{Atomic density} = \frac{1}{d^3} = \frac{1}{(2.82 \times 10^{-8} \text{ cm})^3}$$

$$= \frac{1}{22.4 \times 10^{-24} \text{ cm}^3} = 4.46 \times 10^{22} \text{ atoms/cm}^3$$

The atomic weight of sodium is 22.99, and that of chlorine is 35.45, so the molecular weight of NaCl is $22.99 + 35.45$, or 58.44. Last, each unit of NaCl

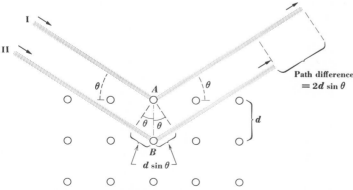

Fig. 24.2   X-ray scattering from cubic crystal.

provides two atoms of the crystal lattice of rock salt. Substituting these various numbers in the above formula for N_0, we find

$$N_0 = 4.46 \times 10^{22} \frac{\text{atoms}}{\text{cm}^3} \times \frac{1}{2} \frac{\text{molecule}}{\text{atom}} \times 58.44 \frac{\text{grams}}{\text{mole}} \times \frac{1}{2.17} \frac{\text{cm}^3}{\text{gram}}$$
$$= 6.03 \times 10^{23} \text{ molecules/mole}$$

This value is the same as values obtained in other ways.

Ionic and Covalent Crystals

Ionic bonds in crystals are very similar to ionic bonds in molecules. Such bonds come into being when atoms which have low ionization energies, and hence lose electrons easily, interact with other atoms which have high electron affinities. The former atoms give up electrons to the latter, and they thereupon become positive and negative ions respectively. In an ionic crystal these ions come together in an equilibrium configuration in which the attractive forces between positive and negative ions predominate over the repulsive forces between similar ions. As in the case of molecules, crystals of all types are prevented from collapsing under the influence of the cohesive forces present by the action of the exclusion principle, which requires the occupancy of higher energy states when electron shells of different atoms overlap and mesh together.

Figure 24.3 shows the arrangement of Na^+ and Cl^- ions in a sodium chloride crystal. The ions of either kind may be regarded as being located at the corners and at the centers of the faces of an assembly of cubes, with the Na^+ and Cl^- assemblies interleaved. Each ion thus has six nearest neighbors of the other kind. Such a crystal structure is called *face-centered cubic*. In NaCl crystals the distance between like ions is 5.63×10^{-10} m; the distance between adjacent ions is half this.

A different structure is found in cesium chloride crystals, where each ion is located at the center of a cube at whose corners are ions of the other kind (Fig. 24.4). This structure is called *body-centered cubic*, and each ion has eight nearest neighbors of the other kind. In CsCl crystals the distance between like ions is 4.11×10^{-10} m.

The cohesive forces in covalent crystals arise from the presence of electrons between adjacent atoms. Each atom participating in a covalent bond contributes an electron to the bond, and these electrons are shared by both atoms rather than being the virtually exclusive property of one of them as in an ionic bond. Diamond is an example of a crystal whose atoms are linked by covalent bonds. Figure 24.5 shows the structure of a diamond crystal. Each carbon atom has four nearest neighbors and shares an electron pair with each of them. The length of each bond is 1.54×10^{-10} m. Silicon, germanium, and silicon carbide are among the substances whose crystal structures are the same as that of diamond.

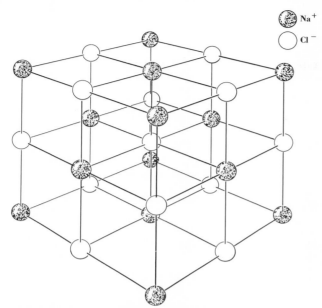

Fig. 24.3   A face-centered cubic crystal.

As in the case of molecules, it is not always possible to classify a given crystal as being wholly ionic or covalent. Silicon dioxide (quartz) and tungsten carbide, for instance, contain bonds of mixed character. Both ionic and covalent crystals are held together with relatively strong binding forces: About 8 ev is required to break each bond in NaCl and diamond crystals, compared with about 4 ev for the metallic bond in iron and 0.1 ev for the van der Waals bond in solid methane (CH_4).

Van der Waals Forces

There are many substances whose molecules are so stable that, when brought together, they have no tendency to lose their individuality by joining together in a collective lattice with multiple linkages like those found in ionic and covalent crystals. Most organic compounds are examples of such noninteracting substances. However, even they can exist as liquids and solids through the action of the attractive *van der Waals* intermolecular forces.

We begin by noting that many molecules, which we called polar molecules in the previous chapter, behave as if negatively charged at one end and positively charged at the other. An example is the H_2O molecule, in which the concentration of electrons around the oxygen atom makes that end of the molecule more negative than the end where the hydrogen atoms are (Fig. 24.6). Such molecules tend to align themselves so that ends of opposite sign

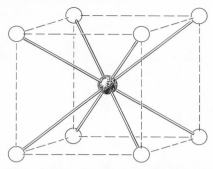

Fig. 24.4   A body-centered cubic crystal.

are adjacent, as in Fig. 24.7, and in this orientation the molecules strongly attract one another.

A polar molecule is also able to attract nonpolar molecules whose charges are normally uniformly distributed. The process is illustrated in Fig. 24.8: The electric field of the polar molecule induces a separation of charge in the other molecule, and the two now attract each other electrostatically.

More remarkably, two nonpolar molecules can attract each other by the above mechanism. Even though the electron distribution in a nonpolar molecule is symmetric *on the average*, the electrons themselves are in constant motion and at *any given instant* one part or another of the molecule has an excess of them. Instead of the fixed charge asymmetry of a polar molecule, a nonpolar molecule has a constantly shifting asymmetry. When two non-

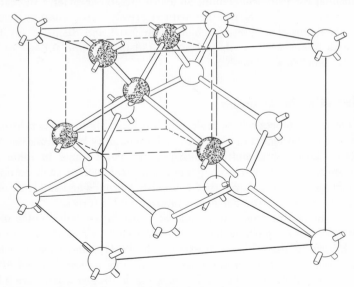

Fig. 24.5   The crystal lattice of diamond.

Fig. 24.6 *Water consists of polar molecules which behave as if negatively charged at one end and positively charged at the other.*

polar molecules are close enough, their fluctuating charge distributions tend to shift together, adjacent ends always having opposite sign (Fig. 24.9) and so always causing an attractive force. This kind of force is named after the Dutch physicist van der Waals, who suggested its existence nearly a century ago to explain observed departures from the ideal gas law; the explanation of the actual mechanism of the force, of course, is more recent, since it is based upon the modern theory of the atom.

Van der Waals forces are present, not only between all molecules, but also between all atoms, including those of the inert gases which do not otherwise interact. Van der Waals bonds are much weaker than ionic and covalent bonds, and as a result molecular crystals, whose lattices are composed of whole molecules rather than ions or atoms, generally have low melting and boiling points and little mechanical strength. Ordinary ice and "dry ice" (solid CO_2) are examples of molecular solids.

The Metallic Bond

The basic concept that underlies the modern theory of metals is that the valence (outermost) electrons of the atoms comprising a metal may be common to the entire atomic aggregate, so that a kind of "gas" of free electrons pervades it. The interaction between this gas and the positive metal ions

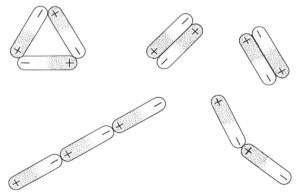

Fig. 24.7 *Polar molecules attract each other.*

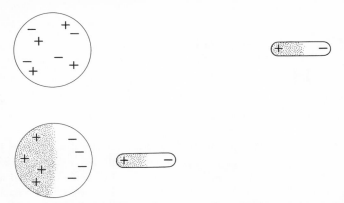

Fig. 24.8   *Polar molecules attract normally nonpolar molecules.*

constitutes a strong cohesive force.   Further, the presence of such free electrons accounts very nicely for the high electrical conductivities and other
unique properties of metals.   To be sure, no electrons in any solid, even a
metal, are able to move about its interior with complete freedom.   All of
them are influenced to some extent by the other particles present, and when
the theory of metals is refined to include these perturbations, a comprehensive
picture emerges that is in excellent agreement with experiment.

A convenient way of understanding the metallic bond is to view it as an
unsaturated covalent bond.   Let us compare the binding processes in hydrogen and in lithium, both members of Group I of the periodic table.   An H_2
molecule contains two $1s$ electrons with opposite spins, the maximum number
of $n = 1$ electrons that can be present.   The H_2 molecule is therefore saturated, since the exclusion principle requires that any additional electrons be
in states of higher energy and the stable attachment of further H atoms cannot occur unless their electrons are in $1s$ states.   Superficially lithium might
seem obliged to behave in a similar way, having the electron configuration
$1s^2 2s$.   However, there are six *unfilled* $2p$ states in every Li atom whose
energies are only very slightly greater than those of the $2s$ states.   When an
Li atom comes near an Li_2 "molecule," it readily becomes attached with a
covalent bond without violating the exclusion principle, and the resulting Li_3
"molecule" is stable since all its valence electrons remain in $n = 2$ states.
There is no limit to the number of Li atoms that can join together in this way,
since lithium forms body-centered cubic crystals (Fig. 24.4) in which each
atom has eight nearest neighbors.   With only one electron per atom available
to enter into bonds, each bond involves one-fourth of an electron on the
average, instead of two electrons as in ordinary covalent bonds.   Hence the
bonds are far from being saturated, which is true of the bonds in other metals
as well.

One consequence of the unsaturated nature of the metallic bond is the weakness of metals as compared with perfect ionic and covalent crystals having saturated bonds. Another is the ease with which metals can be deformed. With so many vacancies in their outermost electron shells, metal atoms do not exhibit directional preferences in the locations of their bonds, and the atoms accordingly can be rearranged in position without the metal as a whole losing strength. A third consequence is the most striking, however: There are so many unoccupied electron states in a metal that an electron can wander from atom to atom without being limited by the exclusion principle, instead of being compelled to remain attached to a particular atom as in an ionic crystal or to resonate between a particular pair of atoms as in a covalent crystal. Thus the valence electrons in a metal behave in a manner similar to that of molecules in a gas. Ohm's law (Chap. 13) can be derived on the basis of this "electron gas" picture of metals.

The Band Theory of Solids

The atoms in almost every crystalline solid, whether a metal or not, are so close together that their valence electrons constitute a single system of electrons common to the entire crystal. The exclusion principle is obeyed by such an electron system because the energy states of the outer electron shells

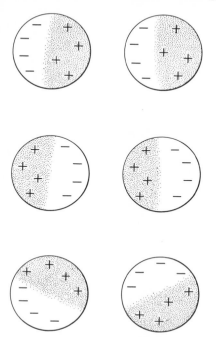

Fig. 24.9 *The fluctuating charge distributions of nearby molecules tend to shift together, leading to an attractive force between them.*

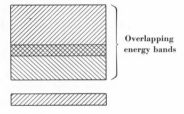

Overlapping energy bands

Fig. 24.10   *The energy bands in a solid may overlap.*

of the atoms are all altered somewhat by their mutual interactions.   In place of each precisely defined characteristic energy level of an individual atom, the entire crystal possesses an *energy band* composed of myriad separate levels very close together.   Since there are as many of these separate levels as there are atoms in the crystal, the band cannot be distinguished from a continuous spread of permitted energies.

The energy bands in a solid correspond to the energy levels in an atom, and an electron in a solid can possess only those energies that fall within these energy bands.   The various energy bands in a solid may overlap, as in Fig. 24.10, in which case its electrons have a continuous distribution of permitted energies.   In other solids the bands may *not* overlap (Fig. 24.11), and the intervals between them represent energies which their electrons cannot possess.   Such intervals are called *forbidden bands*.   The electrical behavior of a crystalline solid is determined both by its energy-band structure and by how these bands are normally filled by electrons.

Figure 24.12 is a simplified diagram of the energy levels of a sodium atom and the energy bands of solid sodium.   A sodium atom has a single 3*s* electron in its outer shell.   This means that the lowest energy band in a sodium crystal is only half-occupied, since each level in the band, like each

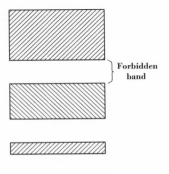

Forbidden band

Fig. 24.11   *A forbidden band separates nonoverlapping energy bands.*

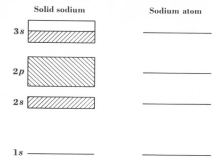

Fig. 24.12   Energy levels in the sodium atom and the corresponding bands in solid sodium (not to scale).

level in the atom, is able to contain *two* electrons.   When an electric field is set up across a piece of solid sodium, electrons easily acquire additional energy while remaining in their original energy band.   The additional energy is in the form of kinetic energy, and the moving electrons constitute an electric current.   Sodium is therefore a good conductor of electricity, as are other crystalline solids with energy bands that are only partially filled.

Figure 24.13 is a simplified diagram of the energy bands of diamond. The two lower energy bands are completely filled with electrons, and there is a gap of 6 ev between the top of the higher of these bands and the empty band above it.   This means that at least 6 ev of additional energy must be provided an electron in a diamond crystal if it is to have any kinetic energy, since it cannot have an energy lying in the forbidden band.   An energy increment of this magnitude cannot readily be given to an electron in a crystal by an electric field.   An electron moving through a crystal collides with another electron after an average of perhaps 10^{-8} m, and it loses much of the energy it gained from any electric field in the collision.   An electric field intensity of 6×10^8 volts/m is necessary if an electron is to gain 6 ev in a path length of 10^{-8} m, well over 10^{10} times greater than the field intensity needed to cause a current to flow in sodium.   Diamond is therefore a very poor conductor of electricity, and is accordingly classed as an insulator.

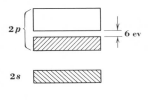

Fig. 24.13   Energy bands in diamond (not to scale).

Silicon has a crystal structure resembling that of diamond, and as in diamond, a gap separates the top of a filled energy band from a vacant higher band. The forbidden band in silicon is only 1.1 ev wide, however. At low temperatures silicon is little better than diamond as a conductor, but at room temperature a small proportion of its electrons have sufficient kinetic energy of thermal origin to jump the forbidden band and enter the energy band above it. These electrons are sufficient to permit a limited amount of current to flow when an electric field is applied. Thus silicon has an electrical resistivity intermediate between those of conductors and those of insulators, and is termed a *semiconductor*.

The resistivity of semiconductors can be significantly affected by small amounts of impurity. Let us incorporate a few arsenic atoms in a silicon crystal. Arsenic atoms have five electrons in their outermost shells, while silicon atoms have four. When an arsenic atom replaces a silicon atom in a silicon crystal, four of its electrons are incorporated in covalent bonds with its nearest neighbors. The fifth electron requires little energy to be detached and move about in the crystal. Such a substance is called an *n-type* semiconductor because electric current in it is carried by negative charges (Fig. 24.14).

If we alternatively incorporate gallium atoms in a silicon crystal, a different effect occurs. Gallium atoms have only three electrons in their outer shells, and their presence leaves vacancies called "holes" in the electron structure of the crystal. An electron needs relatively little energy to enter a hole, but as it does so it leaves a new hole in its former location. When an electric field is applied across a silicon crystal containing a trace of gallium, electrons move toward the anode by successively filling holes. The flow of current here is conveniently described with reference to the holes, whose behavior is like that of positive charges since they move toward the negative electrode (Fig. 24.15). A substance of this kind is called a *p-type*

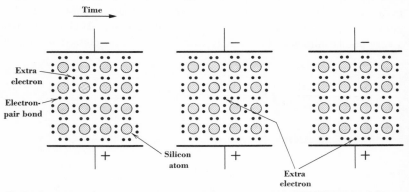

Fig. 24.14   *In an* n-type *semiconductor, current is carried by excess electrons that do not fit into the electron structure of the crystal.*

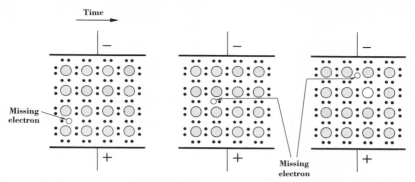

Fig. 24.15 *In a* p-type *semiconductor, current is carried by the motion of sites of missing electrons. Such "holes" in the electron structure of the crystal migrate toward the negative electrode as electrons successively fill them.*

semiconductor. The unusual properties of *n-* and *p-type* semiconductors have made possible the development of such compact and efficient electronic devices as the transistor.

Self-examination

1. A "gas" of freely moving electrons is present in
   a. ionic crystals
   b. covalent crystals
   c. molecular crystals
   d. metal crystals

2. Avogadro's number is the number of
   a. atoms per unit volume in a crystal
   b. grams per mole
   c. molecules per mole
   d. atoms per molecule

3. The individual particles in an ionic crystal are
   a. atoms
   b. molecules
   c. ions
   d. electrons

4. The individual particles in a covalent crystal are
   a. atoms
   b. molecules
   c. ions
   d. electrons

5. The individual particles in the van der Waals crystal of a compound are
   a. atoms
   b. molecules
   c. ions
   d. electrons

6. Van der Waals forces between atoms and between molecules arise from
   a. symmetric charge distributions
   b. asymmetric charge distributions
   c. electron transfer
   d. electron sharing

7. Energy bands exist in crystals in place of specific energy levels because of
   a. the uncertainty principle
   b. the exclusion principle
   c. Ohm's law
   d. the electron gas

8. Current in an *n*-type semiconductor is carried by
   a. electrons
   b. protons
   c. holes
   d. metallic ions

Problems

1. State the four principal types of binding in solids and give an example of each.   What is the fundamental physical origin of all of them?

2. Electrons and neutrons are used to study crystal structure in addition to X rays.   What property of these particles do you think makes them useful for this purpose?

3. Van der Waals forces are strong enough to hold inert gas atoms together to form liquids at low temperatures, yet they do not lead to inert gas molecules at higher temperatures.   Why?

4. Metal crystals are said to be weaker than ionic or covalent crystals, yet in our experience metals are stronger than most other substances.   Can you think of any reasons why ionic and covalent crystals might not be able to exhibit their theoretical strength while metals can?

CHAPTER 25 | *IONS AND SOLUTIONS*

As we have seen, the forces that bind atoms together to form molecules, solids, and liquids are electric in origin. In this chapter we shall further explore the role of electricity in chemical processes, with special emphasis on the behavior of ions in solution.

Electrolysis

Electricity is conducted through gases and non-metallic liquids by a mechanism quite different from that characteristic of metals. The current almost always consists not of moving electrons but of moving *ions*. Ions, as we have mentioned before, are electrically charged atoms or groups of atoms—structures resembling ordinary atoms and molecules but possessing either fewer or more than enough electrons to neutralize the nuclear charges present. Conduction through a gas or liquid usually involves movement of both positive and negative ions.

Air and other gases can be ionized by various radiations: X rays, for example, and the alpha, beta, and gamma radiations from radioactive elements. These are capable of stripping off one or two outer electrons from some of the air molecules in their paths, producing positive ions; the liberated electrons attach themselves temporarily to adjacent neutral molecules, making them negative ions. Left to themselves, positive and negative ions in the course of a few minutes neutralize each other by an exchange of electrons. If a charged electroscope is present when the ions are produced, ions of opposite sign are attracted to it and the instrument is quickly discharged, and this fact can be used as a test for the presence of radiation. In the cloud chamber positive and negative ions form the nuclei for fog droplets, which make visible the paths of high-speed particles.

The light and heat of an electric spark are due to the violent disturbance created by ionized gas molecules moving rapidly between the electrodes.

Ionic compounds like ordinary salt are good conductors when liquefied. These compounds, as we have seen, at ordinary temperatures are solids with crystal structures made up of positive and negative ions. The solids are nonconductors, since their ions are held firmly in position, but in the liquid state the ions are free to move about and hence are free to conduct electricity from one electrode to another.

Molten salt is made up of the two ions Na^+ (sodium ion, a sodium atom with its outer electron missing) and Cl^- (chloride ion, a chlorine atom with one excess electron). When two electrodes connected to the terminals of a battery are immersed in the liquid, Na^+ ions are attracted to the cathode (negative electrode) and Cl^- ions to the anode (positive electrode), as in Fig. 25.1. At the anode each Cl^- is *neutralized;* it gives up its extra electron to the electrode and becomes a normal chlorine atom. At the cathode each Na^+ is neutralized by the addition of an electron from the electrode and becomes an atom of ordinary metallic sodium. Thus electrons move from the electrode to the liquid at the cathode, from the liquid to the electrode at the anode. In effect, a current passes through the liquid, the current in the liquid itself consisting of a movement of ions.

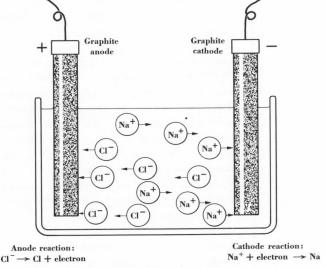

Anode reaction:
$Cl^- \rightarrow Cl + electron$

Cathode reaction:
$Na^+ + electron \rightarrow Na$

Fig. 25.1   The electrolysis of molten sodium chloride.

The current sent through the molten salt breaks up the compound NaCl into its constituent elements:

$$2NaCl \rightarrow 2Na + Cl_2$$

The sodium, a liquid at the temperature of molten salt, collects around the cathode, and chlorine gas bubbles up from the anode. A process of this sort, in which free elements are liberated from liquids by an electric current, is called *electrolysis*. In the preparation of many elements and in electroplating, electrolysis finds important commercial applications; for example, the procedure just outlined is commonly used to prepare metallic sodium.

Electrolysis is usually carried out in water solutions rather than in molten salts. Pure water contains an exceedingly small number of ions, and hence is practically a nonconductor. But ionic compounds dissolve in water as separate ions: Thus a solution of ordinary salt contains Na^+ and Cl^-; a solution of copper bromide ($CuBr_2$) contains Cu^{++} (a Cu atom with its two valence electrons missing) and Br^- (a Br atom with one electron added to its normal outer shell of seven). The ability of these dissolved ions to move through a solution makes the solution a good conductor.

Details of electrolysis are much the same in solutions and in molten salts. In the electrolysis of a $CuBr_2$ solution, for example, Cu^{++} ions move to the cathodes and Br^- ions to the anode. The cathode gives two electrons to each Cu^{++}, changing the ion to a Cu atom; the anode takes one electron from each Br^-, changing the ion to neutral Br. Thus copper is plated out at the cathode, and free bromine is liberated and goes into solution at the anode. Every time one Cu^{++} ion and two Br^- ions are neutralized, two electrons are in effect transferred from cathode to anode, so that a continuous current is maintained across the solution.

Faraday's Laws of Electrolysis

Today, with our knowledge of electricity and atomic structure, it is easy to understand electrolysis. A century ago, however, a great deal of mystery surrounded this phenomenon, and Michael Faraday's discovery of the two laws of electrolysis in 1834 is further testimony to his remarkable ability as an experimenter. After many measurements, Faraday found that the mass of any particular substance liberated at an electrode is directly proportional to (1) the total charge Q that has passed through the liquid and to (2) the atomic weight of the substance divided by its valence. These are Faraday's laws of electrolysis. A charge of 96,500 coul was found to liberate 1 g-atom of elements of valence ± 1, ½ g-atom of elements of valence ± 2, and so on. We can combine this latter observation with Faraday's laws in the formula

$$m = \frac{Q}{96,500 \text{ coul}} \times \frac{\text{atomic weight}}{\text{valence}} \qquad (25.1)$$

where m is the liberated mass. The name *faraday* has been given to 96,500 coul of charge in honor of Faraday's pioneer work.

The above equation is a direct consequence of the atomic nature of matter and charge. A gram atom of any element contains Avogadro's number N_0 of atoms. If the element has unit valence, one electron must be added or removed from it (depending upon whether it is a metal or nonmetal, respectively) in order to convert its ions to neutral atoms. Thus the total amount of charge that must be transferred to liberate a gram atom of a univalent element is equal to N_0, the number of individual atoms, multiplied by e, the charge of the electron, and hence the charge that is absorbed or given off per atom. Inserting the values of N_0 and e to four significant figures,

$$Q = N_0 e = 6.024 \times 10^{23} \text{ atoms/g-atom} \times 1.602 \times 10^{-19} \text{ coul/atom}$$
$$= 96,500 \text{ coul/g-atom}$$
$$= 1 \text{ faraday}$$

Actually, since Q and e can both be measured more or less directly, electrolysis provides a valuable method for determining Avogadro's number that is independent of the method described in Chap. 24.

When the element involved has a higher valence than 1, more than one electron per atom must be transferred, and proportionately less than a gram atom of the element will be liberated by the passage of a faraday during electrolysis. This factor is taken into account in Eq. (25.1), where the atomic weight appears divided by the valence.

As an illustration of the use of Eq. (25.1), let us calculate how much sodium metal is produced by sending a current of 10 amp through molten NaCl for 1 hr. Since current i is the rate of flow of electric charge,

$$Q \text{ (coul)} = i \text{ (amp)} \times t \text{ (sec)}$$

Here
$$t = 1 \text{ hr} \times 60 \text{ min/hr} \times 60 \text{ sec/min} = 3,600 \text{ sec}$$

and
$$Q = 10 \text{ amp} \times 3,600 \text{ sec} = 36,000 \text{ coul}$$

The atomic weight of sodium is 22.99, and its valence is $+1$; hence

$$m = \frac{36,000 \text{ coul}}{96,500 \text{ coul}} \times \frac{22.99 \text{ g}}{1}$$
$$= 8.58 \text{ g}$$

The mass of sodium liberated is 8.58 g.

What volume of chlorine is evolved in the above process? At $0°C$ and atmospheric pressure, 1 mole of any gas occupies 22.4 liters. The valence of chlorine is -1, so 1 faraday will produce 1 g-atom of chlorine. However, chlorine molecules contain *two* atoms of chlorine each, so 2 faradays is needed to produce 1 mole of Cl_2. Here the charge involved is 36,000 coul, which is

$$\frac{36,000 \text{ coul}}{96,500 \text{ coul/faraday}} = 0.373 \text{ faraday}$$

We therefore can write

$$\text{Volume evolved} = \frac{22.4 \text{ liters/mole}}{2 \text{ faradays/mole}} \times 0.373 \text{ faraday}$$
$$= 4.18 \text{ liters}$$

Solubility

Chemical combination, we have learned, takes place either by the transfer of electrons from one atom to another or by the sharing of pairs of electrons between atoms. The distinction is not sharp but serves as the basis for a convenient separation of two kinds of compounds: ionic compounds formed by electron transfer and covalent compounds formed by electron sharing. An ionic compound nearly aways contains a metal and one or more non-metals; its crystal lattice is made up of ions; it has a high melting point, since melting involves separating its ions; and in the liquid state or in solution it conducts an electric current, since its ions are free to move about. A covalent compound most commonly contains two nonmetals; the crystal lattice of its solid state consists of molecules or of atoms; and it is a poor conductor either in the liquid state or in solution.

With these ideas in the background, let us inquire into the properties of solutions and the processes by which they are formed.

A solution is a very intimate mixture of two or more different substances. Solutions can be formed of any of the three states of matter; air is a solution of several gases, sea water is a solution of various solids and gases in a liquid, and many alloys are "solid solutions" of two or more metals. Here our chief concern will be solutions in liquids.

In a solution containing two substances, the substance present in larger amount is called the *solvent,* the other the *solute.* When solids or gases dissolve in liquids, the liquid is always considered the solvent. Thus, when sugar is stirred into water, the sugar is the solute and the water is the solvent. Water is by far the commonest and most active of all solvents.

Solutions, like compounds, are homogeneous, but unlike compounds they do not have fixed compositions. To a solution of 10 g of salt in 100 g of water, for example, a little more salt or a little more water may be added; the composition of the solution is altered, but it remains homogeneous. Some pairs of liquids form solutions in all proportions; any amount of alcohol may be mixed with any amount of water to form a homogeneous liquid. More commonly, however, a given liquid will dissolve only a limited amount of another substance. Common salt can be stirred into water at 20°C until the solution contains 36 g of salt for every 100 g of water; further additions of salt will not dissolve, no matter how prolonged the stirring. This figure, 36 g per 100 g of water, is called the *solubility* of salt in water at 20°C. In other words, the solubility of a substance is the maximum amount that can be dissolved by stirring in a given quantity of solvent at a given temperature.

It is most often expressed in grams of solute per 100 g of water but may be given as grams per liter, ounces per quart, etc. A solution that contains the maximum amount of solute is called a *saturated* solution.

Solubilities of gases decrease as the temperature rises; solubilities of most solids increase (Fig. 25.2). If a solution of a solid is saturated at a high temperature and allowed to cool to a temperature at which its solubility is smaller, some of the solid usually crystallizes out. Thus the solubility of KNO_3 is 136 g per 100 g at 70°C and 31 g per 100 g at 20°C; cooling 236 g of saturated solution through this 50° range would force 105 g of solid KNO_3 to crystallize out. Sometimes, if the cooling is allowed to take place slowly and without disturbance, a solute may remain in solution even though its solubility is exceeded to form a *supersaturated* solution. Supersaturated solutions are in general unstable, with the solute crystallizing out suddenly when the solution is jarred or otherwise disturbed.

Solubilities of different materials vary widely. Water, for example, dissolves readily such diverse susbtances as salt, sugar, alcohol, and ammonia, but it will not dissolve materials like camphor, fat, sulfur, or diamond. Gasoline, on the other hand, dissolves fat, but will not affect salt or sugar. Can we account for these relationships in terms of molecular and atomic structure?

The explanation in part depends on the electrical structures of different kinds of molecules. Water, for example, has polar molecules which behave as if negatively charged at one end and positively charged at the other. This

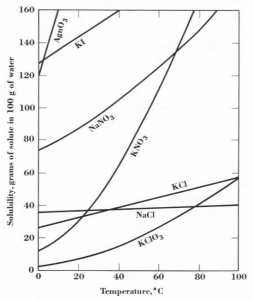

Fig. 25.2 *Variation of solubility with temperature for various substances dissolved in water.*

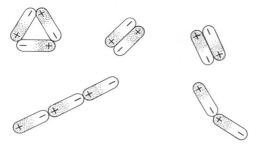

Fig. 25.3   Aggregates of water molecules.

occurs because, as we saw in the previous chapter, water molecules are "bent," with the electrons shared between O and H considerably closer to the oxygen. We call water a *polar liquid;* a liquid like gasoline, whose molecules have positive and negative charges symmetrically arranged, is *nonpolar.*

Water and other strongly polar liquids consist in large part of molecular aggregates rather than simple molecules. The molecules join together in groups, positive charges against negative charges (Fig. 25.3). Water molecules can pair up similarly with polar molecules of other substances, such as alcohol and sugar (Fig. 25.4), so water dissolves these substances readily. Molecules of fats and oils, on the other hand, are less strongly polar or are nonpolar and are not so strongly attracted by water molecules. If oil is shaken with water, the strong attraction of the polar molecules of water for one another "squeezes out" the oil molecules from between them, so the liquids separate quickly into layers. Oil or fat molecules mix readily, however, with the similar nonpolar molecules of gasoline (Fig. 25.5).

The solubility of a covalent substance that has distinct molecules, then, depends primarily on the electrical structure of its molecules. It dissolves only in liquids whose molecules have similar electrical structures.

Ionic compounds are highly polar in the sense that negative charges

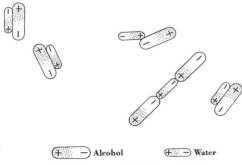

$\underset{\text{Alcohol}}{\boxed{+ \quad -}}$ $\underset{\text{Water}}{\boxed{+ \quad -}}$

Fig. 25.4   Alcohol dissolved in water.

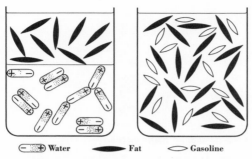

⊂═▒▒+⊃ Water   ▬▬▶ Fat   ⊂▷ Gasoline

Fig. 25.5   *Gasoline dissolves fat; water does not.*

are concentrated on some atoms, positive charges on others, although in the solid state they do not consist of distinct molecules. They dissolve only in highly polar liquids. The process of solution, somewhat different from that for polar covalent compounds, can be visualized with the aid of Fig. 25.6, which represents the solution of NaCl in water. At the surface of the salt crystal water molecules cluster around the ions, positive ends toward negative ions and negative ends toward positive ions. The attraction of so many water molecules is sufficient to overcome the electric forces within the crystal lattice, and each ion moves off into the solution with its retinue of solvent molecules. As each layer is removed, the next is attacked until the salt is completely dissolved or until the solution becomes saturated. Since this process depends on the overcoming of forces within the crystal by electric forces exerted by the solvent molecules, it is understandable that ionic compounds will not dissolve in any but the most polar solvents.

These highly simplified explanations do not tell the complete story of solubility by any means, but do suggest the principal reasons for the differences in solubility of different substances.

Ions in Solution

Since water is the most polar of all ordinary liquids, it has a unique capacity for dissolving ionic compounds according to the mechanism just described. This ability to dissolve materials *as ions* is a major reason why water is such an immensely important substance on our planet.

The ions that a compound releases on dissolving are, as we know, simply its constituent atoms or atom groups, with electric charges determined by their excess or deficiency in electrons. In the example of the last section, every sodium ion is a sodium atom minus its outer electron, and every chloride ion is a chlorine atom with eight electrons instead of the normal seven in its outer shell—precisely the structures, of course, that are present in the original crystal lattice. A potassium nitrate crystal contains positive **potassium** ions, which are potassium atoms shorn of their outer electrons, and negative nitrate ions, which are nitrate groups with one electron in excess of the total number of protons; when the crystal dissolves, these same two ions are free in the solution. We say commonly that an ionic compound ionizes when it dissolves, but ionization in this sense means only that ions already present in the crystal are set free to move about independently in the solution.

Formulas for ions are the symbols of the atoms or atom groups with enough + or − signs attached to indicate their charges. The two ions of NaCl are Na^+ (Na minus an electron) and Cl^- (Cl plus an electron), and those of KNO_3 are K^+ and NO_3^-. $CaCl_2$ ionizes to form Ca^{++} and Cl^- (two of these for every one calcium ion), Na_2SO_4 to form Na^+ and $SO_4^=$. Since the charge on an ion is determined by how many electrons it has gained or lost in electron transfer, the charge is the same as the valence of the atom or atom group.

Substances that separate into free ions on solution in water are called *electrolytes*. Electrolytes include all ionic compounds that are soluble in water and some covalent compounds containing hydrogen (for example HCl) that form ions by reaction with water. Other soluble covalent compounds, like sugar and alcohol, that do not ionize in solution are *nonelectrolytes*.

A property of electrolytes by which they may be recognized quickly— the property, in fact, that gives them their name—is the ability of their solutions to conduct an electric current. Conduction is possible because the ions are free to move; positive ions migrate through the solution toward the negative electrode, negative ions toward the positive electrode. The migration of ions, together with the reactions that occur at the electrodes, made up the process of electrolysis, as we saw.

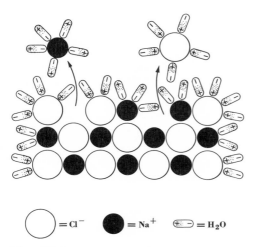

$\bigcirc = Cl^-$ $\bullet = Na^+$ $\oplus\!\!-\!\!\ominus = H_2O$

Fig. 25.6   Solution of a sodium chloride crystal in water.

Arrhenius

The hypothesis that many substances exist in solution as ions was proposed in 1887 by a young Swedish chemist, Svante Arrhenius. So radical was the idea that older chemists derided it, and Arrhenius all but ruined his career at its beginning by defending his hypothesis vigorously. Later, as the weight of accumulating evidence supported him more and more strongly, Arrhenius won world-wide acclaim.

Today the idea of ions in solution follows naturally from the electrical structure of matter. We know that some compounds are formed by the loss of electrons from one kind of atom to another, so that some of the atoms gain a positive charge and the others a negative charge, and we find no difficulty in imagining that a liquid like water can separate these electrically charged atoms. But in 1887 this modern picture of the atom was not even dreamed of. Without this modern knowledge Arrhenius' contemporaries had reason to consider his idea of neutral substances breaking up into electrically charged fragments farfetched.

The only direct experimental evidence that suggested the existence of charged particles in solution was that provided by electrolysis. When a current passes through a solution, one kind of material patently migrates to the anode and another to the cathode, just as if the two kinds had opposite electric charges. Faraday had supposed that passage of the current *caused* the substance in solution to break down into ions, and this explanation of electrolysis was generally accepted.

Arrhenius instead proposed that in solution ions are formed, not by the passage of a current, but *whenever an electrolyte dissolves.* Positive and negative charges are formed in equal numbers, so that both the solution and the original solute appear to be electrically neutral. Of the detailed evidence that Arrhenius presented in support of his theory, we shall mention only two major points:

1. Reactions between electrolytes which take place instantaneously in solution often are very slow or do not occur at all if the electrolytes are dry. An example is the reaction between silver nitrate and sodium chloride. If solutions of the two electrolytes are mixed, a white *precipitate* (ppt)—a solid that forms as a result of a chemical reaction in solution—of the insoluble substance silver chloride appears immediately, at first as a general cloudiness through the solution, later as tiny crystals which settle to the bottom. If the liquid is separated from these crystals by filtration and then evaporated to dryness, another solid, sodium nitrate, will be left. The equation for the reaction may be written

$$AgNO_3 + NaCl \rightarrow AgCl \text{ (ppt)} + NaNO_3 \text{ (in soln)}$$

The silver and sodium seem to have "exchanged partners." Now if dry salt is mixed with dry silver nitrate, no reaction of this sort occurs. Apparently, the exchange of partners is aided by solution, which suggests that the "partners" are already free in the solutions, ready to react as soon as they are mixed.

2. Solutions of electrolytes have abnormally low freezing points. Any substance dissolved in water lowers its freezing point somewhat: We take advantage of this fact, for instance, by dissolving various materials in the water of automobile radiators during cold weather to keep the water from freezing. For nonelectrolytes, careful study shows that the amount by which the freezing point is lowered depends only on the number of molecules of dissolved material present, not on the nature of the material. Equal numbers of sugar, alcohol, and glycerin molecules dissolved in the same quantity of water lower the freezing point by almost exactly the same amount. But the same number of "molecules" of salt (assuming the molecule to be NaCl) lowers the freezing point nearly twice as much; so also do the same number of molecules of $MgSO_4$, KBr, and $AgNO_3$, to give a few more examples. Arrhenius concluded that, in solutions of these substances, twice as many particles were actually present as would be indicated by the simple formulas because the substances were broken down into ions. Similarly a substance like $CaCl_2$ lowers the freezing point nearly three times as much as sugar does, because each "molecule" is broken down into three particles, one calcium ion (Ca^{++}) and two chloride ions ($Cl^- + Cl^-$). Boiling points and vapor pressures of electrolytic solutions show similar abnormalities when compared with solutions of nonelectrolytes, and these abnormalities also find ready explanation in terms of ions.

Arrhenius' hypothesis, based on the careful study and evaluation of these and other experimental observations, has been confirmed by modern research into the electrical structure of the atom. Not all Arrhenius' ideas are still accepted; he believed, for instance, that electrolytes consisted of separate molecules in the solid state, which has been disproved by X-ray studies of crystals. But the basic notion that electrolytes dissolve in water to form free ions capable of moving about in solution remains the foundation of all modern work on solutions in water. Thus the 1923 Debye-Hückel theory of electrolytes, a largely successful quantitative treatment that takes into account the electrostatic attractive forces between ions in solution, is an elaboration of Arrhenius' hypothesis and does not represent a change in his essential argument.

Properties of Ions

One of the early objections to the ionic theory of solutions was that sodium chloride was assumed to break down into separate particles of sodium and chlorine and yet the solution remains colorless. Why, if chlorine is present as free ions, should we not find the characteristic greenish-yellow color of chlorine in the solution? We might reply that chloride ion has altogether different properties from chlorine gas—a different color, a different taste, different chemical reactions. This answer is straightforward enough, but its full significance is not easy to grasp.

We must regard a solution of sodium chloride not as a solution of NaCl but as a solution of two substances with the formulas Na^+ and Cl^-. Further, each of these substances has its own set of properties, properties that are quite different from those of the active metal Na and the poisonous gas Cl_2. We must change our point of view toward all electrolytic solutions, so that we think of each ion as a new and separate material with characteristic properties of its own.

By the *properties of an ion,* we mean, of course, the properties of solutions in which the ion occurs. A solution of a single kind of ion, all by itself, cannot be prepared; positive ions and negative ions must always be present together, so that the total number of charges of each sign will be the same. But each ion gives its own characteristic properties to all solutions containing it, and these properties can be recognized whenever they are not masked by other ions. For example, a property of copper ion (Cu^{++}) is its blue color, and all solutions of this ion are blue (unless some other ion is present that has a stronger color). A characteristic of hydrogen ion (H^+ or H_3O^+) is its sour taste, and all solutions containing this ion (acids) are sour. Silver ion (Ag^+) shows the property of forming a white precipitate, AgCl, when mixed with solutions of chloride ion (Cl^-); any solution of an electrolyte containing silver when mixed with a solution of any chloride will give this precipitate.

To emphasize the difference between the properties of an ion and the properties of the corresponding neutral substance, we may set down in tabular form a comparison of the properties of the two substances Cl^- and Cl_2:

Cl_2	Cl^-
Greenish-yellow color	Colorless
Strong, irritating taste and odor	Mild, pleasant taste
Combines with all metals	Does not react with metals
Combines readily with hydrogen	Does not react with hydrogen
Does not react with Ag^+	Forms AgCl with Ag^+
Very soluble in CCl_4	Insoluble in CCl_4

In general, Cl_2 is much more active—as might be expected, since its atoms have only seven valence electrons while chloride ions have eight and hence closed outer shells.

For each ion we may write down a list of properties, which means a list of the properties common to all its solutions. In general, the properties of a solution of an electrolyte are the sum of the properties of the ions that it contains. The properties of sodium chloride are the properties of Na^+ and the properties of Cl^-; the properties of copper sulfate are the properties of Cu^{++} and $SO_4^=$. This is one of the reasons why the ionic hypothesis is so valuable in the study of solutions: Instead of learning the individual properties of several hundred different electrolytes, we need learn the properties of only a few ions to be able to predict the properties of an electrolytic solution that contains them.

Ionic Equations

Reactions involving ions can be expressed in equation form by following the basic principle that a chemical equation is a summary of an actual chemical change. We may use the formula of a solid compound, as we have done previously, to indicate the relative number of atoms present. Thus the formula of solid sodium chloride is NaCl, even though the crystal actually consists of sodium ions and chloride ions. In solution, we write the formula of an electrolyte in terms of its ions, signifying that the ions are now independent substances rather than parts of a crystal. The change from solid salt to salt in solution, for example, may be represented

$$NaCl \rightarrow Na^+ + Cl^-$$

The equation means that sodium ions and chloride ions have been set free to move about in the solution. If the solution is cooled or evaporated so that solid sodium chloride crystallizes out, the re-formation of the crystal structure may be written

$$Na^+ + Cl^- \rightarrow NaCl$$

Once an electrolyte is dissolved, each ion is independent and its reactions need not involve the other ions present. For example, consider again the reaction between silver nitrate and sodium chloride discussed before. Both $AgNO_3$ and NaCl, when dissolved, are completely dissociated into ions. Of the products, $NaNO_3$ is soluble and completely ionized, but AgCl is a solid precipitate not appreciably ionized. Hence we might write the equation

$$Ag^+ + NO_3^- + Na^+ + Cl^- \rightarrow AgCl + Na^+ + NO_3^- \qquad (25.2)$$

On each side of this equation appear the formulas Na^+ and NO_3^-; these substances have not changed during the reaction but have merely remained in solution. Actually, the only chemical change that has occurred is the disappearance of Ag^+ and Cl^- and the formation of solid AgCl:

$$Ag^+ + Cl^- \rightarrow AgCl \qquad (25.3)$$

This brief equation is a complete summary of the reaction. The other ions are present but take no part. If KCl had been used instead of NaCl, or $AgC_2H_3O_2$ instead of $AgNO_3$, the ions would have been different but the actual chemical change would still have been the union of Ag^+ and Cl^- to form AgCl. Equation (25.2) is not wrong, but Eq. (25.3) expresses more clearly that the reaction with chloride ion is a property of Ag^+ and not of some particular silver compound.

Another similar example is furnished by the precipitation of the white solid calcium carbonate ($CaCO_3$) when a solution of calcium ion is added to a solution of carbonate ion. If $CaCl_2$ is used to supply Ca^{++} and Na_2CO_3 to supply $CO_3^=$, the equation may be written

$$Ca^{++} + 2Cl^- + 2Na^+ + CO_3^= \rightarrow CaCO_3 + 2Cl^- + 2Na^+$$

Sodium ions and chloride ions take no part in the reaction, so we may simplify the equation to

$$Ca^{++} + CO_3^= \rightarrow CaCO_3$$

When two electrolytes are mixed, no reaction occurs unless some undissociated substance like AgCl and $CaCO_3$ can form. If solutions of $Cu(NO_3)_2$ and NaCl are mixed, for example, a possible reaction might be an exchange of partners to form $NaNO_3$ and $CuCl_2$. But both of these are soluble salts, completely ionized in solution, so no reaction can occur. In symbols,

$$Cu^{++} + 2NO_3^- + Na^+ + Cl^- \rightarrow Cu^{++} + Cl^- + Na^+ + 2NO_3^-$$

The same substances are represented on each side of the "equation," and no chemical change has taken place.

For a further example of an ionic process we shall consider the reaction between an active metal and an acid, such as

$$Zn + H_2SO_4 \rightarrow H_2 + ZnSO_4$$

for the reaction between zinc and sulfuric acid. Let us try to express this equation in terms of ions. Zinc is a solid metal, and hence is not ionized; H_2 represents the covalent molecule of a gas, and is also not ionized. Sulfuric acid and zinc sulfate, however, are ionized in solution, and so we have

$$Zn + 2H^+ + SO_4^= \rightarrow H_2 + Zn^{++} + SO_4^=$$

This is one way to write the ionic equation, but inspection shows that it can be simplified. $SO_4^=$ appears on both sides of the equation, and so may be omitted. The actual reaction is therefore

$$Zn + 2H^+ \rightarrow Zn^{++} + H_2$$

This shorter statement implies that the only chemical changes are the formation of zinc ion from zinc metal and the formation of hydrogen gas from hydrogen ion.

Self-examination

1. When an electric current is passed through a solution of sodium chloride,
   a. sodium metal is deposited at the positive electrode
   b. sodium ions are deposited at the positive electrode
   c. chlorine gas is liberated at the positive electrode
   d. chlorine ions are liberated at the positive electrode

2. A saturated solution is a solution that
   a. contains the maximum amount of solute
   b. contains the maximum amount of solvent
   c. is in process of crystallizing
   d. contains polar molecules

3. Polar molecules
   a. contain tiny magnetic poles
   b. are completely symmetric in every way
   c. do not dissolve ionic compounds
   d. behave as though positively charged at one end and negatively charged at the other

4. The most strongly polar liquid is
   a. water
   b. alcohol
   c. hydrochloric acid
   d. gasoline

5. The ions and atoms (or molecules) of an element
   a. have very nearly the same properties except that the ions are electrically charged
   b. may have strikingly different properties
   c. always exhibit different colors
   d. differ in that the ions are more active chemically than the atoms or molecules

6. The mass of any substance liberated at an electrode during electrolysis is directly proportional to its
   a. atomic number
   b. atomic weight
   c. valence
   d. concentration

7. The amount of charge that must be passed through a solution containing Cu^{++} in order to deposit 1 g of copper is
   a. 1,520 coul
   b. 3,040 coul
   c. 6,080 coul
   d. 96,500 coul

Problems

1. Into what kind of energy is electric energy converted during electrolysis? In what common device is this energy transformation reversed?

2. Why is the solubility of one gas in another unlimited?

3. How can you tell whether a sugar solution is saturated or not?

4. Give examples of (*a*) polar and (*b*) nonpolar liquids, and state several substances soluble in each.

5. How could you distinguish experimentally between an electrolyte and a nonelectrolyte?

6. Contrast the properties and electron structures of Na and Na^+. Which would you expect to be more active chemically?

7. Name one property by which you could distinguish
   a. Cl^- from NO_3^-
   b. Ag^+ from Na^+
   c. Ca^{++} from Na^+
   d. Cu^{++} from Ca^{++}

8. Why do so many substances dissolve in water? Why do oils and fats not dissolve in water?

9. A current of 50 amp flows through a solution of NaCl for 10 min. What mass of metallic sodium will be deposited at the negative electrode?

10. A current of 1 amp is passed through a solution that contains 0.5 mole of $CuSO_4$. How long will it take for all the copper to be removed from the solution?

11. One faraday of electricity is passed through a water bath. How many grams of water are decomposed?

12. A total of 400,000 coul is passed through a sample of molten lithium chloride. What volume of chlorine gas at 0°C and atmospheric pressure is liberated?

13. With the help of Fig. 25.2, predict what will happen when a concentrated solution of sodium nitrate at 50°C is added to a saturated solution of potassium chloride at the same temperature.

14. At 10°C, which is more concentrated, a saturated solution of potassium nitrate or a saturated solution of potassium chloride? At 60°C?

CHAPTER 26 | ACIDS, BASES, AND SALTS

We have made a considerable detour from Chap. 11, where we first learned about the periodic table, to the last chapter, where we learned about the electrical aspects of chemistry. We now return to what most of us tend to think of as the real subject matter of chemistry, chemical reactions and the properties of common types of chemical compounds. We shall begin by considering the three important classes of electrolytes, acids, bases, and salts, and then we shall go on to some general considerations affecting chemical reactions.

Acids

Acids have been described earlier as substances containing hydrogen whose water solutions taste sour and change the color of a dye called litmus from blue to red. Strong acids like hydrochloric acid (HCl) and sulfuric acid (H_2SO_4) are poisonous, cause painful burns if allowed to remain on the skin, and are injurious to clothing. Weak acids like carbonic acid (H_2CO_3) and citric acid, far from being harmful, add a pleasant sour taste to foods and drinks.

What is it that gives an acid its characteristic properties? Following the line of reasoning in the last chapter, we note (1) that solutions of acids conduct electricity and hence must contain ions, and (2) that acids contain hydrogen united with one or more nonmetals. It is reasonable, then, to express the dissociation of acids into ions with equations such as

$$HCl \rightarrow H^+ + Cl^- \qquad (26.1)$$

and $\qquad H_2SO_4 \rightarrow 2H^+ + SO_4^= \qquad (26.2)$

453

and to conclude that the characteristic properties of acids are the properties of the free hydrogen ion H^+.

There are difficulties with this simple picture. For one thing, pure acids when liquefied do not conduct current, as NaCl does, so we cannot properly speak of a pure acid as made up of ions. It is as if acids formed free ions, not by simple separation of the positively and negatively charged atoms already present, but only by reaction with water. (In more general terms, acids are covalent rather than ionic substances, and they can form ions only by reaction with a polar liquid like water or alcohol.) A second difficulty is the nature of the ion H^+, which is nothing more than a single proton—the nucleus of a hydrogen atom shorn of its lone electron. All other ions are particles of the same general size as atoms, particles whose structures consist of nuclei and electron clouds. This one ion would be entirely different, a naked positive charge with a volume about 10^{-15}—one-quintillionth—as great. It seems very doubtful that such a particle could have an independent existence in a liquid, and is far more likely to be attached to some other atom or molecule.

To eliminate these difficulties, we could write more correctly

$$HCl + H_2O \rightarrow H_3O^+ + Cl^- \tag{26.3}$$

Here the acid is shown taking part in a specific reaction with water instead of simply splitting up into ions, and the proton is shown attached to a water molecule (H_3O^+) rather than free in solution. The ion H_3O^+ is called the *hydronium ion;* it is a combination of H^+ with H_2O that gives a *hydrated* hydrogen ion. The characteristic properties of acids are described more correctly as properties of the hydronium ion than as properties of the simple hydrogen ion.

Nevertheless, it is customary in chemistry to write the characteristic ion of acids with the formula H^+ rather than H_3O^+. This is chiefly for convenience. H_3O^+ is more correct than H^+, but it is still not entirely correct; if we strove for strict accuracy, we should have to write sometimes $H_5O_2^+$ and $H_7O_3^+$ as well as H_3O^+, and we should have to use hydrates for other ions also —$Na(H_2O)^+$ instead of Na^+, $Cl(H_2O)^-$ instead of Cl^-, and so on. Our equations would quickly become too cumbersome for easy use. In most chemical reactions the water of hydration does not play an important role, and the reactions can be adequately represented by equations from which it is omitted.

For our purposes, then, an *acid* may be defined as a *substance containing hydrogen whose solution in water contains hydrogen ions.* Free hydrogen ions are present in all acid solutions and give these solutions their common properties. When we say that acid solutions taste sour, turn litmus pink, and liberate hydrogen gas by reaction with metals, we mean that the hydrogen ion does these things.

Acids differ greatly in their *degree of ionization.* Some acids, called *strong acids,* ionize completely. For example, when HCl dissolves in water it breaks down completely into H⁺ and Cl⁻, with no molecules of undissociated HCl. Other acids, called *weak acids*, ionize only slightly. The greater ionization of strong acids means that, in solutions of similar total concentration, a strong acid has a much larger proportion of hydrogen ions than a weak acid: It has a much sourer taste, it is a better conductor of electricity, and if the two acids are poured on zinc, the evolution of hydrogen gas is much faster from the reaction with strong acid.

An interesting example of a weak acid is carbonic acid (H_2CO_3), which is formed by the solution of CO_2 gas in water:

$$CO_2 + H_2O \rightarrow H_2CO_3$$

The carbonic acid then dissociates into H⁺ and HCO_3^-:

$$H_2CO_3 \rightarrow H^+ + HCO_3^-$$

Very little H⁺ is found in a solution of CO_2 in water, which means that we can think of carbonic acid as being weak. Actually, it seems unlikely on the basis of experimental evidence that much H_2CO_3 ever exists as such, so that perhaps a better way to express the "ionization of carbonic acid" is simply to write

$$CO_2 + H_2O \rightarrow H^+ + HCO_3^- \tag{26.4}$$

Thus the "weakness" of carbonic acid may simply reside in the unlikelihood of its formation, rather than in any tendency it may have to remain as undissociated H_2CO_3. However, it is convenient to speak of carbonic acid as being formed when CO_2 is dissolved in water and to regard it as a weak acid, which is an acceptable summary of the situation provided that the correct picture of what is happening is kept in mind.

The three most common strong acids are HCl (hydrochloric), H_2SO_4 (sulfuric), and HNO_3 (nitric). Some familiar weak acids besides carbonic acid are acetic acid ($HC_2H_3O_2$), the acid in vinegar; boric acid (H_3BO_3), found in every medicine cabinet; and citric acid, the acid of citrus fruits.

The stronger an acid, the weaker is the attachment of hydrogen in its molecules. In a strong acid like HCl the attachment is so weak that the H⁺ and Cl⁻ are split apart completely and go their separate ways in solution. In a weak acid like "H_2CO_3," on the other hand, the attachment is strong enough so that most of the molecules remain undissociated. For instance, in a saturated solution of CO_2, only 1 CO_2 molecule in every 1,000 combines with H_2O to yield H⁺. Acetic acid, which is not quite so weak as carbonic and which therefore holds its hydrogen ions less securely, has about 10 molecules out of every 1,000 broken up into ions in a saturated solution. In hydrochloric acid, where the attachment of hydrogen in the molecule is very weak, every one of the 1,000 molecules would be split up.

Other substances besides CO_2 that do not contain hydrogen in their formulas are capable of giving acid solutions because they react with water to liberate H^+ from H_2O molecules. Solutions of many iron and copper salts (compounds like $CuSO_4$, $FeCl_2$, $FeCl_3$) give slight acid reactions, as do solutions of nonmetal oxides like SO_2 and NO_2.

Bases

We have already described bases as substances whose solutions in water have a bitter taste and an ability to turn red litmus to blue. Their formulas, for example NaOH and $Ba(OH)_2$, show that bases consist of a metal united with one or more hydroxide groups (OH). On dissolving in water, bases dissociate into ions according to reactions such as

$$NaOH \rightarrow Na^+ + OH^-$$

and $$Ba(OH)_2 \rightarrow Ba^{++} + 2OH^-$$

Just as H^+ is the characteristic ion of acid solutions, so OH^- is the characteristic ion in water solutions of bases. The bitter taste and the ability to change the color of dyes are properties of the OH^- ion. We may define a *base*, therefore, as a *substance that contains an OH group and that gives OH^- on dissolving in water*.

Like acids, bases may be grouped according to their degree of ionization as strong bases and weak bases. Thus NaOH is a strong base because it breaks up completely into Na^+ and OH^- on dissolving. Bases differ from acids, however, in that soluble weak bases with simple formulas are rare. The most common weak base is ammonium hydroxide (NH_4OH), in which the NH_4 group plays the role of a metal. Ammonium hydroxide, like carbonic acid, is considered a compound only for the sake of convenience, since a "solution of ammonium hydroxide" is more correctly just a solution of ammonia gas (NH_3) in water. The "dissociation of ammonium hydroxide" is really a reaction between the dissolved NH_3 and H_2O:

$$NH_3 + H_2O \rightarrow NH_4^+ + OH^- \qquad (26.5)$$

The former belief that this process first goes through the intermediate step

$$NH_3 + H_2O \rightarrow NH_4OH$$

was a consequence of the highly polar nature of both ammonia and water molecules, which leads to the great solubility of ammonia. The "weakness" of ammonium hydroxide means that the reaction of Eq. (26.5) is relatively infrequent; we can take the liberty of referring to NH_4OH as a compound as a kind of verbal shorthand, but we must remember that Eq. (26.5) is what is really involved in its dissociation.

The three strong bases most widely used are KOH (ordinary lye, or caustic potash), NaOH (soda lye, or caustic soda), and $Ba(OH)_2$. These substances are quite as poisonous and quite as destructive to flesh and clothing as the strong acids and, like the strong acids, are extensively used in chemical industry. Another hydroxide that gives a fairly basic solution is

$Ca(OH)_2$, which makes ordinary limewater. Insofar as it dissolves, $Ca(OH)_2$ ionizes completely, but the amount of OH^- obtainable is limited because the compound is not very soluble. All other common hydroxides, like $Al(OH)_3$, $Fe(OH)_3$, $Cu(OH)_2$, are practically insoluble in water. These substances contribute only negligible amounts of OH^- to solution, both because they are weak bases and because they dissolve to such a slight extent.

Many substances that do not contain OH in their formulas give basic solutions because they are capable of reacting with water to produce OH^- from H_2O molecules. Familiar examples besides ammonia water (NH_3 dissolved in water) are washing soda (sodium carbonate, Na_2CO_3) and borax (sodium tetraborate, $Na_2B_4O_7$). These will be recognized as common household items, useful as cleaning agents because of their ability to dissolve grease. Ordinary soap also gives a slightly basic solution, but its cleaning ability is due more to its emulsifying action than to its basic nature.

A name often used for any substance that dissolves to give a basic solution is *alkali*, an old Arabic term that referred originally to the bitter extract obtained by leaching the ashes of a desert plant. The alkali that crystallizes in desert basins is chiefly Na_2CO_3. Because NaOH and KOH are strong alkalies, sodium and potassium are often called *alkali metals*. An *alkaline solution* is any solution with appreciable quantities of the hydroxide ion OH^-; the terms *alkaline* and *basic* are practically synonymous.

More general definitions of acids and bases cover systems from which water may be absent. Thus a "Brønsted-Lowry acid" is a substance that acts as the proton donor in a chemical reaction and a "Brønsted-Lowry base" is a substance that acts as the proton acceptor. A still broader definition was suggested by G. N. Lewis: A "Lewis acid" is a substance that acts as an electron-pair acceptor in sharing electron pairs provided by a "Lewis base."

Neutralization

When sodium hydroxide solution is added slowly to hydrochloric acid, there is no visible sign that a reaction is taking place. Both the original solutions are colorless, and the resulting solution is colorless also. That a reaction does occur can be shown in several ways: (1) the mixture becomes warm, showing that chemical energy is changing to heat energy; (2) the taste of the acid becomes less and less sour as the base is added; (3) if small samples of the acid are taken out while the base is being added, the samples show progressively less and less active evolution of hydrogen gas when poured on zinc. The base evidently destroys, or *neutralizes*, the characteristic acid properties, and the reaction is accordingly called *neutralization*. In the same way the characteristic properties of a base can be neutralized by adding a strong acid.

What is the chemical change in the neutralization of HCl by NaOH? We could write the preliminary equation

$$HCl + NaOH \rightarrow H_2O + NaCl$$

To make the equation more precise, we consider the ions involved. HCl, a strong acid, ionizes completely in water to give H^+ and Cl^-; NaOH, a strong base, ionizes into Na^+ and OH^-; the product NaCl, likewise a soluble electrolyte, remains ionized in solution. Of the four substances shown, only water is a nonelectrolyte, so it alone should appear un-ionized in the equation:

$$H^+ + Cl^- + Na^+ + OH^- \rightarrow H_2O + Na^+ + Cl^-$$

Since Na^+ and Cl^- appear on both sides, they may be omitted, leaving

$$H^+ + OH^- \rightarrow H_2O \qquad (26.6)$$

This is the actual chemical change, stripped of all nonessentials. The neutralization of a strong acid by a strong base in water solution is essentially a reaction between hydrogen ions and hydroxide ions, forming water.

To carry out a neutralization reaction in the laboratory, some method is necessary to determine when just enough acid has been added to neutralize all the base present, or vice versa. Otherwise the resulting solution will be either acidic or basic, depending on which is in excess. One convenient method for determining the "neutral point" is to add a few drops of litmus solution to the base before the reaction is carried out, giving the basic solution a blue color. As the acid is added, the blue color persists until all the base is used up, then changes to pink. Similarly, if a base is to be added to an acid, the acid may first be made pink with litmus solution; then its color will change to blue as soon as enough base has been added to neutralize the acid.

A substance like litmus, whose color enables a chemist to tell whether a solution is acidic or basic and whose sharp change in color shows when neutralization has occurred, is called an *indicator*. Many different indicators are used in chemical laboratories, some being more useful than litmus because changes in their color during neutralization are more abrupt. Two common ones are phenolphthalein, which is pink in basic solution and colorless in acid, and methyl orange, which is yellow in basic solution and salmon pink in dilute acid. All indicators are complex compounds that contain carbon, hydrogen, and oxygen; several are commercial dyes. One familiar "indicator" is the red coloring matter of cherry juice: When a red cherry stain is washed with soap (which gives a weakly alkaline solution), its color changes abruptly to blue, showing that the acid of the fruit juice has been neutralized.

Salts

When an NaOH solution is neutralized with HCl, the resulting solution should contain nothing but the ions Na^+ and Cl^-. If the solution is evaporated to dryness, the ions combine to form the white solid NaCl. This substance, ordinary *salt*, gives its name to an important class of compounds, most of which are crystalline solids at ordinary temperatures and most of which consist of a metal combined with one or more nonmetals. Typical salts are KBr, $MgSO_4$, $Al(NO_3)_3$, and $ZnCO_3$. Crystal structures of salts consist of alternate positive and negative ions, which means that practically all soluble salts will ionize (that is, dissociate into free ions) completely in a water solution. No salt is completely insoluble in water, but some, like AgCl and $CaCO_3$, are so very slightly soluble that we often refer to them as insoluble; such salts, of course, can give only a very few ions in solution.

The solubilities of most common salts can be summarized as follows:

All nitrates (salts containing the NO_3 group) are soluble.
All acetates (salts containing the $C_2H_3O_2$ group) are soluble.
All chlorides are soluble, except AgCl and a very few others.
All sulfates are soluble, except $BaSO_4$ and a few others.
All carbonates are insoluble, except Na_2CO_3, K_2CO_3, and $(NH_4)_2CO_3$.
All sulfides are insoluble, except Na_2S, K_2S, $(NH_4)_2S$, CaS, and BaS.
All salts of Na, K, and NH_4 are soluble.

Any salt can be formed by mixing the appropriate acid and base and evaporating the solution to dryness. Thus KNO_3 is formed when solutions of KOH and HNO_3 are mixed and evaporated; $CuSO_4$ is formed when H_2SO_4 is poured on the insoluble hydroxide $Cu(OH)_2$ and the resulting solution is evaporated. We could say, in general, that neutralization reactions give water and a solution of a salt. It is important to remember, however, that the salt itself is not produced directly by the neutralization. Neutralization is essentially a reaction between hydrogen ion and hydroxide ion; as a result of this process ions may be left in solution that on evaporation will unite to form a salt.

Strong Base and Weak Acid

Neutralization is a more complicated process when the acid or the base is weak. As an example, suppose that NaOH is added slowly to the weak acid, acetic acid $(HC_2H_3O_2)$. (The formula for acetic acid is written $HC_2H_3O_2$ because only one of the four H's has any tendency to be set free as H^+; the other three remain always a part of the acetate ion $C_2H_3O_2^-$.) As the base is added, the vinegarlike odor of $HC_2H_3O_2$ decreases and finally disappears. To describe the reaction we might write

$$NaOH + HC_2H_3O_2 \rightarrow NaC_2H_3O_2 + H_2O$$

The $NaC_2H_3O_2$ (sodium acetate) could be obtained as a white salt by evaporating the solution. So far there is nothing new, and the reaction seems entirely similar to the neutralization of HCl by NaOH. By studying the process quantitatively, however, we can detect certain differences. If we use amounts of solution containing equal numbers of molecules of base and acid, we find that the resulting mixture is basic (that is, it contains an excess of OH⁻), whereas equal amounts of NaOH and HCl would give a strictly neutral solution.

Why is there any difference? We can see the reason by writing the equation in terms of ions. To do this, we recall that NaOH, as a strong base, must be completely ionized in solution; that $NaC_2H_3O_2$, as a soluble salt, must also be completely ionized; that water is practically un-ionized; and that acetic acid, as a weak acid, is present chiefly as un-ionized molecules. So we write

$$Na^+ + OH^- + HC_2H_3O_2 \rightarrow Na^+ + C_2H_3O_2^- + H_2O \qquad (26.7)$$

which reduces to

$$OH^- + HC_2H_3O_2 \rightarrow C_2H_3O_2^- + H_2O \qquad (26.8)$$

Evidently H⁺ is taken away from the acetate ion by OH⁻, the H⁺ and OH⁻ uniting to form water and the acetate ion being left free in solution. Another way of saying this is to picture the OH⁻ and the $C_2H_3O_2^-$ as competing for the H⁺; the $C_2H_3O_2^-$ ions, although they are attached to the H⁺ ions originally, lose most of them because the attraction of OH⁻ ions is stronger. Now the important point is that the $C_2H_3O_2^-$ ions lose most of the H⁺ ions, *but not all of them.* When we say that acetic acid is weak, we mean that there is a strong attraction between H⁺ and $C_2H_3O_2^-$; it is not as strong as the attraction between H⁺ and OH⁻ in water, but it is nevertheless strong enough to hold *some* of the H⁺ out of reach of the OH⁻. Hence some of the OH⁻ is not neutralized but remains free in the solution, and the solution is therefore basic.

Generalizing from this reaction, we could say that the neutralization of a weak acid by a strong base is essentially a reaction of OH⁻ with undissociated acid molecules to form water and set free the negative ion of the acid. If equal numbers of acid molecules and OH⁻ ions are used, some of the OH⁻ will be left over because the acid retains some of its H⁺ ions.

Suppose, now, we try to reverse the reaction of Eq. (26.7) by mixing $C_2H_3O_2^-$ with H_2O. The most direct way to do this is to dissolve solid sodium acetate in water. The salt ionizes, giving

$$NaC_2H_3O_2 \rightarrow Na^+ + C_2H_3O_2^-$$

We now have a mixture of $C_2H_3O_2^-$ and water. Some Na⁺ is present also, of course, but this ion is relatively inert and will not interfere. Next we add litmus or another indicator to the solution, and we find that the solution is slightly basic: Evidently some OH⁻ has been set free. A plausible explanation is that the reaction of Eq. (26.8) has proceeded backward:

$$C_2H_3O_2^- + H_2O \rightarrow HC_2H_3O_2 + OH^- \qquad (26.9)$$

It has not gone very far in this direction, since the concentration of OH⁻ is small, but apparently acetate ion has enough attraction for hydrogen ion so that it can take a little away from water and leave the OH⁻ free.

The same sort of reaction takes place whenever the ion of a weak acid is added to water. If K_2CO_3 is used in place of $NaC_2H_3O_2$, for example, the salt ionizes to give K^+ and $CO_3^=$ in solution; the $CO_3^=$, being the ion of a weak acid, reacts with water to a slight extent in this way:

$$CO_3^= + 2H_2O \rightarrow H_2CO_3 + 2OH^- \qquad (26.10)$$

The solution is therefore basic, because of the OH⁻ set free. The ion K^+, like the ion Na^+, plays no part in the reaction. This kind of reaction is called *hydrolysis,* and we say in general that any salt consisting of the ion of a strong base and the ion of a weak acid will hydrolyze on dissolving in water to give a basic solution. This is one of the reactions mentioned earlier by which substances whose formulas do not contain OH can react with water to give basic solutions. The alkalinity of solutions of washing soda (Na_2CO_3), borax ($Na_2B_4O_7$), water glass (Na_2SiO_3), and soap are all explained by similar hydrolysis reactions.

Weak Base and Strong Acid

We might guess that reactions will take place involving weak bases and their ions that are analogous to those described in the preceding section. When ammonium hydroxide is neutralized with hydrochloric acid, for example, the molecular reaction may be written

$$NH_4OH + HCl \rightarrow NH_4Cl + H_2O$$

The soluble salt NH_4Cl (ammonium chloride) can be obtained as a solid by evaporating the solution. If equal numbers of molecules of the acid and base are used, the resulting solution is slightly acid. This can be explained by writing the ionic equation

$$NH_4OH + H^+ + Cl^- \rightarrow NH_4^+ + Cl^- + H_2O$$

in which HCl is written in terms of its ions because it is a strong acid, NH_4Cl is written in terms of ions because it is a soluble salt, and NH_4OH is written in molecular form because it is a weak base. The chloride ion may be omitted because it appears on both sides of the equation. Hence the true reaction is

$$NH_4OH + H^+ \rightarrow NH_4^+ + H_2O \qquad (26.11)$$

The essential process is the taking away of OH⁻ from NH_4OH by reaction with H^+, the NH_4^+ ion then being left free. Or we could say that NH_4^+ and H^+ are in competition for OH⁻, the H^+ getting the lion's share because its attraction for OH⁻ is greater. Most of the OH⁻ goes with H^+, but not all;

some remains with NH_4^+ since ammonium hydroxide is a weak base. Because some of the H^+ is not neutralized, the resulting mixture is acid.

The reverse reaction to Eq. (26.11) takes place when NH_4Cl is dissolved in water to give

$$NH_4Cl \rightarrow NH_4^+ + Cl^-$$

Such a solution gives an acid reaction with litmus, indicating that the reaction

$$NH_4^+ + H_2O \rightarrow NH_4OH + H^+ \qquad (26.12)$$

occurs. The ion of any other weak base will react similarly with water to set free a small amount of H^+. For example, a solution of $FeCl_3$ is slightly acid because Fe^{3+} reacts with water as follows:

$$Fe^{3+} + 3H_2O \rightarrow Fe(OH)_3 + 3H^+ \qquad (26.13)$$

Such reactions account in part for the fact mentioned earlier, that many substances whose formulas contain no hydrogen can give acid solutions by reacting with water.

Reactions like those that occur when NH_4Cl and $FeCl_3$ are dissolved in water are further examples of hydrolysis. This term refers, in general, either to the formation of free OH^- by reaction of water with the ion of a weak acid or to the formation of free H^+ by reaction of water with the ion of a weak base. (In the chemistry of carbon compounds it has a wider significance, but this definition is sufficient for our present purposes.)

Weak acids can be formed by the action of strong acids on salts. For example, acetic acid may be prepared by mixing solutions of hydrochloric acid and sodium acetate:

$$HCl + NaC_2H_3O_2 \rightarrow HC_2H_3O_2 + NaCl$$

In terms of ions this would be written simply

$$H^+ + C_2H_3O_2^- \rightarrow HC_2H_3O_2 \qquad (26.14)$$

In other words, the original solutions supply the two ions needed to make the acid, and the ions unite spontaneously because the acid is weak. The reaction of Eq. (26.14) is the reverse of the dissociation of acetic acid, whose extent is very limited; in fairly dilute solution only about 1 molecule in 100 is ionized. The reaction of Eq. (26.14) correspondingly dominates, and most of the H^+ and $C_2H_3O_2^-$ unite to form molecules. The procedure of adding a strong acid to a salt containing the ion of a weak acid is a general method for preparing weak acids, widely used both in industry and in research laboratories.

As might be expected, a similar process can be used for the preparation of weak bases. To make ammonium hydroxide, for example, a common procedure is to add sodium hydroxide to an ammonium salt:

$$NaOH + NH_4Cl \rightarrow NH_4OH + NaCl$$

or $$OH^- + NH_4^+ \rightarrow NH_4OH \qquad (26.15)$$

Again the two ions are supplied by the original solutions, and they unite because NH_4OH is a weak base. Similarly, iron hydroxide may be formed in the reaction

$$3NaOH + FeCl_3 \rightarrow Fe(OH)_3 + 3NaCl$$

or $\qquad 3OH^- + Fe^{3+} \rightarrow Fe(OH)_3$ $\hfill (26.16)$

The formation of $Fe(OH)_3$ takes place both because it is a weak base and because it is an almost insoluble compound.

Ammonia and Ammonia Ion

The weak base ammonium hydroxide deserves special attention. It is a common substance in the laboratory, in chemical industry, and around the house ("ammonia water"). It differs from most other common bases in that its positive ion is a combination of two nonmetal atoms rather than a metal.

Ammonium hydroxide may be thought of as being formed by the reaction of Eq. (26.15)—adding a strong base to an ammonium salt—or by dissolving ammonia (NH_3) in water:

$$NH_3 + H_2O \rightarrow NH_4OH \hfill (26.17)$$

Ammonia is a gas with a strong odor that is extremely soluble in water. Just how much of the NH_3 dissolved in water actually reacts to form NH_4OH is uncertain, and in all likelihood the latter does not ever exist as such. As we said earlier, for most purposes it is immaterial whether we regard a solution of ammonia as containing NH_4OH or as a mixture of NH_3 and H_2O. In any event, the solution is a weak base in the sense that the concentration of OH^- ions is only a tiny fraction of the total amount of dissolved ammonia.

NH_4OH is neutralized by a solution of HCl, as we have seen in Eq. (26.11), and a similar reaction takes place between gaseous NH_3 and gaseous HCl:

$$NH_3 + HCl \rightarrow NH_4Cl \hfill (26.18)$$

This reaction is conspicuous when bottles of HCl and NH_4OH solutions are opened side by side: The two gases, escaping from the solutions, mix and form a dense white cloud consisting of tiny particles of NH_4Cl.

Ammonium chloride (commercially called "sal ammoniac"), although made up of three nonmetals, is a white crystalline substance that behaves like a salt. Its crystals are made up of the ions NH_4^+ and Cl^-, the NH_4^+ (ammonium ion) playing the role of a metal ion like K^+. Similar ionic compounds, called in general *ammonium salts*, are formed by the reaction of ammonia or ammonium hydroxide with the other acids: ammonium sulfate, $(NH_4)_2SO_4$, ammonium nitrate, NH_4NO_3, ammonium carbonate, $(NH_4)_2CO_3$, and so on.

Ammonium sulfate and ammonium nitrate, like ammonium chloride, give slightly acid solutions because the ammonium ion hydrolyzes. Ammonium carbonate, on the other hand, gives a basic solution because both of its ions hydrolyze and the hydrolysis of carbonate ion is more effective than that of ammonium ion:

$$(NH_4)_2CO_3 \rightarrow 2NH_4^+ + CO_3^=$$
$$NH_4^+ + H_2O \rightarrow NH_4OH + H^+$$
$$CO_3^= + 2H_2O \rightarrow H_2CO_3 + 2OH^-$$

Ammonia is readily driven out of solution by heating, which reduces the solubility of NH_3. If we wish, we can regard the process as NH_4OH decomposing by a reaction that is the reverse of Eq. (26.17):

$$NH_4OH \rightarrow NH_3 + H_2O$$

This reaction is the basis of a delicate test for the presence of ammonium salts in any solution: One need only add a strong base to give NH_4OH, as in Eq. (26.15), and then heat the solution to produce the characteristic odor of NH_3. Similarly, the presence of a solid ammonium salt in a mixture can be tested for by heating with a solid hydroxide:

$$(NH_4)_2SO_4 + Ca(OH)_2 \rightarrow CaSO_4 + 2H_2O + 2NH_3 \qquad (26.19)$$

Acidic and Basic Oxides

In an earlier chapter we learned that one important distinction between metals and nonmetals is the fact that oxides of the former often react with water to form bases, whereas oxides of the latter often react with water to form acids. For example,

$$CaO + H_2O \rightarrow Ca(OH)_2$$
$$SO_3 + H_2O \rightarrow H_2SO_4$$
$$CO_2 + H_2O \rightarrow H_2CO_3$$

Not only do these oxides dissolve in water to give acidic and basic solutions, but in some reactions they may themselves play the roles of acids or bases. For example, Na_2O can "neutralize" H_2SO_4 quite as effectively as can NaOH, in the sense that it destroys its acidic properties:

$$Na_2O + 2H^+ + SO_4^= \rightarrow 2Na^+ + H_2O + SO_4^=$$

or
$$Na_2O + 2H^+ \rightarrow 2Na^+ + H_2O$$

Some oxides (CuO, Fe_2O_3, SiO_2) will not dissolve in water. Their relationship with acids and bases is shown, however, by the fact that they can be prepared by reactions of the type

$$Cu(OH)_2 \rightarrow CuO + H_2O$$
$$2Fe(OH)_3 \rightarrow Fe_2O_3 + 3H_2O$$
$$H_4SiO_4 \rightarrow SiO_2 + 2H_2O$$

These equations show what happens when copper hydroxide, iron hydroxide, and silicic acid, respectively, are heated.

Because any oxide may be regarded as derived from an acid or base (although sometimes the acid or base is purely hypothetical), oxides of metals in general are referred to as *basic oxides* and oxides of nonmetals as *acidic oxides*. Thus SiO_2 (the chief constituent of ordinary sand) is called an acidic oxide, although it is insoluble in water and neither tastes sour nor turns litmus red, while Fe_2O_3 (the chief constituent of hematite ore) is called a basic oxide, although it neither tastes bitter nor turns litmus blue.

Certain oxides have the ability to neutralize both acids and bases. An example is zinc oxide (ZnO), which can undergo both of the following reactions:

$$ZnO + 2H^+ \rightarrow Zn^{++} + H_2O$$
$$ZnO + 2OH^- + H_2O \rightarrow Zn(OH)_4^-$$

An oxide of this kind is called *amphoteric*.

Self-examination

1. The reason that pure acids in the liquid state are not dissociated is that their chemical bonds are
   a. ionic
   b. covalent
   c. metallic
   d. van der Waals

2. While it is convenient to regard acid solutions as containing H^+ ions, it is more correct to describe them as containing
   a. hydronium ions
   b. hydroxide ions
   c. polar molecules
   d. hydrogen atoms

3. A common strong acid is
   a. acetic acid
   b. boric acid
   c. nitric acid
   d. citric acid

4. A base dissolved in water liberates
   a. H
   b. H^+
   c. OH
   d. OH^-

5. A substance whose formula does not contain OH yet which yields a basic solution when dissolved in water is
   a. NH_3
   b. CO_2
   c. HCl
   d. NaCl

6. Water is formed during
   a. hydrolysis
   b. electrolysis
   c. neutralization
   d. crystallization

7. When an equivalent amount of a strong base is added to a weak acid, the resulting solution will be
   a. neutral
   b. acid
   c. basic
   d. opaque

Problems

1. How can you tell whether an unknown solution is acidic, basic, or neutral?

2. Which of the following are weak acids, and which are weak bases? H_2SO_4, $HC_2H_3O_2$, NH_4OH, H_2CO_3, HCl, NaOH, H_3BO_3.

3. Would you expect HBr to be a weak or strong acid? Why?

4. Write the ionic equation for the neutralization of KOH by HNO_3. What actual chemical changes does this equation show?

5. How could you tell whether an unknown mixture of salts contains (*a*) a salt of ammonium ion, (*b*) a salt of carbonate ion?

6. What reaction would take place if $FeCl_3$ solution were added to KOH solution?

7. Boric acid (H_3BO_3) is a weaker acid than carbonic acid. What would happen if solutions of sodium borate (Na_3BO_3) and HCl were mixed? Would you expect a solution of Na_3BO_3 to be acidic, basic, or neutral?

8. If the following salts are dissolved in water, which would give acidic solutions, which alkaline solutions, which neutral solutions? Na_2CO_3, KCl, $KC_2H_3O_2$, $BaCl_2$, $(NH_4)_2SO_4$, $NaNO_3$.

9. How could you prepare the weak acid H_2S from the salt Na_2S (sodium sulfide)?

10. From the fact that H_2S is a weak acid, would you predict that a solution of Na_2S would be acidic, basic, or neutral? Explain.

11. Which hydrolyzes more, $CO_3^=$ or $C_2H_3O_2^-$? What is the general relation between the extent of hydrolysis of a negative ion and the weakness of the corresponding acid?

12. One common type of baking powder ("alum" baking powder) contains a salt of aluminum, such as $Al_2(SO_4)_3$. Explain how such a salt can furnish acid to liberate CO_2 (from $NaHCO_3$) when the baking powder is mixed with water. [Use the fact that $Al(OH)_3$ is insoluble and a weak base.]

13. What reaction takes place when a solution of $Ca(C_2H_3O_2)_2$ is added to a solution of H_2SO_4?

CHAPTER 27 | CHEMICAL REACTIONS

Chemical reactions have significant aspects quite apart from the changes that occur when the reactants combine to yield the products. For instance, some reactions evolve energy while others require energy to be supplied externally if they are to take place. Even those reactions that liberate energy may not occur unless an initial amount of energy is furnished to start the process. Chemical changes may be almost instantaneous or may take years to be completed, depending upon many factors. And not all reactions can ever actually be "completed": Often an equilibrium situation exists with the products undergoing reverse reactions to form the starting substances just as fast as the primary reaction proceeds. These and still other considerations are involved in actual chemical reactions, and they form the subject of this chapter.

Chemical Energy

Ever since our ancestors learned the value of fire, mankind has been putting chemical energy to practical use. Today we transform it not only into heat and light but into mechanical energy and electric energy as well. Locked up in the atoms of matter, chemical energy long remained a mystery. Modern theories of the atom and of the chemical bond, however, have given us a great deal of insight into the origin of this energy.

Chemical changes that *liberate* heat are called *exothermic reactions*. Familiar examples are the burning of coal and the explosion of a mixture of hydrogen and oxygen. The heat liberated is often expressed in the equation for the process:

$$C + O_2 \rightarrow CO_2 + 94.4 \text{ kcal}$$

$$2H_2 + O_2 \rightarrow 2H_2O + 117 \text{ kcal}$$

These figures represent the heat produced when an amount of each substance is used equal to its molecular weight expressed in grams multiplied by its coefficient in the equation. When 12 g of carbon is burned, 94.4 kcal is produced; when 4.032 g of hydrogen is burned, 117 kcal is produced. These particular amounts are chosen so that heats liberated for similar numbers of molecules may be compared for different reactions.

Chemical changes that take place only when heat or some other kind of energy is *supplied* are called *endothermic reactions*. Thus water can be decomposed into hydrogen and oxygen only by heating to very high temperatures or by supplying electric energy (during electrolysis):

$$2H_2O + 117 \text{ kcal} \rightarrow 2H_2 + O_2$$

The formation of nitric oxide (NO) from its elements is an endothermic reaction, which takes place only at high temperatures:

$$N_2 + O_2 + 43.2 \text{ kcal} \rightarrow 2NO$$

From the law of conservation of energy we might predict that, if a given reaction is exothermic, the reverse reaction will be endothermic and, further, that the amount of heat liberated by one reaction must be equal to the amount absorbed by the other. This prediction is borne out in the case of water, as we can see above, and might be checked by any number of other reactions. For example, sodium burning in chlorine liberates 197 kcal for every 46 g of sodium:

$$2Na + Cl_2 \rightarrow 2NaCl + 197 \text{ kcal}$$

and NaCl is decomposed in an endothermic process requiring the absorption of this same amount of heat:

$$2NaCl + 197 \text{ kcal} \rightarrow 2Na + Cl_2$$

Energy changes accompanying ionic reactions are measured and represented in equations in the same manner as energy changes for other reactions. The ionization of most salts is an endothermic process; for example, when KNO_3 is dissolved in water, the container becomes cold, since ionization of the salt absorbs heat from its surroundings:

$$KNO_3 + 8.5 \text{ kcal} \rightarrow K^+ + NO_3^-$$

Neutralization is a good example of an exothermic ionic process. If concentrated solutions of NaOH and HCl are mixed, for instance, the mixture quickly becomes too hot to touch:

$$H^+ + OH^- \rightarrow H_2O + 13.7 \text{ kcal}$$

The neutralization of any strong acid by any strong base liberates almost precisely this same amount of heat for each 1.008 g of H, as might be expected, since the actual chemical change in all cases is simply the joining together of hydrogen ions and hydroxide ions.

The general interpretation of chemical-energy changes in terms of electrons follows readily from earlier discussions of chemical combination. When sodium reacts with chlorine, for example, an electron from each sodium atom is transferred to the outer shell of a chlorine atom, a position in which it has a smaller amount of potential energy with respect to the atomic nuclei. When carbon reacts with oxygen, the atoms are joined by electron pairs, the formation of pairs involving a decrease in the potential energy of the electrons. Thus *chemical energy is initially potential energy of electrons;* when the electrons move to new positions, some of this potential energy is transformed into other kinds. Apparently the excess energy of the shifted electrons causes a violent disturbance in the new-formed molecules: It may give the molecules themselves motions that constitute heat energy or it may displace outer electrons into new orbits from which they jump back with emission of radiant energy. In endothermic reactions, some other form of energy must be supplied to increase the potential energy of electrons.

Activation Energies

Coal burns in air to give great quantities of heat; how then can coal be kept indefinitely at ordinary temperatures in contact with air? The decomposition of nitric oxide liberates considerable energy; why does it not therefore break up spontaneously? How can the compound exist at all? A mixture of hydrogen and oxygen will produce a violent explosion; why should heat or an electric spark be necessary to start the explosion? Why, in general, do not all exothermic reactions take place instantaneously of their own accord?

Experience indicates that many exothermic processes occur only if some energy is provided to start them. A mixture of hydrogen and oxygen may be likened to the car of Fig. 27.1, whose potential energy may be converted into kinetic energy if it moves down into the large valley. However, it can move of its own accord only if it is first given sufficient energy to climb to the top of the first hill. Similarly, the chemical energy stored in the electrons of hydrogen and oxygen can be liberated as heat only if the molecules have sufficient energy, or are sufficiently *activated*, to make the reaction start. The energy necessary for activation, corresponding to the energy required to move the car up the first hill, is called the *activation energy* of the reaction.

The electronic picture of chemical combination gives a plausible reason why activation should be necessary. The combination of oxygen and hydrogen involves the formation of electron-pair bonds between O and H atoms, a process that gives out energy, but before these bonds can be formed, the

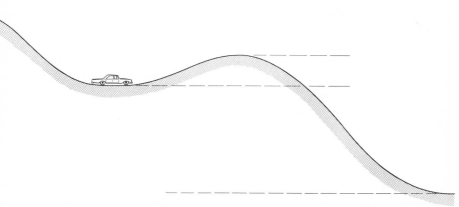

Fig. 27.1   *The potential energy of the automobile will be converted into kinetic energy if it moves down into the valley. However, it requires an initial kinetic energy in order to climb the hill between it and the valley, analogous to the activation energy required in many exothermic reactions.*

electron pairs that bind hydrogen atoms in H_2 molecules and oxygen atoms in O_2 molecules must be broken.   To break these bonds requires energy.   The energy is in part supplied by the thermal energy of the molecules and, after the reaction starts, by the energy it gives out, but initially some additional energy must be supplied to loosen the bonds.

A molecule with sufficient energy above the average to enable it to react is called an *activated molecule.*   In some gas reactions an activated molecule may be actually broken down into atoms.   Other activated molecules may simply have high kinetic energy, or they may have one or two electrons displaced from their normal orbits.   In reactions that take place spontaneously at room temperatures (for example, the reaction between hydrogen and fluorine), enough of the molecules have sufficient heat energy to break the necessary bonds without further activation.   In many ionic reactions no bonds need be broken; ions are, so to speak, already activated and react almost instantaneously.   But a great number of exothermic reactions require the preliminary activation of some molecules before they can take place at appreciable rates.

Once an exothermic reaction is started, it usually supplies its own activation energy.   In other words, the energy given out when some of the molecules react supplies neighboring molecules with sufficient energy to activate them in turn, so the reaction spreads quickly.   Thus a mixture of hydrogen and oxygen need only be touched with a flame for the reaction to spread so rapidly that an explosion results.   When a bed of coal is set on fire it continues to burn, since the heat liberated in one part is sufficient to ignite the coal in adjacent parts.

Reaction Rates

Some chemical changes are practically instantaneous. In neutralization, **for** example, acid and base react as soon as they are stirred together; silver chloride is precipitated immediately when solutions of silver ion and chloride ion are mixed; the reaction involved in a dynamite explosion is immeasurably rapid. Other chemical changes, like the formation of ammonia, the souring of milk, and the rusting of iron, take place slowly. For many of these slow reactions we can set up experiments to measure exactly how fast they **are** going, that is, what fractions of the original substances have disappeared at various times after the reactions start.

Reaction rates depend, first of all, on the nature of the reacting substances. Obviously some materials undergo a given chemical change more rapidly than others: Meat decays more quickly than wood; iron corrodes more rapidly than copper. For any particular reaction the rate is influenced by four principal factors: (1) temperature, (2) concentrations of the reacting substances, (3) amount of surface exposed (in reactions involving solids), and (4) catalysts.

Temperature. Reaction rates are always increased by a rise in temperature. We use this simple fact, of course, when we put food in the refrigerator to retard its decay and when we use hot water rather than cold for washing. As a rule of thumb, reaction rates are approximately doubled for every $10°C$ rise in temperature.

The kinetic theory of matter suggests one obvious reason for the increase of rate with temperature: Most reactions depend on collisions between particles, and the number of collisions increases with rising temperature because molecular speeds are increased. But a $10°C$ rise at ordinary temperatures is not nearly sufficient to double the collision rate. To find an adequate explanation, we must go back to the idea of activation energy.

If molecules must be activated before they can react, reaction rates should depend not on how many ordinary collisions occur each second but on the number of collisions between *activated* molecules. Now activated molecules in a fluid may be produced by ordinary molecular motion as a result of exceptionally energetic collisions; these remain activated for only a small fraction of a second, losing their excess energy by further collisions unless they react in the meantime. In any fluid, then, provided the temperature is not too low, a fraction of the particles should be activated at any one instant. The fraction may be very small at ordinary temperatures, but it increases rapidly as the temperature rises and molecular motion speeds up. Reaction rates increase with temperature, therefore, chiefly because the number of activated molecules grows larger.

A mixture of hydrogen and oxygen, for example, contains at room temperature very few molecules with sufficient energy to react, and the reaction is so exceedingly slow that the gases may remain mixed for years without appreciable change. Even at 400°C the rate is negligibly small, but at 600° enough of the molecules are activated to make the reaction fast, and at 700° so many are activated that the mixture explodes. This kind of behavior is typical of many reactions, especially those involving molecules whose bonds must be broken: At low temperatures the chemical change is so slow that for all practical purposes it does not occur; in a range of intermediate temperatures the reaction is moderately rapid; and at high temperatures it becomes instantaneous. Reactions between ions, on the other hand, are instantaneous even at room temperatures, for the ionic state itself is a form of activation.

Concentration. The general effect of concentration on reaction speed is well shown by rates of burning in air and in pure oxygen; the pure gas has almost five times as many oxygen molecules per cubic centimeter as air has, and rates of burning are accordingly greater. The concentration effect appears even more spectacularly in the burning of iron wire in liquid air; despite the low temperature, oxygen molecules are so abundant and so close together in the liquid that the metal burns brightly. As a general rule, the rate of a chemical reaction is directly proportional to the concentration of each reacting substance. This is an experimental result, for which the kinetic theory gives a simple and reasonable explanation: The number of collisions between activated molecules, which determines the reaction speed, should depend on the total number of collisions and thus, in turn, on how many molecules each cubic centimeter contains.

Surface. When a reaction takes place between two solids or between a fluid and a solid, its rate depends markedly on the amount of solid surface exposed. A finely powdered solid presents vastly more surface than a few large chunks, and reactions of powders are accordingly much faster. Granulated sugar dissolves more rapidly in water than lump sugar; finely divided zinc is attacked by acid quickly, larger pieces only slowly; ordinary iron rusts slowly, but if the metal is very finely powdered, its oxidation is fast enough to produce a flame. A kinetic explanation is obvious enough: The greater the surface, the more quickly molecules can get together to react. For a similar reason, efficient stirring speeds up reactions between fluids.

Catalysts. Harder to explain is the action of catalysts. These are substances with the remarkable property of changing the rate of a chemical reaction without being themselves altered or used up. A catalyst may either speed up or retard a reaction. For a simple example, hydrogen peroxide solutions are unstable at ordinary temperatures and slowly decompose into water and oxygen. If a little of the black powder called manganese dioxide is added to hydrogen peroxide, the decomposition becomes much more rapid, and oxygen bubbles from the solution in large quantities. At the end of the reaction the manganese dioxide catalyst can be recovered unchanged. Ordinary solutions of hydrogen peroxide contain a little of a carbon compound called acetanilid, a catalyst of the opposite sort which slows down the decomposition.

An extremely important example of *catalysis* (the name given to the action of a catalyst) occurs in nature. This is the formation of carbohydrates in the leaves of green plants, which involves a direct conversion of radiant energy from sunlight into chemical energy. Carbohydrates are complex compounds of carbon, including sugar, starch, and cellulose—the first two vitally important foods, the last a major constituent of wood, paper, and cloth. Plants are able to manufacture carbohydrates out of water, which enters through their roots, and CO_2, which is taken from the air, according to the reaction

$$6CO_2 + 5H_2O + 671 \text{ kcal} \rightarrow C_6H_{10}O_5 + 6O_2$$

This reaction is highly endothermic, and the necessary energy comes from sunlight. The energy is absorbed, not by the CO_2 and H_2O directly, but instead by a substance called *chlorophyll,* which is part of the green coloring matter of leaves; the catalyst chlorophyll is not changed by the reaction, but serves to pass on the sun's energy to the reacting molecules. This reaction is often called *photosynthesis,* since light is necessary for its occurrence. It has not been duplicated in the laboratory, and its details are imperfectly understood; mankind depends on it, not only for the chemical energy in carbohydrates, but also for the constant replenishment of oxygen in the atmosphere.

Catalysts may affect reaction rates in several ways. In some cases, the catalyst is known to form an unstable intermediate compound with one of the reacting substances, which decomposes again as the reaction proceeds. Other catalysts, notably certain metals, can affect reaction rates by producing activated molecules at their surfaces. For the action of many others no adequate explanation has been suggested. In general, a given reaction is influenced only by a few catalysts, and these may or may not affect other reactions. Catalysts are highly important in many industrial processes, but in searching for new ones a chemist must usually rely more on experience and trial-and-error methods than on any definite knowledge of how catalysts work.

Chemical Equilibrium

Most chemical reactions are *reversible;* that is, the products of a chemical change, under suitable conditions, can usually be made to react to give the original substances. We have discussed many examples in other connections. Hydrogen and oxygen combine to form water when ignited, and water can be decomposed into its elements by extreme heat or by electricity. Mercury and oxygen combine when heated moderately, and mercuric oxide decomposes when heated more strongly. Carbon dioxide reacts with water to form hydrogen and carbonate ions, and these recombine into carbon dioxide and water.

There is no reason, of course, why the forward and backward processes of a chemical change cannot take place simultaneously, provided their rates are approximately equal. If CO_2 is kept over water in a stoppered bottle, for instance, some of the gas reacts with water. But a number of the resulting ions join together to give CO_2 and H_2O as soon as an appreciable concentration is built up. The recombination rate increases with concentration until, finally, as many ions recombine each second as are formed by the dissolving of CO_2. At this point the rates of the forward and backward reactions are the same, and no further change occurs in the amounts of the various substances. We may represent this situation by the single equation

$$H_2O + CO_2 \leftrightharpoons H^+ + HCO_3$$

in which the double arrow indicates that reactions in both directions occur together.

A situation of this kind is called *chemical equilibrium*. It is a state of balance determined by two opposing processes. The two processes do not reach equilibrium and stop, but continue indefinitely to maintain a balance because one constantly undoes what the other accomplishes. As a crude analogy, we might imagine a man walking down an escalator while the escalator is moving upward; if he walks as fast in one direction as the escalator carries him in the other, the two motions will be in equilibrium and he will remain at the same place indefinitely.

A great many chemical changes reach a state of equilibrium instead of going to completion in one direction or the other. Equilibrium may be established when a reaction is very nearly complete, or when it is only just starting, or when both products and reacting substances are present in comparable amounts. At what point equilibrium occurs depends entirely on the rates of the opposing reactions; one reaction takes place until a sufficient concentration of products is built up for the reverse reaction to go at the same rate. The ionizations of different acids offer good examples. HCl dissociates completely into H^+ and Cl^-; here there is no reverse reaction and no equilibrium, except in very concentrated solutions. On the other hand, $HC_2H_3O_2$ ionizes to only a slight extent, and when a small concentration of ions is built up, the recombination goes at the same rate as the dissociation. The extent to which an acid is ionized depends on how fast its molecules break down into ions compared with how fast the ions recombine.

Frequently a chemist encounters this problem: He wishes to prepare a compound but finds that the reaction that produces it reaches equilibrium before much of the compound has been formed. Once equilibrium is established, waiting for more of the product to form is futile since its amount thereafter does not change. How can the equilibrium conditions be altered so that the yield of the product will be larger?

Since equilibrium depends on a balance between two rates, a solution to this problem depends on finding a way to change the speed of one reaction or the other. Speeding up or retarding only one of the reactions in an equilibrium is not quite so simple as changing the rate of a single reaction, but we might expect that the same general factors that affect reaction rates would influence equilibrium also. The chemist has three chief methods at his disposal for shifting an equilibrium in one direction or another: (1) changing the concentration of one or more substances, (2) changing the temperature, and (3) changing the pressure (especially in gas reactions). Since, generally, the two opposite reactions involved in a chemical equilibrium are affected differently by these three factors, proper adjustment often gives a yield of the desired reaction product larger than would otherwise be possible. We may note that neither using a catalyst nor changing the amount of exposed surface influences equilibrium, since these factors always affect forward and backward actions alike.

Oxidation and Reduction

As we know, the valence of an element in a compound is the number of electrons that each atom has gained, lost, or shared. In ionic compounds, the valence of the metal is positive, that of the nonmetal (or nonmetals) negative. In covalent compounds, valences are properly neither positive nor negative, but the more active nonmetal is often arbitrarily assigned a negative valence. The valence of an ion is the amount of its charge. Elements in the free state are regarded as having a valence of zero.

Earlier in this book we used the term *oxidation* to mean the chemical combination of a substance with oxygen. A related term often employed is *reduction,* which refers to the removal of oxygen from a compound. It is often convenient to use these terms in a much broader sense: The *oxidation* of an element is defined in general as a chemical change in which its positive valence is increased or its negative valence decreased; the *reduction* of an element is a chemical change in which its positive valence is decreased or its negative valence increased.

Let us examine several examples of oxidation and reduction. When zinc is oxidized by burning in oxygen to form ZnO, its valence increases from 0 to $+2$. Similarly, when zinc burns in chlorine,

$$Zn + Cl_2 \rightarrow ZnCl_2$$

its valence again increases, and this reaction is considered oxidation even though no oxygen is involved. The solution of zinc in hydrochloric acid is a further example of oxidation, for the valence of the metal there goes from 0 to $+2$:

$$Zn + 2H^+ + 2Cl^- \rightarrow Zn^{++} + H_2 + 2Cl^-$$

The decomposition of mercuric oxide on heating means an oxidation of oxygen itself, for the negative valence of oxygen decreases from -2 to 0:

$$2HgO \rightarrow 2Hg + O_2$$

The reduction of iron by heating its oxide in a stream of hydrogen

$$Fe_2O_3 + 3H_2 \rightarrow 2Fe + 3H_2O$$

gives a valence change in the opposite direction, for the original valence of +3 changes to 0. In similar fashion iron in ferric chloride may be reduced by hydrogen:

$$2FeCl_3 + 3H_2 \rightarrow 2Fe + 6HCl$$

When chlorine reacts with sodium, its negative valence increases from 0 to −1, so this too is an example of reduction:

$$2Na + Cl_2 \rightarrow 2NaCl$$

An increase in the positive valence of a metal means that its atoms have lost electrons; a decrease means that its atoms have gained electrons. Thus iron atoms combine with either oxygen or chlorine by losing electrons to the nonmetal atoms; to reduce iron from these compounds to the free metal requires that electrons be given to the iron atoms. When a nonmetal increases in negative valence, on the other hand, its atoms gain electrons; when it decreases in negative valence, its atoms lose electrons. So we may simplify our definitions of oxidation and reduction to read: *An element is oxidized when its atoms lose electrons, reduced when its atoms gain electrons.*

We run into difficulties, of course, in trying to apply this definition to covalent compounds. Carbon we say is oxidized by burning in oxygen,

$$C + O_2 \rightarrow CO_2$$

since its valence increases from 0 to +4. The + sign indicates merely that carbon is a less active nonmetal than oxygen, not that electrons are transferred from carbon atoms to oxygen atoms. Again, when phosphorus reacts with chlorine,

$$2P + 3Cl_2 \rightarrow 2PCl_3$$

the phosphorus gains in positive valence, although electrons are shared between its atoms and chlorine atoms. For these compounds we shall find it best to keep the definition of oxidation and reduction in terms of valence rather than loss or gain of electrons.

Note that oxidation of one element is always accompanied by reduction of another. For example, the burning of zinc in chlorine means the reduction of chlorine as the zinc is oxidized; in other words, electrons *lost* by the zinc atoms are *gained* by chlorine atoms. When carbon burns in oxygen, the oxidation of carbon is accompanied by the reduction of oxygen from a valence of 0 to a valence of −2; for each electron shared by a carbon atom, one electron must, of course, be shared by an oxygen atom. Since in chemical reactions atoms cannot lose, gain, or share electrons all by themselves, oxidation and reduction must take place together. Reactions involving changes of valence are often called *oxidation-reduction reactions*. They make up a large and important group of chemical changes, some of which we have already studied. Below we shall examine in more detail a few typical oxidation-reduction processes.

Displacement Reactions

If a piece of copper wire is covered with a solution of silver nitrate and allowed to stand for a few hours, the wire becomes coated with gray crystals and the solution turns pale blue. The crystals are metallic silver, and the telltale blue color shows the presence of copper ions in the solution. Evidently some copper has become ionized, and at the same time silver has been set free. This reaction is summarized by the equation

$$Cu + 2Ag^+ + 2NO_3^- \rightarrow Cu^{++} + 2Ag + 2NO_3^-$$

Or since the nitrate ion is not affected, we may write

$$Cu + 2Ag^+ \rightarrow Cu^{++} + 2Ag$$

This is an oxidation-reduction reaction in the simplest form. Each copper atom has lost two electrons, to become a copper ion; each silver ion has gained one electron, to become a neutral silver atom. Copper is oxidized; silver is reduced. We may describe this reaction by saying that copper has *displaced* silver from solution.

A similar reaction takes place when a steel knife blade is held in a solution of copper sulfate. After a few moments the blade is coated with a reddish film of copper, and chemical tests would show the presence of iron ions in solution. The equation is therefore

$$Fe + Cu^{++} \rightarrow Fe^{++} + Cu$$

Iron reduces copper ion to free copper and is itself oxidized to a positive ion. Or we may say that iron has displaced copper from solution.

Iron gives up electrons to copper ion; copper gives up electrons to silver ion. Thus we might arrange the three metals in the order Fe, Cu, Ag, showing their relative abilities to give up electrons. By studying other displacement reactions, we should find that other metals may be added to this series, each metal being capable of giving electrons to the ions of metals that follow it:

Na	Sodium
Ca	Calcium
Mg	Magnesium
Al	Aluminum
Zn	Zinc
Fe	Iron
Pb	Lead
(H)	(Hydrogen)
Cu	Copper
Hg	Mercury
Ag	Silver
Au	Gold

This sequence is in order of decreasing ability to lose electrons or of decreasing ability to reduce the ions of other metals. Magnesium placed in a solution of copper chloride gives its electrons to the copper ions; lead placed in a silver nitrate solution reduces the silver ions. This is precisely the order we described earlier as the *order of activity* of the metals (Chap. 11). Oxidation-reduction reactions, in fact, furnish a precise measure for the activities of different metals.

Hydrogen may be placed in the above sequence, for the solution of a metal in acids is a typical displacement reaction:

$$Zn + 2H^+ \rightarrow Zn^{++} + H_2$$

Zinc gives up electrons to hydrogen ions, going into solution as zinc ions and setting hydrogen free. To find where hydrogen belongs in the series, we need only see which metals will dissolve in acids and which will not. We find that all the metals from Na to Pb will reduce H^+, but those from Cu to Au are unaffected by ordinary acids. Hence H belongs between Pb and Cu.

Displacement reactions among nonmetals are shown especially well by the halogens. If chlorine is added to a solution of potassium bromide, for example, the solution turns brownish because bromine is set free:

$$Cl_2 + 2Br^- \rightarrow Br_2 + 2Cl^-$$

Chlorine oxidizes bromide ion; in other words, each chlorine atom takes an electron from Br^-, setting free a bromine atom and itself becoming ionized. Similarly, bromine displaces iodine, and fluorine displaces any one of the other halogens. By means of these reactions, nonmetals also may be arranged in an activity series:

F	Fluorine
Cl	Chlorine
Br	Bromine
O	Oxygen
I	Iodine
S	Sulfur

This sequence is in order of decreasing ability to gain electrons, or of decreasing ability to oxidize the ions of other nonmetals. Note that the activity of nonmetals is measured by their oxidizing ability, that of metals by their reducing ability—which is just another way of stating the fundamental facts that metals enter chemical combination by losing electrons to other elements and that nonmetals enter chemical combination by gaining electrons.

Iron Compounds

Many elements show two or more different valences in their compounds. Mercury, for example, forms compounds in which it has a valence of $+1$, like Hg_2O, Hg_2Cl_2, $Hg_2(NO_3)_2$, Hg_2SO_4 (mercur*ous* oxide, mercur*ous* chloride, etc.), and other compounds in which it has a valence of $+2$, like HgO,

$HgCl_2$, $Hg(NO_3)_2$, $HgSO_4$ (mercur*ic* oxide, etc.). Tin in some compounds ($SnCl_2$, SnO) has a valence of $+2$; in others, a valence of $+4$ ($SnCl_4$, SnO_2). Carbon forms the two oxides CO and CO_2; sulfur, the two oxides SO_2 and SO_3. Changes from one valence state to another are, of course, oxidation-reduction reactions. For example, carbon is oxidized when carbon monoxide is burned:

$$2CO + O_2 \rightarrow 2CO_2$$

and sulfur is reduced when sulfur trioxide is strongly heated:

$$2SO_3 \rightarrow 2SO_2 + O_2$$

Especially noteworthy are valence changes among the compounds of iron. This element shows two principal valences, $+2$ and $+3$; thus it forms the two oxides FeO (ferr*ous* oxide) and Fe_2O_3 (ferr*ic* oxide), the two chlorides $FeCl_2$ and $FeCl_3$, and the two sulfates $FeSO_4$ and $Fe_2(SO_4)_3$. Many compounds of each type are soluble in water and ionize to give, respectively, the ions Fe^{++} and Fe^{3+}. Most ferrous compounds in solution are pale green in color, most ferric compounds pale yellow. (Solutions of ferric compounds often show stronger tints of yellowish to reddish brown because ferric ion has a tendency to form complex ions by attaching itself to water molecules and to other ions.) As a general rule, iron compounds are strongly colored, both in solution and in the solid state: Ferric compounds have shades ranging from yellow to brown and red; ferrous compounds are gray, green, or black.

Changes from one valence state of iron to the other are easily brought about. If chlorine, for example, is bubbled into a solution of ferrous sulfate, the greenish color of the solution changes quickly to yellow, showing that Fe^{++} has been converted to Fe^{3+}:

$$Cl_2 + 2Fe^{++} \rightarrow 2Cl^- + 2Fe^{3+}$$

Each chlorine atom oxidizes a ferrous ion by taking one electron away from it. One way of effecting the opposite change is to add an iodide, say KI, to a solution of a ferric compound. Now the yellow solution changes to deep brown as iodine is liberated:

$$2I^- + 2Fe^{3+} \rightarrow I_2 + 2Fe^{++}$$

Each iodide gives an electron to a ferric ion, thereby reducing it to ferrous ion. Many other oxidizing and reducing substances besides Cl_2 and I^- can be used in these reactions.

In the presence of air, most ferrous compounds are slowly oxidized to ferric compounds by atmospheric oxygen. Deep in the earth, however, at high temperatures and out of reach of the atmosphere, ferrous compounds are more stable than ferric compounds. Most of the iron in rocks formed at these depths, therefore, goes into ferrous compounds, chiefly ferrous silicates. When such rocks appear at the surface, either brought up by volcanic activity or exposed by long erosion, their iron compounds are no longer stable. Slowly, oxygen attacks the iron, aided by the slight solvent action of carbonic acid in streams and rain water. The complex silicates are broken down, and the iron is oxidized as in ordinary rusting to various hydrates of Fe_2O_3. The rusty stains on the surfaces and in cracks of so many common rocks are due to this iron oxide, formed by slow oxidation of ferrous compounds present in the rocks.

Many of the bright and somber hues in nature we owe to the colorful compounds of this one element. Not only the rusty surface stains but yellow-brown and reddish-brown colors in rocks themselves are nearly always due to ferric compounds. Many black rocks and green rocks get their colors from ferrous compounds. Sand, clay, and soil likewise owe their brown tints to ferric compounds, their gray and black shades often to ferrous compounds. The colors of ferric compounds are so strong that only a little iron is needed to color a rock or a soil conspicuously.

Reduction of ferric compounds at the earth's surface is accomplished chiefly by carbon compounds produced by plants and animals. Soils containing much organic matter are usually black, since their iron is in the form of ferrous compounds whose relatively weak colors do not obscure the dark carbonaceous materials. Often we find a thin layer of black soil resting on brown soil, the dark color showing the depth to which decaying organic matter keeps the iron of the soil reduced.

Thus in nature we find continuous transformations of ferric compounds to ferrous compounds and back again, an unending series of oxidation-reduction reactions.

Self-examination

1. Chemical energy is stored within atoms, molecules, and ions as
   a. activation energy
   b. electron kinetic energy
   c. electron potential energy
   d. thermal energy

2. Chemical reactions that evolve energy are said to be
   a. exothermic
   b. endothermic
   c. activated
   d. electrolytic

3. Chemical reaction rates in solution do *not* depend to any great extent upon
   a. pressure
   b. temperature
   c. concentration
   d. catalysts

4. Plants manufacture carbohydrates from water and carbon dioxide during photosynthesis with the help of chlorophyll, which acts
   a. to extract oxygen from the atmosphere
   b. to shield the reacting molecules from the sun's rays
   c. to prevent the water from evaporating
   d. to catalyze the reaction

5. At equilibrium,
   a. both forward and reverse reactions have ceased
   b. the forward and reverse reactions are proceeding at the same rate
   c. the forward reaction has come to a stop, and the reverse reaction is just about to begin
   d. a considerable amount of heat is evolved

6. Oxidation occurs when
   a. atoms lose electrons
   b. atoms gain electrons
   c. positive valence is decreased
   d. negative valence is increased

7. When fluorine is said to be a more active nonmetal than chlorine, what is meant is that
   a. fluorine dissolves more readily in water
   b. fluorine has greater ability to acquire electrons than chlorine
   c. fluorine has greater ability to lose electrons than chlorine
   d. fluorine is a better reducing agent

Problems

1. Which of the following are exothermic reactions and which endothermic?
   a. the explosion of dynamite
   b. the burning of methane
   c. the decomposition of water into its elements
   d. the decomposition of water into ions
   e. the burning of iron in chlorine
   f. the combination of zinc and sulfur to form zinc sulfide

2. From the observation that the slaking of lime [addition of water to CaO to form $Ca(OH)_2$] gives out heat, would you conclude that the following reaction is endothermic or exothermic?
   $$Ca(OH)_2 \rightarrow CaO + H_2O$$

3. In what fundamental way is the explosion of an atomic bomb different from the explosion of dynamite?

4. Give two examples of reactions that are
   a. practically instantaneous at room temperatures
   b. fairly slow at room temperatures

5. Suggest three ways to increase the rate at which zinc dissolves in sulfuric acid.

6. Under ordinary circumstances coal burns slowly, but the fine coal dust in mines sometimes burns so rapidly as to cause an explosion. Explain the difference in rates.

7. Explain why a reaction with high activation energy is slow at room temperature.

8. Ammonia gas dissolves in water and reacts according to the equation
$$NH_3 + H_2O \rightleftharpoons NH_4^+ + OH^-$$
How would the amount of ammonium ion in solution be affected by
   a. increasing the pressure of NH_3?
   b. pumping off the gas above the solution?
   c. raising the temperature?
   d. adding a solution of HCl?

9. Which of the following equations represent oxidation-reduction reactions?
   a. $Zn + S \rightarrow ZnS$
   b. $H^+ + OH^- \rightarrow H_2O$
   c. $MnO_2 + 2Cl^- + 4H^+ \rightarrow Cl_2 + Mn^{++} + 2H_2O$
   d. $CaO + H_2O \rightarrow Ca^{++} + 2OH^-$

10. In each of the following reactions, pick out (a) the element that is oxidized, (b) the element that is reduced, (c) the element whose atoms gain electrons, (d) the element whose atoms lose electrons:
$$Mg + 2H^+ \rightarrow H_2 + Mg^{++}$$
$$Ca + S \rightarrow CaS$$
$$2Na + 2H_2O \rightarrow 2Na^+ + 2OH^- + H_2$$
$$F_2 + 2Br^- \rightarrow Br_2 + 2F^-$$
$$2Fe^{3+} + 3H_2S \rightarrow 2FeS + S + 6H^+$$

11. Which loses electrons more easily, Na or Fe? Al or Ag? I^- or Cl^-? Which gains electrons more easily, Cl or Br? Hg^{++} or Mg^{++}?

12. In what part of the periodic table are the elements that are most easily reduced? In what part are those that are most easily oxidized?

13. What would you expect to happen when a knife blade is held in a solution of silver nitrate? Write an equation to show the reaction. (The iron forms Fe^{++}.)

14. Which of the halogens will displace bromine from solution? Which will bromine displace from solution? Write an equation for one of these reactions.

15. How could you demonstrate that magnesium is a better reducing agent (that is, more easily oxidized) than hydrogen?

CHAPTER 28 | ORGANIC CHEMISTRY

In many ways the most remarkable element, carbon is a constituent of hundreds of thousands of compounds. There are more than ten times as many known carbon compounds as there are all other compounds. Further, carbon compounds are the chief constituents of living things; hence the name *organic chemistry* to describe the chemistry of carbon and the name *inorganic chemistry* to describe the chemistry of all the other elements.

At one time it was thought that carbon compounds, with the exception of the oxides, the carbonates, and a few others, could be produced only by plants and animals or from other compounds produced by plants and animals. Carbon was supposed to unite with other elements only under the influence of a mysterious "vital force" possessed by living things. This ancient idea was exploded in 1828 by the German chemist Friedrich Wöhler, who prepared the organic compound urea by heating the inorganic compound ammonium cyanate. Since Wöhler's time a great number of organic compounds have been made in the laboratory from inorganic materials, but the general distinction between the chemistry of carbon compounds and inorganic chemistry nevertheless remains useful.

Carbon Compounds

What properties of carbon enable it to be so prolific in forming compounds? Let us first examine the periodic table. Carbon is at the head of the middle group of elements, which means that it is a small atom with four valence electrons. Carbon atoms are unable readily either to lose all the electrons in their outer shells or to gain the four more required to complete the shells, and so they form compounds exclusively by sharing electron pairs. Carbon bonds with other atoms are covalent, and because of the small size of the carbon atom and the consequent strong attraction of its nucleus for electrons, these bonds are especially strong.

A carbon atom can form firm attachments not only to many different metallic and nonmetallic atoms but to *other carbon atoms* as well. The strength of the attraction between carbon atoms is demonstrated by the hardness of diamond, a crystalline form of carbon in which each atom is linked to four others by electron-pair bonds. It is this unique capacity of carbon atoms to join together that makes possible the immense number and variety of carbon compounds. A few elements near carbon in the periodic table— boron, silicon, nitrogen—have this same ability to a small extent, but their chains of atoms are short and unstable.

Because the bonds formed by carbon atoms are covalent, carbon compounds are mostly nonelectrolytes and their reaction rates are usually slow. The great attraction of carbon atoms and hydrogen atoms for oxygen makes many organic compounds subject to slow oxidation in air and to rapid oxidation if heated. Even in the absence of air, organic compounds are, in general, stable only at ordinary temperatures, and few of them resist decomposition at temperatures over a few hundred degrees centigrade.

The Paraffin Hydrocarbons

The simplest organic compounds are the *hydrocarbons*, compounds that contain only the two elements carbon and hydrogen. Even these relatively simple compounds exist in tremendous variety.

One group of hydrocarbons, called the *paraffin* (or methane) hydrocarbons, includes substances like CH_4 (methane), C_2H_6 (ethane), C_3H_8 (propane), C_4H_{10} (butane), and so on up to compounds with 30 or more carbon atoms per molecule. We can express the composition of these compounds by the general formula C_nH_{2n+2}, indicating that the number of hydrogen atoms is always two more than twice the number of carbon atoms. Information on some members of this group is given in Table 28.1. Evidently boiling point and freezing point increase regularly as molecular weight increases, which is also true of the densities of these compounds. Many other series of organic compounds show similar changes as the number of carbon atoms per molecule grows larger.

The paraffin hydrocarbons occur as constituents of natural gas and petroleum. The lighter ones, methane to butane, make up natural gas; the heavier ones are found in liquid oil. These hydrocarbons are also among the products obtained by heating soft coal in the absence of air. Methane itself has a more widespread occurrence, as a constituent of volcanic gases,

Table 28.1.   The paraffin series of hydrocarbons.*

Formula	Name	Freezing point, °C	Boiling point, °C	Commercial name
CH_4	Methane	−184	−161	
C_2H_6	Ethane	−172	−88	
C_3H_8	Propane	−190	−45	Fuel gases
C_4H_{10}	Butane	−135	1	
C_5H_{12}	Pentane	−132	36	Petroleum ether
C_6H_{14}	Hexane	−94	69	(naphtha)
C_7H_{16}	Heptane	−90	98	
C_8H_{18}	Octane	−57	125	Gasoline
C_9H_{20}	Nonane	−51	154	
$C_{10}H_{22}$	Decane	−32	174	
$C_{16}H_{34}$	Undecane	−27	197	
. . . .				Kerosene
$C_{46}H_{34}$	Hexadecane	20	288	

$C_{17}H_{36}$ to $C_{22}H_{46}$, semisolids, constituents of petroleum jelly and lubricating oil
$C_{23}H_{48}$ to $C_{29}H_{60}$, constituents of paraffin

* The data above refer to the normal, or straight-chain, compounds.   Isomers of these hydrocarbons (page 489) have somewhat different properties.

for example, and as a minor product of organic decay.   The gas that bubbles up from the black ooze at the bottom of stagnant pools is largely methane; hence the common name *marsh gas.*

The separation of petroleum into its constituent compounds is a difficult problem because the properties of the compounds are so similar.   We might, for example, try to separate a mixture of pentane and hexane by boiling. Seemingly, pentane should boil off first, since its boiling point is lower (36°C—only a little higher than room temperature); thus we could leave hexane behind and then condense the vapor to recover the pentane.   The difficulty is that hexane evaporates readily at 36°C, since its own boiling point is only about 30°C higher, and so the condensed vapor would contain considerable hexane as well as pentane.   By this procedure we should therefore obtain a vapor relatively rich in the low-boiling compound and a residue relatively rich in the high-boiling compound, but not a complete separation.

Fortunately, for commercial purposes a complete separation is not necessary.   The refining of petroleum involves a process of partial separation called *fractional distillation,* in which the oil is heated and its vapors are led off and condensed at progressively higher temperatures.   The material coming off at the lowest temperature is largely pentane and hexane, with minor amounts of both lighter and heavier hydrocarbons; it forms a colorless, volatile liquid used as a solvent and cleaning agent (petroleum ether or naphtha).   The next fraction, consisting largely of hydrocarbons from hexane to decane, is gasoline. A still heavier and less volatile fraction is kerosene. At higher temperatures lubricating oils are formed, and at still higher temperatures the solid hydrocarbon mixtures called petroleum jelly and paraffin.

Of all these products the most valuable, of course, is gasoline. Unfortunately the constituents of gasoline make up only a minor fraction of most petroleums. In order to increase the yield of gasoline, it is common practice to supplement the refining process in two ways: by *cracking* the heavier hydrocarbons, which means heating them under pressure in the presence of a catalyst so that they break down into the simpler molecules of gasoline, and by *polymerizing* the lighter hydrocarbons, which means joining together small molecules into larger ones, again under the influence of heat and catalysts.

Molecules of the paraffin hydrocarbons have chains of carbon atoms linked together to form symmetric or nearly symmetric structures. Such structures, as we might expect, give nonpolar molecules, that is, molecules with neither end appreciably more positive or negative than the other. Because of this nonpolar character the paraffin hydrocarbons are insoluble in water. Chemically they are fairly unreactive, and neither concentrated acids and bases nor most oxidizing agents will affect them at ordinary temperatures. When ignited, as we know, they burn readily in air or oxygen.

Structural Formulas

So far the chemistry of the hydrocarbons seems simple enough. The only complexity we have introduced is the ability of carbon atoms to join together in chains, which makes possible an unusually large number of compounds of the same two elements. But further study of the hydrocarbons shows that this is only one respect in which organic compounds differ from the inorganic compounds that we have discussed. Another important difference is that two or more organic compounds may have the same formula; thus two different gases share the formula of butane (C_4H_{10}) and three different liquids share the formula of pentane (C_5H_{12}). Among inorganic compounds we never think of a formula like NaOH or $FeCl_3$ as representing more than a single substance.

The formula of an organic compound is determined in the same manner as other formulas: The molecular weight is found, perhaps by measuring the density of its vapor, and the proportions by weight of the different elements are found by analysis. Like inorganic formulas, the formula of a carbon compound tells us how many atoms of each kind are present in a molecule. Evidently, however, this information is not sufficient to describe an organic compound accurately, since more than one compound can show the same molecular composition. The additional information we need is the *arrangement* of atoms in the molecule.

To illustrate, we may write the formulas of methane (CH_4) and ethane (C_2H_6) in the pictorial form

$$
\begin{array}{cc}
\text{H} & \text{H \quad H} \\
\overset{..}{} & \overset{..}{} \quad \overset{..}{} \\
\text{H}:\text{C}:\text{H} & \text{H}:\text{C}:\text{C}:\text{H} \\
\overset{..}{} & \overset{..}{} \quad \overset{..}{} \\
\text{H} & \text{H \quad H} \\
\text{Methane} & \text{Ethane} \\
\text{CH}_4 & \text{C}_2\text{H}_6
\end{array}
$$

where the dots represent valence electrons (four from each C atom, one from each H atom) arranged in pairs to form covalent bonds. Dashes are often used instead to represent electron pairs:

$$
\begin{array}{cc}
\text{H} & \text{H \quad H} \\
| & | \quad | \\
\text{H—C—H} & \text{H—C—C—H} \\
| & | \quad | \\
\text{H} & \text{H \quad H} \\
\text{Methane} & \text{Ethane} \\
\text{CH}_4 & \text{C}_2\text{H}_6
\end{array}
$$

Diagrammatic formulas of this sort are called *structural formulas*; the simpler CH_4 and C_2H_6 are called *molecular formulas*. Besides the information that the molecular formulas give, these structural formulas show that, in both methane and ethane molecules, each hydrogen atom is attached to a carbon atom and that in ethane the two carbon atoms are linked together.

Structural formulas are written according to the ordinary rules of valence. Each carbon atom, with its valence of 4, must be connected with other atoms by four bonds, or dashes. Each hydrogen or chlorine atom can have only one dash; each oxygen atom has two. Since the bonds to carbon atoms are all covalent, the positive or negative character of the valence is immaterial. The following formulas illustrate the valence rules:

$$
\begin{array}{ccc}
\text{H \ H \ H} & \text{H} & \text{Cl} \\
| \ \ | \ \ | & | & | \\
\text{H—C—C—C—Cl} & \text{H—C—O—H} & \text{Cl—C}=\text{O} \\
| \ \ | \ \ | & | & \\
\text{H \ H \ H} & \text{H} & \\
\text{Propyl chloride} & \text{Methyl alcohol} & \text{Phosgene} \\
\text{C}_3\text{H}_7\text{Cl} & \text{CH}_4\text{O} & \text{COCl}_2
\end{array}
$$

For methane and ethane the structural formulas given above are the only possible arrangements of carbon and hydrogen atoms that will satisfy the valence rules. Butane, on the other hand, may have its four C atoms and 10 H atoms arranged in two *different* ways:

$$
\begin{array}{cc}
\text{H \ H \ H \ H} & \text{H \ H \ H} \\
| \ \ | \ \ | \ \ | & | \ \ | \ \ | \\
\text{H—C—C—C—C—H} & \text{H—C—C—C—H} \\
| \ \ | \ \ | \ \ | & | \ \ | \ \ | \\
\text{H \ H \ H \ H} & \text{H \ C \ H} \\
& \diagup | \diagdown \\
& \text{H \ H \ H}
\end{array}
$$

These formulas show that there are two different compounds with the molecular formula C_4H_{10}. To give another example, in pentane (C_5H_{12}) the five C atoms can be arranged in three different patterns, corresponding to the three known kinds of pentane:

$$
\begin{array}{ccccc}
\text{H} & \text{H} & \text{H} & \text{H} & \text{H} \\
| & | & | & | & | \\
\text{H—C—C—C—C—C—H} \\
| & | & | & | & | \\
\text{H} & \text{H} & \text{H} & \text{H} & \text{H}
\end{array}
$$

Compounds that have the same molecular formulas but different structural formulas are called *isomers*. The number of possible isomers increases rapidly with the number of carbon atoms in the molecule; $C_{13}H_{28}$ has 813 theoretically possible isomers, and $C_{20}H_{42}$ has 366,319. Only a few of the possible isomers have actually been prepared.

Figuring out the possible structural arrangements corresponding to a given molecular formula is an interesting, though not too difficult, game. The big question is, which structural formula goes with which isomer? This is a difficult question to answer, often requiring extensive laboratory tests. To show how the problem is attacked, let us use, instead of hydrocarbons, some more reactive substances that contain oxygen. We choose two that have the molecular formula C_2H_6O. One is the familiar liquid ethyl alcohol, or grain alcohol; the other is a gas named dimethyl ether (not the anesthetic called "ether," but a related compound). The valence rules permit two possible structures for C_2H_6O:

Our problem is to match these structures with the properties of the two substances. Tests such as the following make a choice possible:

1. Sodium reacts with alcohol, liberating hydrogen and forming the compound C_2H_5ONa. No further reaction with the other five H's of the alcohol molecule takes place, so one H must be attached in a different manner from the others.

2. Alcohol reacts with HCl to give water and the gas ethyl chloride (C_2H_5Cl). An O and an H have been replaced by a Cl atom, which suggests that the O and H were together in the original molecule.

We need go no further to assign the first of the above formulas to ethyl alcohol; so the second must represent dimethyl ether.

Many simple examples of this sort give the organic chemist a background of experience which enables him to handle more difficult problems. He learns, for example, that evolution of hydrogen on addition of Na to any organic compound indicates an H attached to an O somewhere in the molecule and that reaction with HCl to form water indicates the presence of an OH group. From other reactions he learns that organic compounds that dissolve in water to form acids contain the more complicated group

$$\overset{O}{\underset{O-H}{-C}}$$

A compound with the group

$$\overset{O}{\underset{H}{-C}}$$

is not an acid itself, but is easily oxidized to an acid.

The organic chemist thus learns to recognize reactions characteristic of certain atom groups, much as the inorganic chemist learns to recognize typical reactions of compounds containing the nitrate group NO_3 or the sulfate group SO_4. The properties of an organic compound are the sum of the properties of its constituent atom groups, each one modified by the presence of the others. By investigating the properties of a substance, an organic chemist can often deduce what groups are present and, by piecing them together, can make a good guess at the formula. Organic chemistry is a study in molecular architecture, dealing with arrangements of atoms in larger units and the fitting together of these units to make molecules.

Structural formulas are not meant to be accurate pictures of molecules. Although they probably do show something about the actual connections between atoms, they obviously cannot portray the true positions of the atoms in space, for molecules are three-dimensional rather than two-dimensional structures. Structural formulas are primarily a means of summarizing concisely the experimentally determined properties of organic compounds. Their ability to accomplish this is largely responsible for the development of modern organic chemistry.

Unsaturated Hydrocarbons

The possible structures obtainable from the two elements carbon and hydrogen alone are far from exhausted with the paraffin series and its numerous isomers. The two gases ethylene (C_2H_4) and acetylene (C_2H_2), for example, introduce another structural complexity, which enormously multiplies the number of possible compounds. Structural formulas for these gases are impossible to write with simple electron-pair bonds; there simply are not enough H atoms to go around. We can stick to the rule of four valences for each carbon atom only by supposing that two carbon atoms can share *more than one* electron pair between them. In ethylene, the atoms apparently share two pairs; in acetylene, three pairs. Such linkages are called *double bonds* and *triple bonds* and are represented by two dashes and three dashes, respectively:

$$
\begin{array}{cc}
\underset{|}{\text{H}}\ \underset{|}{\text{H}} \\
\text{H}-\text{C}{=}\text{C}-\text{H} & \text{H}-\text{C}{\equiv}\text{C}-\text{H} \\
\text{Ethylene} & \text{Acetylene} \\
\text{C}_2\text{H}_4 & \text{C}_2\text{H}_2
\end{array}
$$

Compounds with double bonds are much more reactive than the paraffin hydrocarbons. Both Cl_2 and HCl combine readily with ethylene, for instance:

$$
\text{H}-\overset{\text{H}}{\underset{}{\text{C}}}{=}\overset{\text{H}}{\underset{}{\text{C}}}-\text{H} + Cl_2 \rightarrow \text{H}-\overset{\text{H}}{\underset{Cl}{\text{C}}}-\overset{\text{H}}{\underset{Cl}{\text{C}}}-\text{H}
$$

$$
\text{H}-\overset{\text{H}}{\underset{}{\text{C}}}{=}\overset{\text{H}}{\underset{}{\text{C}}}-\text{H} + HCl \rightarrow \text{H}-\overset{\text{H}}{\underset{H}{\text{C}}}-\overset{\text{H}}{\underset{Cl}{\text{C}}}-\text{H}
$$

The other halogens and many other acids react similarly. Since compounds with double and triple bonds can thus combine by *adding* other atoms to their molecules, they are called *unsaturated compounds,* as distinct from *saturated compounds* like the methane hydrocarbons.

Unsaturated hydrocarbons of a special type, called *benzene* or *aromatic* hydrocarbons, are obtained as by-products when coal is heated to form coke and are also found as constituents of some petroleums. These hydrocarbons have closed rings of carbon atoms in their structural formulas. The two simplest are benzene (C_6H_6) and toluene (C_7H_8) :

Benzene   Toluene

Naphthalene, the white solid used in moth balls, is a hydrocarbon with a more complicated ring structure in its molecule. In general, these compounds do not react by addition as readily as other unsaturated hydrocarbons do, for the ring structure apparently makes the double bonds more stable.

Hydrocarbon Derivatives

The variety and complexity of organic compounds containing only two elements are amply demonstrated by the hydrocarbons. With one or two other elements added, the number of possible compounds becomes immense. To simplify the problem of classifying these compounds, they are often regarded as *derivatives* of hydrocarbons—that is, as compounds obtained by substituting other atoms or atom groups for some of the H atoms in hydrocarbon molecules. Ordinarily carbon compounds are not prepared in this manner, but their structural formulas suggest that they might be. For example, ethyl alcohol and acetic acid may be regarded as derivatives of ethane and methane respectively:

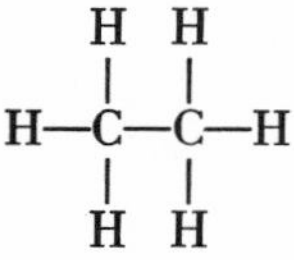

Ethane 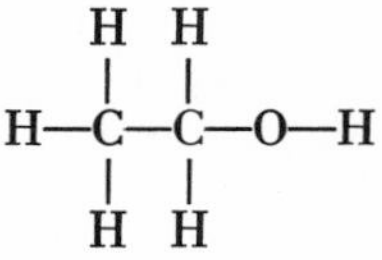   Ethyl alcohol

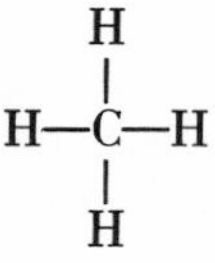

Methane 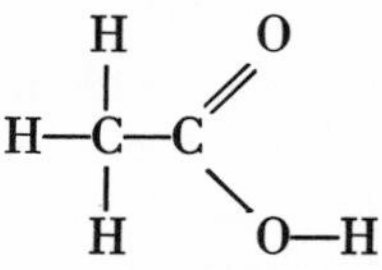   Acetic acid

The formula of alcohol is derived from that of ethane by substituting an OH group for an H atom, and that of acetic acid is derived from CH_4 by substituting a COOH group for an H atom.

The carbon-hydrogen atom groups that appear in hydrocarbon derivatives are named from the hydrocarbons. Groups corresponding to the hydrocarbons methane, ethane, and propane are

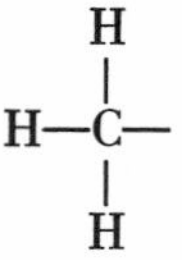

Methyl group   Ethyl group   Propyl group
CH_3 C_2H_5 C_3H_7

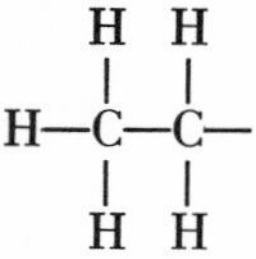

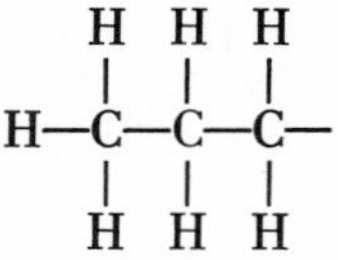

Thus the compound CH_3Cl is methyl chloride, C_3H_7I is propyl iodide, C_2H_5OH is ethyl alcohol, and $CH_3C_2H_5SO_4$ is methyl ethyl sulfate.

Let us examine briefly several important classes of hydrocarbon derivatives.

Halogen derivatives. One or more of the H atoms in a hydrocarbon molecule may be replaced by halogen atoms to give compounds like CH_3Br, CH_2I_2, C_2H_5Cl, and C_7H_7Cl. The simpler compounds of this sort are gases and volatile liquids, and, as in the methane series, their boiling points and melting points rise with increasing molecular weight. They can be prepared by the addition of halogens and halogen acids to unsaturated hydrocarbons, as we have seen, but are more conveniently made indirectly from alcohols. The halogen derivatives are particularly important to the organic chemist because the halogen atoms are easily replaced by other groups in building up complex molecules. A few of the simpler of them are useful for other purposes: $CHCl_3$ is the anesthetic chloroform; CCl_4 is carbon tetrachloride, an important cleaning fluid; and CCl_2F_2 (dichlorodifluoromethane) is one of the gases used in refrigeration under the name "Freon."

Alcohols. These form a group of hydrocarbon derivatives in which one or more H atoms in the molecule have been replaced by OH groups. The two commonest members of the group are ethyl alcohol (grain alcohol), C_2H_5OH, and methyl alcohol (wood alcohol), CH_3OH. The OH group makes alcohol molecules somewhat polar, so the simpler alcohols are soluble in water. The polarity is not great enough, however, to prevent alcohols from mixing also with a great variety of less polar organic substances. These properties make alcohols, especially ethyl and methyl alcohol, valuable as solvents.

A familiar alcohol with more than one OH group in its molecule is the sweetish, viscous liquid *glycerin:*

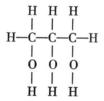

Substitution of an OH group in the molecule of a benzene hydrocarbon produces a compound with properties somewhat different from ordinary alcohols. The simplest is the antiseptic *phenol* (carbolic acid), C_6H_5OH, a very weak but highly poisonous acid.

Esters. Alcohols are, so to speak, organic hydroxides, but unlike inorganic hydroxides, they do not ionize appreciably in water. They react slowly with acids to form compounds called *esters.* These reactions are superficially similar to the neutralization of an acid by a base, but, in contrast to neutralization, are slow and incomplete. Esters are analogous to the salts of inorganic chemistry but are nonelectrolytes. They can be formed from either organic acids or inorganic acids. For example, the ester methyl sulfate can be prepared from methyl alcohol and sulfuric acid:

$$2CH_3OH + H_2SO_4 \rightarrow 2H_2O + (CH_3)_2SO_4$$

| Methyl alcohol | Sulfuric acid | Water | Methyl sulfate |

When the organic acid acetic acid (which we write here "backward" as HOOCCH$_3$, to show how it combines structurally) is added to ethyl alcohol, the ester ethyl acetate results:

$$C_2H_5OH + HOOCCH_3 \rightarrow H_2O + C_2H_5OOCCH_3$$

| Ethyl alcohol | Acetic acid | Water | Ethyl acetate |

Many esters have pleasant flowerlike or fruitlike odors and find extensive use in perfumes and flavors. The explosive *nitroglycerin* is an ester formed by the reaction of nitric acid with glycerin:

$$C_3H_5(OH)_3 + 3HNO_3 \rightarrow C_3H_5(NO_3)_3 + 3H_2O$$

Organic acids. Partial oxidation of ethyl alcohol gives CH_3COOH (acetic acid). We have sometimes written this $HC_2H_3O_2$; either formula indicates that only one of the four H atoms is capable of ionizing, but the former shows a little more about the molecular structure. Acetic acid itself is a colorless liquid, freezing at 17°C and boiling at 118°C, miscible with water in all proportions. It is used industrially as a solvent and in the manufacture of dyes, drugs, flavors, and plastics.

In general, any organic compound whose molecule contains the group

$$-C\overset{\displaystyle O}{\underset{\displaystyle O-H}{\big\backslash\!\!\!\big/}}$$

which we have abbreviated COOH, is an acid, the H atom of this group being capable of ionizing. Most organic acids are very weak. Acids corresponding to the methane hydrocarbons form a series, as do the halogen derivatives and the alcohols, in which the boiling points and freezing points increase steadily with increasing molecular weights. The simpler members of the series, like acetic acid, are soluble in water; the more complex are insoluble. Three members of the series are butyric acid (C_3H_7COOH), which is the acid of rancid butter; capric acid ($C_9H_{19}COOH$), which has an odor like that of goats; and stearic acid ($C_{17}H_{35}COOH$), whose sodium salt is a constituent of soap. More complex organic acids are the citric acid of citrus fruits, the tartaric acid of grapes, and the lactic acid of sour milk.

Organic acids are often produced as intermediate steps in the decay of organic matter. Black soils with abundant decaying plant material, for instance, may be too acidic for the successful growing of crops unless lime or some other basic substance is added to neutralize the acidity. The acids of decay often aid in the slow disintegration of rocks.

Industrial Organic Chemistry

The industrial applications of organic chemistry are so many in number and so wide-ranging in scope that it is hopeless even to try to summarize them in a short space. What we shall do instead is briefly examine three important classes of synthetic products created by the chemist, the plastics, the elastomers, and the fibers.

Earlier in this chapter the unsaturated hydrocarbon ethylene,

$$H—\overset{\displaystyle \overset{H}{|}}{C}=\overset{\displaystyle \overset{H}{|}}{C}—H$$

was mentioned. Because of the double bond, ethylene molecules can, under the proper conditions, polymerize to form long chains whose formula we might write as

$$\cdots—\overset{\displaystyle \overset{H}{|}}{\underset{\displaystyle \underset{H}{|}}{C}}—\overset{\displaystyle \overset{H}{|}}{\underset{\displaystyle \underset{H}{|}}{C}}—\overset{\displaystyle \overset{H}{|}}{\underset{\displaystyle \underset{H}{|}}{C}}—\overset{\displaystyle \overset{H}{|}}{\underset{\displaystyle \underset{H}{|}}{C}}—\overset{\displaystyle \overset{H}{|}}{\underset{\displaystyle \underset{H}{|}}{C}}—\overset{\displaystyle \overset{H}{|}}{\underset{\displaystyle \underset{H}{|}}{C}}—\cdots$$

This material is *polyethylene,* which is widely used as a packaging material because of its inertness and pliability. The ethylene is called the *monomer* in this process, and polyethylene the *polymer.* Ethylene is the simplest member of a class of hydrocarbons called the *olefins* that, because they possess unsaturated bonds, undergo polymerization fairly readily. Thus the olefin derivative vinyl chloride,

$$H_2C=\overset{\displaystyle \overset{H}{|}}{C}—Cl$$

is the monomer in preparing the polymer polyvinyl chloride, sometimes abbreviated PVC, which is used, among other applications, in plastic tubing and in sheet form (Koroseal). Another olefin derivative, methyl methacrylate,

$$H_2C=\overset{\displaystyle \overset{CH_3}{|}}{C}—COOCH_3$$

polymerizes to form the transparent plastics Lucite and Plexiglas.

Those olefins that contain two double bonds in each molecule are known as *dienes.* The polymers of dienes are, in general, flexible and elastic and are accordingly called *elastomers.* Rubber is a natural elastomer. A widely used synthetic elastomer is Neoprene (actually polychloroprene) a polymer of the monomer chloroprene,

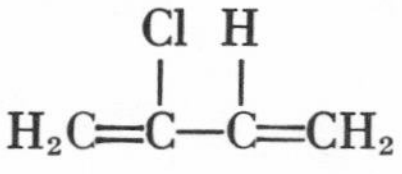

$$\begin{array}{cc} Cl & H \\ | & | \\ H_2C{=}C{-}C{=}CH_2 \end{array}$$

A valuable property of Neoprene is that liquid hydrocarbons such as gasoline do not affect it, while they interact with natural rubber.

Synthetic fibers are of various kinds. Orlon (actually polyacrylonitrile) is a polymer of the olefin derivative acrylonitrile,

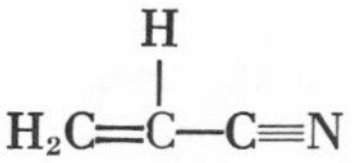

$$\begin{array}{c} H \\ | \\ H_2C{=}C{-}C{\equiv}N \end{array}$$

Saran, which can be manufactured in sheet form also, is a *copolymer* formed by the mutual polymerization of the different monomers vinyl chloride and vinylidiene chloride,

$$H_2C{=}CCl_2$$

Usually the proportions are 90 percent vinylidiene chloride and 10 percent vinyl chloride. Nylon and Dacron are composed of chains of structural elements, just like polymers, but they are produced by chemical reactions rather than by the polymerization of monomer molecules. Thus one type of nylon is prepared by reacting hexamethylene diamine,

$$H_2N{-}(CH_2)_6{-}NH_2$$

with adipic acid,

$$HOOC{-}(CH_2)_4{-}COOH$$

The result is a chain whose elements can be written

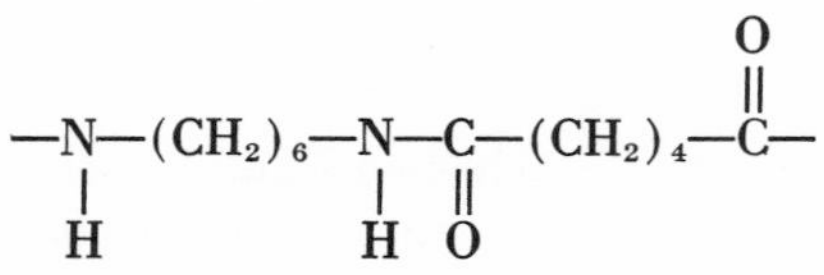

$$\begin{array}{c} O \\ || \\ {-}N{-}(CH_2)_6{-}N{-}C{-}(CH_2)_4{-}C{-} \\ | \quad\quad | \;\; || \\ H \quad\quad H \; O \end{array}$$

The atom group

$$\begin{array}{c} O \; H \\ || \; | \\ {-}C{-}N{-} \end{array}$$

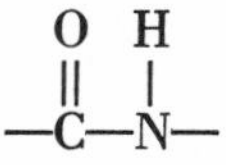

is known as an amide linkage, so nylon is called a polyamide. In a similar way Dacron, whose structural elements are different from those of nylon, is a polyester because its elements are linked together by OH groups.

The Organic Chemistry of Life

The chemistry of carbon that we have considered thus far, though interesting and important industrially, does not indicate why the somewhat grandiose name *organic* chemistry has been applied to this subject. The reason that we have not encountered living things in discussing the basic aspects of organic chemistry is that the carbon compounds characteristic of plants and animals are incredibly complex, often containing tens of thousands of atoms arranged in intricate three-dimensional patterns. Until recently only a few of the simpler molecules of living matter had been analyzed and understood, but with the development of advanced techniques, such as those involving the use of radioactive *tracer* atoms which can be followed through various reactions by means of their radioactive emissions, it has been possible to elucidate the structure and behavior of a number of the compounds directly involved in the essential phenomena of life.

There are four chief classes of organic compounds found in living matter: carbohydrates, fats, proteins, and nucleic acids. We shall discuss each of these briefly.

Carbohydrates. Carbohydrates are compounds of carbon, hydrogen, and oxygen whose molecules contain two atoms of hydrogen for every one of oxygen. They are manufactured in the leaves of green plants from carbon dioxide and water by the process of photosynthesis, energy for the reaction being absorbed from sunlight by the catalyst chlorophyll.

Sugars are carbohydrates of fairly simple structure, characterized by their sweet taste. The important sugars belong to two groups of isomers, one group having the formula $C_6H_{12}O_6$ and the other the formula $C_{12}H_{22}O_{11}$. As an example of a structural formula for a sugar, the molecule of *glucose* (also called *dextrose*) is represented by

$$\begin{array}{ccccccc}
H & H & H & H & H & H & \\
| & | & | & | & | & | & \\
H-C & -C & -C & -C & -C & -C & =O \\
| & | & | & | & | & & \\
O & O & O & O & O & & \\
| & | & | & | & | & & \\
H & H & H & H & H & &
\end{array}$$

All sugars have similar chains of carbon atoms in their molecules, with several OH groups attached. They are, then, complex alcohols somewhat similar to glycerin and show many of the characteristic alcohol reactions.

Fats. Fats are esters of glycerin with long-chain organic acids; for example, a typical fat is the ester of stearic acid, $C_3H_5(OOCC_{17}H_{35})_3$. Like carbohydrates, fats contain only the elements C, H, and O, but the atoms are combined in different ratios. Liquid fats, or *oils*, are esters of unsaturated acids; solid fats are esters of saturated acids. The digestion of a fat breaks it down into glycerin and acid. These are absorbed into the blood and oxidized directly to produce energy, like the simple sugars.

Proteins. The proteins, which are the principal constituent of living cells, are compounds of carbon, hydrogen, oxygen, nitrogen, and often sulfur and phosphorus; some proteins contain still other elements. The basic chemical units of which the protein structures are composed are called *amino acids*, of which 23 are known. Hundreds to thousands of these amino acids are joined together in chains to form protein molecules, which consequently have almost incredible molecular weights; protein molecular weights range from about 13,000 for the simplest to about 10 million for the most complex. As an example, the approximate formula of one of the proteins found in milk is $C_{1,864}H_{3,012}O_{576}N_{468}S_{21}$!

Plant and animal tissues contain proteins both in solution, as part of the fluid present in cells and in other fluids such as blood, and in insoluble form in the skin, muscles, hair, nails, horns, etc., of animals. Silk is an almost pure protein. The human body contains about 100,000 different proteins, all of which it must make from the amino acids it obtains from the digestion of the food proteins it ingests. One of the great problems of modern biochemistry is to discover how living cells are able to duplicate the incredibly complex arrangements of amino acids that are found in the proteins they are composed of.

Nucleic acids. These acids are very minor constituents of living matter from a quantitative viewpoint, but because they control the processes of heredity by which cells and organisms reproduce their proteins and themselves, they are extremely important to biologists. *Desoxyribonucleic acid* (DNA for short), which is the active ingredient in the chromosomes of every cell, occurs in very long molecules, each consisting of two long, very thin chains of atom groups twined together, with the two chains connected together at various places. The specific pattern of each DNA molecule carries the information required to control the development of the cell it is in. DNA molecules are able to reproduce themselves, so that when a cell divides, all the new cells have the same characteristics (that is, the same *heredity*) as the original cell. Apparently the DNA molecules represent a kind of biological code which is translated into the processes of life.

Another nucleic acid, *ribonucleic acid* (or RNA), seems to have a quite different function. It is located in cell cytoplasms (the bodies of cells, rather than their nuclei) and is somehow involved in the manufacture of protein from the amino acids the cells take in as food. RNA, DNA, and the many proteins are enormously complex organic compounds, and their properties, whose bare outlines are all that we now know, are currently under intensive scrutiny.

Self-examination

1. The science of organic chemistry has as its subject
   a. compounds produced by plants and animals
   b. carbon compounds
   c. compounds with complex molecules
   d. the determination of structural formulas

2. Carbon atoms do *not*
   a. form covalent bonds by sharing electrons
   b. form bonds with other carbon atoms
   c. have stability at high temperatures
   d. exist only in combination with other elements

3. In general, in the paraffin series of hydrocarbons, a high molecular weight implies
   a. a low boiling point
   b. a high boiling point
   c. a low freezing point
   d. an artificial origin

4. Compounds that have the same molecular formulas but different structural formulas are called
   a. hydrocarbons
   b. isomers
   c. polymers
   d. derivatives

5. Unsaturated hydrocarbon molecules are characterized by
   a. double or triple bonds between carbon atoms, so that additional atoms can be added readily
   b. the ability to absorb water
   c. the ability to dissolve in water
   d. benzene rings in their structural formulas

6. Hydrocarbon derivatives in general are
   a. formed by burning hydrocarbons in air
   b. alcohols
   c. hydrocarbons that have had H atoms replaced by other atoms or atom groups
   d. hydrocarbons that have more than one bond between carbon atoms

7. Organic acids are
   a. strong and highly corrosive
   b. rather weak
   c. not found in nature but must be artificially made
   d. characterized by simple molecules

8. Living matter does *not* contain as an essential constituent
   a. proteins
   b. carbohydrates
   c. nucleic acids
   d. paraffin hydrocarbons

9. Proteins consist of combinations of
   a. amino acids
   b. nucleic acids
   c. esters of glycerin with organic acids
   d. DNA and RNA molecules

10. The process by which small hydrocarbon molecules join together to form heavier ones under the influence of heat and catalysts is called
    a. cracking
    b. esterification
    c. polymerization
    d. saturation

Problems

1. Write structural formulas for three of the isomers of hexane (C_6H_{14}).

2. Show by means of structural formulas the reaction between methyl alcohol and acetic acid to produce methyl acetate.

3. Compare the properties of a simple ester, for instance methyl chloride, with those of a salt, for instance sodium chloride.

4. In each of the following pairs, which substance would you expect to have (a) the higher melting point, (b) the lower density?

C_6H_{14}	and	$C_{11}H_{24}$
$C_6H_{13}Br$	and	$C_{11}H_{23}Br$
$C_5H_{11}COOH$	and	$C_{10}H_{21}COOH$

5. Which of the following would (a) dissolve in water, (b) turn a litmus solution red, (c) be gases at ordinary temperatures, (d) react with Na to liberate hydrogen, (e) react with ethyl alcohol to give esters, (f) react with acetic acid to give esters?

C_2H_5COOH	C_3H_8
C_2H_4	C_2H_5OH
HCl	$C_3H_5(OH)_3$ (glycerin)

6. Name one property by which you could distinguish
   a. C_2H_4 from CH_4
   b. CH_3COOH from CH_3OH

    c. C_3H_7OH from $C_5H_{11}OH$
    d. C_2H_5OH from H_2O
    e. CH_4 from O_2

7. Name two unsaturated hydrocarbons, two esters, two organic acids, two alcohols, two sugars, and two derivatives of methane.

8. Explain why structural formulas are so much more useful in organic chemistry than in inorganic chemistry.

9. Why are there more carbon compounds than compounds of any other element?

10. Can you name three very different forms of pure carbon?

11. Distinguish between saturated and unsaturated hydrocarbons, giving examples of each. What is a hydrocarbon derivative?

12. In what ways do organic compounds, as a class, differ from inorganic compounds?

Answers to Self-examinations

Chapter 1
1. *a.*   2. *c.*   3. *d.*   4. *a.*   5. *c.*   6. *c.*   7. *b.*   8. *c.*   9. *a.*

Chapter 2
1. *c.*   2. *b.*   3. *d.*   4. *a.*   5. *c.*   6. *d.*   7. *c.*   8. *b.*   9. *b.*   10. *d.*

Chapter 3
1. *c.*   2. *b.*   3. *d.*   4. *b.*   5. *a.*   6. *b.*   7. *a.*   8. *b.*   9. *a.*

Chapter 4
1. *b.*   2. *a.*   3. *c.*   4. *c.*   5. *d.*   6. *d.*   7. *a.*   8. *d.*   9. *b.*

Chapter 5
1. *b.*   2. *c.*   3. *c.*   4. *a.*   5. *c.*   6. *b.*   7. *d.*

Chapter 6
1. *b.*   2. *b.*   3. *a.*   4. *c.*   5. *c.*   6. *b.*   7. *c.*   8. *d.*   9. *a.*

Chapter 7
1. *a.*   2. *a.*   3. *b.*   4. *a.*   5. *d.*   6. *c.*   7. *c.*   8. *c.*   9. *b.*

Chapter 8
1. *c.*   2. *d.*   3. *a.*   4. *d.*   5. *d.*   6. *c*   7. *a.*

Chapter 9
1. *b.*   2. *b.*   3. *a.*   4. *b.*   5. *c.*   6. *d.*   7. *c.*   8. *c.*

Chapter 10
1. *c.*   2. *b.*   3. *c.*   4. *c.*   5. *d.*   6. *a.*   7. *d.*

Chapter 11
1. *a.*   2. *c.*   3. *b.*   4. *d.*   5. *a.*   6. *b.*   7. *a.*   8. *b.*

Chapter 12
1. *b.*   2. *c.*   3. *b.*   4. *d.*   5. *c.*   6. *c.*   7. *c.*   8. *c.*

Chapter 13
1. *d.*   2. *b.*   3. *c.*   4. *a.* Ohm.   *b.* Ampere.   *c.* Volt.   *d.* Watt.   5. *a.*   6. *c.*   7. *c.*   8. *d.*

Chapter 14
1. *c.* 2. *d.* 3. *b.* 4. *a.* 5. *b.* 6. *d.* 7. *c.* 8. *c.* 9. *b.* 10. *d.*

Chapter 15
1. *b.* 2. *c.* 3. *c.* 4. *b.* 5. *c.* 6. *c.* 7. *b.* 8. *b.*

Chapter 16
1. *d.* 2. *b.* 3. *a.* 4. *c.* 5. *c.* 6. *c.* 7. *d.* 8. *c.*

Chapter 17
1. *c.* 2. *c.* 3. *d.* 4. *d.* 5. *d.* 6. *d.* 7. *a.*

Chapter 18
1. *d.* 2. *c.* 3. *c.* 4. *a.* 5. *a.* 6. *c.* 7. *d.*

Chapter 19
1. *b.* 2. *a.* 3. *b.* 4. *b.* 5. *b.* 6. *d.* 7. *b.* 8. *b.*

Chapter 20
1. *a.* 2. *a.* 3. *c.* 4. *d.* 5. *d.* 6. *d.* 7. *b.*

Chapter 21
1. *b.* 2. *d.* 3. *a.* 4. *d.* 5. *d.* 6. *c.* 7. *c.*

Chapter 22
1. *b.* 2. *b.* 3. *a.* 4. *d.* 5. *c.* 6. *a.* 7. *d.* 8. *c.*

Chapter 23
1. *b.* 2. *d.* 3. *a.* 4. *b.* 5. *b.* 6. *c.* 7. *a.*

Chapter 24
1. *d.* 2. *c.* 3. *c.* 4. *a.* 5. *b.* 6. *b.* 7. *b.* 8. *a.*

Chapter 25
1. *c.* 2. *a.* 3. *d.* 4. *a.* 5. *b.* 6. *b.* 7. *b.*

Chapter 26
1. *b.* 2. *a.* 3. *c.* 4. *d.* 5. *a.* 6. *c.* 7. *c.*

Chapter 27
1. *c.* 2. *a.* 3. *a.* 4. *d.* 5. *b.* 6. *a.* 7. *b.*

Chapter 28
1. *b.* 2. *d.* 3. *b.* 4. *b.* 5. *a.* 6. *c.* 7. *b.* 8. *d.* 9. *a.* 10. *c.*

Answers to Problems

Chapter 1

1. Planets change their positions relative to the stars, which form a fixed pattern.

3. If the moon is seen near a particular star on one evening, by the next evening it will be some distance east of that star.

5. The moon does not rise at the same hour every night because of its revolution about the earth.

7. The sun's apparent diameter is a maximum when the earth is closest to it and a minimum when the earth is farthest from it.

9. To be drawn.

11. Speed of light $= 3 \times 10^5$ km/sec $= 186,000$ mi/sec.

13. 4.8 sec.

15. 16.7 (mi/hr)/sec $= 60,000$ mi/hr^2.

17. -1.5 ft/sec^2.

19. 19.8 m/sec downward; 59 m/sec downward.

21. 3 sec; 6 sec; 96 ft/sec downward.

23. 12 sec.

25. *a.* 0.61 sec. *b.* 0.59 sec.

Chapter 2

1. The moon's motion around the earth is accelerated because the moon's direction of motion continually changes. Because it is accelerated, a force must be acting upon it. The force is directed toward the earth.

3. 30 newtons.

5. The force here is his weight plus his mass times his acceleration, or 944 newtons.

7. 60 newtons.

9. 963 lb.

11. 50 miles.

13. 33 mi/hr at 158° from the boat's heading.

15. 300 m/sec; 304 m/sec; 316 m/sec.

17. If you throw something away from you, you will then begin moving backward since the force exerted on you by the thing will be equal and opposite to the force you exert on it in the act of throwing it.

19. 7.66 newtons horizontal, 6.43 newtons vertical.

Chapter 3

1. Sprinters could not improve their time in the 60-yd dash on the moon because their masses are the same there as on the earth. With the force that their legs can exert also unchanged, their acceleration will be the same, and hence their motion will not differ from that on the earth.

3. At the equator; at the poles. The reason is that the equator is farthest from the earth's axis of rotation, while the poles are on the axis.

5. 0.78 lb.

7. 1 lb; 5 lb; 3 lb.

9. The sun's gravitational pull on the earth varies through the year since the distance from the earth to the sun varies.

11. The earth must travel faster when it is nearest the sun in order that the centrifugal force increase sufficiently to counterbalance the greater gravitational force of the sun.

13. 26,000 ft/sec = 7,900 m/sec = 18,000 mi/hr.

15. 6.4 lb.

Chapter 4

1. 0.102 m; 1 m.

3. 5 kg.

5. Yes.

7. 11.3 m; 10,000 joules.

9. 57 ft/sec.

11. 22 ft/sec; 53,000 ft-lb.

13. 16 ft/sec.

15. 2.67 mi/hr opposite to the other boy.

Chapter 5

1. −297°F.

3. 37.8°C.

5. 3.72 kcal; 3.72 kcal.

7. A piece of ice at 0°C is more effective in cooling a drink than the same weight of water at 0°C because of the latent heat of fusion which must be added to it before it melts. Hence the ice will absorb more heat from the drink than the cold water.

9. 620 kcal.

11. 9,800 joules; 2.34 kcal; 0.0002344°C.

13. 516 kcal.

Chapter 6

1. 1.6 ft.

3. 1 cm.

5. 163 atm.

7. The can collapses because, when the steam inside cools and condenses into water, the internal pressure is then much lower than the external pressure on the can.

9. 8 lb/in.^{2}.

11. 0.20 lb.

Chapter 7

1. Bombardment by air molecules does not produce Brownian movement in large objects because the mass of the air molecules is so much smaller than that of the objects.

3. Oxygen; 2.83×10^4 cm/sec.

5. 0.267 mi/sec.

7. The thermal energy of a solid resides in oscillations of molecules about their equilibrium positions.

9. By heating it gradually; if it is glass, it will sag slowly, which will not occur if it is a crystalline solid.

11. The temperature will rise because of the conversion of the mechanical and electric energy of the fan into heat.

Chapter 8

1. The change from water to ice is a physical change because chemically the substance remains the same; the only differences between ice and water are in their physical properties.

3. Water may be shown to be a compound rather than a mixture by decomposing it into hydrogen and oxygen and showing that the ratio between the amounts of these evolved gases is a constant.

5. The candle goes out when it has used up all the oxygen in the air trapped by the jar.

7. Yes; yes; no; no.

Chapter 9

1. 42 g; 567 g.

3. These formulas represent the ratios in which the atoms of the various elements are present in the respective compounds. They do not provide information on the constitutions of the individual molecules or the physical properties of the compounds.

5. It is possible to show that air is a mixture by showing that the ratio between its nitrogen and oxygen constituents is not constant; nitric oxide, on the other hand, is a compound because the ratio between its nitrogen and oxygen constituents is constant. Also, the boiling point of nitric oxide is a single specific temperature at a given pressure, while air boils over a range of temperatures since it is a mixture of different substances.

7. The ratio of the weights of nitrogen and hydrogen in ammonia is 14:3. Since each nitrogen atom is fourteen times as heavy as a hydrogen atom, the ratio between the numbers of nitrogen and hydrogen atoms in ammonia is $\frac{14}{3} \times \frac{1}{14} = \frac{1}{3}$; there are three hydrogen atoms for every nitrogen atom.

9. 9.03×10^{19}.

11. 1.27×1^{28}.

13. 1.5.

15. Ag_5SbS_4.

Chapter 10

1. Like hydrogen, sodium reduces many metallic oxides to the pure metal and burns brightly in oxygen. Hydrogen and the more active metals burn brilliantly in oxygen as well as in chlorine.

3.
$MgCO_3$	Magnesium carbonate
$HgSO_4$	Mercuric sulfate
SiO_2	Silicon dioxide
$AgNO_3$	Silver nitrate
$AgCl$	Silver chloride

Na_3N	Sodium nitride
K_2CO_3	Potassium carbonate
NiS	Nickel sulfide
$Al_2(SO_4)_3$	Aluminum sulfate
$Zn(NO_3)_2$	Zinc nitrate
UF_6	Uranium hexafluoride

5. $$CaCO_3 \rightarrow CaO + CO_2$$
Calcium carbonate $\rightarrow$ calcium oxide + carbon dioxide

7. *a.* Phosphorus trioxide, phosphorus pentoxide.
   b. Mercurous chloride, mercuric chloride.
   c. Ferrous hydroxide, ferric hydroxide.

9. $2HCl \rightarrow H_2 + Cl_2$; yes, since the same numbers of molecules are liberated.

11. *a.* $2H_2 + O_2 \rightarrow 2H_2O$
    b. $2C + O_2 \rightarrow 2CO$
    c. $SO_3 + H_2O \rightarrow H_2SO_4$
    d. $2K + S \rightarrow K_2S$
    e. $Ba + H_2O \rightarrow BaO + H_2$

Chapter 11

1. Sodium is a very active metal, and so it combines readily, while platinum is highly inactive, and therefore does not tend to combine at all.

3. $+2$; -3; $+4$; $+3$; $+2$; $+2$; $+4$.

5. *a.* Solid. *b.* 2. *c.* Slightly soluble. *d.* HAt. *e.* KAt, CaAt$_2$. *f.* About 215.
   g. Less stable.

7.
Aluminum oxide	Al_2O_3
Magnesium iodide	MgI_2
Lithium carbonate	Li_2CO_3
Calcium sulfide	CaS
Sodium nitride	Na_2N
Rubidium hydroxide	RbOH
Potassium sulfate	K_2SO_4
Barium nitrate	$Ba(NO_3)_2$

Chapter 12

1. The various possible experiments include the use of an electroscope to show that all charges either add to or cancel out charges of vitreous or resinous origin placed on it initially, and the use of suspended pith balls to show that all electrostatic charges act as though of either vitreous or resinous origin.

3. Bring up a glass rod that has been stroked with a silk cloth so that it is positively charged. Then, without touching the rod to the electroscope, ground the electroscope. Remove the ground, and then remove the rod; the electroscope will now be negatively charged.

5. The electrostatic repulsion is 4.2×10^{34} greater; hence electrostatic forces are far more important than gravitational ones in atomic phenomena.

7. *a.* 0.00022 newton. *b.* 0.004 newton. *c.* 0.018 newton. *d.* 0.001 newton.

9. Electric fields may be attractive or repulsive, while gravitational fields are always attractive. Electric fields may be created or destroyed, while gravitational fields are present whenever mass is present. Electric fields affect only certain objects, while gravitational fields affect everything with mass.

11. *a.* 180 newtons, attractive. *b.* 22.5 newtons, repulsive.

13. 10^{-6} coul.

Chapter 13

1. Charge accumulated on the truck can flow through the conducting chain to the road.

3. Metals are good electrical conductors, nonmetals good electrical insulators. Liquids may be either. Gases are good insulators if un-ionized. Good electrical conductors are good heat conductors, and vice versa.

5. The movement of electricity in air involves the motion of both positive and negative ions in opposite directions, while in a copper wire only electrons contribute to the current.

7. 6.25×10^{18} electrons must be added. Their total mass would be 5.7×10^{-12} kg. This is an almost impossible experiment since the mutual repulsion of the electrons is so great that they would continually fly off the pith ball.

9. 480 coul; 48 watts; 57,600 joules.

11. 28.8 kg of water.

13. 1.25×10^{19} electrons.

15. 3×10^6 m/sec.

Chapter 14

1. To prepare such a map, world-wide measurements of the magnitude and direction of the earth's magnetic field are required.

3. *a.* Alternating current. *b.* Direct current. *c.* Alternating current.

5. With a direct current, the coil rotates in the magnetic field until it is in equilibrium; with an alternating current, the coil oscillates back and forth.

7. The moving electrons constitute electric currents, which are surrounded by magnetic fields.

9. The earth's rotation and the heat of the inner core.

11. Because the flux through the loop undergoes both an increase and a decrease in each rotation.

13. The additional current is required to build up the various magnetic fields in the motor.

Chapter 15

1. The electric and magnetic fields of an electromagnetic wave are perpendicular to its direction of propagation and to each other.

3. 600 m; 200 m; 30 m.

5. The 60 cycle/sec frequency of most alternating-current power lines is too low to be received by radios.

7. 133 revolutions per second.

Chapter 16

1. When light is absorbed, the absorber is heated.

3. For paths of the order of a wavelength or less, the wave aspects of light are dominant; for paths much greater than a wavelength, light may be more conveniently considered as a ray.

5. The object appears to be its normal size but to be farther above the water surface than it actually is.

7. Large bodies of water appear bluish because they are reflecting the blue light of the sky. The sky would appear black to an astronaut above the earth's atmosphere during both day and night.

9. Light perpendicularly incident is not deflected, so the component colors remain together in the beam.

11. The flashes of color are the result of dispersion. In red light the flashes would be red only.

Chapter 17

1. The two postulates are (1) all laws of nature are the same in all systems of reference moving uniformly relative to one another; and (2) the speed of light in vacuum is the same in all systems of reference moving uniformly relative to one another. These postulates had to have experimental verification.

3. The velocity of an electron whose kinetic energy is 10^{-16} joule is 1.5×10^7 m/sec; its mass is 9.1×10^{-31} kg, since the relativistic mass increase at this velocity is negligible. The velocity of an electron whose kinetic energy is 10^{-13} joule, however, is 2.7×10^8 m/sec, and its mass is 20.8×10^{-31} kg.

5. 2.6 ft.

7. No; yes; yes.

Chapter 18

1. Electrons possess mass, while photons do not. Electrons possess charge, while photons do not. Electrons may be stationary or move with velocities of up to

almost the speed of light, while photons always travel with the speed of light. Electrons are constituents of ordinary matter, while photons are not. The energy of a photon depends upon its frequency, while that of an electron depends upon its velocity.

3. *a.* 3.6×10^{-12} m. *b.* 1.5×10^{-38} m.

5. In the photoelectric effect, the entire photon energy is absorbed by an electron, while in the Compton effect, only part of the photon energy is absorbed.

7. 2.3×10^{23} photons/cm²-sec.

9. 1.2×10^{19} sec⁻¹.

11. Interference is easier to exhibit than the photoelectric or Compton effects.

Chapter 19

1. *a.* The statement is no longer exact. Experiments involving the bombardment of atomic nuclei with other particles have shown that atoms may be changed into other atoms or even be completely decomposed into their constituent neutrons, protons, and electrons. A correct statement would be that atoms are indivisible and indestructible by ordinary chemical or physical means.

   b. This statement is still correct.

   c. This statement is no longer exact, since it does not take into account the conversion of mass into energy and energy into mass. A correct statement would be that the total amount of energy plus mass energy in the universe is constant.

   d. This statement is still correct.

   e. This statement is no longer exact, since the atoms of which an element consists may be decomposed as in (*a*).

   f. This statement is no longer exact, since the experiments of Thomson, Aston, and others have shown that isotopes, which are atoms of an element having different atomic weights, exist. A correct statement would be that all atoms of any one element have the same number of protons in their nuclei and the same number of electrons in their electron shells.

3. Radium is considered an element because its spontaneous decomposition into radon and helium cannot be affected by ordinary chemical or physical means.

5. Nuclei are extremely small and therefore present poor targets to bombarding particles.

7. *a.* Its atomic number increases by 1, while its atomic weight is unchanged.
   b. Its atomic number decreases by 1, while its atomic weight is unchanged.
   c. Neither its atomic number nor atomic weight changes.

9. The straightness of alpha particle tracks means that atoms and molecules are mostly empty space.

11. The actual existence of isotopes can be demonstrated, which is not true of phlogiston.

Chapter 20

1. *a.* 9×10^{13} joules.
   b. 4.18×10^9 joules/ton of TNT. Hence 21,500 tons of TNT is equivalent to 1 kg of U235.

3. The chief difference is that in fission heavy nuclei split into lighter ones, while in fusion light nuclei join to form heavier ones. The chief similarity is that in both processes mass is converted into energy.

5. $_1H^3$: 0.0092 amu, 1.37×10^{-12} joule; $_2He^3$: 0.0084 amu, 1.25×10^{-12} joule.

7. 6, 12; carbon.

Chapter 21

1. *a.* An absorption spectrum, since the continuous spectrum emitted by the sun must pass through the cooler solar atmosphere.
   b. A continuous emission spectrum.
   c. A discontinuous emission spectrum.
   d. An absorption spectrum.

3. The Bohr theory assumes that the position and velocity of each electron in an atom may be definitely known at the same time, which is prohibited by the uncertainty principle.

5. 2.6×10^{74}.

7. 2.42×10^{-19} joule, 0.87×10^{-19} joule.

9. 9.1×10^{-8} m.

Chapter 22

1. The results of quantum mechanics are in better quantitative agreement with experiment than those of the Bohr theory.

3. 182.

Chapter 23

1. Both are ionic compounds.

3. Electrons are liberated from metals illuminated by light more easily than from nonmetals because their outer electrons are more easily removed, which is also the reason for the positive valence of metals. Electrons are most readily liberated from metals in Group I of the periodic table.

5. The two isotopes of chlorine are identical in atomic structure except for a difference in the number of neutrons in their respective nuclei. Since their electron structures are the same, the chemical behavior of the two isotopes is the same.

7. Lithium atoms must lose an electron each in forming such a molecule, and sharing electrons does not permit this to occur.

Chapter 24

1. Ionic, NaCl; covalent, diamond; van der Waals, ice; metallic, copper. Electrostatic attraction.

3. These forces are too weak to hold inert gas atoms together to form molecules against the forces exerted during collisions in the gas phase.

Chapter 25

1. During electrolysis, electric energy is converted to chemical energy. This energy change is reversed in batteries.

3. There are two simple ways of determining if a sugar solution is saturated:

(1) add some additional sugar and see if it dissolves; (2) cool the solution and see if any sugar crystallizes out.

5. A solution of an electrolyte conducts electricity, while a solution of a non-electrolyte does not.

7. *a.* When Ag^+ is added to a solution containing Cl^-, $AgCl$ is precipitated, while nothing happens if Ag^+ is added to a solution of NO_3^- since $AgNO_3$ is soluble.
   b. When Cl^- is added to a solution containing Ag^+, $AgCl$ is precipitated, while nothing happens if Cl^- is added to a solution of Na^+ since $NaCl$ is soluble.
   c. When $CO_3^=$ is added to a solution containing Ca^{++}, $CaCO_3$ is precipitated, while nothing happens if $CO_3^=$ is added to a solution containing Na^+ since Na_2CO_3 is soluble.
   d. Cu^{++} is blue in color, while Ca^{++} is colorless.

9. 7.13 g.

11. 9 g.

13. NaCl will precipitate out.

Chapter 26

1. An indicator can be used. Thus blue litmus turns red in an acid solution, while red litmus turns blue in a basic solution. In a neutral solution neither red nor blue litmus will change color. Another method is taste: Acids are sour, bases are bitter.

3. HBr is a strong acid because, like HCl, it is completely dissociated into ions in solution.

5. Dissolve in water and heat. If (a), ammonia will be evolved, and if (b), carbon dioxide will be evolved.

7. $3Na^+ + BO_3{}^{3-} + 3H^+ + 3Cl^- \rightarrow H_3BO_3 + 3Na^+ + 3Cl^-$; basic.

9. Add a strong acid, for instance: $HCl : 2Na^+ + S^= + 2H^+ + 2Cl^- \rightarrow H_2S + 2NaCl$.

11. $CO_3^=$ hydrolyzes more because H_2CO_3 (or better, $CO_2 + H_2O$) is less dissociated than $HC_2H_3O_2$. The weaker the acid, the greater the extent to which its ion hydrolyzes.

13. $Ca(C_2H_3O_2) + H_2SO_4 \rightarrow 2 HC_2H_3O_2 + CaSO_4$.

Chapter 27

1. Exothermic: *a, b, e, f.*

3. In an atomic-bomb explosion, the liberated energy comes from rearrangements of particles within atomic nuclei, while in a dynamite explosion, the liberated energy comes from rearrangements within the electron clouds of atoms.

5. *a.* Increase the temperature. *b.* Increase the concentration of the sulfuric acid. *c.* Use powdered zinc or zinc filings to increase the exposed surface area.

7. At room temperature few of the molecules will have energies as great as the activation energy, and since only these few molecules can react, the process is a slow one.

9. *a, c.*

11. Na, Al, I$^-$; Cl, Hg^{++}.

13. When a knife blade is held in a solution of silver nitrate, the iron is oxidized and the silver reduced; hence the iron goes into solution while metallic silver deposits out. The equation is

$$Fe + 2Ag^+ \rightarrow Fe^{++} + 2Ag$$

15. To show that magnesium is a better reducing agent than hydrogen, it may be placed in an acid solution. Hydrogen gas is evolved, meaning that the magnesium has reduced hydrogen ions in the solution.

Chapter 28

3. Esters are nonelectrolytes, while salts in solution are electrolytes. Salts (such as sodium chloride) are crystals in their pure state, while the simpler esters (such as methyl chloride) are liquids or gases.

5. *a.* C_2H_5COOH; C_2H_5OH; HCl; $C_3H_5(OH)_3$.
   b. C_2H_5COOH; HCl.
   c. C_3H_8; C_2H_4.
   d. C_2H_5COOH; HCl; C_2H_5OH; $C_3H_5(OH)_3$.
   e. C_2H_5COOH; HCl.
   f. C_2H_5OH; $C_3H_5(OH)_3$.

7. *a.* Ethylene and benzene are unsaturated hydrocarbons.
   b. Ethyl acetate and nitroglycerin are esters.
   c. Acetic acid and citric acid are organic acids.
   d. Ethyl alcohol and glycerin are alcohols.
   e. Glucose and sucrose are sugars.
   f. Acetic acid and methyl chloride are derivatives of methane.

9. There are more carbon compounds than those of any other element because of the ability of carbon atoms to form bonds with one another.

11. In a saturated hydrocarbon, for example ethane, adjacent carbon atoms share only a single pair of electrons. In an unsaturated hydrocarbon, for example ethylene, adjacent carbon atoms share more than one pair of electrons. A hydrocarbon derivative is a compound obtained by substituting other atoms or atom groups for some of the hydrogen atoms in hydrocarbon molecules.

Index

521